THE IRON AND STEEL INDUSTRIES OF THE SOUTH

Printed Series Number 17

Bureau of Business Research

School of Commerce and Business Administration

University of Alabama

THE IRON AND STEEL INDUSTRIES

OF THE SOUTH

BY H. H. CHAPMAN

WITH THE COLLABORATION OF
W. M. ADAMSON, H. D. BONHAM
H. D. PALLISTER, AND E. C. WRIGHT

1953

UNIVERSITY OF ALABAMA PRESS
UNIVERSITY, ALABAMA

Copyright 1953 by University of Alabama

Printed and Bound by Birmingham Printing Company

Birmingham, Alabama

PREFACE

The project that nas resulted in this book had its origin in the spring of 1945. Dean Lee Bidgood of the School of Commerce and Business Administration and Professor James R. Cudworth, Director of the School of Mines (now Dean of the College of Engineering) of the University of Alabama, had become very much interested in the possible impact on the Southern industry of the approaching exhaustion of the high grade Lake Superior iron ores. They arranged for a meeting at the University of Alabama with representatives of the Tennessee Valley Authority. The results of the meeting were (1) a decision to further explore the possibilities of a comprehensive study of the iron and steel industries in the South and (2) the appointment of a committee consisting of Professor Cudworth and the present writer to represent the University of Alabama and Mr. W. K. McPherson to represent the Tennessee Valley Authority to develop a proposal.

Immediately, two problems faced the committee. The first was to prepare a preliminary statement outlining the objectives of the proposed study and the topics to be covered and to determine whether there was sufficient interest to warrant attempting such a project. The second was to explore the possible means of securing adequate funds for financing the program. It is not necessary to recount the details of this preliminary planning stage of the work. Approval of the project was secured and the following agencies agreed to participate in providing the necessary funds: the Tennessee Valley Authority, the University of Alabama, the State of Alabama (through Governor Chauncey Sparks), and the General Education Board. The primary responsibility for housing the project, carrying on the research, and preparing the report was assigned to the Bureau of Business Research of the University of Alabama, with the collaboration of the School of Mines and the Tennessee Valley Authority.

Although adequate funds and appropriate physical facilities were assured, the problem of securing a staff to carry on the work now became critical. Trained personnel was almost impossible to locate. The great influx of the veterans as students had placed a tremendous burden on university faculties, and government, business, and industry were offering attractive possibilities to the limited number of trained persons who were available. The Bureau of Business Research had its regular program of research and publication to maintain and the work on the iron and steel study had to be done largely by a special staff. The Bureau was extremely fortunate in the staff that worked on the study. These were as follows:

Mr. Hugh D. Pallister, Geologist and Mining Engineer. Formerly with the Alabama School of Mines and the U. S. Bureau of Mines, now geologist with the Geological Survey of Alabama.

Dr. Ernest F. Burchard, Consulting Geologist. Retired from U. S. Geological Survey.

Professor Harry D. Bonham, Marketing Department, School of Commerce and Business Administration, University of Alabama.

Professor Wendell M. Adamson, Department of Business Statistics and formerly Statistician, Bureau of Business Research, University of Alabama.

Professor E. C. Wright, Department of Metallurgical Engineering, College of Engineering, University of Alabama, and formerly assistant to the president of the National Tube Company.

Mr. Pallister and Dr. Burchard dealt primarily with the natural resource phases of the subject. Professors Bonham and Adamson were concerned largely with the collection, analysis, and interpretation of economic and statistical data. Professor Wright, because of his experience in the industry, handled the operating and technical problems and advised on many of the general questions that arose from time to time.

Valuable assistance was received from so many persons and agencies that it is impossible to acknowledge all. In addition to direct financial aid, the Tennessee Valley Authority made available information from its files and the advice of specialists on its staff and prepared Maps 1-16 that appear in this book. The Tennessee Coal, Iron and Railroad Company permitted the use of maps and furnished valuable assistance. The aid and encouragement of Mr. LeRoy Holt, Mr. John Hunter, and Mr. Arthur Blair especially should be acknowledged. The Bureau of the Census, particularly Mr. Maxwell Conklin and Mr. O. C. Gretton, provided special tabulations that were of basic importance. A number of questionnaires were used, a large number of manufacturers were interviewed, and many letters were written that made inquiry concerning particular problems or asked for information. The response obtained was extremely gratifying and is greatly appreciated.

In the preparation of a report of this type, a great deal of detailed and routine work is required. Often the contribution of those who perform these services is overlooked. Among those who have had a part in preparing the report are the following:

Mrs. Irene Huchison and Mrs. Jerry Hoit, compilation of statistical data.

Mr. Norman Ponder, preparing the drawings for the charts and Maps 17-22.

Mrs. Marion Hawley, Analyst, Bureau of Business Research, detailed checking of tables.

Miss Mable Mills, Statistician, Bureau of Business Research, format for text, tables, and charts.

Mrs. Frank Oakes, editing manuscript.

Finally, it should be pointed out that the research members of the special staff had teaching and other duties that made it impossible for them to participate fully in the preparation of the final copy of the manuscript. The present writer brought the various parts together and attempted to prepare a unified report. The credit for the collection of the information and the assembly of the basic facts belongs to the several members who worked on special phases. It is entirely possible that the co-ordinator of the entire project has not succeeded fully in reflecting the individual opinions of all the staff members. To the extent that this may be true, the present writer accepts full responsibility.

H. H. Chapman

TABLE OF CONTENTS

Part I. Introduction

Part II. Natural Resource Base of the Iron and Steel Industry of the South

MAPS

TABLES

CHARTS

PART I

INTRODUCTION

CHAPTER I

SCOPE AND PLAN OF THE STUDY

What Constitutes the Iron and Steel Industry

Iron and steel enter into the commodities and services of our modern world at so many places and in so many ways that a serious problem of definition is encountered at the outset of a study of the iron and steel industry. What should be included as belonging to the industry? If all plants that have some part in making or using iron and steel are included, there might well be a question as to what remains. Some users have need for only very small quantities. The demand of others for iron and steel is indirect or derived since their use is almost enirely for buildings, machinery and other equipment or supplies, such as cans or containers to use in packaging their product. The extent of dependence varies by small degrees, so that there is a gradual shading from the users who are concerned almost entirely with iron and steel to those whose interest in the metals is very small and almost incidental. This situation makes the setting of definite limits a difficult task.

Also, iron and steel are often used in conjunction with other metals and other materials. Sometimes the connection is a very intimate one, as where two metals are joined by a process that makes them inseparable, such as in tin plating or silver plating. A large proportion of such items as buildings and machinery and equipment consist of a number of parts, some of which may be wood or plastic or ceramic or one of the nonferrous metals. This again complicates the problem of classification.

Still another complicating factor arises when sources of available data are examined. The Census of Manufacturers, the American Iron and Steel Institute, the War Production Board, and other agencies have defined and classified industries for their various purposes. These classifications do not always correspond. However, much of the information must necessarily be in terms of the various groups and classes used by the several reporting agencies. As a result of all of these complicating factors, the definitions given and the classifications used in this study cannot be considered as either precise or logically perfect. They attempt to provide a working basis for an examination of the part that iron and steel plays in the economy of the South.

In this study the iron and steel industry is considered to include all establishments which have a direct part in the production of pig iron and steel and also those whose activities consist of processing iron and steel or manufacturing a product for which iron and steel is one of the major raw materials. This includes on the one hand concerns that mine iron ore and coal and produce coke to provide the raw materials for the blast furnaces and foundries and on the other hand the manufacturers of automobiles, industrial machinery, tin cans, household appliances and a host of other products. In attempting to reduce this definition to specific terms, it was decided to select from the industries as set up in the 1947 Census of Manufactures a list of those that will be considered as constituting the iron and steel industries for purposes of this study. In cases where retabulations of the 1939 Census of Manufactures reports are available, the definition can be applied to the earlier data without great difficulty. There are, however, many types of data, particularly on a state and local basis, that have not been retabulated, and the classifications used by agencies other than the Bureau of the Census for the period from 1939 to 1948 differ frequently from Census practice. In such cases attempts have been made to select industries and to combine statistics into broad general groups that are sufficiently comparable to indicate general characteristics and trends.

The industries selected from the 1947 classification are as follows:

Group 33—Primary Metals — all industries except nonferrous metals.

Group 34—Fabricated Metal Products—all industries except collapsible tubes and foils.

Group 35—Machinery—all industries.

Group 36—Electrical Machinery, Equipment, and Supplies—all industries except those considered to have little connection with metals.

Group 37—Transportation Equipment—all industries.

Group 38—Instruments and Related Products—all industries.

Group 39—Miscellaneous Industries—selected industries.

Group 25—Furniture and Fixtures—selected industries in whose products metal is important.

The industries in the last of the above named groups, Groups 38, 39, and 25, are relatively small and may be omitted in some of the analyses.

A further problem of getting a working basis for analysis is that of breaking the entire field into subdivisions that permit closer examination of the data and yet are not so numerous as to be unwieldy. The various agencies dealing with industrial data use several classification systems. A primary breakdown that has much to recommend it from the point of view of logic is one that divides the iron and steel industries into three main groups: (1) the basic industries, (2) the processing or converting industries, and (3) the fabricating industries.

The basic industries include those that have to do directly with the production of pig iron and steel. These are ore mining, coal mining to provide raw materials for coke for metallurgical purposes, coke ovens, blast furnaces, steel works, and electrometallurgical plants.

The processing or converting industries include those whose primary function is to perform some process required in preparing iron or steel for further use. Examples are foundries, wire-drawing plants, enameling, forging, and machine shops. They partake somewhat of the character of service industries.

The fabricating plants are those that are concerned with the manufacture of a finished product. Examples are the manufacturers of saws, files, and other hand tools; stoves, ranges, and furnaces; steam engines; tractors and agricultural machinery; machine tools; refrigerators; automobiles; locomotives; and numerous other products.

At first glance this may seem like a very simple classification. In application, however, it becomes quite difficult. Actually, industries do not confine themselves to activities in a single field. One reason is that many plants, perhaps particularly the smaller ones, may have a product that they manufacture and sell to as great an extent as their market will permit, and at the same time they hold themselves out to perform various processes for other concerns on a contract or service basis. Also, there has been a very large degree of vertical integration in the iron and steel industries. Most of the larger corporations that own and operate blast furnaces have extended their operations back to the mines and forward to include steel works and rolling mills. Some of the companies have extended their holdings to include plants that fabricate the steel for buildings, bridges, and other identified structures. Then too, the rolling mills produce such items as nails, staples, bolts, and woven wire fence which might well be classed as finished products. To the extent that the fact-gathering agencies have set up these different lines of activity as separate plants under their appropriate classifications, no great problem is involved. However, steel works and rolling mills almost universally are considered as one industry, and this constitutes the biggest flaw in the practical application of the classification. In addition, there are industries where there is a practical difficulty in determining what is the most appropriate class. An example is the cast iron pipe industry, which is engaged in producing a finished product but one that must be assembled in order to be put into use. Also, this industry is so intimately associated with foundries and foundry practice that it scarcely seems proper to attempt to separate it from the foundry industry. In fact, many of the fact-collecting agencies place cast iron pipe and gray iron foundries together as constituting only one industry.

Because of the difficulty of distinguishing between processing and fabricating, it was decided to use only two classes: the basic industries and the processing and fabricating industries. Even then, there can be no assumption that the assignment to a particular group is always logically perfect or that totals for the several groups based upon these assignments can be used as precise measurements. The objective is to secure as close an approach to a sound analysis of the existing conditions and problems as the nature of the subject and the available information permit.

What Constitutes the Southeast, the Southwest, and the South

Over the years there has come into common use a number of terms designating geographical divisions or regions of the United States which lack greatly in precision of definition. These terms include the Middle West, the West, the South, the Southeast, and the Southwest. A very extensive literature has been produced which makes available regional breakdowns of data of a statistical nature or presents the results of analyses on a regional basis of a wide variety of social and economic problems. An examination of this literature shows that there is little agreement in the assignment of states to the Southeast and the Southwest. Consequently, the problem of defining the areas to be used in this study cannot be solved on the basis of conformance to common or accepted usage.

In this study the Southeast will consist of the following nine states: North Carolina, South Carolina, Georgia, Florida, Tennessee, Alabama, Mississippi, Arkansas, and Louisiana. The Southwest will include the two states of Oklahoma and Texas. When the eleven states are considered as a whole, they will be referred to as the South.

While no elaborate defense of this delimitation of the area will be attempted, some of the considerations which led to the decision may be mentioned. The basic iron and steel industry in the South by quite common agreement centers in the Birmingham district. It seemed reasonable, therefore, to approach the study from the point of view of the areas most related to that district in the production and marketing of iron and steel. The South as setup for this study corresponds directly to the area designated by the United States Steel Corporation as the Southern District and assigned to the Tennessee Coal, Iron and Railroad Company as its market or sales responsibility. Also, it corresponds reasonably well to an area in which Birmingham has a freight rate differential on basic iron and steel products as compared with other leading iron and steel centers.

In this study the analyses of raw material resources, operating problems, and other subjects directly related to the basic industry will be confined largely to the Southeast. However, in the discussions of the market for iron and steel and the analysis of processing and fabricating industries, the entire South will be used. It is felt that the Southeast as defined gives a logical unit for the discussion of the basic industries and one that is sufficiently self-contained to permit analysis. On the other hand, the market is a wider concept and the Southwest most certainly is an area that should be included.

It should be remembered that market areas cannot be marked off with sharp boundary lines. The choice of the place from which to buy is influenced by many factors which are given different weights by different people at any given time and by the same people at different times. As a result, a market area is at best one in which a particular center tends to be dominant and is bounded by a sort of twilight zone or "no man's land" rather than a line. Consequently, the area designated as the South should not be interpreted to mean either (1) that steel made in the South has an advantage in selling in every point in the area, or (2) that all southern-made steel is sold in these states. There are areas particularly along the Atlantic Coast and in west Texas in which southern-made steel is at a market disadvantage. On the other hand, a very considerable proportion of southern steel has been sold outside the South, for example, on the Pacific Coast and in export trade.

The Outlook of the Study and the General Approach

The outlook of the study is toward the future rather than the past. The questions for which sound foundations for answers, if not direct and positive answers, are being sought, have to do with the developments which are logical and feasible for the future. However, the approach to such problems must come from a careful analysis of the past and the present. It is only by such study that an understanding of the factors that control or influence the development of the iron and steel industry can be secured. The successes and failures of the past carry lessons which cannot be ignored, and a knowledge of the trends of the past provides important clues as to what can be expected in the future. As a result, the first effort must be directed toward developing an understanding of present conditions and problems. Having provided a foundation of facts, problems of future potentialities can then be considered.

The intricate relationship between the iron and steel industry of the South and of the nation as a whole presents a difficult problem of presentation. It also involves troublesome questions with regard to the concepts involved. So many of the published industrial studies deal with national totals and speak of an industry in such a manner that one is very likely to fall into the habit of thinking of a national industry as something quite apart from the units which together make the whole. This study is concerned with the South and will present the factual material and make the analyses from the point of view of the South.

On the other hand, a study of the iron and steel industry of the South must necessarily keep constantly in mind the fundamental fact that the southern industry is an integral part of the American iron and steel industry. As a result, the problems of the industry in the region must always be considered in light of the characteristics of the national industry. This will necessitate from time to time the introduction of data and the discussion of topics that do not deal immediately or specifically with the South.

A very important characteristic, though elementary, is that the production of iron and steel in the United States has come to be distributed to a number of centers or districts which are dispersed quite widely over the nation. What constitutes proper relationships between these centers has become one of the important problems of the industry. At one time Pittsburgh was in such a predominant position that one could almost say that it was the American iron and steel industry. With the passage of the years, the growth of a number of other centers has gradually changed the character of the industry. Important among these centers are Sparrows Point, Maryland, on the Atlantic Tidewater; Bethlehem in eastern Pennsylvania; Pittsburgh and Youngstown in close proximity to coal; the lake ports of Buffalo, Cleveland, Detroit, and Chicago; Birmingham in the Southeast; Pueblo, Colorado, Provo and Geneva, Utah, Fontana, Torrance, and Pittsburg, California, in the Far West; and the beginnings of a steel industry in Texas. These centers are quite widely scattered, but no one of them is so far distant from the others that the markets which they strive to serve are not also within the reach of several of the other centers. Furthermore, the assembling of raw materials, the production of iron and steel, and the merchandising of products present problems in each of the several centers that are quite distinctive, with the result that there is a nice balancing of the various cost factors in determining what center can sell in what market.

The American economy is sufficiently well knit that it is unlikely that any segment of an industry, whether it be in the basic, processing, or fabricating groups, can depart to a very marked degree from the technical, production, and marketing practices which have been found to be effective and sound for the industry generally. If variations do occur, they can best be evaluated in light of general characteristics. This study, therefore, attempts to give the general characteristics of the industry their proper place in the analysis of the region and to avoid the danger of thinking of the southern industry as a detached fragment.

Another general observation which should be made is that the development of the iron and steel industry cannot be divorced from the general economic and industrial development of the nation and the region. If the future is to see a general geographic decentralization or diffusion of American industry, the future of the Southeast will be much different from what it would be should the trends prove to be in the opposite direction. Again, if the future holds extensive further mechanization of agriculture, manufacturing, mining, and other phases of our life, the effects on iron and steel are certain to be important. Shifts in population and in purchasing power, modifications in freight rates, changes in pricing policies, and the initiation of new measures to eliminate restrictive trade practices—all are certain to have their effects, favorable or unfavorable, upon the regional economy and hence upon an industry whose products have such diverse uses as do those of iron and steel.

Plan of Presentation

In developing the subject, the plan of presentation is first to discuss some of the very general aspects of the industry and in this way to provide a basis for the more detailed sections that follow. This is the function of the present and the following two chapters. The next main division will present an analysis of the natural resource base of the iron and steel industry in the South. Then follow in order divisions on the basic iron and steel industries of the South, the processing and fabricating industries and the market for iron and steel in the South, and the potentials of the iron and steel industries in the South. Included in these divisions will be discussions of the history, trends, and operational problems of the basic industries, the characteristics of the South that influence the market for iron and steel, the kinds and locations of the processing and fabricating industries, estimates of consumption of iron and steel products, and the economic characteristics of the industries that must be taken into consideration in evaluating potentials.

CHAPTER II

GENERAL BACKGROUND FACTORS IN THE STUDY OF THE
IRON AND STEEL INDUSTRY

In discussions of the iron and steel industry in the Southeast, the tendency has been to center attention upon the fact that iron ore, coal, and limestone or dolomite occur in close proximity at several places. The inference is that since this is true, a great iron and steel industry is assured. While the presence of iron, coal, and fluxing materials is of very great importance, there are other factors of equal or greater importance, and it is necessary to keep these in mind if the problems of the industry are to be seen in their proper perspective. The ability to find markets for the products of industry is always the most powerful factor in determining whether natural resources will be developed and the extent and manner in which they will be exploited. Even from the point of view of assembling raw materials for processing, the distance which these materials must be transported is only one factor. The quality of the raw materials, the physical conditions under which they occur, the quantities available, all exercise powerful influences upon the uses which will be made of natural resources.

In an economy in which commodities are produced to be sold at a profit, a common denominator is the total cost to deliver to the buyer. If we look at the problem from the point of view of Birmingham (or any other iron and steel center), the most pressing question during any except very abnormal periods becomes the price at which a specified kind of iron and steel can be delivered at a designated market. In an industry like iron and steel, the cost structure is very complex and one which permits an almost endless number of combinations and permutations. The costs of mining ore and coal and other necessary materials and of transporting them to the blast furnaces are the resultants of an intricate interrelation of factors, but costs of raw materials form only a part of the picture. The costs of producing the desired kinds of iron or steel and of transporting them to the market are just as important. Complicating the whole question is the fact that the iron and steel industry is one with a heavy investment in plant and other fixed and highly specialized equipment and, consequently, one in which fixed costs are very important. It is an industry in which the economics of large-scale production play very important parts. As a result of all these factors, the calculation of costs is a difficult problem, and one in which concepts of what constitutes cost are likely to vary from time to time depending upon business conditions, the volume of demand, and the control that a producer may have over the disposition of his product. However, it is almost axiomatic that production will be limited to the total of the quantities that the managements of the several producing firms decide that they can afford and are willing to deliver to buyers in markets, A, B, C, etc., at the going market prices and under current marketing practices and policies. Conditions such as these place great emphasis upon the careful examination of the operating problems of the several industries and the formation of conclusions only after evaluation of the evidence with regard to the many factors involved. There is no room for hasty generalizations.

Not only are the operating and cost problems many and complicated, but there are distinctive factors which exercise an influence over demand and markets which must be understood. As has been suggested in Chapter I, the uses of iron and steel are extremely numerous and varied. This must inevitably lead to the examination of the conditions and forces which control or influence the market demands of a wide variety of iron or steel-consuming industries. It is important to know something of the factors that control the quantities and kinds of products which these industries can sell and that influence the enterprisers in their choices of locations for plants or sources of supply of iron and steel products.

To an overwhelming degree, iron and steel enter into products of a durable nature. Exceptions such as safety razor blades are few and, so far as the quantity of steel is concerned, of little consequence. Furthermore, a large proportion of the total use is in products which may be said to have a derived demand. These products include such items as machinery, industrial and commercial buildings, agricultural implements and the various items used in the production of other goods and services. These two factors play an important part in making the demand for iron and steel highly sensitive to cyclical fluctuations.

Another general characteristic of the demand for iron and steel products is that there is a very close association with such factors as urbanization, industrialization and mechanization. The implications of this characteristic with respect to the demand in a region that has been predominantly rural and agricultural and whose farming has not been mechanized should be obvious.

The Influence of the Northern District

While there has come about a very considerable degree of decentralization in the iron and steel industry, at least in the sense that no one center any longer holds an overwhelmingly predominant position, it must be recognized that the northern segment of the industry, extending from Buffalo and Pittsburgh on the east to Chicago on the west, does exercise such a strong influence that it practically sets the pace for the whole country.

The blast furnaces and steel works in this northern area are founded upon four basic conditions which have so molded developments that centers in other sections to a very large degree have the patterns of their operations set for them. These conditions are: (1) a great body of easily-mined and high-grade ore, (2) huge reserves of suitable coal, (3) excellent transportation facilities with a large portion of the hauls by water, and (4) the largest highly industrialized area in the world within easy reach as a market. The result of these four factors has been the development of an industry which has carried large-scale production to such a degree that it is able to market its products in such quantities and at such prices as to make iron and steel components of a wide range of the commodities that are in everyday use in American life. Furthermore, these conditions mean that iron and steel from the northern mills can be sold at almost any point in the United States at prices that can be met by mills in other centers only if these mills, too, can operate on a large-scale basis. Consequently, quantity is an extremely important requirement if ore and coal deposits are to be of significance or if a mill is to attempt to meet the demand for a particular kind of iron or steel product.

Large integrated steel plants require a tremendous initial investment. It is estimated that a figure approaching $250 per ton of ingots produced in a year, or $250,000,000 for a plant to make a million tons of ingots per year, is now required. The southern district has to face this investment factor in any program for future expansion.

Ownership Concentration in the Iron and Steel Industries

Not only are the basic industries and many of the fabricating industries in iron and steel characterized by large plants, but also in many cases by very large corporations which directly or through subsidiaries control a number of plants. These plants may perform similar operations and be located at different points, or the combination may represent an attempt to integrate several of the stages required to convert raw materials into finished products. Thus the United States Steel Corporation owns blast furnace plants at several points in the United States. It also controls ore and coal mines, lake ore boats, railroads, coke plants, steel works and rolling mills, and structural steel fabricating plants. A list of the largest manufacturing corporations[1] in the United States ranked according to total capital assets in 1943, plus the public-financed facilities operated in September of 1944, showed that 48 of the first hundred corporations were in basic iron and steel or in such fabricating industries as automobiles, airplanes, electrical equipment and machinery, farm machinery, industrial equipment, business machines, railroad equipment, shipbuilding, can manufacturing, and plumbing and heating products.

The existence of this general condition has an important bearing upon lines of development. The fact that the large companies hold such important places in many of the industries with which this study is concerned naturally means that decisions concerning the establishment of new plants, the enlargement of old ones, or the development of new products in an area lie largely with the managements of a relatively small number of corporations. In other words, the management policies of those corporations are certain to be potent factors in shaping the future.

The huge investments of the large companies in existing plants and raw material reserves naturally make the boards of directors and officers cautious about taking steps in the establishment of plants in new locations which might endanger the returns on existing investments. It is reasonable to expect that concerns in well established positions will tend to be conservative with regard to changes that are likely to break into trade connections

[1]*Economic Concentration and World War II.* Report of the Smaller War Plants Corporation to the Special Committee to Study Problems of American Small Business of U.S. Senate. 79th Congress 2nd Session, Senate Document No. 206, pp. 347-349.

and business practices that have been profitable in the past. Such an attitude is not necessarily bad and most certainly has a stabilizing influence on the economy, but it does constitute a condition which influences very decidedly the lines of development that can be expected in the future.

Influence of Governmental Policy on the Iron and Steel Industry

A number of conditions combine to make government policy a factor of very great importance to the iron and steel industry. For many years the federal government took an active part in fostering an American iron and steel industry through protective tariffs. The industry is one which moves bulky products in large tonnages for relatively long distances, and as a result, railroad freight rates have occupied a place of great interest to the industry. Many of its products have a comparatively low value in relation to weight, and for the most part freight tariff schedules have been so designed as to permit the wide distribution of iron and steel. Consequently, continued increases in rates or changes in levels of rates as between different areas can be factors of considerable importance in modifying the flow of commodities.

The prominent place occupied by large plants and the concentration of ownership has tended to direct a great deal of attention to problems of regulating the competitive practices in the industry. The mergers and combinations in the industry have been continuously under question, and there is a very real possibility that the ownership structure of the industry may undergo significant changes through the application of existing or new antitrust legislation. The pricing policies of the industry have long been a subject of much discussion by the public generally and of controversy between the industry and government agencies. For many years Pittsburgh plus pricing was held by many to be an important means of protecting the position of

Pittsburgh and discouraging the growth of competing centers. After the abandonment of that pricing policy, the multiple basing point price policy became the accepted practice. Freight absorption and other alleged discriminatory practices soon led to criticism, and recently a new policy has been adopted, f.o.b. mill pricing. It is not the purpose of this report to render judgment on the moral issues involved in these policies or to conduct a crusade either for or against any particular pricing or other competitive practice, but these are questions that deal with important factors in the economics of the industry, and an effort must be made to know the facts and to be acquainted with the probable effects of alternative policies if one is to evaluate the prospects for the future.

Having discussed some of the general background factors that exercise important influences on the iron and steel industry, the next chapter will summarize the location of raw material for iron and steel and the iron and steel producing centers in the United States.

CHAPTER III

LOCATION OF RAW MATERIALS AND IRON AND STEEL PRODUCING CENTERS IN THE UNITED STATES

In the early history of the nation, small iron furnaces were located at a great many strategic spots throughout the eastern United States close to a deposit of iron ore and to a supply of timber because most of these early furnaces used charcoal for fuel. Small forge shops and cast iron foundries, whose principal products were bar iron, nails, and castings, came into being near the early furnaces. In the relatively simple economy, the demand for iron products was small in quantity and local in character. Transportation facilities did not provide for rapid or cheap movements of commodities over long distances. The dependence on charcoal for fuel tended to prevent large-scale operations, because a relatively large forest area was required for quantity production, and the process of preparing the charcoal was slow.

With the development about 1860 of the Bessemer and open hearth processes for making steel, a transformation of the whole industrial economy occurred. The metal steel, available in large quantities at low cost, provided the basis for the development of machines, structures, and railroads, which had hitherto been impossible. The sudden expansion in steel production caused, and in turn was augmented by, the substitution of coke for charcoal. This was a fuel that could be provided in huge quantities from coking coal that was mined in restricted areas. These developments resulted in Pittsburgh becoming the center of the iron and steel industry. The main production area extended out from that city up and down the river valleys in all directions. Water transportation by rivers, the Ohio, the Monongahela, the Allegheny, and even the Mississippi, was cheap, and large quantities of raw and finished products moved in that manner. Iron ores from Pennsylvania, New York, and Ohio were smelted with coke produced from Pennsylvania, West Virginia, Kentucky, and Ohio coals.

The second great factor in the transformation of the iron and steel industry was the discovery and development after 1870 of the high grade ores of northern Minnesota, Michigan, and Wisconsin. Two conditions under which these ores occur were of the greatest importance. One was that they are located within easy reach of the chain of lakes that forms one of the greatest systems of inland waterways in the world. The other condition was that the ores were very rich and occurred in huge deposits which in many cases were on or very near the surface and of a character that encouraged cheap mining and handling by mechanical means. As a result, quantity production and transportation of ore in large cargo vessels provided a source of cheap ore which could be transferred to railroad cars at the lower lake ports and dispatched to Pittsburgh and vicinity.

The development of the use of coke and lake ores was paralleled by a great industrial development in the eastern states which rapidly extended to the lower lake ports and the Middle West generally. The railroads sought return loads for cars that carried iron ore to Pittsburgh, and a movement of coal to the lake ports resulted. The establishment of iron and steel plants around Buffalo, Cleveland, Lorain, Detroit, Chicago, and Gary naturally followed.

In the meantime, conditions favorable to the establishment of modern iron and steel plants developed in other parts of the United

States, but it is significant that the factors that created Pittsburgh destroyed the small localized industries and resulted in the large integrated and highly mechanized enterprises which have become established in well-defined centers. The remainder of this chapter will be devoted to describing the main ore, coal, and limestone areas of the United States and to showing how the iron and steel centers are located with respect to sources of raw materials.

Location of the Principal Iron Ore Districts[1]

The greatest production of iron ore (about 85 per cent) comes from a small area west and south of Lake Superior and west of the northern end of Lake Michigan in northern Minnesota, Wisconsin, and Michigan. This is known as the Lake Superior Region, and the ores are known as the lake iron ores. The most important locations are the Mesabi, Vermilion, and Cuyuna ranges in Minnesota, the Marquette Range in northern Michigan, and the Gogebic and Menominee ranges which lie partly in Wisconsin and partly in Michigan. Some ore is also imported from the Canadian Steep Rock deposit on the northwest side of Lake Superior and from the Michipicoten Range, which is located to the east of Lake Superior. Of all these, the Mesabi is by far the most important and is the largest producer of iron ore in the world. The location and importance of the several iron ore ranges is indicated by the tabulation below.

The second important producing area is the Southern Region, which supplies about 9

[1]See Map 2.

per cent of the United States total. Production is concentrated in a small area around Birmingham, Alabama, but there are other deposits that provide supplementary sources of supply. The iron ores used in the Southeastern District are of two kinds, (1) the red hematite ores and (2) the brown iron ores. The former supplies about 90 per cent of the production of the district, and the mines are located in Red Mountain, within 4 or 5 miles of the blast furnaces of Birmingham and Bessemer. The brown ores come from a number of locations which are rather widely scattered. In Alabama, deposits occur in the vicinity of Woodstock and Russellville and in many scattered locations in the eastern part of the state. Brown ores also are found in northwest Georgia and in Tennessee.

From the standpoint of production, the Northeastern Region is the third in importance, with about 4 per cent of the total. It embraces the magnetite deposits in northern and eastern New York, eastern Pennsylvania, and in New Jersey. These deposits in most instances require some form of magnetic concentration and sintering of the fines before being ready for furnace use. Important occurrences are in the Adirondacks in the area immediately west of Lake Champlain and extending as far west as the St. Lawrence River. An important center of mining is Mineville, N. Y., which is approximately 350 miles from Buffalo and 550 miles from Pittsburgh. Another part of the area extends from the southern portion of the Highlands of the Hudson southwest across New Jersey and southeastern Pennsylvania. The eastern Pennsylvania and New Jersey ores are approximately 300 miles from Pittsburgh.

Name of range	Principal lake port	Direction of range from port	Approximate distance of range from port	Approximate per cent of production of lake ores
Mesabi	{ Duluth { Two Harbors	North	45 miles	75+
Vermilion	Two Harbors	North	55 "	2
Cuyuna	Superior	West	85 "	3
Marquette	Marquette	West	15 "	5
Gogebic	Ashland	Southeast	20 "	6
Menominee	Escanaba	West	40 "	4

A fourth area with about 2 per cent of total production is called the Western Region, with deposits in Utah, Wyoming, and New Mexico, with small additional sources in adjoining states. In New Mexico the magnetite deposits near Fierro furnish ore to the blast furnaces at Pueblo, from which they are some 300 miles distant to the southwest. The Sunrise District of eastern Wyoming lies 250 miles north of Pueblo. In southwestern Utah at Iron Springs there is located a large deposit from which ore is shipped some 200 miles to Provo and Geneva, Utah.

The fifth area is designated as the West Coast Region and has less than one per cent of United States production. California is the largest producer. The most important iron ore deposit in this state is at Eagle Mountain, which is approximately 100 miles from Fontana. There are also scattered iron ore deposits in Oregon, Washington, Nevada, and in other sections of California.

A sixth area is called the Gulf and Central Region and includes Texas and the Missis-

sippi River Valley as far north as Missouri. At Iron Mountain and several other points in southern Missouri, small deposits of iron ore have been worked at various times. Shipments have been for the most part to furnaces near St. Louis and occasionally to Alabama furnaces. Northeast Texas has brown ore deposits scattered over a large part of the area. Some carbonate ore also occurs. Shipments have been made to Houston and in the form of sinter to Birmingham, Alabama.

The average annual production for the states in the above regions is shown in Table 1 for two five-year periods: 1935 to 1939 and 1940 to 1944, and for a four-year period: 1945 to 1948. The location of the iron ore deposits is shown on Map 2.

Sources of Imported Iron Ores[2]

From 1875 to 1900, imports into the United States of iron ore exceeded one million tons in

[2]A more detailed discussion of foreign ores is given in Chapter VIII.

Table 1

Average Annual Production of Iron Ore by Producing
Regions of the United States, 1935-1939, 1940-1944, and 1945-1948
(in gross tons)

Region	Average annual production, 1935-1939	Per cent of United States total	Average annual production, 1940-1944	Per cent of United States total	Average annual production, 1945-1948	Per cent of United States total
1. Lake Superior Region (Michigan, Minnesota, and Wisconsin)...............	38,359,101	82.8	79,302,922	85.3	73,256,350	83.4
2. Southern Region (Alabama, Georgia, Mississippi, Tennessee, and North Carolina)*...	4,839,183	10.5	8,064,217	8.7	7,111,927	8.1
3. Northeastern Region (New Jersey, New York, Pennsylvania, Virginia, and Connecticut)†.	2,397,309	5.2	3,597,896	3.9	3,662,186	4.2
4. Western Region (Colorado, New Mexico, Arizona, Wyoming, Utah, and South Dakota)‡	676,942	1.5	1,592,934	1.7	2,969,391	3.4
5. West Coast Region (California, Nevada, and Washington)	26,925	...	367,341	0.4	314,359	0.3
6. Central and Gulf Region (Texas, Oklahoma, Missouri, and Arkansas) §	18,711	...	96,445	...	502,651	0.6
Total United States**.........................	46,318,171	100.0	93,021,755	100.0	87,816,864	100.0

* Virginia included with Tennessee in 1938, 1939, and 1940.
† South Dakota included with Virginia in 1936. Texas included with Virginia in 1936, 1937, and 1942.
‡ Virginia and Texas included with South Dakota in 1941.
§ Texas included with Oklahoma in 1935.
** The Bureau of Mines could not allocate 340 gross tons to any particular state for the year 1936.
Source: *Minerals Yearbook*, 1935-1948.

only three of the years. Cuba was the largest supplier. Spain followed in order of importance, while French Africa, Italy, Greece, and Newfoundland and Labrador were erratic suppliers. Small quantities also came from the United Kingdom, Portugal, France, Turkey, and Canada. Over 90 per cent of these early imports were divided almost equally between the ports of Baltimore and Philadelphia. Other east coast customs districts that reported imports were Delaware, New York, Boston, and Newport News. Small tonnages also were entered at the eight lake ports of Cape Vincent, Buffalo Creek, Champlain, Genesee, Oswegatchie, all in New York; Cuyahoga, Ohio; Detroit, Michigan; and Vermont. A few tons were credited to Saluria, Texas, a Gulf port; Puget Sound, Washington, a Pacific port; and Pittsburgh, Pennsylvania, an interior port.

Some of these imports were undoubtedly purchased at very favorable prices or were brought in as ballast or at very low rates by vessels for which no other return cargo was available.

In the early part of the twentieth century, several of the iron and steel companies began to be interested in foreign sources of iron ore. The high grade ores of Chile, Venezuela, Canada, Brazil, and even more distant deposits were considered. In 1916, the Bethlehem Steel Corporation acquired the Maryland Steel Company, which had been importing ores mainly from Cuba. The Corporation increased these imports and built a modern plant at Sparrows Point, Maryland, which is largely dependent on foreign ores for raw materials. In 1922, Bethlehem began importing ores from deposits which are located near the coast of Chile.

By 1920, imports of iron ore had reached one and one quarter million tons and from that year through 1941 imports exceeded 2 million tons in 14 of the 22 years but reached 3 million tons only in 1929. The war brought a sharp reduction, but an increase began in 1945, and the unprecedented figure of 6 million tons was reached in 1948. For the twenty-year period from 1920 to 1939 inclusive, a total of some 19.7 million tons of ore came from Chile. The next largest source was Cuba, which had a total for the period of slightly more than 7 million tons, but there was a tendency for this country to be a less important source in the thirties than in the twenties. Norway and Sweden with a total of 4.7 million tons ranked third. Slightly more than 3 million tons were imported from Africa, and imports came quite consistently but in small quantities from Spain, the United Kingdom, and Canada. The Bethlehem Steel Corporation was the leading importer, and Maryland was the leading customs district of entry.

The postwar years have seen a great increase in interest, with particular attention directed to the Steep Rock deposits of Canada and to Venevuela and Labrador and Newfoundland.

Fluxes

The fluxes, limestone and dolomite, are widely distributed and are abundant in most parts of the country, within reasonable shipping distance of the coal or the iron producing areas. Consequently, in most instances the location of an iron and steel industry is quite independent of fluxing materials. The following states arranged in order of production are the largest suppliers of fluxing stone (limestone and dolomite): Pennsylvania, Michigan, Ohio, Alabama, West Virginia, Illinois, Virginia, Colorado, Utah, and Oklahoma. The producing iron and steel centers are close to one or more of these areas.

In the open hearth and electric processes of making steel, fluorite or fluorspar, a calcium fluoride, is used as a flux to an extent that approximates 2 per cent of the slag weight. The purpose is to improve the fluidity of the slag. The principal deposits of fluorspar are in western Kentucky and southern Illinois. There are also scattered deposits in the western states, with important occurrences in New Mexico, Colorado, and Utah.

Location of Important Coal Fields

The bituminous coal fields of the United States are more widely scattered than the iron ore districts. Twenty-six states have deposits of coal worthy of note, and at least nine others have smaller deposits. Map 3 shows the location of the coal fields.

The United States Geological Survey has divided the nation into six coal provinces, namely: the Eastern, Gulf, Interior, Northern Great Plains, Rocky Mountain, and Pacific Coast. These divisions provide convenient bases for description of coal resources.

The Eastern Province, which includes four subdivisions or regions, has some of the finest coals in the United States, both anthracite and bituminous (coking, steam, and domestic). Very little of the coal from the Rhode Island meta-anthracite region and the Pennsylvania anthracite region are used in making coke. The Atlantic Coast region includes the small fields of Farmville and Richmond in Virginia and the Deep River in North Carolina, none of which have been important as sources of coal for coke, although recent tests have demonstrated that coke can be made from Deep River coal.

The Appalachian region, the largest and most important bituminous coal area in the United States, extends from northwestern Pennsylvania to central Alabama and is divided into many fields. It has produced some of the best coking coal in the world. It includes such fields as the Connellsville, Windber, Broadtop, Meadow Branch, Georges Creek, Upper Potomac, New River, Pocahontas, Brushy Mountain, Eastern Kentucky, Northern and Southern Tennessee, Sand Mountain, Lookout Mountain, Warrior, Cahaba, and Coosa. The coals in the Appalachian region range from medium high volatile to low volatile, and, by blending, most of them can be used in producing an excellent coke.

The Gulf Province is divided into the Mississippi region and the Texas region and includes the Alabama, Mississippi and Texas lignites, which have been of little importance to the iron and steel industry.

The Interior Province is divided into four regions: the Northern (Michigan); the Eastern (Illinois, Indiana, and Western Kentucky); the Western (Iowa, Missouri, and Oklahoma); and the Southwestern (Central and South Texas). Large quantities of coal are produced in this province, but only a small tonnage from Kentucky, Illinois, Indiana and Oklahoma has been made into suitable coke.

The Northern Great Plains Province is confined to eastern Montana, North Dakota, northern South Dakota, and northeastern Wyoming. The beds in the northeastern part of the area are largely lignites. While some coke has been produced from the coal of the Cambia field in Wyoming, it is of minor importance.

The Rocky Mountain Province is the largest in area and includes many scattered regions and small districts. Much of the coal is subbituminous and not suitable for making coke. However, there are a few areas of good coking coal. The Great Falls field, Montana, is close to the Anaconda copper smelters, and coals from there have been used for making coke for the blast furnaces in the smelting of Montana copper ores. The Raton-Trinidad coal fields have supplied coke to the Colorado Fuel and Iron Company furnaces at Pueblo, Colorado. The Sunnyside-Castlegate field in Utah is the source of coke for the Provo and Geneva, Utah, blast furnaces. Coal from this field is even being shipped to California furnaces. Other fields are distant from points of use and therefore of little present importance.

The Pacific Coast Province includes the states of California, Oregon, and Washington, and needs little discussion at this time, as the deposits are small and not attractive for making coke.

Having described briefly the coal provinces, the statistics of production of the leading states will be presented to show the relative importance of the various coal producing areas. These data are summarized in Table 2.

The total production of bituminous coal since early mining began is as follows: over

Table 2

Production of Coal in the United States by States
Average Annual Production 1935-1939, 1940-1944, and 1945-1947; and Total to End of 1947
(thousands of net tons)

State	Average annual production 1935-1939	Average annual production 1940-1944	Average annual production 1945-1947	Total production from earliest record to end of 1947
West Virginia	107,580	149,216	157,404	4,670,271
Pennsylvania (B)	96,516	135,604	135,180	7,142,034
Illinois	47,150	63,961	68,113	3,018,733
Kentucky	43,294	59,930	73,462	1,811,107
Ohio	21,864	30,197	34,200	1,628,013
Indiana	16,632	23,954	24,110	944,889
Virginia	12,187	18,744	17,644	521,540
Alabama	11,257	17,200	17,822	790,543
Wyoming	5,491	7,856	8,511	351,048
Colorado	6,299	7,623	6,631	460,854
Tennessee	4,827	7,131	6,049	313,657
Utah	3,247	5,391	6,701	184,893
Kansas	2,770	3,725	2,822	261,482
Montana (B & L)	2,850	3,925	3,789	151,599
Missouri	3,686	3,770	3,984	249,798
Iowa	3,460	2,806	1,839	334,338
North Dakota (L)	2,089	2,386	2,612	61,712
Arkansas	1,323	1,741	1,785	88,752
Oklahoma	1,360	2,370	2,992	152,291
Maryland	1,531	1,802	1,939	257,496
Washington	1,726	1,699	1,155	140,330
New Mexico	1,434	1,525	1,402	119,072
Georgia	*	*	*	*
North Carolina	*	...	...	*
Texas (B & L)	*	308	66	60,805
Michigan	*	252	73	46,348
Other states	212	357	433	65,014
Total United States	400,078	553,473	580,721	23,826,619

NOTE: B signifies bituminous and L lignite. In the western states of Montana and Texas, the lignite production is not separated from the bituminous coal; in North Dakota and South Dakota, the entire production is lignite. The Texas 1945-1947 average annual production is lignite.
* Included in "other states."
Source: *Minerals Yearbook*, 1935-1947.

seven billion tons in Pennsylvania, four and one-half billion in West Virginia, three billion in Illinois, over one and three-quarters billion in Kentucky, over one and one-half billion in Ohio, almost one billion in Indiana, three-quarters billion in Alabama, approximately a half billion each in Virginia and Colorado, and approximately one-third billion each in Tennessee, Wyoming, and Iowa, with Missouri, Kansas, and Maryland not far behind.

The ranks of the states in average annual bituminous coal production for the five-year period from 1940 to 1944 were: first, West Virginia; second, Pennsylvania; third, Illinois; fourth, Kentucky; fifth, Ohio; sixth, Indiana; seventh, Virginia; eighth, Alabama; ninth, Wyoming; tenth, Colorado; eleventh, Tennessee; and twelfth, Utah. These ratings are based on total bituminous, and not on coking, coal production.

Coking Coal

Although 631 million net tons of bituminous coal and lignite were mined in the United

States in 1947, only about 105 million tons were used in the production of coke. Also, very little if any of the coal mined in such important producing states as Ohio, Indiana, Illinois, Kansas, Iowa, and Missouri was made into coke.

As shown by Table 3, Pennsylvania continues to furnish the largest quantity of coal purchased for manufacture of by-product coke. West Virginia is second but was almost equal to Pennsylvania in 1947, eastern Kentucky third, and Alabama fourth. These four states in 1947 furnished 92.5 per cent of the coal used for making coke. After these come in

the order named: Utah, Virginia, Colorado, New Mexico, Illinois, Oklahoma, Arkansas, Tennessee, Indiana, and Maryland. Table 3 shows the states of origin of coal used in 1947 in the manufacture of by-product coke with the states in which the coal was coked.

Iron and Steel Producing Centers in the United States

As has been stated previously, the beginning of the modern iron and steel industry of the United States centered around Pittsburgh where the high-grade coking coals of western

Table 3

Coal Purchased for Manufacture of By-Product Coke in the United States
in 1947 by State of Origin and State Where Coked
(in net tons)

State of origin	Tons	State where coked
Pennsylvania (bituminous)	33,951,973	New York, Pennsylvania, Maryland, Ohio, Minnesota, Illinois, Indiana, West Virginia, Michigan, Wisconsin, New Jersey
(anthracite)	263,913	Michigan, Pennsylvania, New York, Ohio, Missouri, Illinois, West Virginia, Wisconsin
West Virginia	33,886,386	Maryland, Pennsylvania, West Virginia, Michigan, New York, Ohio, Massachusetts, New Jersey, Connecticut, Illinois, Kentucky, Indiana, Wisconsin, Missouri, Rhode Island, Minnesota, Alabama
Kentucky	13,901,468	Indiana, Michigan, Ohio, New York, Illinois, New Jersey, Massachusetts, Minnesota, Pennsylvania, Connecticut, West Virginia, Maryland, Wisconsin, Tennessee
Alabama	8,255,050	Alabama and Texas
Utah	2,121,856	Utah and California
Virginia	2,076,318	Pennsylvania, Ohio, Michigan, Indiana, Massachusetts, Wisconsin, New York, Tennessee, New Jersey, Maryland, Illinois
Colorado	906,407	Colorado and Utah
New Mexico	588,395	Colorado and Texas
Illinois	505,099	Illinois, Indiana, Minnesota, Missouri
Oklahoma	363,306	Texas and Colorado
Arkansas	179,338	California, Colorado, Texas, Illinois, Utah
Tennessee	154,910	Tennessee, Minnesota, Ohio
Indiana	128,931	Illinois, Wisconsin, Indiana
Maryland	42,115	Pennsylvania
Total	97,325,465	

Source: *Minerals Yearbook*, 1947, p. 414.

Pennsylvania and the iron ores from Pennsylvania and the lake region could be brought together. According to Table 4, the Pittsburgh district still holds first place, but the district around Chicago and Gary is a close second in blast furnace capacity. From Pittsburgh the iron and steel industry spread down the Ohio River Valley, which in 1948 ranked seventh, and up the Mahoning Valley, which was third. The development which includes the Lake Erie ports, centering around Cleveland, was in fourth place in 1948. The Southeastern area, including Alabama and Tennessee, was fifth. Buffalo and western New York ranks sixth, and eastern Pennsylvania, eighth. The large plant of the Bethlehem Steel Corporation at Sparrows Point placed Maryland and Virginia ninth. Michigan (Detroit) ranks tenth and Utah, with the Columbia Steel Company and Geneva Steel Company at Provo,

Ironton, and Geneva, was eleventh. Following these in order of importance were Colorado (Pueblo), Texas, Minnesota (Duluth), St. Louis (including Granite City, Illinois), California, and, last, Massachusetts (Everett). The statistics of blast furnace capacities and of capacities for making steel by districts are shown in Tables 4 and 5. Map 4 shows the locations of iron centers.

Location of Iron and Steel Centers with Reference to Their Sources of Supply

In the preceding paragraphs, the locations of the main producing areas of iron ore and coal have been briefly described, the main iron and steel centers have been named, and their relative importance has been indicated by the production capacities of their blast furnaces and steel furnaces. The next step is to relate the centers with the areas from which

Table 4

Blast Furnace Capacity of United States by Districts, 1948

District	Furnaces for production of pig iron		Furnaces for production of ferro-alloys		All furnaces
	Number	Annual capacity (net tons)	Number	Annual capacity (net tons)	Annual capacity (net tons)
1. Pittsburgh and vicinity.......	47	14,857,500	6	491,200	15,348,700
2. Chicago and vicinity.........	41	13,654,230	..	...	13,654,230
3. Youngstown and vicinity.....	25	7,463,820	..	...	7,463,820
4. Lake Erie	19	5,531,580	..	...	5,531,580
5. Alabama and Tennessee......	20*	4,145,460	3†	99,400	4,244,860
6. Buffalo and vicinity..........	14	3,952,180	1	120,000	4,072,180
7. Ohio River Valley...........	13	3,796,600	2	180,000	3,976,600
8. Eastern Pennsylvania and eastern New York...........	14	3,581,000	3	170,400	3,751,400
9. Maryland, including Virginia..	8	3,252,000	1	36,000	3,288,000
10. Michigan	5	1,604,000	..	...	1,604,000
11. Utah	4‡	1,349,200	..	...	1,349,200
12. Colorado	4	850,000	..	...	850,000
13. Texas	2§	668,800	..	...	668,800
14. Minnesota	3	581,060	..	...	581,060
15. St. Louis and vicinity........	2	465,000	..	...	465,000
16. California	1	413,100	..	...	413,100
17. Massachusetts	1	176,400	..	...	176,400
Total.................	223	66,341,930	16	1,097,000	67,438,930

* One of these is a charcoal furnace.

† One of these furnaces is idle and the capacity is not included. Another furnace is included under those for the production of pig iron but the capacity is included under furnaces producing ferro-alloys.

‡ One furnace which was last operated in 1943 is not included.

§ One charcoal furnace which was under construction in 1948 is not included.

Source: American Iron and Steel Institute, *Directory of Iron and Steel Works*, 1948.

Table 5

Furnace Ingot and Steel for Castings Capacities of United States by Districts, 1948

District	Open Hearth		Bessemer		Crucible and electric		Total
	Number	Annual capacity (net-tons)	Number	Annual capacity (net-tons)	Number	Annual capacity (net-tons)	Annual capacity (net-tons)
1. Pittsburgh and vicinity	244	18,439,170	11	1,466,000	61	924,010	20,829,180
2. Chicago and vicinity	165	16,609,200	8*	830,000	18	967,600	18,406,800
3. Youngstown and vicinity	84	7,453,730	4	1,484,000	11	522,000	9,459,730
4. Ohio River Valley	72	7,244,180	6†	576,000	7	84,000	7,904,180
5. Lake Erie	47	4,391,550	2	558,000	30	1,278,100	6,227,650
6. E. Penn, New Jersey and eastern New York	91	5,725,260			38	443,640	6,168,900
7. East Coast (Massachusetts, Rhode Island, Virginia, Connecticut, Delaware and Maryland)	54	5,550,280	3	312,000	13	107,300	5,969,580
8. Buffalo and vicinity	43	4,130,000			8	59,100	4,189,100
9. Birmingham, Ala., Georgia and Tennessee	34	3,719,000	3‡		6	118,400	3,837,400
10. Michigan (Detroit)	26	3,082,800	2‡		12	390,300	3,473,100
11. West Coast	33	2,034,100			17	480,000	2,514,100
12. Utah	9	1,283,400					1,283,400
13. Colorado	16	1,272,000					1,272,000
14. St. Louis and vicinity	17	946,020					946,020
15. Minnesota	7	690,000					690,000
16. Texas and Oklahoma	7	614,000			2	22,320	636,320
17. Missouri (other than St. Louis)	5	426,000					426,000
Total	954	83,610,690	39	5,226,000	223	5,396,770	94,233,460

* Three furnaces used in melting charge for open-hearth furnaces.
† Two furnaces used in melting charge for open-hearth furnaces.
‡ Used in melting charge for open-hearth furnaces.

Source: American Iron and Steel Institute, *Directory of Iron and Steel Work*, 1948.

Table 6

Distance Raw Materials Must Be Transported to Blast Furnaces At Important Centers in the United States

District	Principal source of iron ore			Principal source of coal			Principal source of flux		
	Place	Distance (miles) Water	Rail	Place	Distance (miles) Water	Rail	Place	Distance (miles) Water	Rail
Birmingham, Alabama	Red Mountain		10	Warrior Field		10	Birmingham Valley		6
Eastern Pennsylvania	N. Y.-Lake-Foreign		100*	Pennsylvania		100	Pennsylvania		50
Sparrows Point, Maryland	Chile	4,900†		W. Virginia‡		300	Pennsylvania		100
Buffalo, New York	Lake Superior	950	100	Pennsylvania		200	New York		50
Pittsburgh, Pennsylvania	Lake Superior	875	200	Pennsylvania		50	Pennsylvania		50
Youngstown, Ohio	Lake Superior	850	200	Ohio, Penn., Ky.		200	Ohio		50
Cleveland, Ohio	Lake Superior	850	100	Ky., W. Va.		150	Marblehead, O.	50	
Detroit, Michigan	Michigan	500	50	Ky., W. Va.		400	Ohio-Michigan	50	
Chicago, Illinois	Lake and Michigan	800	100	Ky., W. Va.		400	Michigan	50	
Duluth, Minnesota	Minnesota		77	Penn., W. Va., Ky.	850	200	Michigan	200	
Houston, Texas	Texas-Mexico		200	Oklahoma		300	Texas		100
Pueblo, Colorado	Utah-Wyoming		500	Colo., New Mexico		100	Colorado		100
Geneva-Provo, Utah	Utah		232	Utah		100	Utah		50
Fontana, California	California		130	Utah		807	California		100

* N. Y.
† One way, but vessels return without cargo.
‡ Grafton W. Va., to Baltimore via B. & O. Ry., approximately 300 miles.

they draw their raw materials. Table 6 gives the distance that raw materials must move from the principal source to the processing center. The data are also presented by Map 5.

From the point of view of location with respect to sources of raw materials, Birmingham occupies a unique position in that it depends primarily on iron ore from Red Mountain, coal from the Warrior field, and limestone and dolomite from neighboring quarries. Thus all the principal materials are available within a radius of 10 miles. The great steel centers of the northern states are located at long distances from at least one of the principal raw materials and in some cases from both iron and coal. Location on or near a waterway is a common characteristic of these centers. Buffalo, Cleveland, Detroit, Chicago, and Gary receive ore shipments from Minnesota or Michigan by lake ore ships. Pittsburgh and near-by plants are located on the Ohio River or its tributaries and thus have the advantage of water transportation for moving coal and are connected by a relatively short rail haul with the Great Lakes. Sparrows Point is located on Chesapeake Bay at tidewater and is accessible to ocean shipping and hence to imported ores. At Pittsburgh, coal is close at hand. However, both coal and ore must be transported to the lake ports from considerable distances. In recent years the iron ore resources of eastern New York, New Jersey, and eastern Pennsylvania have been taking on greater significance to Pittsburgh and the steel centers in eastern Pennsylvania and Maryland, but long rail hauls are involved.

The district in the vicinity of St. Louis, Missouri, including Alton and Granite City, Illinois, has operated in a small way on Lake Superior, Missouri, and Texas ores.

During World War II, the United States Government financed a blast furnace at Rusk, Texas, and a larger plant at Daingerfield (concentrator, coke plant, and blast furnace) which were to use Texas brown iron ore and Oklahoma coal. The Rusk furnace is still unfinished and the Daingerfield did not become fully

productive until after the war. The Sheffield Steel Company of Texas at Houston was able to get into production and used Texas ores, scrap iron, and some Mexican ore and Oklahoma coal.

The Colorado Fuel and Iron Corporation at Pueblo, Colorado, has been a producer of iron and steel mainly to supply the demand in the West Central and Mountain States. For many years the iron mines of Colorado and New Mexico were the principal sources of supply, but in recent years the company has been securing a large part of its supply of iron ore from Wyoming. The coking coal for this plant comes from southern Colorado and northern New Mexico. A coal field in western Colorado is said to have a large tonnage of coking coal.

In Utah, the Columbia Steel Company built a small blast furnace at Provo in 1924 which operated successfully on Utah iron ores and coke made from Utah coals and shipped pig iron to the company's steel mills at Pittsburgh and Torrance, California. During World War II, the Geneva Steel Company, a subsidiary of the United States Steel Corporation, operated a steel plant in the same district on behalf of the Defense Plant Corporation for whom the plant was built. This plant was acquired in 1946[3] by the United States Steel Corporation. The production is intended primarily for West Coast consumption, and the raw materials are obtained in Utah. The iron ore comes from southwest Utah and the coal from northeast Utah.

The facts presented in this chapter suggest that the occurrence of the necessary basic materials in close proximity to each other is not a necessary prerequisite to the establishment and growth of an iron and steel industry. It follows that there must be other important factors. Among these are location with reference to cheap means of transportation, and access to markets for finished products, the quality of ore and coal, and the size of reserves.

[3]Purchase was approved June 17, 1946.

MAPS

Map 1 Areas to be discussed.

Map 2 Based on maps of the Iron Ore Deposits of the United States by E. F. Burchard and Iron Ore Deposits of the Western United States by C. E. Dutton and Martha S. Carr, 1947. Both United States Geological Survey maps.

Map 3 Based on United States Geological Survey map of Coal Fields of the United States, prepared by Paul Aveiett in 1942.

Map 4 Based on Blast Furnace Capacities as given in publications of American Iron and Steel Institute.

Map 5 Composite of principal data on Map 2, 3, and 4.

Map 6 Drawn from maps in publications of United States and State Geological Surveys.

Map 7 Drawn from maps in publications of United States and State Geological Surveys.

Map 8 Principal limestone and dolomite deposits in Southeast.

Map 9 Index of detailed maps.

Map 10 Based on Map of Birmingham District by E. F. Burchard in Bulletin 400 of the United States Geological Survey, 1910.

Map 11 Taken from Tennessee Coal, Iron and Railroad Company Map, showing locations of mining and metalurgical operations in Birmingham District.

Map 12 Based on Map of Northern Alabama of E. F. Burchard in his "Iron Ore Outcrops of the Red Mountain Formation in Northern Alabama," Special Bulletin 19 of the Geological Survey of Alabama, 1947.

Map 13 Based on Georgia Department of Mines, Mining and Geology and Tennessee Valley Authority, Geological Map of Northwest Georgia by Charles Butts, 1946.

Map 14 Based on map of Red Ores and Coal Fields in East Tennessee by E. F. Burchard in Bulletin 540 of the United States Geological Survey, 1913.

Map 15 Based on map of Brown Iron Ores of the Western Highland River of Tennessee by E. F. Burchard, in Bulletin 39 of Tennessee Geological Survey, 1934.

Map 16 Based on map of the Cranberry Magnetite Iron Ore Belt on Tennessee-North Carolina line by W. S. Bayley in Bulletin 29 of the Tennessee Geological Survey 1923 and Bulletin 32 of the North Carolina Geological Survey, 1923.

MAP 1

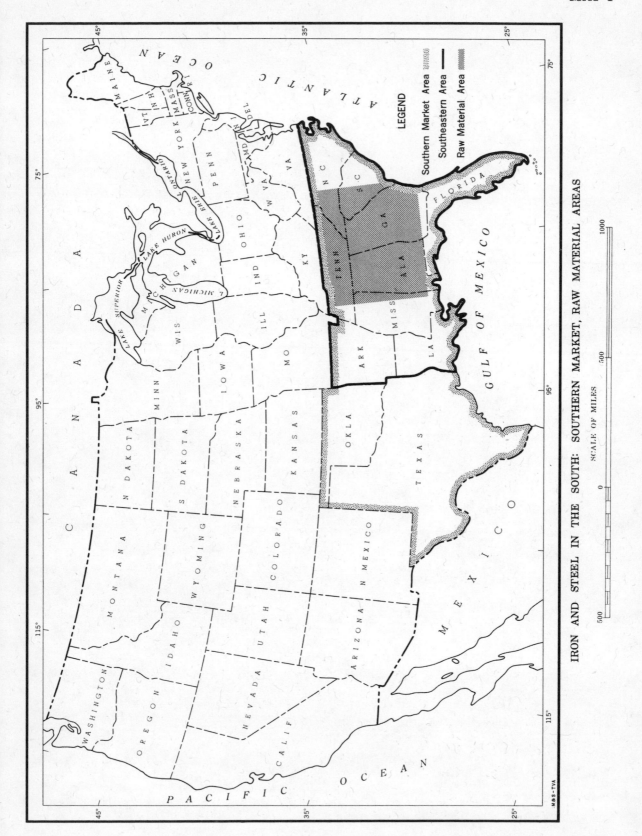

IRON AND STEEL IN THE SOUTH: SOUTHERN MARKET, RAW MATERIAL AREAS

LEGEND

Southern Market Area

Southeastern Area

Raw Material Area

SCALE OF MILES

M&S-TVA

MAP 2

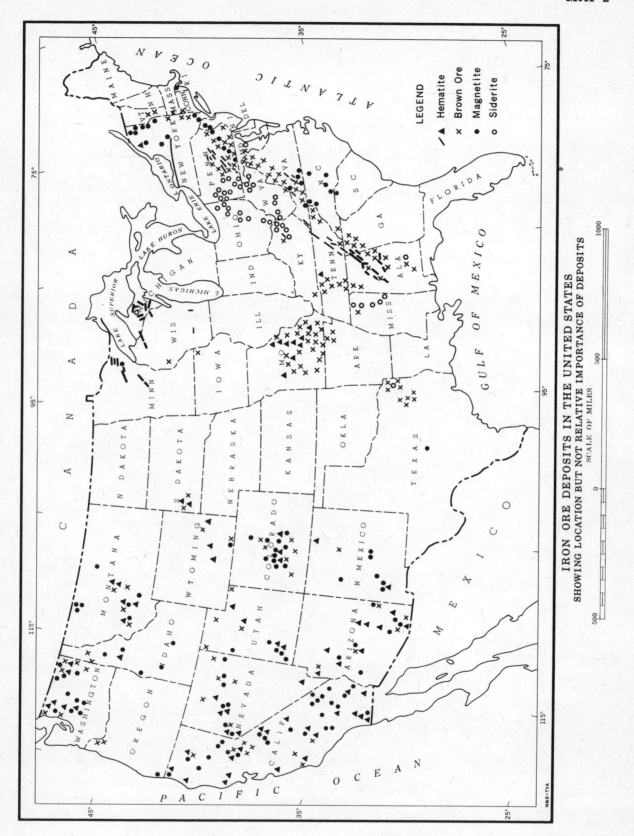

LEGEND

Hematite	▲
Brown Ore	✕
Magnetite	●
Siderite	○

IRON ORE DEPOSITS IN THE UNITED STATES
SHOWING LOCATION BUT NOT RELATIVE IMPORTANCE OF DEPOSITS

SCALE OF MILES

500   0   500   1000

M&S—TVA

MAP 3

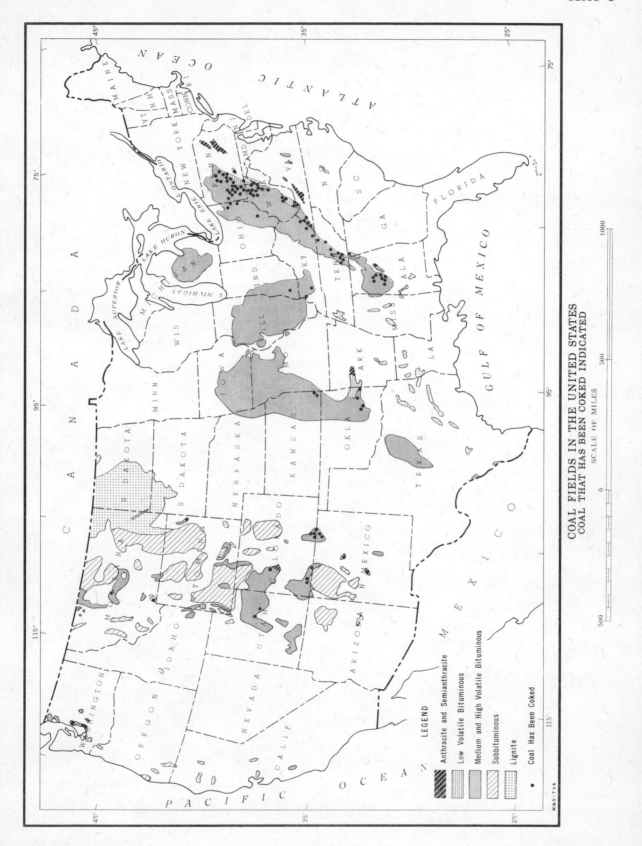

COAL FIELDS IN THE UNITED STATES
COAL THAT HAS BEEN COKED INDICATED

SCALE OF MILES

LEGEND

Anthracite and Semianthracite

Low Volatile Bituminous

Medium and High Volatile Bituminous

Subbituminous

Lignite

• Coal Has Been Coked

M&S-TVA

MAP 4

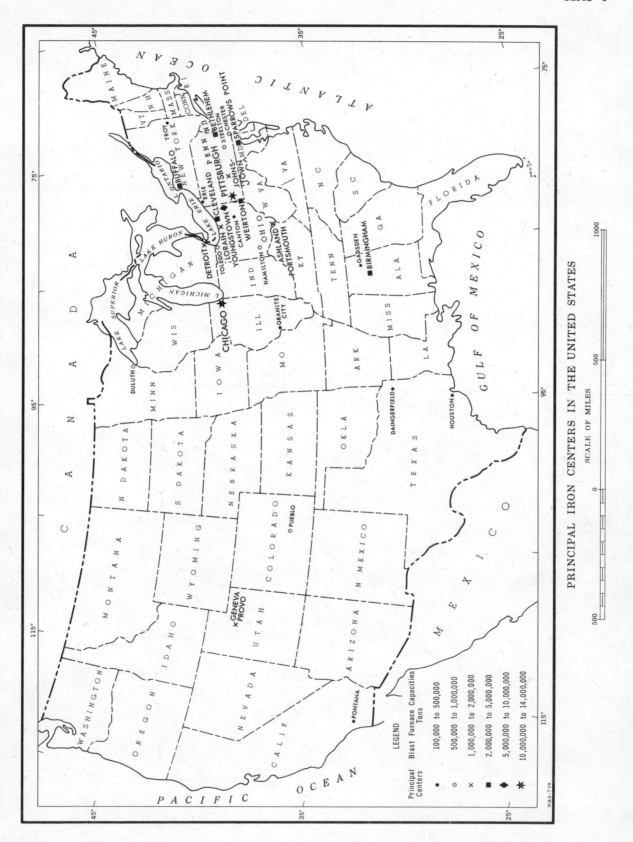

PRINCIPAL IRON CENTERS IN THE UNITED STATES

LEGEND

Principal Iron Centers	Blast Furnace Capacities Tons	
•	100,000 to 500,000	
○	500,000 to 1,000,000	
×	1,000,000 to 2,000,000	
■	2,000,000 to 5,000,000	
◆	5,000,000 to 10,000,000	
★	10,000,000 to 14,000,000	

SCALE OF MILES
500   0   500   1000

M&S—TVA

MAP 5

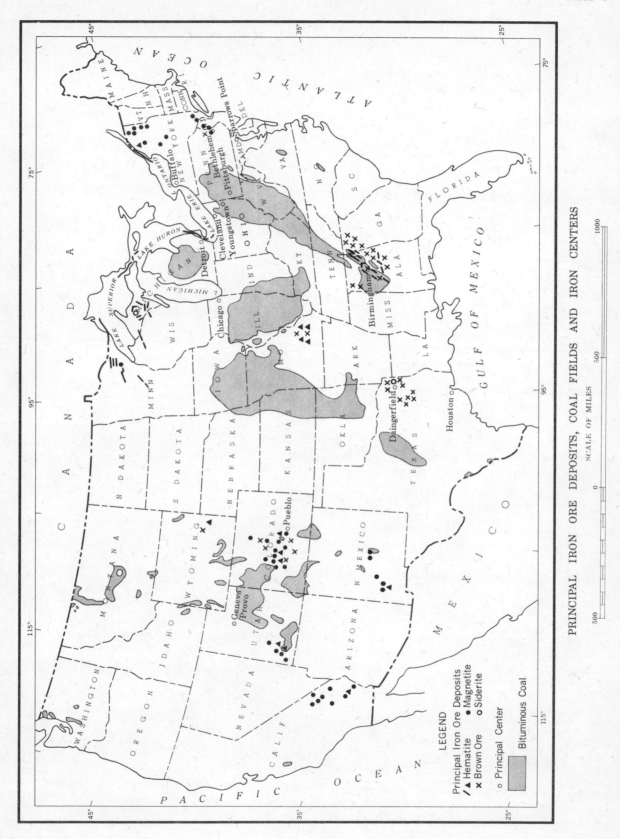

PRINCIPAL IRON ORE DEPOSITS, COAL FIELDS AND IRON CENTERS

SCALE OF MILES

LEGEND

Principal Iron Ore Deposits

/ Hematite   • Magnetite

× Brown Ore   ○ Siderite

○ Principal Center

Bituminous Coal

MAP 6

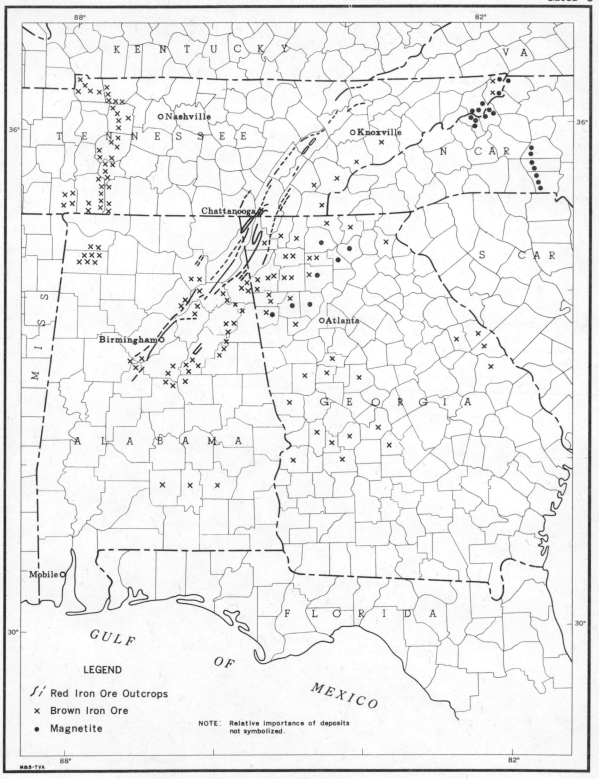

LEGEND

∫∫ Red Iron Ore Outcrops

✗ Brown Iron Ore

● Magnetite

NOTE: Relative importance of deposits
not symbolized.

M&S-TVA

88°   82°

IRON ORE DEPOSITS IN THE SOUTHEASTERN STATES

SCALE OF MILES

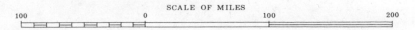

100   0   100   200

MAP 7

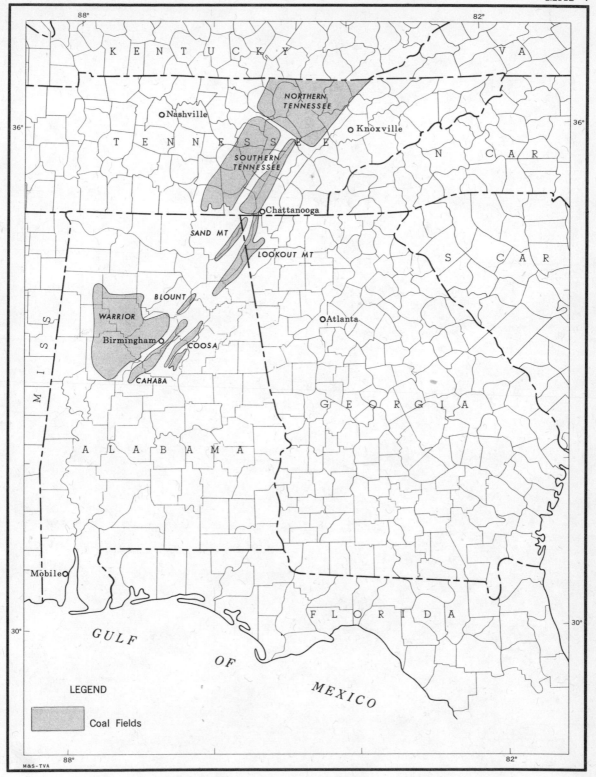

COAL FIELDS IN THE SOUTHEASTERN STATES

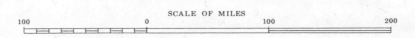

MAP 8

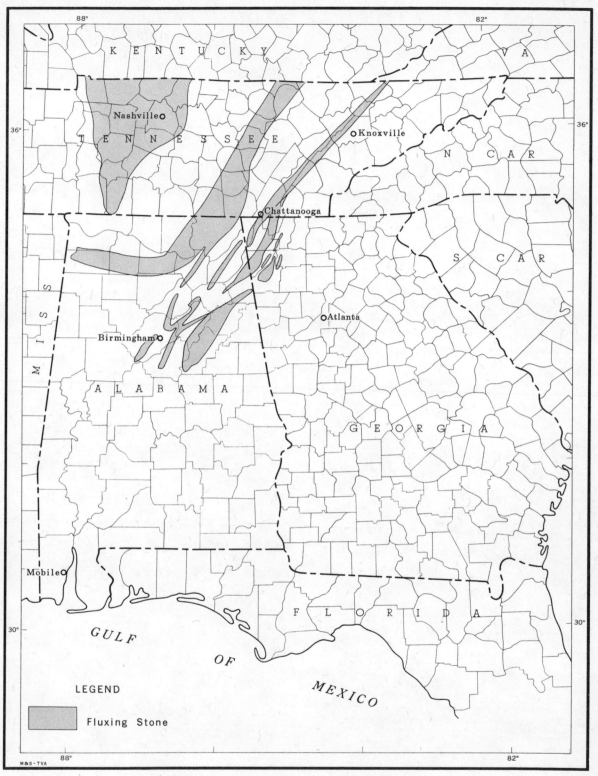

FLUXING STONE IN THE SOUTHEASTERN STATES

SCALE OF MILES

100   0   100   200

MAP 9

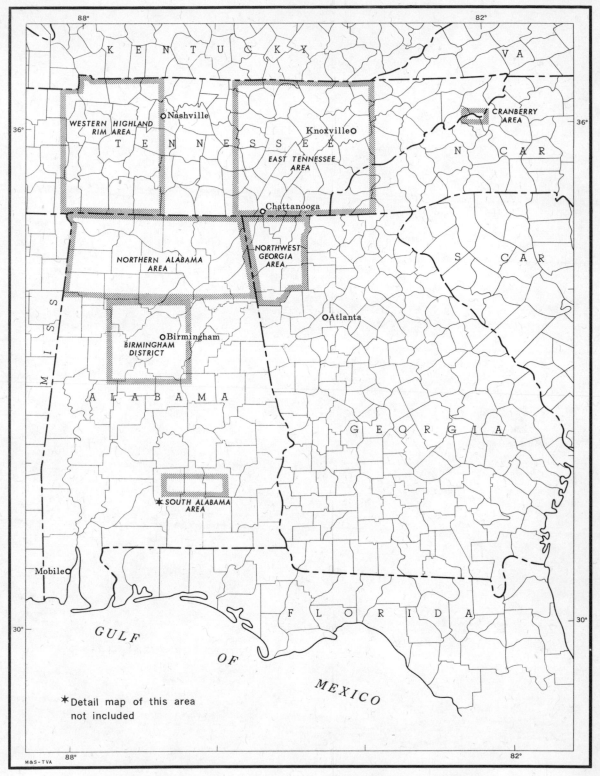

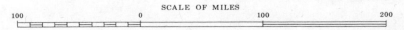

RAW MATERIAL AREAS IN THE SOUTHEASTERN STATES

SCALE OF MILES

MAP 10

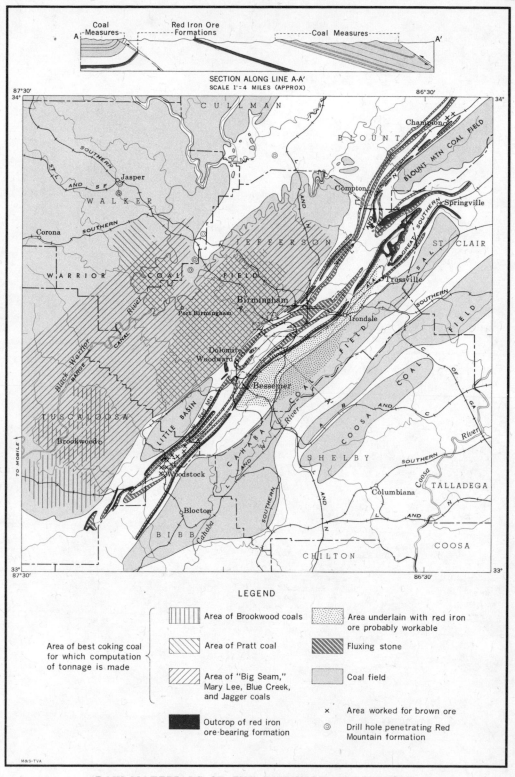

Coal Measures — Red Iron Ore Formations — Coal Measures

SECTION ALONG LINE A-A'
SCALE 1"= 4 MILES (APPROX)

LEGEND

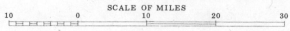

Area of best coking coal for which computation of tonnage is made

⊟ Area of Brookwood coals

▧ Area of Pratt coal

▨ Area of "Big Seam," Mary Lee, Blue Creek, and Jagger coals

■ Outcrop of red iron ore-bearing formation

▦ Area underlain with red iron ore probably workable

▨ Fluxing stone

▨ Coal field

× Area worked for brown ore

◎ Drill hole penetrating Red Mountain formation

RAW MATERIALS OF THE BIRMINGHAM DISTRICT
IRON ORE, COAL, AND FLUXING STONE

SCALE OF MILES

10   0   10   20   30

MAP 11

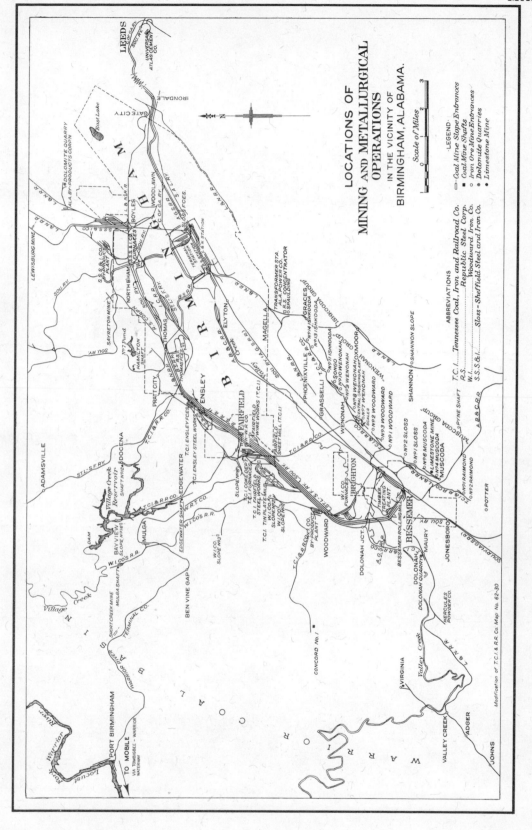

LOCATIONS OF
MINING AND METALLURGICAL
OPERATIONS
IN THE VICINITY OF
BIRMINGHAM, ALABAMA.

Scale of Miles

LEGEND:
⊐ Coal Mine Slope Entrances
■ Coal Mine Shafts
○ Iron Ore Mine Entrances
● Dolomite Quarries
● Limestone Mine

ABBREVIATIONS
T.C.I. .... Tennessee Coal, Iron and Railroad Co.
R.S. .... Republic Steel Corp.
W.I. .... Woodward Iron Co.
S.S.S.&I. ..... Sloss-Sheffield Steel and Iron Co.

Modification of T.C.I.& R.R. Co. Map No. 62-30

MAP 12

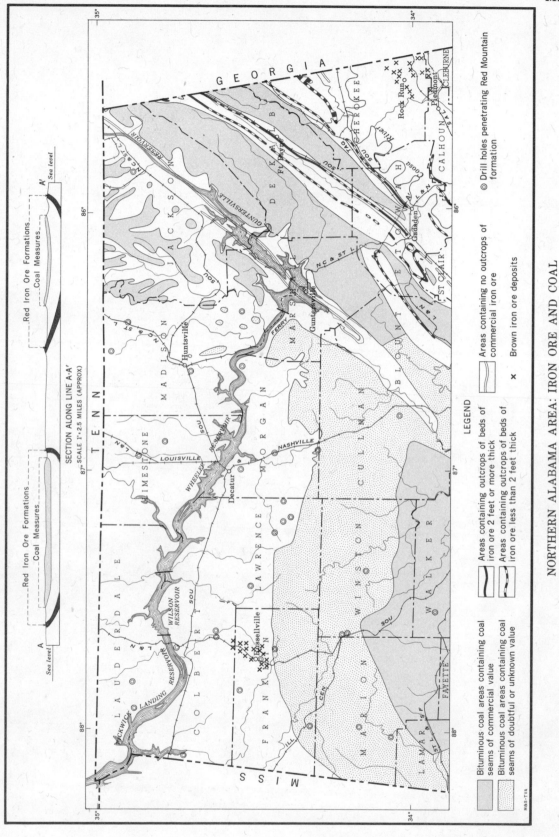

NORTHERN ALABAMA AREA: IRON ORE AND COAL

SCALE OF MILES

10   0   10   20   30   40   50

SECTION ALONG LINE A-A'
8" SCALE 1"·2.5 MILES (APPROX)

A   A'
Sea level   Sea level

---Red Iron Ore Formations---   ---Red Iron Ore Formations---
------Coal Measures------   ------Coal Measures------

LEGEND

Bituminous coal areas containing coal
seams of commercial value

Bituminous coal areas containing coal
seams of doubtful or unknown value

Areas containing outcrops of beds of
iron ore 2 feet or more thick

Areas containing outcrops of beds of
iron ore less than 2 feet thick

Areas containing no outcrops of
commercial iron ore

Brown iron ore deposits

⊙ Drill holes penetrating Red Mountain
formation

×

M&S—TVA

MAP 13

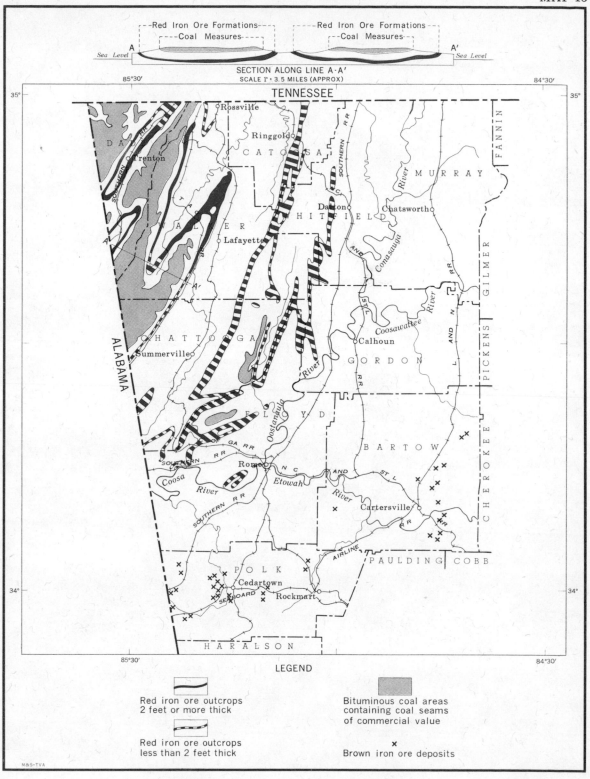

Red Iron Ore Formations
Coal Measures
Red Iron Ore Formations
Coal Measures

A

Sea Level

A'

Sea Level

SECTION ALONG LINE A-A'
SCALE 1" = 3.5 MILES (APPROX)

85°30'

84°30'

35°

35°

TENNESSEE

Rossville

Ringgold

CATOOSA

DADE

SOUTHERN RR

Trenton

WALKER

Lafayette

WHITFIELD

Dalton

SOUTHERN RR

Chatsworth

MURRAY

Conasauga River

FANNIN

Coosawattee River

L AND N RR

PICKENS

GILMER

CHATTOOGA

Summerville

Calhoun

GORDON

STL

ALABAMA

FLOYD

Oostanaula River

BARTOW

×
×
×

×

CHEROKEE

COAL OF GA RR

SOUTHERN RR

Rome

Coosa River

Etowah River

NC AND STL RR

Cartersville

×

×
×
×
×
×
×

SOUTHERN RR

AIRLINE

PAULDING COBB

×
×
×

POLK

Cedartown

SEABOARD

Rockmart

×
×
×
×
×
×
×

×

34°

34°

HARALSON

85°30'

84°30'

LEGEND

Red iron ore outcrops
2 feet or more thick

Bituminous coal areas
containing coal seams
of commercial value

Red iron ore outcrops
less than 2 feet thick

×
Brown iron ore deposits

M&S-TVA

NORTHWEST GEORGIA AREA: IRON ORE AND COAL

SCALE OF MILES

10   0   10   20   30

MAP 14

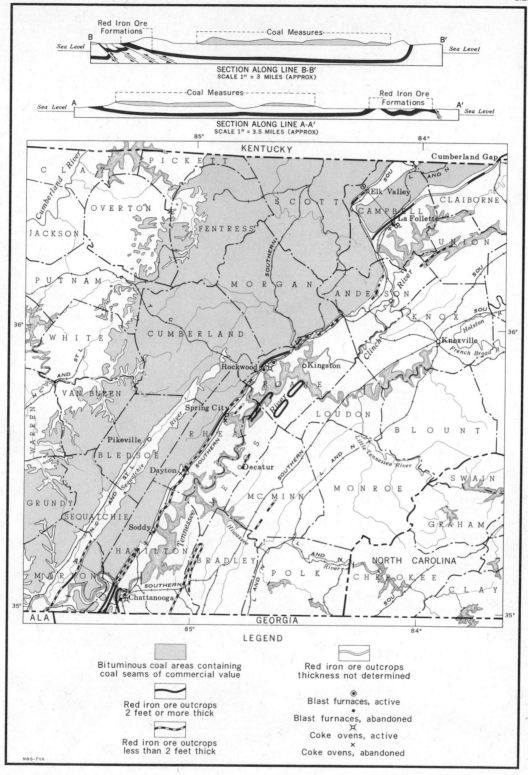

SECTION ALONG LINE B-B'
SCALE 1" = 3 MILES (APPROX)

SECTION ALONG LINE A-A'
SCALE 1" = 3.5 MILES (APPROX)

LEGEND

Bituminous coal areas containing
coal seams of commercial value

Red iron ore outcrops
2 feet or more thick

Red iron ore outcrops
less than 2 feet thick

Red iron ore outcrops
thickness not determined

Blast furnaces, active

Blast furnaces, abandoned

Coke ovens, active

Coke ovens, abandoned

M&S-TVA

EAST TENNESSEE AREA: RED IRON ORE AND COAL

SCALE OF MILES

10   0   10   20   30   40   50

MAP 15

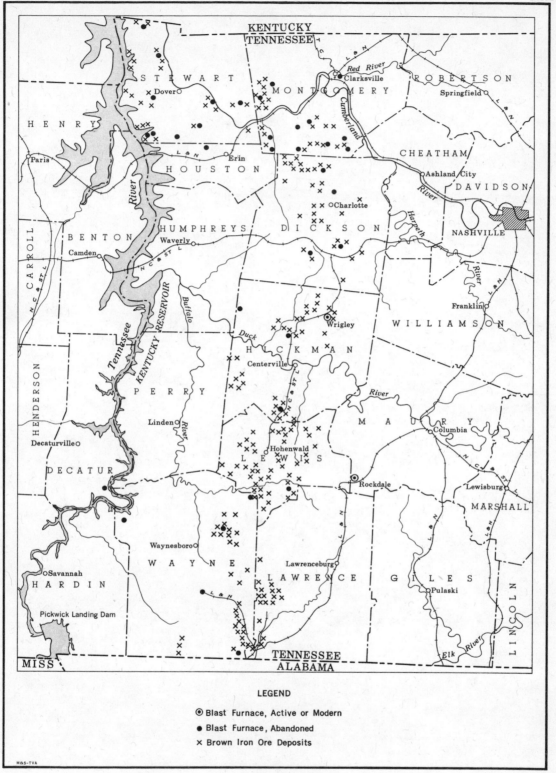

LEGEND

⊚ Blast Furnace, Active or Modern
● Blast Furnace, Abandoned
✕ Brown Iron Ore Deposits

WESTERN HIGHLAND RIM TENNESSEE AREA: IRON ORE

SCALE OF MILES
10   0   10   20   30   40

MAP 16

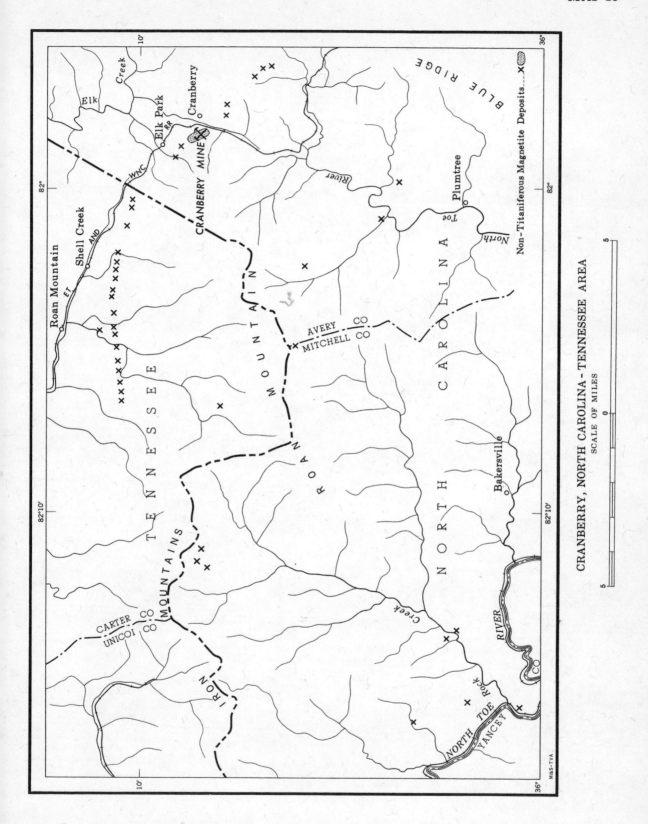

CRANBERRY, NORTH CAROLINA - TENNESSEE AREA

SCALE OF MILES

PART II

NATURAL RESOURCE BASE OF THE IRON AND STEEL INDUSTRY OF THE SOUTH

CHAPTER IV

CRITERIA FOR THE ANALYSIS OF NATURAL RESOURCES FOR IRON AND STEEL

As has been pointed out previously, the problems of assembling raw materials must ultimately be considered in relation to those which arise in manufacturing and marketing, but before this can be done it is necessary to develop the main characteristics of the raw materials situation in the Southeast. To provide criteria for appraising the data on the natural resources, the characteristics which influence the utilization of the mineral deposits needed for the basic industry will be reviewed briefly.

The important factors may be grouped under the following eight headings.

1. Location of raw materials and distances from assembly points.

2. Quality of raw materials.

3. Physical conditions under which the mineral deposits occur.

4. Reserves of iron ore and coal, or size of mineral deposits.

5. Supply of iron and steel scrap.

6. Accessibility of imported ores.

7. Transportation facilities for bringing the materials together.

8. Assembly costs of raw materials.

The present chapter will discuss some of the general problems which arise in connection with the first four of the factors mentioned above. The four chapters[1] that follow will deal with the iron ore deposits of the Southeast; the coal deposits of the Southeast and their relation to the iron and steel industry; fluxing materials in the Southeast; iron and steel scrap supplies and imported ores as a

source of raw materials. Transportation facilities and assembly costs will be discussed in Part III, in which the basic iron and steel industries of the Southeast are described.

Significance of Location of Mineral Deposits

In an industry that must handle great quantities of raw materials, the advantage of having the several different kinds located in near proximity to each other is quite obvious. This advantage is further emphasized in an industry, such as blast furnace products, whose chief finished product, pig iron, represents in bulk a relatively low percentage of the quantity of raw materials put in process. On the other hand, it has already been pointed out that other factors such as high quality and location with respect to convenient and cheap means of transportation, as for instance the Lake Superior ores, may overcome the apparent handicap of great distance from the point of final use. Also, the policies of railroads or the federal government as represented by the Interstate Commerce Commission may provide a compensating factor in the form of low commodity freight rates. Therefore location of ore and coal deposits with reference to each other and to an iron and steel producing center must be studied with reference to means of transportation as well as distance and must be related to the other important factors which influence utilization.

The Quality Factor in Iron Ore

The quality characteristics of an iron ore which should be kept in mind are (1) the iron content of the ore, (2) the foreign materials present in the ore, and (3) the particle size,

[1]The analysis of the natural resources available to the basic iron and steel industry of the South is primarily the work of H. D. Pallister, Dr. E. F. Burchard, and Prof. E. C. Wright.

density, moisture content, and magnetic properties of the ore. Each of these will be discussed.

Iron Content of Ore

It is elementary to say that the higher the iron content of an ore the lower the proportions of other ingredients and therefore the larger the yield of metallic iron per ton of ore handled. This, however, is the quality characteristic which must always have first consideration. Iron ore as mined from the earth may be considered as consisting of two parts: the iron ore proper (the ferrous of ferric oxide or the ferrous carbonate) and the nonferrous (or gangue) materials that are included in the crude ore. The iron content of the ore is a resultant of the iron content of the iron compounds and the quantity of the gangue materials.

The four common iron bearing minerals with their chemical formulas and iron content are listed below.

It is evident that the highest theoretical iron content is 72.4 per cent for pure magnetite. For hematite, the most commonly used ore, the maximum possible is 70 per cent and for limonite or brown ore the presence of additional hydrogen and oxygen reduces the theoretical iron content to 59.8 per cent.

As is indicated above, the iron content of mined ore is always reduced by the presence of extraneous materials. The more common of the "gangue" materials are silica, limestone, clay and shale. Also present in many iron ores are varying percentages of sulphur, phosphorus, and many other chemical elements which are very detrimental to steel. The presence of foreign materials varies from relatively small proportions in the high grade ores to such large proportions that the metallic iron becomes scarcely more than a trace. Unless means can be found of raising the iron content by relatively inexpensive processes, ores that contain less than 30 per cent of iron are not considered to be of economic significance for direct smelting because of the high fuel consumption required in the process of separating the iron from the gangue materials.

Gangue Materials in Ore

The quality of an ore is not to be judged alone by its iron content. Another important consideration is the kind of gangue materials which are present. From the point of view of metallurgical reaction in the furnace, such materials may be classified as follows: (1) those constituents such as water and carbon dioxide which are volatilized, (2) those components such as lime, silica, magnesia, and alumina which mainly enter the slag, and (3) substances such as sulphur, phosphorus, arsenic, titanium and zinc which are not separated from the iron in smelting. From the point of view of the effect in processing, an alternative classification may be used: (1) those elements that generally have a beneficial effect in processing the ore, (2) those that are neutral in effect and are significant because they lower the iron content and are materials that must be handled in the early stages and separated from the iron in the smelting process, and (3) those elements whose presence give rise to serious technical problems and that can be classed as detrimental.

Name of ore	Chemical composition	Per cent metallic iron
Hematite (red ore)	Fe_2O_3	70.0
Limonite (brown ore)	$2Fe_2O_3 3H_2O$	59.8
Magnetite (magnetic ore)	$FeO.Fe_2O_3$	72.4
Siderite (carbonate ore)	$FeCO_3$	48.3

The smelting of iron in modern blast furnaces requires the use of a sufficient quantity of coke to reduce the iron oxides in the ore and to supply the heat necessary to melt the reduced iron and the slag. Lime or magnesia or both are required to react with the silica and alumina always present in the coke ash and gangue of the ore. If limestone or dolomite is not a part of the mined ore itself, it must be added to secure a proper furnace charge. The presence of lime in considerable quantities offsets in part a low iron content and is one of the factors that makes it possible to use the lower grade ores. This is particularly true of certain of the hematites of the Red Mountain area whose lime content is high enough to make them self-fluxing.

The most common of the gangue materials is silica, which may vary from as low as a few per cent to above 40 per cent. Except for relatively small quantities that are reduced to silicon and unite with the iron, silica must be removed during the blast furnace operation by slagging it out with added limestone or dolomite. When it occurs in excessive amounts it increases the slag volume, thereby increasing coke and lime consumption and other smelting costs.

Where the percentage of lime in an iron ore equals the combined percentages of silica and alumina, some furnacemen consider the ore as self-fluxing. There are other furnacemen who consider the alumina as neutral in the charge and balance the percentage of silica by a fixed ratio of lime. Ore at the outcrop and for sometimes as much as 100 feet under cover is called weathered ore, the lime being leached out. This ore is higher in iron content than the unweathered ore that occurs farther from the outcrop. However, the silica will also be higher, and lime in the form of limestone or dolomite must be added to the charge to replace the lime removed by leaching in the weathered ore.

Among the elements which tend to cause technical difficulties, even though they may be present in small proportions, are phosphorus, sulphur, titanium, arsenic, zinc, and copper. Sulphur is not an important factor in southern ore, and the other elements will be discussed briefly.

Phosphorus is found in small amounts in most iron ores, limestone, dolomites, and coke. It has an affinity for iron, and none is removed in the blast furnace. The percentage of phosphorus in the ore and the resultant pig iron determines the use for which the pig iron can be employed. Ores graded as Bessemer should contain less than 0.045 per cent phosphorus. Non-Bessemer ores range from 0.045 to 0.180 per cent phosphorus, while ores above 0.180 per cent phosphorus are classed as high phosphorus ores.

Unlike silica, which is a strong acid under all conditions, alumina may perform either as an acid or as a base depending on the conditions imposed. With silica it may form an aluminum silicate. On the other hand, with a strong base such as sodium, a sodium aluminum silicate may result, or with calcium, a calcium aluminum silicate may result. Alumina in large quantities gives the furnaceman a difficult problem in its removal, due to its high melting temperature and its tendency to increase the viscosity of the slag.

Titanium oxide in excess is troublesome because in the process of smelting a small quantity is reduced to metal, enters the pig iron and is detrimental, particularly in the making of Bessemer steel. It also acts similarly to alumina since it increases slag viscosity and requires additional lime for fluxing. However, titaniferous magnetite iron ore deposits, which for many years were rejected as a source of iron ore, have recently been exploited due to the demand for titanium oxide. Magnetic separation has resulted in the production of a magnetite containing varying amounts of ilmenite $(Fe,Ti)_2O_3$, and a titanium concentrate. It is reported that the magnetite concentrate containing as much as 9 per cent of TiO_2 or 5.4 per cent titanium is now being sent to the blast furnace.

Arsenic is seldom separated from phosphorus and in very small amounts has little effect in steel. It is not known to occur in Lake Superior ores. It is known to occur occasionally in southern ores but only in very small amounts.

Zinc even in small amounts is detrimental in its effect. It is reduced in the upper part of the blast furnace stack to zinc powder, vaporizes, and condenses in the blast furnace gas passages, eventually closing them. Zinc also combines with the alumina in the brick lining, causing swelling of the brickwork. Iron ores do not ordinarily contain zinc, but sintered iron residue from complex sulphide ores used in sulphuric acid plants may contain troublesome quantities of zinc oxide.

PARTICLE SIZE, DENSITY, MOISTURE CONTENT, AND MAGNETIC PROPERTIES OF IRON ORE

Some ores occur in the form of very small particles which when dry might be described as a dust or an iron sand; some are in the form of lumps of varying sizes; and still others are hardrock masses of great size. Likewise some ores are mixed with very heavy gangue materials, others with relatively light foreign elements; some are compact and others are porous with much air space in their structures. The variations in these properties have at least some effect upon the general desirability of the ores and a very direct connection with the kinds of equipment and the technical methods best adapted to their mining and smelting.

When water is present in any considerable proportion it has the immediate effect of adding to the weight of the materials which must be transported. In *The Making, Shaping and Treating of Steel* the authors point out that the marketing of the ores and all the metallurgical calculations involving them are based on the analysis of samples dried at 100°-150° C. "It will be observed that drying at this temperature may not drive off water of crystallization and that in the case of the brown hematites a much higher temperature than the drying temperature is required to drive off all the combined water."[2]

2J. M. Camp and C. B. Francis, *The Making, Shaping and Treating of Steel*, p. 74.

In the case of the magnetites the iron particles are attracted by a magnet. The possession of this property is of very great importance in low grade ores where beneficiation is necessary to make utilization feasible.

Quality of Coal as Related to Production of Coke

A high-grade coking coal is an important asset in the production of iron and steel. The qualities of a coal for making a good coke are four in number. First, a coal is required which decomposes on distillation in a coke oven, gives off its volatile matter, leaves a residue in the form of a porous pasty mass, and hardens on cooling into a coke with a strong cellular structure of uniform character. Only a high grade bituminous coal will do this. Some coals can be improved to make better coke by adding small amounts of low volatile coal, or in some cases anthracite coal can be substituted. Second, since phosphorus remains in the coke and unites with the iron, a low phosphorus content in the coal is desirable. If the content is high, it may produce a non-Bessemer iron from a Bessemer ore in the blast furnace. All southern coals are low in phosphorus. Third, sulphur is also to be avoided, as about one-half of it goes into the coke. Since coke is the chief source of sulphur carried into the iron, it is desirable to keep this element as low as possible. Sulphur in coal occurs in two forms: (a) pyritic sulphur, part of which can be removed in washing, and (b) organic sulphur which cannot be removed by ordinary coal-washing plants. Fourth, it is desirable to have the ash as low as possible. With modern mechanical mining, ash usually exceeds 10 per cent and must be reduced as low as possible by washing. Under 6 per cent ash is preferred.

Physical Features of Mineral Deposits as Related to Utilization

In this technical age with its great emphasis upon large scale production, conditions favorable to mechanization have taken on special significance in such industries as iron and steel. Generally speaking, modern methods can be applied best where operations can be reduced to repetitive routines which can be continued for long periods with little more than minor adjustments. This puts a premium upon uniformity of materials and conditions. As has already been pointed out, the freezing of large investments in capital equipment has placed emphasis upon a large and continuous flow of ore, coal, and fluxing materials to the steel plants. The physical characteristics of deposits and the conditions under which they occur therefore exert a very great influence upon their adaptability to modern mining methods and hence upon their economic significance.

Eight important characteristics will be discussed briefly to develop criteria which can be applied to the more important of the iron ore and coal deposits.

The first characteristic is the shape and dimensions of the deposit. The advantages of large deposits that are regular in shape as compared with those that are cut into irregular shapes (or even cut into detached pieces by erosion of valleys) scarcely need elaboration. Several other features can be included under this general heading. The deposits may take the form of more or less continuous and well-defined seams in the strata, or they may occur in occasional pockets or irregular masses. Again the deposits may be in relatively small lenses or in large masses. In case of beds or seams, the thickness of the bed is a consideration of great importance.

The second characteristic has to do with the structural irregularities of the deposit. The entire Appalachian region of the United States was molded by a great upheaval which created many irregularities in the strata of the area. The folding of the strata created differences in the angle that a seam may have with the horizontal at different places. If the foldings were severe enough the stresses often caused complete breaks or faults in the seam and displacements which require costly connecting tunnels or passageways and special equipment to link the working area with the part of the seam extending beyond the fault. Also the break may create a water hazard which must be sealed off by leaving unmined the mineral in the immediate vicinity of the fault. The stresses may also have caused pinched out areas which produce little or no product of value and which must be bypassed to get to the more profitable workings.

There are also other types of structural irregularities. For example sometimes prehistoric valleys were cut by erosion and then filled with clay or shale, thus creating an interruption in what promised to be a continuous seam.

A third characteristic which applies to the red hematite ores and the coal beds of the Southeast but not to the brown ores is the dip or angle of incline of the seam with the horizontal. One of the important problems in mining is to find the most economical means of transporting the product to the surface from the place where it is detached from its original position. Naturally the steeper the dip of the seam the greater the power that must be exerted to overcome the force of gravity. Also the degree of dip is a factor in determining the distance that a seam will be from the surface at any given spot. Finally, modern mining methods try to make the maximum use of gravity in the handling and transportation of minerals, and the dip of the seam influences greatly the mine layout, equipment, and methods.

The fourth question has to do with the characteristics of the enclosing materials. By this is meant the kinds of strata that over- and underlie the deposit in question. If the deposit is close to the surface or if operations consist of working outcrops, the depth and kinds of overlying or overburden materials will determine whether strip or open-pit mining is practicable. If the seam is so deep below the surface that underground mining is necessary, the character of the material immediately above the seam determines the kind of roof problems that must be solved. The roof must be handled in such a way as to provide properly for safety in the operations. If the overlying material is a kind of rock which can be depended upon to withstand stresses, all the mineral deposit may be removed except for that needed for roof pillars. On the other hand, if the strata above consists of soft or weak materials, careful timbering may be necessary. Finally, the kind of overlying materials determines the reactions that will occur when a particular part of a seam is worked out and it becomes desirable to mine out the supporting pillars. Naturally this can be expected to introduce a certain amount of caving. The question is whether the displacements will be sufficiently serious to cause surface disturbances, to cause squeezes or other adverse conditions in working areas, or to open breaks to water-bearing strata.

The underlying materials exercise an influence because they determine the kind of floor if all of the seam is removed. If the next lower strata is of suitable character, it may be preferable to have at least the main passageways, or slopes, in this underlying strata rather than in the mineral seam itself. On the other hand, soft or sticky materials may make such an unsatisfactory floor that the lower part of the seam may be left to act as a floor.

The fifth criterion is the variation in mineral make-up. A mineral deposit or seam is likely to have variations in its composition. There may be variations in the richness or chemical composition of the basic mineral itself, and there is likely to be a mixture of extraneous materials. Slate, shale, clay, and many other materials are often present, sometimes in quite well-defined layers or partings and at other times in more or less random occurrences. Such materials must be removed. One way is by hand sorting or picking within the mine, and the other is by some one of the various kinds of mechanical separation. In mechanized mines the tendency is to remove everything and depend on separation later. Naturally, excessive quantities of such waste materials make operations costly, and variations in the composition of the seam increase the problem of securing the best adjust-

ments of equipment and methods to produce ore or coal at a minimum cost.

The sixth characteristic is the distribution of minable ore or coal. If the seam is thick and continuous so that slopes and other passageways are always in productive areas, low costs and satisfactory production records can be expected. On the other hand, unfavorable conditions exist if the development strikes places where the seam pinches out and barren or low grade ore or coal areas are encountered or where faults or other obstructions make it necessary to tunnel through unproductive materials.

The seventh question is that of water. In most mining operations the handling of water is a problem that requires constant attention. If water-bearing strata are struck, the problem of keeping the mine dry enough for operation leads to the use of equipment that is costly both to install and to operate. In open pit operations surface water is almost certain to require attention. Also the breaking into underground water-bearing strata may interfere with the wells and water supplies on the surface and cause trouble to mine operators.

The eighth and final general consideration has to do with the relation that a given bed or deposit has to other deposits in the vicinity. Often several different seams appear in a vertical section. This is true of the iron ore seams in the Red Mountain area and the coal seams of the Warrior Basin. If two seams are close to each other or are separated by a very unstable intervening strata, it is entirely possible that the mining of the bottom bed may result in displacements that will render the upper one unminable. The point, therefore, is that intelligent exploitation will plan development along lines that will make the best use of all the mineral resources rather than of a single bed or area.

The Significance of Reserves or the Quantity Factor in Mineral Deposits

As mentioned at several previous places, the introduction of the modern blast furnace which used coke as a fuel quickly led to large-scale production of pig iron and later of steel. This placed increasing emphasis on the importance of deposits of iron ore and coal that were large enough to provide a steady flow of raw materials in sufficient quantities to keep the furnaces in operation and for a period of sufficient length to permit the recovery by amortization of the capital investment in the large and costly plants required by modern technology. Thus the increase in size of blast furnaces in the last century serves to emphasize the increasing importance of large mineral deposits. Around 1850, blast furnaces used charcoal only as a fuel and had daily outputs of one to 25 tons. By the first years of the twentieth century, coke had replaced charcoal, and the size of the furnaces had increased so that heights ranged from 40 to 85 feet, diameters from 10 to 20 feet, and daily capacities from 200 to 500 tons. In recent years furnaces have been built that are over 100 feet in height, with diameters of 28 feet at the hearth and 30 feet across the boshes and have daily capacities of 1,000 to 1,500 tons. Such furnaces consume up to a million tons per year of iron ore and a battery of five blast furnaces, five million tons annually. These installations can only be predicated on deposits of ore of usable grade that exceed a hundred million tons. The capacities of other

items of equipment have increased correspondingly.

Limestone (or dolomite) in adequate quantities is usually available at low cost to all iron and steel centers, and so interest centers primarily on the problem of securing a large, uniform and continuous supply of iron ore and coal for coking. As a result the discussion of size of deposits will be concerned primarily with these two essential minerals.

Estimates of the reserves of a mineral are at best approximations of the quantities that are available. The geologist or mining engineer must take into consideration the accumulated data on the formation of an area which have resulted from observations of outcrops, test drilling, and experience in existing or abandoned mines, and in the light of his scientific knowledge of geology and mining arrive at the most logical figures that the then existing conditions permit. It is important that the reader keep this tentative and approximate character of statistics of reserves in mind throughout the discussion.

Having pointed out some of the important factors with regard to location, quality, physical conditions under which deposits occur, and quantity of minerals that may be available, the following two chapters will undertake to describe and evaluate the iron ore and the coal deposits of the Southeast.

CHAPTER V

IRON ORE RESOURCES OF THE SOUTHEAST

The Southeast has a large number of iron ore deposits which extend from below Bessemer, Alabama, on the south, to northern Tennessee and include northwest Georgia and western North Carolina. At one time or another, many of these deposits have been worked for the purpose of making iron, but the present industry is built principally on the resources of a restricted area in and around Birmingham, Alabama. Three common types of iron ore are represented by the deposits of the Southeast—red hematite, or red ore; brown ore, or limonite; and magnetite. This classification provides a convenient division for the study of the several deposits.

Since location and the physical characteristics surrounding the occurrence of ore are closely associated, the first main section will deal with these topics. After a brief general statement, the location and physical conditions of each of the important deposits will be described in some detail. The second main section will discuss the quality factor, and the reserves of iron ore in the Southeast will be the topic of the third section.

Location and Physical Conditions: Red Ores

In the Southeastern states, red iron ores (hematite) crop out near Cumberland Gap on the northern Tennessee line and continue southwest, paralleling the ridges and valleys of eastern Tennessee, northwest Georgia, and northeastern Alabama. After being exposed at many places by outcrops, such as those near LaFollette, Rockwood, and Chattanooga in Tennessee, near Trenton and Estelle in northwest Georgia, and near Attalla, Gadsden, Birmingham, and Bessemer in Alabama, the formations disappear under overlying younger formations to the southwest of Bessemer. The locations of the outcrops are shown by Map 6.

The red iron ores of the Southeast occur as bedded deposits of large extent and originally were of regular shapes. Also, they were more or less horizontal, but have been folded and faulted into many angles between the horizontal and the vertical. The folding was followed by erosion which has removed the tops from the anticlinal folds, and outcrops of the ore beds are exposed on many hillsides. The beds frequently extend downward along synclinal[1] folds of the formation under the ridges and tend to have a pitch to the southwest and a dip either to the southeast or northwest, depending on the side of the basin on which they are exposed. The angles of dip are almost vertical near Gadsden, Alabama, approach the horizontal in some places under Shades Valley, and vary between 12 and 35 degrees with an average of 20 degrees to the southeast where they outcrop along the northwest face of Red Mountain. The intense folding produced considerable faulting, which frequently tends to parallel the trend of the mountains—northeast to southwest, but some faults are roughly at right angles to the trend of the mountains.

The red iron ores in the southeastern states can be divided for the purpose of more specific location into the following geographic districts:

Red iron ores of the Birmingham District
Red iron ores of Northeast Alabama
Red iron ores of Northwest Georgia
Red iron ores of Eastern Tennessee
Red iron ores of Tellico Sandstones,
    Tennessee
Red iron ores of Grainger Shales,
    Tennessee.

[1] For those not familiar with geological terms, anticlinal refers to a bend or fold of rock strata with the convex side up. Synclinal refers to a bend or fold of rock strata presenting a concave structure or trough.

RED IRON ORES: BIRMINGHAM DISTRICT

The largest production of iron ore in the Southeast has come from the red iron ore beds of the Birmingham district in Alabama.[2] The red iron ore beds crop out near the crest of Red Mountain from about 30 miles southwest of Bessemer to near Springville, Alabama, on the northeast, a distance of approximately 75 miles (see Map 10). The northeast and the southwest ends of this outcrop are thin and poor in grade and only the thicker beds of higher grade ore between Bessemer and Birmingham (a distance of about 12 miles) are being actively mined (see Map 11).[3]

There are four named seams, or beds, of red hematite ores in the Red Mountain formation. These are the Ida, the Hickory Nut, the Big Seam (upper and lower benches), and the Irondale. Of these, the Big Seam is the only one of great present significance. In addition there are two layers of ferruginous sandstone.

The red iron ores occur in the Red Mountain formation which outcrops along the northwest crest of Red Mountain and dips at angles of 15 to 35 degrees to the southeast under Red Mountain, Shades Valley, and Shades Mountain. There is reason to believe that, at one time, the formation reached a crest somewhere above the present Jones Valley (the site of the present city of Birmingham) and dipped sharply from the top of the anticline to the northwest and to the southeast. This crest was destroyed by the processes of erosion that formed the present valley, thus bringing underlying limestone and dolomite to the surface in the valley.

To the west of Birmingham, along the ridge that is known as West Red Mountain, there are outcrops of red ore which intrigued many of the earlier prospectors and promoters of iron mining, but the thin beds with their almost vertical dips have discouraged exploitation. It seems probable that the formation continues to the west, since it is known that the red iron ore formation exists beneath the Warrior Basin and extends northwest nearly to Russellville. Near Praco it is 3000 feet below the surface. There are coal and limestone beds above the red iron ore formation. The red ore formation is brought closer to the surface, however, by a great anticlinal uplift which runs northeast and southwest through the center of the coal field. Most of the deep drilling in this area was done with churn drills and for purposes other than exploring for iron ore. The results of this work are difficult to interpret, but one deep diamond drill core record shows an iron ore bed of interest. Further drilling with careful core analyses will be of great value in providing more reliable evidence as to the potential importance of the westward extension of the red ore beds.

The extensive development and mining operations under Red Mountain have provided more information concerning conditions in that area than exists on any of the other red ore deposits of the Southeast. This fact, along with the predominant position of these deposits as sources of ore, accounts for the more detailed description which follows.

The red ores occur in a series of superimposed and relatively thin beds or seams over an area extending some 20 miles along the ridge opposite Birmingham and Bessemer and under mountains and valleys for at least 3 miles east of the outcrop. This series contains the important bed known as the Big Seam and three minor beds, two of which are above the Big Seam and are known as the Ida and the Hickory Nut Seams; the other, the Irondale, is beneath. In the formation there are also beds of ferruginous sandstone which have an iron content of 15 to 25 per cent.

The Ida and Hickory Nut beds have not been mined. These beds vary from an over-all thickness of 9 feet at Red Mountain Gap with a fair iron content to an over-all thickness of 7 feet at a distance of about 3 miles south. At

[2] Two reports on the iron ores of the Birmingham District of basic importance are: E. F. Burchard and Charles Butts, *Iron Ores, Fuels and Fluxes of the Birmingham District* and W. R. Crane, *Red Iron Ores and Ferruginous Sandstones of the Clinton Formation in the Birmingham District, Alabama.*

[3] For location of mines and discussion of mining problems see Chapter XIII, "Problems of Mining and Preparation of Iron Ore in the Southeast."

6½ miles south of the gap, the Hickory Nut bed is too highly siliceous to have value, and the Ida Seam is only about 2 feet thick. The Ida Seam then increases in thickness to 5 feet, but is only 3½ feet thick at the south end of the area.

A large quantity of ore has been extracted from the Irondale bed near the north end of the district, where it is 4 or 5 feet thick and is of fair grade. It decreases in thickness and practically disappears in the southern half of the area.

Two layers of ferruginous sandstone are shown in the sections on Chart 1. One is immediately above the Big Seam and is about 15 feet thick at Red Mountain Gap. It increases to a thickness of 25 to 28 feet at a distance of about 10 miles to the south, and then thins to 17 feet at the south end of the district. The other is above the sandstone bed overlying the Ida Seam and is 32 feet thick at a point 6½ miles south of Red Mountain Gap, nearly 50 feet thick at 12⅖ miles south, and 40 feet thick at the south end. The latter of these two fer-

CHART I

SAMPLES AND ANALYSES OF SECTIONS TAKEN AT INTERVALS INDICATED ALONG RED MOUNTAIN
WEATHERED ORE NEAR OUTCROP

SHOWING THICKNESS AND ANALYSES OF FERRUGINOUS MATERIAL IN RELATION TO BIG SEAM

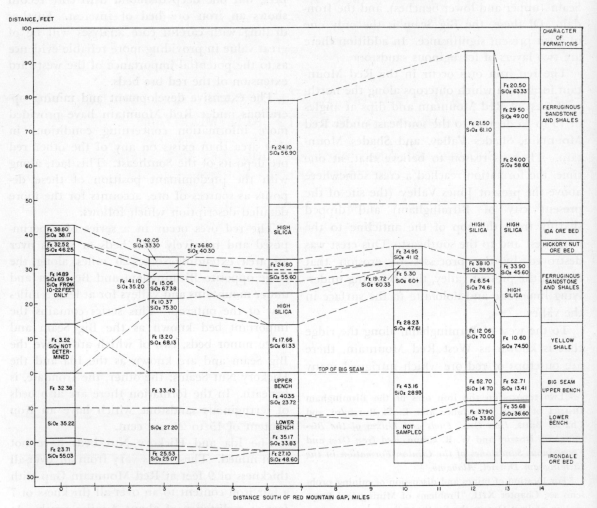

SOURCE: U.S. BUREAU OF MINES, TECHNICAL PAPER 377.

ruginous sandstone beds is near the top of the formation and is exposed for a considerable distance on the southeast slope of Red Mountain where the slope of the mountain and the dip of the bed are at nearly the same angle. These beds have a low phosphorus content and are located conveniently for mining. If they could be beneficiated to bring the iron content to a more desirable figure, they might well become important sources of Bessemer iron ore.

While the Birmingham district does have other potential sources of ore that deserve further exploration, the main domestic source of ore at present, and very probably for many years in the future, is the Big Seam, and for that reason attention will now be concentrated upon the physical features of that bed.

The underground condition of folds and faults under Red Mountain and Shades Valley has been disclosed by drill holes and by mining developments. The displacements along the faults are usually not great but may range from a few feet to as much as 500 feet. The angle of the fault plane with the vertical, the hade, is usually high and may be either with or against the slope of the mountain. It may be noted in passing that the displacement of the ore beds caused by the faults interferes with the mine passages and mining methods. Also the dips of the ore beds are frequently at different angles on the two sides of the fault. The accompanying section through Red Mountain, Chart 2, illustrates some adverse conditions caused by faults and folds of the Big Seam in the Birmingham district. The heavy black line indicates the Big Seam, the heavy dotted line the haulage way, and the short light steeply

CHART 2

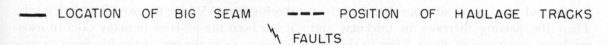

FAULTED SECTION THROUGH RED MOUNTAIN AND SHADES VALLEY
AT RIGHT ANGLES TO RED MOUNTAIN

SHOWING FOLDING AND FAULTING OF ORE BEDS,
CONDITIONS BELOW NORMAL

—— LOCATION OF BIG SEAM   ――― POSITION OF HAULAGE TRACKS
⚡ FAULTS

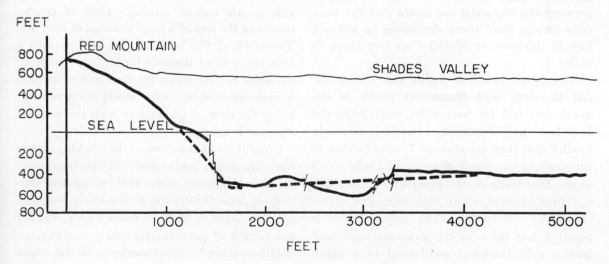

SOURCE: U.S. BUREAU OF MINES, TECHNICAL PAPER 407.

inclined lines show fault planes. Water under high pressure in some faults creates mining hazards.

A few of the faults extend for several miles along Red Mountain but most of them are rather short in length and often feather out into minor folds. Where the latter is the case, mining may be carried out on one side of the fault, then carried around the end of the fault and the deposit mined from the far side of the fault. Should the fault, as is frequently the case, carry water under pressure, there is a considerable loss of ore in the barrier pillars which must be left on either side of the fault to protect the mine workings from flooding.

While the thickness of the beds does not change greatly down the dip, there is a very considerable variation both in thickness and in other characteristics, as one goes north or south along Red Mountain. This variation has been brought out in the discussion of the Hickory Nut, Ida, and Irondale beds and becomes especially significant in considering the potentialities of the Big Seam.

The Big Seam is separated into two beds that are known locally as the upper and lower benches. At the north end and for over 9 miles to the south, the parting is merely a line of demarcation between the fossiliferous upper bench and the more siliceous bench below. Then the parting increases in thickness and reaches a maximum of about 3 feet in the area between the Sloss red ore mines and the Muscoda group, from there decreasing to about a foot in thickness at Spark's Gap (see Maps 10 and 11).

The upper bench is highly siliceous at the old Rueffner and Hammond mines at the north end and for four miles south from the East Lake neighborhood. Then it increases in fossiliferous lime content for 7 miles farther to the south or to a place about ¾ of a mile south of the Spaulding mine. From this point south the lime content is so high that the ore is classed as self-fluxing. The upper bench is about 8 feet thick at the Rueffner mine and increases in thickness southward to a maximum of over 10 feet between the Spaulding

and Sloss red ore mines. This area, the best in the district, includes also the Ishkooda, Wenonah, and Woodward groups of mines. From the Sloss red ore mines south, the thickness decreases to about 7 feet at Sparks Gap.

The lower bench of the Big Seam for 4 miles south of East Lake, like the upper bench, is so highly siliceous that it can be classed only as potential ore and not as commercial ore until it can be beneficiated. From 6 feet in thickness, it increases to about 8 feet in the 4 miles. Then, for the next 10½ miles farther south to near the Woodward slope mines, it increases in thickness, reaching a maximum of about 11 feet in the Ishkooda mines. The ore is siliceous but can be beneficiated. From the Woodward slope mines south to Sparks Gap, shale partings and ferruginous sandstone replace the ore, and the bench thins to about 5 feet.

Since underground mining must be used in exploiting the Big Seam, attention must be given to the top above and bed beneath the seam. Chart 3 shows the kind of strata above and below the ore beds. It will be noted that over a great part of the mountain the Big Seam is overlain by a low grade ferruginous sandstone. This sandstone makes a very good roof and can be used for that purpose. However, in some places a ferruginous slate overlies the Big Seam. Where the overlying slate is soft, it has been the practice in many cases to leave a foot or so of the top of the Big Seam to provide a safe top in mining. This, of course, results in the loss of a large tonnage of iron ore. Therefore, if the layer of slate is thin with a firm top a short distance higher up, it may be advisable to take down the slate and either gob it underground, or, with mechanized mining, bring the slate to the surface with the ore and separate it there.

Conditions of the floor of the workings along Red Mountain are varied. At the north end of Red Mountain from Red Mountain Gap and for 3 or 4 miles south, the lower bench of the Big Seam is high in silica and is usually not mined at present. However, it makes an excellent floor for mine workings in the upper bench of the Big Seam. Farther south, the

CHART 3
SECTIONS OF BIG SEAM
AT SELECTED LOCATIONS
SHOWING ANALYSES

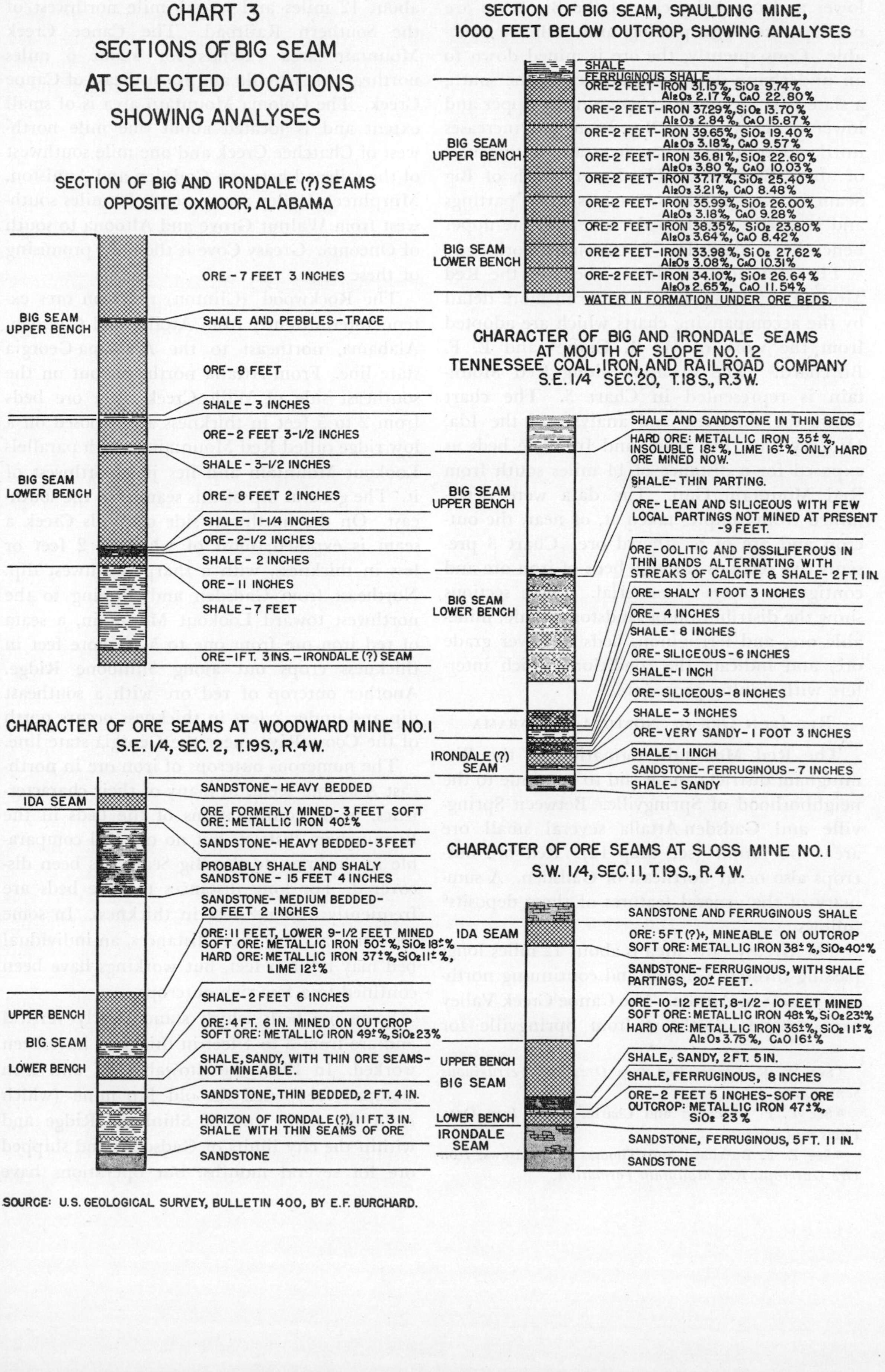

SECTION OF BIG AND IRONDALE (?) SEAMS
OPPOSITE OXMOOR, ALABAMA

BIG SEAM UPPER BENCH
- ORE - 7 FEET 3 INCHES
- SHALE AND PEBBLES - TRACE
- ORE - 8 FEET
- SHALE - 3 INCHES
- ORE - 2 FEET 3-1/2 INCHES

BIG SEAM LOWER BENCH
- SHALE - 3-1/2 INCHES
- ORE - 8 FEET 2 INCHES
- SHALE - 1-1/4 INCHES
- ORE - 2-1/2 INCHES
- SHALE - 2 INCHES
- ORE - 11 INCHES
- SHALE - 7 FEET
- ORE - 1 FT. 3 INS. - IRONDALE (?) SEAM

CHARACTER OF ORE SEAMS AT WOODWARD MINE NO.1
S.E. 1/4, SEC. 2, T.19S., R.4W.

IDA SEAM
- SANDSTONE - HEAVY BEDDED
- ORE FORMERLY MINED - 3 FEET SOFT ORE: METALLIC IRON 40±%
- SANDSTONE - HEAVY BEDDED - 3 FEET
- PROBABLY SHALE AND SHALY SANDSTONE - 15 FEET 4 INCHES
- SANDSTONE - MEDIUM BEDDED - 20 FEET 2 INCHES

UPPER BENCH / BIG SEAM / LOWER BENCH
- ORE: 11 FEET, LOWER 9-1/2 FEET MINED SOFT ORE: METALLIC IRON 50±%, SiO₂ 18±% HARD ORE: METALLIC IRON 37±%, SiO₂11±%, LIME 12±%
- SHALE - 2 FEET 6 INCHES
- ORE: 4 FT. 6 IN. MINED ON OUTCROP SOFT ORE: METALLIC IRON 49±%, SiO₂ 23%
- SHALE, SANDY, WITH THIN ORE SEAMS - NOT MINEABLE.
- SANDSTONE, THIN BEDDED, 2 FT. 4 IN.
- HORIZON OF IRONDALE(?), 11 FT. 3 IN. SHALE WITH THIN SEAMS OF ORE
- SANDSTONE

SECTION OF BIG SEAM, SPAULDING MINE,
1000 FEET BELOW OUTCROP, SHOWING ANALYSES

- SHALE
- FERRUGINOUS SHALE

BIG SEAM UPPER BENCH
- ORE - 2 FEET - IRON 31.15 %, SiO₂ 9.74% Al₂O₃ 2.17%, CaO 22.80%
- ORE - 2 FEET - IRON 37.29%, SiO₂ 13.70% Al₂O₃ 2.84%, CaO 15.87%
- ORE - 2 FEET - IRON 39.65%, SiO₂ 19.40% Al₂O₃ 3.18%, CaO 9.57%
- ORE - 2 FEET - IRON 36.81%, SiO₂ 22.60% Al₂O₃ 3.80%, CaO 10.03%
- ORE - 2 FEET - IRON 37.17%, SiO₂ 25.40% Al₂O₃ 3.21%, CaO 8.48%
- ORE - 2 FEET - IRON 35.99%, SiO₂ 26.00% Al₂O₃ 3.18%, CaO 9.28%

BIG SEAM LOWER BENCH
- ORE - 2 FEET - IRON 38.35%, SiO₂ 23.80% Al₂O₃ 3.64%, CaO 8.42%
- ORE - 2 FEET - IRON 33.98%, SiO₂ 27.62% Al₂O₃ 3.08%, CaO 10.31%
- ORE - 2 FEET - IRON 34.10%, SiO₂ 26.64% Al₂O₃ 2.65%, CaO 11.54%
- WATER IN FORMATION UNDER ORE BEDS.

CHARACTER OF BIG AND IRONDALE SEAMS
AT MOUTH OF SLOPE NO. 12
TENNESSEE COAL, IRON, AND RAILROAD COMPANY
S.E. 1/4 SEC.20, T.18 S., R.3 W.

- SHALE AND SANDSTONE IN THIN BEDS
- HARD ORE: METALLIC IRON 35±%, INSOLUBLE 18±%, LIME 16±%. ONLY HARD ORE MINED NOW.

BIG SEAM UPPER BENCH
- SHALE - THIN PARTING.
- ORE - LEAN AND SILICEOUS WITH FEW LOCAL PARTINGS NOT MINED AT PRESENT - 9 FEET.
- ORE - OOLITIC AND FOSSILIFEROUS IN THIN BANDS ALTERNATING WITH STREAKS OF CALCITE & SHALE - 2 FT. 1 IN.

BIG SEAM LOWER BENCH
- ORE - SHALY 1 FOOT 3 INCHES
- ORE - 4 INCHES
- SHALE - 8 INCHES
- ORE - SILICEOUS - 6 INCHES
- SHALE - 1 INCH
- ORE - SILICEOUS - 8 INCHES
- SHALE - 3 INCHES
- ORE - VERY SANDY - 1 FOOT 3 INCHES
- SHALE - 1 INCH

IRONDALE (?) SEAM
- SANDSTONE - FERRUGINOUS - 7 INCHES
- SHALE - SANDY

CHARACTER OF ORE SEAMS AT SLOSS MINE NO. 1
S.W. 1/4, SEC.11, T.19 S., R.4 W.

- SANDSTONE AND FERRUGINOUS SHALE

IDA SEAM
- ORE - 5 FT. (?)±, MINEABLE ON OUTCROP SOFT ORE: METALLIC IRON 38±%, SiO₂40±%
- SANDSTONE - FERRUGINOUS, WITH SHALE PARTINGS, 20± FEET.

UPPER BENCH / BIG SEAM
- ORE - 10-12 FEET, 8-1/2 - 10 FEET MINED SOFT ORE: METALLIC IRON 48±%, SiO₂23±% HARD ORE: METALLIC IRON 36±%, SiO₂ 11±% Al₂O₃ 3.75%, CaO 16±%
- SHALE, SANDY, 2 FT. 5 IN.
- SHALE, FERRUGINOUS, 8 INCHES

LOWER BENCH / IRONDALE SEAM
- ORE - 2 FEET 5 INCHES - SOFT ORE OUTCROP: METALLIC IRON 47±%, SiO₂ 23%
- SANDSTONE, FERRUGINOUS, 5 FT. 11 IN.
- SANDSTONE

SOURCE: U.S. GEOLOGICAL SURVEY, BULLETIN 400, BY E.F. BURCHARD.

lower and upper benches of the Big Seam are
not separated by a parting, and both are mineable. Consequently, the ore is mined down to
an underlying slate. Still farther to the south,
a slate parting comes in between the upper and
lower benches of the Big Seam and increases
until, opposite Bessemer, it attains a thickness
of about 30 inches. The lower bench of Big
Seam is also split by numerous shale partings
and is usually not mined; therefore, the upper
bench has a slate floor in the mine workings.

The variations in the ore beds of the Red
Mountain formation are shown in more detail
by the accompanying charts which are adopted
from the work of W. R. Crane[4] and E. F.
Burchard.[5] The variation along Red Mountain is represented in Chart 3. The chart
shows the thickness and analyses of the Ida,
Hickory Nut, Big Seam, and Irondale beds as
exposed for a distance of 14 miles south from
Red Mountain Gap. The data were determined from samples taken at, or near, the outcrop and are of weathered ore. Chart 3 presents five sections through beds of iron ore and
contiguous layers of material. These sections
show the distribution of sandstone, shale, mineable ore, and ferruginous beds of lower grade
ore, and indicate the conditions which interfere with mining procedure.

RED IRON ORE OF NORTHEAST ALABAMA

The Red Mountain formation of the Birmingham district can be said to continue to the
neighborhood of Springville. Between Springville and Gadsden-Attalla several small ore
areas are found (see Map 12). Red ore outcrops also occur northeast of Gadsden. A summary of the general features of these deposits[6]
follows.

The Greasy Cove area is about 12 miles long,
passing through Gallant and continuing northeast almost to Attalla. The Canoe Creek Valley
area extends northeast from Springville for

---

[4] See W. R. Crane, *Red Iron Ores and Ferruginous
Sandstones.*

[5] See E. F. Burchard and Charles Butts, *Iron Ores,
Fuels and Fluxes.*

[6] See E. F. Burchard and Thomas G. Andrews, *Iron
Ore Outcrops, Red Mountain Formation.*

about 12 miles and is one mile northwest of
the Southern Railroad. The Canoe Creek
Mountain area extends for about 6 miles
northeast of Ashville and is southeast of Canoe
Creek. The Coloma Mountain area is of small
extent and is located about one mile northwest of Chatchee Creek and one mile southwest
of the railroad between Gadsden and Anniston.
Murphree's Valley area extends 20 miles southwest from Walnut Grove and Altoona to south
of Oneonta. Greasy Cove is the most promising
of these areas.

The Rockwood (Clinton) red iron ores extend intermittently from Attalla and Gadsden,
Alabama, northeast to the Alabama-Georgia
state line. From Attalla northeast, but on the
southeast side of Wills Creek, iron ore beds
from 2 to 5 feet in thickness are exposed on a
low ridge called Red Mountain, which parallels
Lookout Mountain and lies just northwest of
it. The general dip of this seam is to the southeast. On the northwest side of Wills Creek a
seam is exposed, most of which is 2 feet or
less in thickness, with a sharp northwest dip.
Northeast from Gadsden and dipping to the
northwest toward Lookout Mountain, a seam
of red iron ore from one to 5 or more feet in
thickness crops out along Shinbone Ridge.
Another outcrop of red ore with a southeast
dip and under 2 feet in thickness occurs north
of the Coosa River near the Georgia state line.

The numerous outcrops of iron ore in northeast Alabama seem, in many of their characteristics, to be continuations of the beds in the
Birmingham district, but no ore bed comparable in thickness to the Big Seam has been discovered. For long distances the ore beds are
frequently under 2 feet in thickness. In some
localities, and for short distances, an individual
bed may reach 5 feet, but workings have been
confined to a few rich outcrops.

Some ore beds which stand nearly vertical
and are from 3 to 4 feet in thickness have been
worked. In 1946, the Etowah Coal and Iron
Company reopened the old Jap mine (which
is in the south end of Shinbone Ridge and
within the city limits of Gadsden) and shipped
ore for several months, but operations have

been suspended. This project is of considerable interest because of the mining methods used and also because the bed itself may have possibilities, for it is higher in iron content than Birmingham ore and also higher in lime and lower in silica. The steep dip of the seam calls for mining methods which differ from those used in the Red Mountain mines, and apparently the problem has not yet been solved satisfactorily. The ore bed is about 3½ feet thick and probably flattens with depth, continuing under Lookout Mountain and outcroping on its west slope. Drilling by United States Bureau of Mines has established its presence and dip west of Shinbone Ridge.

On the west side of Lookout Mountain from Attalla to Fort Payne and at the head of Big Wills Valley near Battelle, the ore beds are 2 or more feet in thickness and have a gradual dip to the southeast. They may be faulted and should be considered only as potential ores. South of Attalla in Greasy Cove, the Bureau of Mines has drilled to determine the physical condition of the Red Mountain formation in that location. Irregular folding and faulting have complicated the structure in the area between Attalla and Springville.

RED IRON ORES OF NORTHWEST GEORGIA

The red iron ores of the Rockwood (Clinton) formation[7] extend from northeast Alabama across northwest Georgia (see Map 13) with a general northeastern trend, but no beds comparable to the Big Seam in the Birmingham district are known to exist. The red iron ore seams outcrop on either side of Lookout Valley from the Alabama line to beyond the Tennessee line. The western outcrop dips to the northwest under Sand Mountain; the eastern outcrop dips to the southeast under Lookout Mountain. Another outcrop follows the east side of Lookout Mountain from the Tennessee line southwest, almost to the Alabama line, where it swings eastward across the upper end of Chickamauga Creek and north-

eastward to beyond Estelle. Here it again swings southwest and continues to the Alabama line. Most of the outcrops described above exceed 2 feet in thickness. In the old mines east of Rising Fawn[8] the thickness approaches 8 feet. Another outcrop of thinner ore with a northeast trend extends from south of Summerville through Ringgold into Tennessee. The total length of red iron ore outcrops in northwest Georgia is approximately 175 miles.

Beds of 2 feet or more in thickness crop out along the west side of Lookout Mountain from Batelle to Rising Fawn where they dip at fairly low angles to the southeast under the mountain. Around Estelle, as well as near Trenton, there are beds at least 2 feet in thickness and with varying directions of dip. In some localities near Estelle, the dip is flat, the overburden is light, and strip mining has been used to recover some of the ore. Further exploration here might be warranted at spots where the beds are as much as 4 feet thick. Shale partings, folds, and faults interfere with mining in northwest Georgia.

RED IRON ORES OF EAST TENNESSEE

The Rockwood iron ore bed[9] (see Map 14) outcrop along the foot of the Cumberland escarpment from the Alabama-Tennessee lines near Chattanooga to the Tennessee-Kentucky line near Cumberland Gap. The continuity of the formation has many interruptions, but there are sections of 15 to 20 miles of continuous outcrop. The aggregate of outcrops, if placed end to end, would extend 160 miles; the workable outcrops would extend approximately 60 miles. The normal dip in this section is to the northwest.

Just west of Chattanooga, three parallel outcrops occur in which a bed of red iron ore up to 3½ feet thick is present. Each of these is about 10 miles long and extends from the

---

[7] E. F. Burchard, "Preliminary Report on the Red Iron Ores," pp. 308-316; R. H. Haseltine. *Iron Ore Deposits of Georgia*, pp. 172-182.

[8] See J. Wentwood Sullivan, *Sand-Lookout Mountain Area*.

[9] See E. F. Burchwood, "Preliminary Report on the Red Iron Ores," pp. 296-303; E. F. Burchard, *The Red Iron Ores of East Tennessee*, pp. 9-40 and 74-150; and G. I. Whitlatch, *Industrial Resources of Tennessee*, pp. 25-27.

Georgia line northward. The westernmost of these dips to the northwest while the other two form a synclinal basin. From Rockford northeast for about 10 miles, a bed of ore, which generally is from 2½ to 4 feet thick with a maximum of 8 feet, crops out and extends for an unknown distance under the Cumberland Plateau to the northwest. Another bed, ranging from 3 feet 10 inches to 8 feet 4 inches (including two partings aggregating 30 inches) in thickness, outcrops for 15 miles northeast of LaFollette and dips to the northwest under the Cumberland Plateau. Probably the same ore bed with a maximum thickness of 4 feet crops out in Elk Valley, 10 miles northwest of LaFollette. This ore bed has a southeast dip under the Cumberland Plateau—a dip which suggests the possibility of a large tonnage of potential ore in this area at a depth of 1200 to 1800 feet under the plateau.

Finally the two synclinal basins, Chamberlain and Barnardsville, should be mentioned. These basins are located about 20 miles southeast of Rockwood on the east side of the Tennessee River and contain a bed of ore 5 to 8 feet thick. However, it is divided into an upper and lower bench by a shale parting except along the eastern edge. The bed is nearly flat, and the comparatively soft cover over a large area is less than 50 feet in thickness. These conditions are favorable to strip mining.

Red Iron Ore in the Tellico Sandstone

Ferruginous beds in the Tellico sandstone,[10] reported to be of Ordovician age, crop out near Sweetwater and east of Knoxville, Tennessee, and at a few localities in northwest Georgia. They are not of economic importance at present.

Red Iron Ore in the Grainger Shale

The Grainger shale,[11] a formation probably of Mississippian age, outcrops in Blount

10 See E. F. Burchard, "Preliminary Report on the Red Iron Ores," 296-313 and E. F. Burchard, *Red Iron Ores of East Tennessee.*

11 See E. F. Burchard, "Preliminary Report on the Red Iron Ores."

County, Tennessee, south of Knoxville. This shale dips to the southeast and carries alternating sandy and shaly beds of iron oxide. These beds of low grade ore range from 3 to 8 feet in thickness, but have many partings. A small amount of red iron ore is reported to have been mined.

Location and Physical Conditions: Brown Ores

The brown iron ores of Alabama, Georgia, and Tennessee consist of heterogeneous mixtures of nodules and fragments most frequently of limonite but sometimes of geothite, siderite, and other iron oxides, with replacements and fine particles of the above iron ores. These pieces of ore are roughly distributed in sand, clay, round pebbles, and angular fragments (some of larger size) of chert, quartz, sandstone, and sometimes limestone. This ore and debris rests upon the eroded irregular surface of older rocks, frequently limestone and occasionally sandstone. This ore mass is often covered by sand, gravel, and clay to a considerable depth. In contrast to the red hematite ores, the brown ores do not occur as regular layers or beds in the strata but as occasional deposits or masses. Consequently, neither the presence nor the extent of a deposit can be predicted by a study of geological formations in the same manner as is possible with the hematites. These characteristics necessitate expensive prospecting by test pits or wells, or by core drilling.

In size, the deposits in the Southeast vary from small pockets to deposits that cover hundreds of acres in area. Generally, the deposits are irregular in shape and may be very thin or, in some cases, extend downward for over 100 feet. In the deeper operations, surface and ground water interferes and must be pumped. Large pits which are partly filled with water are characteristic features of areas in which worked out deposits are located.

The most important past and present areas in which these deposits are found are:

1. Woodstock, Alabama
2. Champion, Alabama

3. Eastern Alabama
4. South Alabama
5. Russellville, Alabama
6. Western Highland Rim, Tennessee
7. Eastern Tennessee
8. Georgia.

The location of these areas and the characteristics of the deposits within each area will be briefly described. In addition, there are many other scattered deposits in the Southeast. For example, considerable ore is known to exist in north central Mississippi between Winona and Oxford.

THE WOODSTOCK AREA

The Woodstock area (see Map 10) of Alabama has supplied a large proportion of the brown iron ore that has been used in the furnaces of the Birmingham district. The known area extends from a point about 6 miles northeast of Bucksville, a road intersection near the county line between Jefferson and Tuscaloosa Counties, southward nearly 17 miles to within a short distance of Bibbville in Bibb County. The area is well located with respect to the blast furnaces at Birmingham with which it has direct connections by the Southern and the Louisville and Nashville railroads. The area has been extensively worked, but in the summer of 1950 only one washer near Adkins was being operated. Many of the large pits are hundreds of acres in area and, in some cases, are limited only by property lines. The deposits vary in thickness from only a few feet to a depth of 125 feet. The underlying hard rock is usually dolomite. The outline of the ore body is very irregular, often being interrupted by pinnacles of the underlying strata. The ore may pass in a few feet into barren ground. Water in large quantities is encountered in the deeper pits.

Extensive drilling by the U. S. Bureau of Mines has been done in the Woodstock district to develop further reserves. Also, modern mining methods make it possible to handle lower grades of material and may result in reworking some areas and in further extensions of the district.

THE CHAMPION AREA

The brown iron ore deposits at Champion, which is in Murphree's Valley about 35 miles northeast of Birmingham, have furnished considerable tonnages but are now reported as practically worked out. For several years the Shook and Fletcher Supply Company operated a mine and washer about 3 miles north of Odenville, but this operation has been closed.

EASTERN ALABAMA AREA

Most of the scattered irregular brown iron ore deposits in eastern Alabama (see Map 12) are in the vicinity of faults. These deposits are generally smaller in area than those in the Woodstock district, but some of them are over 100 acres in area and may occasionally exceed 50 feet in depth. Many of the deposits seem to contain a softer ore of finer size than those in the Woodstock district. The underlying material is usually limestone. One central washer sometimes serves several small pits.

During World War I and World War II, and at other times when the demand for iron ore was strong and the price was high, many scattered brown iron ore deposits in eastern Alabama were mined either by hand or by power excavating machinery, and the ore was shipped to the blast furnaces of Birmingham and Gadsden.

Among the counties in eastern Alabama which have produced brown iron ore are: Marshall, Cherokee, Etowah, Calhoun, St. Clair, Shelby, Cleburne,[12] Talladega, Clay, Coosa, and Chilton. In some cases the quantities have been small.

At Shelby, Alabama, in Shelby County, there was a large deposit of brown iron ore which kept one blast furnace operating for about 50 years and a second blast furnace for 20 years. Following the shutdown of the furnaces, one firm of mine operators continued to mine, wash, and ship concentrates to Birmingham until 1932. Little iron ore has been shipped since that year. Two open pit mines and two washers are producing brown ore near Bluff-

[12] See J. W. Huddle, *Brown Iron Ore of the Chulafinnee District.*

ton, Cherokee County, near the Georgia-Alabama line.

SOUTH ALABAMA AREA

Brown and carbonate iron ores are known to be present in workable quantities in Butler, Crenshaw, and Pike counties, Alabama, about 150 miles south of Birmingham (see Map 9). These deposits are scattered. No large quantities of ore have been found at any one point, and as a result, only selected high grade ores have any economic significance at present.

THE RUSSELLVILLE AREA OF ALABAMA

The Russellville district[13] in Franklin, Colbert, and Lauderdale counties in northwestern Alabama long has been noted for its contribution of brown iron ore to the blast furnaces of the Birmingham and other districts. This and the northwest Georgia area are the most active brown ore mining districts in the Southeast at the present time.

The ore occurrence is somewhat similar in general physical characteristics to that of other southern brown ore deposits. Lenses and irregular masses of brown iron ore, up to hundreds of acres in area and varying in thickness from a few feet to 100 feet or more, are underlain by the irregular surface of older limestones or sandstones. Sometimes the brown iron ore extends downward from the surface, but in other places it is covered by unconsolidated clay, sand, gravel, or soil to a depth of 10 to 20 feet. Water in considerable quantity is encountered with depth.

WESTERN HIGHLAND RIM AREA

Extending due northward from the brown iron ore deposits of northwestern Alabama to the Kentucky line, a distance of 115 miles, is a belt containing scattered deposits of brown iron ores which is from 15 to 40 miles in width and is known as the Western Highland Rim area of Tennessee (see Map 15).[14] In former

times, these brown iron ores were worked at many places for use in small local blast furnaces but now only serve as a potential reserve. The deposits vary from a few feet to 60 feet in thickness and show evidences of lateral extent from 5 acres to over 100 acres. The ore and gangue mixture lies on the eroded surface of older rocks and is overlain by unconsolidated clay, sand, gravel, or soil. Many of the deposits occupy high ground and are self-draining. The remains of the last two washers in this area are reported to have been junked in 1946.

EASTERN TENNESSEE AREA

The brown iron ores of eastern Tennessee (see Map 14) consist of widely scattered deposits in the valley region flanking the western edge of the Blue Ridge Mountains from Georgia to the Virginia line. None of these deposits is being mined, and, due to their distance from the Birmingham district, little interest has been shown in recent years in their exploration.

BROWN IRON ORES OF GEOGRIA

The brown iron ores of Georgia[15] (see Maps 6 and 13) can be divided into four groups according to the formations on which they were deposited.

1. Brown iron ore deposits of the Paleozoic Area
2. Brown iron ore deposits of the Metamorphosed Paleozoic Area
3. Brown iron ore deposits of the Crystalline Area
4. Brown iron ore deposits of the Coastal Plain Area

BROWN IRON ORE DEPOSITS: PALEOZOIC AREA OF GEORGIA

The brown iron ores in the Paleozoic area are the most important of the brown iron ores in Georgia. They are found in the northwest counties of Georgia extending from Cedartown and Cartersville northeast to the Tennessee line. The nearest deposits in this district are only 40 miles from Gadsden, Alabama. Ore

[13] See E. F. Burchard, "Brown Iron Ores, Russellville District," pp. 152-160.

[14] See E. F. Burchard, "Brown Iron Ores, Russellville District," pp. 152-160; Whitlatch, pp. 25-27; E. C. Echel, *Iron Ores and Iron Industries*, p. 5; and E. F. Burchard, *The Brown Ores of the Western Highland Rim, Tennessee.*

[15] Hazeltine, R. H., *Iron Ore Deposits of Georgia*, pp. 7-171.

was shipped to Alabama during World War II for use in blast furnaces there, and activity continued after the close of hostilities. In January, 1947, at least four brown ore mines were in operation and were shipping ore either to Gadsden, 70 miles away, or to Birmingham, 130 miles away. Some of these pits are hundreds of acres in extent and have ore bodies of 50 to 150 feet or more in thickness. One pit is among the largest in the Southeast. The ore mixture here seems to contain a smaller proportion of the large boulders of ore than is found in some Alabama deposits and more of the gravel and sandy ore of a fragmental nature. The deposits are underlain by limestone, schist, or quartzite and overlain by clay, sand, or soil. Portions of the deposit are low in iron and high in alumina and silica. In addition, a high ratio of waste material to ore must be handled in the washers. The brown ore varies both laterally and vertically, but in many places may extend from the surface to the underlying hard rock. Naturally, with deep pits, both surface and underground waters are a problem.

BROWN IRON ORE DEPOSITS: METAMORPHOSED
PALEOZOIC AREA OF GEORGIA

The brown iron ores in the metamorphosed Paleozoic area of Georgia start at the Tennessee line in Farris County and continue southward to the Alabama-Georgia line near Rockmart, Georgia. This irregular belt is about 40 miles wide at the north Georgia line. It narrows to 2 miles near Allatoona in Bartow County, where the most productive area was found in World War II, and then increases to 20 miles at the Alabama-Georgia line. These deposits are about 75 miles northeast of Gadsden, Alabama.

BROWN IRON ORE DEPOSITS: CRYSTALLINE
AREA OF GEORGIA

The deposits in this area occur mainly in a small section in north Georgia from Blalock to Dahlonega, and other around Griffin and Thomaston in west central Georgia.

BROWN IRON ORE DEPOSITS: COASTAL PLAINS

The brown iron ores of the Coastal Plains occur at numerous points along the fall line from Columbus, Georgia, on the Alabama line, to Augusta on the South Carolina line. The widest distribution is from Lumpkin to Fort Valley and around Augusta. It would require extensive prospecting to determine whether sufficient iron ore were present to warrant mining operations. Most of the deposits are too small and scattered and too far from blast furnaces for use at the present time.

Location and Physical Conditions: Magnetite Ores

The magnetic iron ores of the southeastern states are found only in the crystalline belt of rocks in eastern Tennessee, western North Carolina, and in a small area in eastern Alabama.[16] Until recently, exploration work has been confined to a few areas where the greatest concentration occurs and where the richer deposits are found.

The three kinds of magnetic iron ores in the Southeast are as follows: (1) nontitaniferous, those that consist primarily of magnetite; (2) titaniferous magnetite, those that contain titanium oxide in amounts greater than 4 per cent; and (3) hematite magnetite, those that contain a mixture of hematite and magnetite.

NONTITANIFEROUS MAGNETITE

The nontitaniferous magnetite iron ores are those that are so low in titanium that satisfactory pig iron may be produced. They can be divided into two classes: the siliceous magnetites and the marble (lime) magnetites. The siliceous magnetites of the mountainous area along the North Carolina-Tennessee line are by far the most important of the magnetic iron ores of the Southeast. These deposits consist of lenticular pockets of a good grade of magnetite in a large vein thousands of feet (or several

[16] See W. S. Bayley, *Magnetic Iron Ores*; E. C. Echel, *Iron Ores and Iron Industries*; Whitlatch, pp. 25-27; Hazeltine, pp. 183-198; and E. C. Harder, "Iron Ores, Pig Iron and Steel."

miles) in length, from a few feet to 200 feet in width, and from 300 feet to an unknown depth. Continuations of the vein, or other veins, can be traced northward along the North Carolina-Tennessee state line into Virginia. The best known development is at Cranberry where a large amount of ore was mined and shipped to Johnson City, Tennessee, for use in a blast furnace formerly located there.

The ore consists of an intimate mixture of magnetite, quartz, epidote hornblende, feldspar, and associated rocks and should readily lend itself to magnetic separation. It is thought that concentration can be so conducted as to supply a furnace grade of ore, with a minimum iron loss, or a high grade magnetite concentrate, with a larger loss of total iron.

Rolls in the hanging wall cause thickening and thinning of the vein, which is frequently intersected at various angles by many pegmatite dikes. The dip of the deposit is from 20 to 30 degrees to the southwest. The vein occurs in the Cranberry granite, but a gouge of shaly chlorite schist lies between the sides of the vein and the granite wall rock.

During the earlier mining only the good ore was shipped, while thousands of tons of lower grade ore which could have been recovered by magnetic concentration was used for ballast along the line of the Eastern Tennessee and Western North Carolina Railroad.

The adit, or horizontal passage from the railroad grade level into the deposit, has been clogged by debris and has backed up water in the lower workings. Drilling has proven the continuation of the ore for some distance down dip. Draining of this adit, followed by further drilling to establish the structural condition of the ore body below the adit, might make it advisable to develop this deposit by means of a vertical shaft to cut the ore body at greater depth. Shrinkage stoping might then be used in mining. Since the magnetite ore is capable of beneficiation by magnetic concentration, this deposit has considerable interest as a future source of iron ore.

The main occurrence of the siliceous magnetites in the Piedmont area of North Carolina is in Catawaba, Lincoln, and Gaston counties. A small area extends southward into northern South Carolina.

The marble magnetites have been found in only two localities: in Ashe County, North Carolina, and in one place in Carter County, Tennessee. These deposits apparently consist of grains and small lenses of magnetite scattered irregularly through a medium-grained white marble. The fact that it contains lime gives the ore a high fluxing property; marble magnetites as low as 35 per cent iron are merchantable. The distance of the magnetite deposits from furnaces preclude their extensive use at present.

TITANIFEROUS MAGNETITES

Deposits of titaniferous magnetites are found in North Carolina, Tennessee, and Georgia. One area extends northeast and southwest along the Tennessee-North Carolina line from Ashe County, North Carolina, and Carter County, Tennessee, into northwest Georgia. Another belt farther east occurs in the Piedmont counties of Caldwell, Rockingham, Guilford, and Davidson, North Carolina. Although these titaniferous magnetites are not mined in the southeast as a source of iron ore, the increasing demand for titanium may result in the separation of the magnetite and the titanium as it is done in New York. In that state, one mine is shipping magnetite containing as high as 9 per cent titanium oxide for use in an iron blast furnace. The general limit, however, is placed at 4 per cent.

HEMATITIC MAGNETITE

In North Carolina and Tennessee, various mixtures of hematite and magnetite constitute what is known as hematitic magnetite. Deposits of this material are to be found on either side of the North Carolina-Tennessee line in the adjoining two northern-most counties in each state. Many of the deposits are small, but some of them, according to Bayley, are of economic importance. The distance from blast furnaces, however, is a serious barrier to their use.

Two other deposits of hematitic magnetite are located in Alabama: one in Talladega County and the other in Shelby County. The Talladega deposit, about 50 miles from Birmingham, is commonly known as gray hematite and has about the same iron content as the red ores of the Big Seam. It is a highly siliceous ore and has not been mined to any great extent. In 1951, it was reported that a new deposit had been discovered and that weathered ore was being mined by open pit methods. The fact that the ore contains considerable quantities of magnetite makes concentration a possibility.

The Quality Factors of Iron Ores of the Southeast

That the iron ores of the Southeast rank low in iron content is a well known characteristic which is shown in quantitative terms by the data in Table 7.

Table 7
Average Iron Content of Ore Mined by States, 1948

State	Iron content natural (Per cent)
Alabama	38.28
California	54.86
Georgia	42.26
Michigan	49.26
Minnesota	49.86
Missouri	52.11
Nevada	65.00
New Jersey	63.97
New York	62.50
Pennsylvania	56.00
Texas	41.19
Utah	53.93
Virginia	35.01
Washington	56.50
Wisconsin	52.84
Wyoming	47.00
Average all mined ore	49.51

Source: *Minerals Yearbook*, 1948.

CHEMICAL ANALYSES OF ORES

It is impossible to give "average" analyses of the iron ores of the southeast because of the great variation in the different deposits. The soft, or weathered, ores that occur near an outcrop are usually higher in iron and silica and lower in lime than the hard ores of the same bed. The hard ores, or those located at some distance from an outcrop, continue fairly uniform in composition with depth on the dip. For the purpose of comparison, the analyses below, compiled from reports of state and United States geological surveys and from reports of the U. S. Bureau of Mines, show range rather than average figures. The analyses of soft red iron ores are omitted in most cases because most of the soft ores have been mined.

Analyses of Iron Ores in the Southeast
(Elements, in per cent)

Hard ores, Irondale Seam, Birmingham district

Fe	31 to 38
SiO_2	13 to 31
Al_2O_3	3 to 4
CaO	4 to 14

Hard ores, Big Seam (both benches), Birmingham district

Fe	31 to 39
SiO_2	8 to 32
Al_2O_3	2.5 to 5
CaO	6 to 28
Mn	0.1 to 0.3
P	0.27 to 0.38
S	0.009 to 0.09

Soft ores, Ida Seam, Birmingham district

Fe	37 to 40
SiO_2	21 to 40
Al_2O_3	3.5 to 4.0
CaO	0.5 to 6.0
P	Trace to 0.24

Hard red ore, northeast Alabama

Fe	21 to 42
SiO_2	11 to 16
Al_2O_3	3 to 8
CaO	11 to 30
MgO	0.5 to 1.5
Mn	Trace to 0.26
P	0.22 to 0.50

Hard red iron ores, northwest Georgia

Fe	26 to 43
SiO_2	4 to 10
Al_2O_3	1 to 5
CaO	15 to 30
MgO	Trace to 1
Mn	Trace to 0.60
P	0.20 to 2.00
S	Trace to 0.10

Tennessee hard red iron ores

Fe	27 to 41
SiO_2	4 to 15

Al_2O_3	1.5 to 8
CaO	7 to 26
MgO	1 to 4
Mn	0.1 to 0.6
P	0.4 to 0.9
S	0.02 to 0.84

Ferruginous sandstone, Red Mountain, Birmingham district

Fe	25
SiO_2	55
P	0.035

Brown iron ores after washing, Woodstock, Alabama

Fe	40 to 50
SiO_2	10 to 21
Al_2O_3	3 to 5
Mn	Trace to 1.2
P	0.2 to 0.9
H_2O	1 to 12

Brown iron ores after washing, Champion, Alabama

Fe	43 to 52
SiO_2	5 to 18
Al_2O_3	2 to 4
Mn	0.6 to 0.85
P	0.18 to 0.3
H_2O	6 to 7

Brown iron ores after washing, Russellville, Alabama

Fe	51 to 57
SiO_2	2.5 to 9.5
P	0.07 to 0.83
S	0.01 to 0.05

Brown iron ores after washing from Tennessee Western Highland Rim

Fe	38 to 52
Insol.	10 to 38
P	0.12 to 1.30
Mn	0.10 to 1.30

Brown iron ores after washing from Georgia Paleozoic area

Fe	38 to 57
SiO_2	4 to 28
Al_2O_3	1 to 9
Mn	Trace to 8
P	Trace to 2
S	Trace to 0.15

Magnetic iron ore at Cranberry Mine, North Carolina

Fe	45 to 48
SiO_2	20 to 23
CaO	8 to 10
MgO	1 to 2
Mn	Low
Al_2O_3	Low
TiO_2	Trace
P	Trace
S	Trace

Titaniferous magnetites

Fe	21 to 67
TiO_2	12 to 23
Cr_2O_3	0.50 to 1.50

CaO	Trace to 1
Al_2O_3	2 to 3
Mn	Trace to 1

An examination of the above analyses of southeastern ores shows that the red ores generally have low iron content—rarely above 40 per cent. The brown ores are better in this respect—the Russellville ores, after washing, have an iron content of more than 50 per cent. The red ores generally show a substantial calcium or lime content, although the ranges in the percentages for particular seams or areas are rather wide. The brown ores do not report lime. Silica is an element that accounts for a large portion of the bulk in all the ores, but here again there is a wide range in many of the seams. Except for the Cranberry ore and the ferruginous sandstone of Red Mountain, none of the Southeastern ores can qualify as being low in phosphorus. On the other hand, sulphur seldom is present in sufficient quantities to present a problem. Alumina is present in all of the ores and, in some of the ores, in amounts which may be troublesome.

The unweathered red iron ores from Bessemer northeast through Alabama, northwest Georgia, and eastern Tennessee frequently are high in limes — sometimes exceeding 25 per cent. When this occurs, the silica is frequently less than 10 per cent and the ore is more than self-fluxing. Such ores can be mixed with red or brown iron ores higher in silica, and little, if any, limestone is needed. Throughout the central part of the Birmingham district, the upper bench of the big seam is high in lime and low in silica, while the lower bench is lower in lime and higher in silica.

Only the ores from the Cranberry nontitaniferous magnetite mine in North Carolina and some of the ferruginous sandstone of the Birmingham district can be classed as Bessemer iron ores. While the phosphorus content can be controlled in the basic open hearth process of making steel, the presence of this element in pig iron made from the Big Seam ores has limited its use, high phosphorus pig iron being considered unsuitable for many types of iron castings.

OTHER QUALITY CHARACTERISTICS

The red hematite ores of the Southeast are in the form of rock layers or beds which must be broken from the ore face in the mine and then broken or crushed into sizes which permit transportation from the mine and handling at the blast furnace. This, of course, influences the mining and handling technique and the kinds of equipment required. As compared with the brown ores or the high grade ores of the Lake Superior region, the red ores are hard. On the other hand, the Birmingham red ores do not pack together as readily as do the Lake Superior ores, and this has some effect on handling and on furnace practice. Also, the Birmingham ores are not as readily reduced to dust or blown away by air blast as the finer ores. Compared with the low grade Lake Superior ores, the taconites, the Birmingham ores are not nearly so hard and can be crushed more easily. This may be a factor of some importance in the application of methods of beneficiation. An offsetting factor is that the Red Mountain ores consist of ferrous oxides cemented intimately around very fine particles of sand (silica), and this makes the separation of the iron and sand particles difficult in a beneficiation process. As a result, there is a quite complex balancing of the good and the less advantageous quality features, and this condition presents many difficult technical problems.

Reserves of Iron Ores in the Southeast

The statistics on the iron ore reserves in the Southeast which are presented in this section were set up as a result of a detailed examination of estimates of many authorities.[17] While care has been taken to present the most authoritative figures possible, the limitations[18]

[17] Visits were made to many of the districts to observe the characteristics of the deposits. Members of the technical staffs of the U. S. Geological Survey, the U. S. Bureau of Mines, the Tennessee Valley Authority, and the Geological Surveys of Alabama, Tennessee, North Carolina, and Georgia were interviewed. Dr. Ernest F. Burchard served as a special consultant.

[18] For a statement of the limitations, see Chapter IV.

which apply to all estimates of reserves must be remembered. In other words, the quantities which are given must always be considered as approximations and not as the results of exact measurements.

The data given in the following paragraphs use two classes: available ore and potential ore. The first includes the tonnages that present conditions and techniques indicate as likely to be mined. The second includes the ore that is in existence and that might come into production if such conditions as scarcity of ore, high prices, or new mining methods make it possible for the ores to be mined in competition with other sources.

RESERVE OF RED ORE IN THE BIRMINGHAM DISTRICT

It is generally conceded that there are some 2 billion net tons of available ore in the Birmingham district. This includes not only high lime or self-fluxing ores but also high silica ores. The reserves are here given as 2.08 billion net tons. These ores contain from 33 to 37 per cent iron. In other words, the reserve represents roughly 600 million net tons of available iron. If an ore recovery of 50 per cent is assumed, the result is a reserve of 300 million net tons of available iron. Actual recovery may fall short of this estimate due to wasteful mine operation, rolls and faults in strata, and employment of mining practices that remove only one bench of the Big Seam. On the other hand, improved mining methods and beneficiation may improve the recovery, effecting an increase in the available reserve.

It is a well-known fact that there is additional potential ore in the Birmingham district, both in extensions of the present areas and by the recovery of the iron contained in the ferruginous sandstones. These average about 25 per cent iron and some can be mined cheaply by open-cut methods. The possibilities of iron ore under the Warrior coal field are also worthy of consideration. It is felt that it would not be amiss to place the figure for these various sources at 3 billion net tons of potential ore.

RESERVES OF RED IRON ORE IN NORTHEAST ALABAMA

The publication of *Iron Ore Outcrops of the Red Mountain Formation in Northeast Alabama* by Ernest F. Burchard and Thomas G. Andrews (Special Report 19, Geological Survey of Alabama, 1947) makes available the results of a detailed and thorough examination of the iron ore resources of that area. The authors give an estimate of 57 million tons of recoverable ore and 2.38 billion net tons of potential ores.

RESERVES OF RED IRON ORE IN NORTHWEST GEORGIA

Garland Peyton, the Director of the Department of Mines, Mining and Geology, State of Georgia, was of the opinion that the existing estimates were low. After careful considera-

tion, it was decided to accept the published estimate of 21 million tons as representing the reserve of available ore and to use 2.04 billion net tons as the reserve of potential ore. This estimate was prepared by Dr. Burchard especially for this report. The evidence indicates that this tonnage is in the ground, but whether it can be used depends upon changes in the conditions which govern the mining of less desirable deposits.

RESERVES OF RED IRON ORE IN TENNESSEE

In considering reserves in Tennessee, the southeastern area as far north as Rockford-Cardiff has been considered separately. An estimate of 40 million net tons of available ore is considered justified, while the potential tonnage is placed at 69 million net tons.

In northeastern Tennessee, no available tonnage is given, and the total of the potential

Table 8

Reserves of Iron Ore in the Southeast
(in millions of net tons)

Type of ore and district	Available ores	Potential ores	Total
All districts			
Red iron ore (hematite)	2,197	8,886	11,356
Brown iron ore (limonite)	54	23	77
Magnetite and gray iron ore	30	33	63
Total all type ores	2,281	8,942	11,496
Red ores			
Birmingham	2,079	3,000	5,079
Northeastern Alabama	57	2,377	2,707
Northwest Georgia	21	2,040	2,061
Tennessee	40	1,469	1,509
Total red ores	2,197	8,886	11,356
Brown ores			
Woodstock, Alabama	1.3	1.3	2.6
Eastern Alabama	4.5	1.2	5.7
Russellville, Alabama	12.3	6.8	19.1
South Alabama	1.7	...	1.7
Georgia	22.4	6.7	29.1
Eastern Tennessee	1.3	1.2	2.5
Western Highland Rim, Tennessee	10.5	5.8	16.3
Total brown iron ore	54.0	23.0	77.0
Magnetite and hematitic magnetite			
Eastern Tennessee-western North Carolina	8	11	19
Talladega, Alabama	22	22	44
Total magnetite and gray iron ore	30	33	63

Source: Estimates by H. D. Pallister and E. F. Burchard from state and federal reports.

reserves is placed at 1.4 billion net tons, mostly in the LaFollette-Elk Valley area.

RESERVES OF BROWN IRON ORE IN THE SOUTHEAST

Estimates of brown iron ore reserves are very difficult to make because there is no reliable way of estimating how far a particular deposit may extend beyond the test pits that have been dug. Also, wide variations may occur in a particular deposit within very short distances. The total reserves for the Southeast were placed at 54 million tons of available ore and 23 million tons of potential ore. The estimates by districts are given in Table 8.

RESERVES OF MAGNETITE AND HEMATITIC MAGNETITE (GRAY) IRON ORES

Evidence provided by the examinations and tests of the United States Geological Survey, the United States Bureau of Mines, and the state surveys of North Carolina and Tennessee indicate that an estimate of 8 million tons of available ore and 11 million tons of potential ore is justified.

The United States Geological Survey and the United States Bureau of Mines have made extensive surveys and drilling exploration of the Talladega gray iron ores. From these surveys, an estimate of 22 million tons of available ore can be made. The potential ores are much greater and a tentative estimate of 22 million tons in this class is reasonable.

SUMMARY OF IRON ORE RESERVES IN THE SOUTHEAST

In Table 8, a summary of the estimates of reserves of various kinds of iron ore is given. It should be kept in mind that these estimates are based on latest available data as well as on information concerning the different deposits which has been obtained from confidential sources.

The estimates presented in Table 8 show that the iron ore of the Southeast which is classed as available is largely concentrated in the Birmingham district. There are considerable tonnages in other areas, but, under pre-

vailing iron and steel-making practices, it seems that these should be considered as possible sources of ore to supplement the Birmingham deposits. Also, the Southeast has a large reserve of potential ores which may become important in the future. A final evaluation of the iron ore reserves of the Southeast involves an examination of the position of the region with reference to other deposits in the United States and in foreign countries, a study of the problems of beneficiation, and a careful consideration of the operating and economic problems of the industry. Such an appraisal will not be attempted in the present chapter.

Conclusion

The data presented in this chapter indicate that the Southeast has a large number of iron ore deposits which generally are of a low grade so far as iron content is concerned. The available ore is concentrated in the great deposits in Red Mountain near Birmingham, and this fits very directly into the needs of the modern large scale methods of making iron and steel. However, many of the smaller deposits are located near enough to Birmingham that ores from these localities may serve as important supplementary raw materials for the blast furnaces of Birmingham and Gadsden.

Southern ores generally belong in the high phosphorous class, and this has influenced greatly the development of the basic iron and steel industry in the Southeast. On the other hand, much of the Red Mountain ore has sufficient lime to make it self-fluxing. The region has a great quantity of ore which has such a high silica content that the problem of beneficiation is one of strategic importance, if the ores are to be used. Consequently, this subject will be given consideration in a later chapter.

The physical conditions under which the ores in the Southeast occur are of such a nature that difficult problems in mining are presented. With the exception of the brown ores and the outcrops of the red ores, underground mining is required. With the exception of the Big Seam, the beds are relatively thin. Many dip at difficult angles. Folds, faults and other irregularities are common. In the case of the brown ores, difficulty of judging the extent or thickness of the beds makes it hazardous to base an iron industry on these deposits.

On the other hand, there are very great tonnages of iron ore in the Southeast, and it is entirely possible that exploration will open up new possibilities and that changes in technical methods and economic conditions may make it feasible to exploit deposits that now seem submarginal.

CHAPTER VI

THE COAL RESOURCES OF THE SOUTHEAST

While the quality characteristics of the several coal deposits will be discussed in one of the sections of this chapter, it will probably be convenient for the reader to have a statement concerning the general classifications of the coal that indicate coking qualities. Knowledge of these characteristics should be helpful in appraising the significance of the data on location, physical conditions, and reserves of the deposits.

It has been general practice to classify bituminous coals into three groups, depending upon their percentages of volatile matter, as follows:

(1) Coals that have less than 25 per cent volatile matter (these are usually designated as steam coals)
(2) Coals that have between 25 and 33 per cent volatile matter (these are usually classified as coking coals)
(3) Coals with more than 33 per cent volatile matter (these are considered as domestic, industrial, or gas coals).

Some authorities use an alternate two-way classification: noncoking and coking.

There seems to be a growing tendency to question the adequacy of the older classification by those who believe that modern coking practices are greatly changing the requirements. A recent study states:

A wide variety of coals, as far as volatile matter and coking power is concerned, are now used for making metallurgical coke. Much of the coal from the central district formerly classified as noncoking, because of the weak fingery character of the coke produced, can be successfully coked in modern ovens. At Provo, Utah, metallurgical coke is being produced from 100 per cent Utah coal containing over 10 per cent oxygen and 40 per cent volatile matter.[1]

Considerations such as these have led many furnacemen to consider all coals in the South-

[1] J. H. Kerrick, J. E. Tobey, and D. R. Mitchell, "Use Specifications for Coal," p. 119.

east as potential coking coals. It is certain that a good grade of coke can be obtained in many instances by blending coals from different seams. Consequently, a survey of coal from the point of view of the iron and steel industry should include all coals and should not be confined exclusively to those that are now serving as the source of raw materials for coke, although the major immediate interest will be upon this last class.

Location and Physical Conditions

Bituminous coal in the Southeast occurs in series of overlying seams or beds, few of which are close enough to the surface (except along the outcrops) for open-cut or strip mining. The coal measures occur in areas which have been subjected to much the same kind of geological disturbances as the red hematite ores. The coal beds are hundreds of feet above the red iron beds, and usually the coal areas are much smaller than those of the red ore beds and frequently are entirely removed by erosion. As a consequence of folding and faulting, changes in the dip of seams and displacements are created. Also, serious irregularities are imposed by erosion of valleys. These conditions have made some areas of little commercial significance and contribute to making the Southeast a high-cost area in terms of man-hours per ton of coal mined.

In many of the fields, the number of seams or beds is large, but for the most part the beds are thin, and consequently comparatively few are of commercial significance. The fact that the beds are often superimposed above each other raises a serious problem as to the methods of mining which are best suited to obtaining the most desirable utilization of the coal resources of the area. The mining and pulling of pillars in one of the deeper seams may make it almost impossible to mine overlying beds,

where the two beds are not far apart strati-
graphically.

Another characteristic shared by most of the
coal beds of the Southeast is the presence of
partings of shale, bone coal, and other foreign
materials. This condition makes washing a
necessary operation in the region, if reasonably
clean coal is to be had. This, of course, is another factor adding to cost. From the point of
view of competition with coal from deposits in
other areas, this factor may be offset in the
future by the depletion of thick clean coal
seams in the North.

The coal area of the Southeast (Map 7) can
be divided into a number of districts by geographic and geologic boundaries as follows:

Alabama district
Warrior coal field
Cahaba coal field
Coosa coal field
Plateau-Blount coal field
Northwest Georgia district
Plateau coal field
Tennessee district
Southern Tennessee coal field
Northern Tennessee coal field
North Carolina district
Deep River coal field

The most important characteristics of each
of these fields will be summarized in the paragraphs that follow.

ALABAMA DISTRICT: WARRIOR COAL FIELD

The Warrior coal field[2] (see Map 10) lies to
the west and southwest of Birmingham and is
the most important source of coking coal in the
Southeast. The coal seams are located within
a few miles of iron ore and limestone deposits
and are close to the blast furnaces and to the
industrial cities of Birmingham, Bessemer, and
Gadsden. The Warrior River passes through
this coal field and provides access, by barge, to
Mobile. The entire area of the Warrior coal
basin includes about 3,500 square miles, and an
unknown quantity of coal extends under the
later formations to the southwest.

[2] Henry McCalley, *Warrior Coal Basin,* p. 327; Charles
Butts, "Warrior Coal Basin in the Brookwood Quadrangle, Alabama," pp. 371-381.

The whole field has a gentle pitch to the
southwest. An anticlinal uplift, passing through
the middle of the field and having synclinal
basins on either side, causes a variation in the
east-west dip of the beds. The folding of the
beds has caused some faulting, with dislocation
of the coal beds. The beds of coal are overlain
by shale or sandstone and underlain by shale,
sandstone, and occasionally by clay. The beds
vary in thickness over wide areas, and this
variation in disposition has resulted in interruptions in coal sequences by layers, or partings, of shale which sometimes occur in as
many as three or four points in the vertical
section of a coal bed.

The coal measures, all of Pennsylvanian age,
are over a thousand feet in thickness at their
thickest exposure and include some twenty
coal beds or seams which may be classified into
six groups. Beginning with the oldest, they are
as follows: the Black Creek, the Mary Lee, the
Pratt, the Cobb, the Gwin and the Brookwood.
The Cobb and Gwin groups are not mined at
present and are of minor importance. The
Black Creek and Brookwood are of less importance than the Mary Lee and Pratt groups.
The Black Creek group (except for two seams
of minor importance, the Brock and the Rosa)
is the lowest group of coal seams in the Warrior field.

The Pratt, the most important seam of the
Pratt group, overlies the Mary Lee, the thickest
seam of the Mary Lee group, with an interval
of 400 to 700 feet. The two seams, because of
the thick interval between them, can be mined
without interfering with each other. However,
it would be best to mine the Pratt seam first.
Together the two make up the large part of
Alabama's coking coal production. A higher
group, the Brookwood, has furnished a good
coking coal but has been almost exhausted.
A lower lying seam, the Blue Creek, is also
used to produce coke.

The general conditions in the Warrior coal
field and details with reference to beds of particular importance are shown in Chart 4. Three
sections of the Pratt coal beds are given. These
sections are taken at different mines where

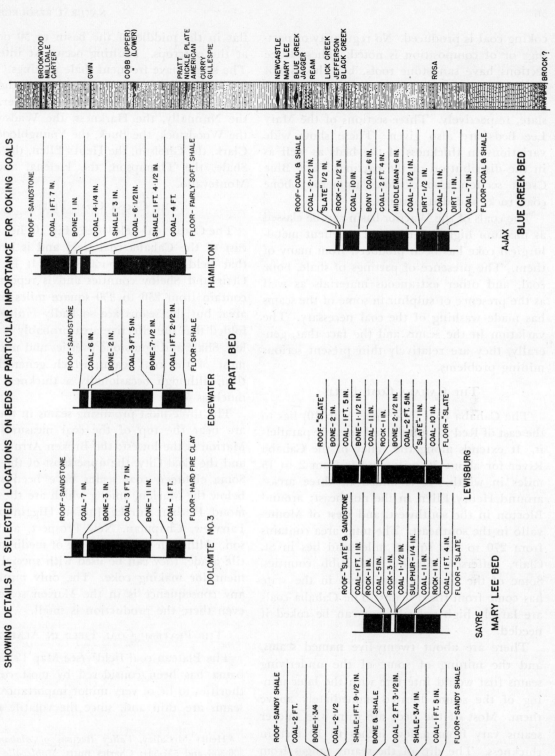

SECTIONS OF THE WARRIOR COAL FIELD

SHOWING DETAILS AT SELECTED LOCATIONS ON BEDS OF PARTICULAR IMPORTANCE FOR COKING COALS

BROOKWOOD
MILLDALE
CARTER
GWIN
COBB (UPPER) **(LOWER)**
PRATT
NICKLE PLATE
AMERICAN
CURRY
GILLESPIE

NEWCASTLE
MARY LEE
BLUE CREEK
JAGGER
REAM
LICK CREEK
JEFFERSON
BLACK CREEK
ROSA
BROCK ?

GENERALIZED SECTION OF WARRIOR COAL FIELD

HAMILTON
ROOF – SANDSTONE
COAL – 1 FT. 7 IN.
BONE – 1 IN.
COAL – 4-1/4 IN.
SHALE – 3 IN.
COAL – 6-1/2 IN.
SHALE – 1 FT. 4-1/2 IN.
COAL – 4 FT.
FLOOR – FAIRLY SOFT SHALE

EDGEWATER
PRATT BED
ROOF – SANDSTONE
COAL – 6 IN.
BONE – 2 IN.
COAL – 3 FT. 5 IN.
BONE – 7-1/2 IN.
COAL – 1 FT. 2-1/2 IN.
FLOOR – SHALE

DOLOMITE NO. 3
ROOF – SANDSTONE
COAL – 7 IN.
BONE – 3 IN.
COAL – 3 FT. 7 IN.
BONE – 11 IN.
COAL – 1 FT.
FLOOR – HARD FIRE CLAY

BLUE CREEK BED
AJAX
ROOF – COAL & SHALE
COAL – 2-1/2 IN.
ROCK – 2-1/2 IN.
"SLATE" 1/2 IN.
COAL – 10 IN.
BONY COAL – 6 IN.
COAL – 2 FT. 4 IN.
MIDDLEMAN – 6 IN.
COAL – 1 FT. 1/2 IN.
DIRT – 1/2 IN.
COAL – 11 IN.
DIRT – 1 IN.
COAL – 7 IN.
FLOOR – COAL & SHALE

LEWISBURG
ROOF – "SLATE"
BONE – 2 IN.
COAL – 1 FT. 5 IN.
BONE – 1-1/2 IN.
COAL – 11 IN.
ROCK – 1 IN.
BONE – 2-1/2 IN.
COAL – 2 FT. 5 IN.
"SLATE" – 1 IN.
COAL – 10 IN.
FLOOR – "SLATE"

SAYRE
MARY LEE BED
ROOF – "SLATE" & SANDSTONE
COAL – 1 FT. 1 IN.
ROCK – 1 IN.
COAL – 5 IN.
ROCK – 3 IN.
COAL – 1-1/2 IN.
SULPHUR – 1/4 IN.
COAL – 2 IN.
ROCK – 1 IN.
COAL – 1 FT. 4 IN.
FLOOR – "SLATE"

RISCO
ROOF – SANDY SHALE
COAL – 2 FT.
BONE – 1-3/4
COAL – 2-1/2
SHALE – 1 FT. 9-1/2 IN.
BONE & SHALE
COAL – 2 FT. 3-1/2 IN.
SHALE – 3/4 IN.
COAL – 1 FT. 5 IN.
FLOOR – SANDY SHALE

SOURCE: U.S. GEOLOGICAL SURVEY, BULLETIN 400.

coking coal is produced. No regularity of partings or of composition is noted. These three sections have sandstone roofs, but this is not necessarily true throughout the Warrior field. The floors are fire clay, shale, and fairly soft slate, respectively. Three sections of the Mary Lee beds are also given. These show wide variations in thickness of the beds as well as in the distribution of the partings. The Blue Creek section also discloses numerous bone coal, rock, and dirt partings.

The coals of the Warrior basin can be classed as medium high volatile, and excellent metallurgical coke has been produced from many of them. The presence of partings of shale, bone coal, and other extraneous materials as well as the presence of sulphur in some of the seams has made washing of the coal necessary. The variation in the seams and the fact that, generally, they are relatively thin present serious mining problems.

The Cahaba Coal Field

The Cahaba coal field[3] (see Map 10) lies to the east of Red Mountain and roughly parallels it. It extends along the valley of the Cahaba River for about 70 miles and is from 2 to 15 miles in width. It is mined in three areas: around Henry Ellen in the northeast; around Blocton in the southwest; and west of Montevallo in the southeast. The total area contains from 270 to 325 square miles and lies in St. Clair, Jefferson, Shelby, and Bibb counties. Some of the finest domestic coal in the state has come from these seams. The Cahaba coals are largely high volatile, but can be coked if needed.

There are about twenty-five named seams, and the mining of some of the underlying seams first would interfere with the later mining of the seams located immediately above them. Most of the beds are thin; the thicker seams vary from a few inches to 10 feet in thickness. The dip of the seams ranges from

flat in the middle of the basin to 30 degrees at the outcrops. Faulting occurs at intervals. The seams have frequent shale partings.

The producing seams, named from the lowest one upward, in approximate order, are: the Nunnally, the Harkness, the Wadsworth, the Woodstock, the Buck, the Youngblood, the Clark, the Gholson, the Henry Ellen, the Black Shale, the Thompson, the Helena, and the Montevallo.

The Coosa Coal Field

The Coosa coal field[4] (see Map 10) lies to the east of the Cahaba coal field and is between that field and the Coosa River. It is in St. Clair and Shelby counties and is reported to contain from 250 to 350 square miles of coal area, but the seams are so badly faulted and folded that the effective area probably is much less. Shale and sandstone overlies and underlies most of the coal seams, which generally are thin, although occasionally a thickness of as much as 6 feet is attained.

The three most promising seams in the field are near the top of the coal measures: the Marion is the lowest; the Broken Arrow, next; and the Coal City, the uppermost of the three. Some eighteen coal seams have been named below the Marion, among which are the Hammond, Herbert Eureka, Judson, Higginbotham, Fairview, Chapman, New Prospect, and Carson. Although these coals are of medium volatile grade, they can be used with special treatment for making coke. The only mining of any consequence is in the Marion seam, and even there the production is small.

The Plateau Coal Field in Alabama

The Plateau coal field[5] (see Map 12) in Alabama has been considered by most coal authorities to be of very minor importance. The seams are thin and, since the volatile matter

3 Joseph Squire, *Cahaba Coal Field,* pp. 3-131; Charles Butts, "The Northern Part, Cahaba Coal Field," pp. 76-115 and "Southern Part, Cahaba Coal Field," pp. 89-146.

4 Henry McCalley, *Valley Regions of Alabama,* pp. 306-308 and 531-534; Charles Butts, *Montevallo-Columbiana,* p. 20.

5 Henry McCalley, *Coal Measures, Plateau Region of Alabama,* pp. 15-109 and 110-215; C. W. Hayes, *Geology of Northeastern Alabama,* pp. 49-51; and Henry McCalley, *Valley Regions of Alabama,* pp. 145-413.

often is only 20 per cent, the coal is close to low volatile in classification. The coal, however, resembles closely the Pocahontas coal of West Virginia and Virginia and has value in that it can replace Pocahontas in blending with the high volatile coals of the Southeast to produce a better coke.

The Plateau coal field includes the Blount coal basin which lies between the north ends of the Warrior and Cahaba coal fields in Blount and Etowah counties and also extends northeast through the Lookout and Sand Mountain area to the Georgia state line. Coal lying to the west of this area is also included. Coal is being produced from the Underwood seam in Blount and Etowah counties. A small amount of coal is produced for local consumption, from time to time, from outcrops throughout the field.

Northwest Georgia Coal Field

The coal field in Georgia[6] (see Map 13) is confined to the northwest corner of the state and is principally in Dade, Walker, Floyd, and Chattooga counties, with small areas in Catoosa, Whitfield, and Gordon counties. It is an extension of the Plateau coal field of northeastern Alabama and has similar characteristics. The field is divided into the Lookout Mountain and the Sand Mountain areas. Some of these Georgia coals resemble Pocahontas coal and are, therefore, classed as low volatile grade.

In the Lookout Mountain area, the coal is apparently in the upper Pottsville formation and has three producing seams. From the uppermost downward they are: the "A" Seam, about 18 inches in thickness; the Durham Seam, which, with the middleman, totals about 62 inches; and the Number Four Seam, about 24 inches. The Durham, according to Sullivan, is almost worked out.

The coals in the Sand Mountain area are of lower Pottsville series and cannot be correlated with those in the Lookout Mountain area, nor can they be made to correspond to

those in the neighboring Alabama area. Naming from the top downward, Sullivan lists four coal seams: the Etna Coal Seam, 18 to 28 inches in thickness; the Dade Coal Seam, 20 to 60 inches; the Rattlesnake Coal Seam, 15 to 30 inches; and the Red Ash Coal Seam, 8 to 12 inches in thickness.

The beds are reasonably flat except along the eastern edge of Sand Mountain, where the gradual dip is to the northwest. These beds are reasonably free from parting in both the Lookout and Sand Mountain areas.

The Tennessee Coal District

The Tennessee coal fields[7] (see Maps 7 and 14) are coextensive with the mountainous Cumberland plateau in the eastern half of the state. The fields embrace a total area of about 4,400 square miles and include all or parts of 21 counties. The entire district is customarily divided into the "southern" and "northern" fields. The line of demarcation is not so much one of structure as it is of chemical analysis. The beds of the northern field are of the high volatile class and are really extensions of the eastern Kentucky high volatile field. The coal beds in the southern field belong to the medium high volatile class. A listing of the counties in the two fields indicates their location.

The southern Tennessee coal field embraces at least parts of the counties of Bledsoe, Cumberland, Franklin, Grundy, Hamilton, Marion, Putnam, Rhea, Sequatchie, Van Buren, Warren, and White.

The northern Tennessee coal field includes Anderson, Campbell, Claiborne, Fentress, Morgan, Overton, Picket, Roane, and Scott counties.

NORTHERN TENNESSEE COAL FIELDS

The area of the northern Tennessee coal field is between 1,000 and 1,500 square miles,

6 John Westworth Sullivan, *Sand-Lookout Mountain Area,* pp. 44-52.

7 G. I. Whitlatch, *The Resources of Tennessee,* pp. 19-22; Wilbur A. Nelson, *The Southern Tennessee Coal Field;* L. C. Glenn, *The Northern Tennessee Coal Field;* Wilbur A. Nelson, *The Herbert Domain;* and Charles Butts and Wilbur A. Nelson, *The Crossville Quadrangle.*

and the thickness of the individual coal beds ranges from a few inches in some places to 8 feet in others. Except where the mountain building pressures forming Cumberland, Pine, Walden, and other uplifts have caused folds and faults, the coal beds are reasonably flat over large areas. Close to the faults, the angle of dip may be nearly vertical.

Shale and sandstones form the roofs and likewise the floors of the seams. Occasionally clay occurs below the seam. Excessive sulphur concentrations, at some places up to 5 per cent, require special care. The coal beds are frequently cut by deep erosion valleys. This characteristic, together with frequent irregularities in thickness of the workable seams, interferes with mining and must be taken into account in mine layout.

SOUTHERN TENNESSEE COAL FIELDS

The area of the southern Tennessee coal field is approximately 2,200 square miles in extent. One of the coal beds which is extensively mined averages 36 inches in thickness, but, in some localities, thicknesses of 6 feet are mined. In some large areas, the beds are reasonably flat, but in many places folds and faults have interrupted the continuity of the beds. A number of major faults are noted. Rolls which cause dips of as much as 45 degrees are common in some parts of the area. The coal is overlain and underlain with shale or sandstone, but occasionally a clay floor is found below the coal seam. Due to the deep erosion valleys, a great deal of the coal has been washed away, leaving the coal beds ex-

Table 9

Analyses of Coals of the Southeast

District and seam	Per cent volatile	Per cent fixed carbon	Per cent ash	Per cent sulphur	B T U pound
Alabama—Pratt seam*					
Unwashed coal	26.12	61.93	11.95	1.62	
Washed coal	27.94	67.02	5.04	1.27	
Alabama—American seam*					
Unwashed coal	27.50	59.50	13.00	0.75	
Washed coal	31.00	65.00	4.00	0.70	
Alabama—Mary Lee seam*					
Unwashed coal	24.36	58.33	17.30	0.88	
Washed coal	27.23	63.52	9.25	0.75	
Alabama—Blue Creek seam*					
Unwashed coal	24.27	59.27	16.49	0.78	
Washed coal	25.78	66.49	7.73	0.72	
Alabama—Cahaba coal fields***					
Harkness seam	32.5	56.2	11.3	1.1	13,300
Montevallo seam	36.0	56.0	8.0	0.9	13,850
Alabama—Coosa field**					
Coal City seam	34.1	61.5	4.4	1.1	15,010
Broken Arrow seam	29.3	61.0	9.7	1.5	14,050
Northwest Georgia***					
Number Four seam					
Face sample	22.0	75.3	1.7	0.8	15,550
Tennessee†					
Northern district††	38.4	56.5	5.1	1.9	14,230
Southern district†††	31.2	60.6	8.3	1.1	13,945

*Steel Making at Birmingham, pp. 12-15.
**Charles Butts, Analyses of Alabama Coals.
***J. W. Sullivan, Sand-Lookout Mountain Area, p. 46.
†P. B. Place, "Tennessee Coals, Their Classification and Analyses" Combustion, VIII No. 3 (September 1936), p. 41.
††Coals averaged from Southern Appalachian, Jellico, LaFollette, Coal Creek, Fentress, and Bon Air.
†††Coals from Tracy City, Walden Ridge, Rockwood, and Soddy.

posed high up on the side hills. This has one advantage, however, in that it provides natural drainage for many of the coal areas.

The Sewanee is one of the best coal seams in the southern Tennessee coal field and frequently has large areas with mineable thicknesses of clean coal. The top is often made up of shale or rashy coal, which sometimes is high in sulphur. Rashy coal (coal mixed with foreign matter) is also found below the coal, but may be replaced by shale or clay. Partings in the clean coal sections are rare.

NORTH CAROLINA COAL DISTRICT

A small coal field is located in central North Carolina[8] (see Map 3) where its production is needed for local consumption.

The Quality Factor

The chemical characteristics of the coals of the Southeast are indicated by the analyses presented in Table 9. These data have been compiled from several sources and may be taken as representative.

The Warrior coal field has been the chief source of coking coal in the Southeast. For many years the Pratt coal seam, after washing, has produced a high grade coke. The Mary Lee, the American, and the Blue Creek are also extensively used. A mixture containing equal parts of each of these four coals would have about the following average content: volatile matter, 28.0 per cent; fixed carbon, 65.5 per cent; ash, 6.5 per cent; and sulphur, 0.86 per cent. If this mixture were coked, approximately one-half the sulphur would be volatized while the other half would go into the coke. About 70 per cent of coal would be converted into coke. The analysis of the resulting coke would approximate 2.0 per cent volatile matter, 88.7 per cent fixed carbon, and 9.3 per cent ash, with a reduction of the sulphur from 0.86 per cent in the coal to 0.61 per cent in the coke. Using Pratt and Mary Lee in a mixture, the sulphur seldom falls below 1.00 per cent in the coke.

The quality of the coal from the better seams in the Cahaba and Coosa fields is good, and some of the coal has been coked. The coal from the northwest Georgia field is in the low volatile class and might be used to blend with the high volatile coals, if it could be produced cheap enough to compete on a cost basis.

The coals of the northern Tennessee field tend to run higher in sulphur than those of the southern field. Coals of the Poplar Creek, Coal Creek, Jellico, and Windrock seams in the northern field are preferred by the steam coal trade, although the Poplar Creek coal was mined for years at LaFollette for coking. Coke is made at Chattanooga and at Coalmont, but Tennessee coal deposits are at considerable distances from important coke plants. Coals from these deposits have been used chiefly for other purposes.

The Coal Reserves of the Southeast

In an estimate of the coal reserves of the United States as of January 1, 1946, W. H. Young of the United States Bureau of Mines placed the reserves in the southern states— Tennessee, North Carolina, Georgia, and Alabama—at 92.84 billion net tons. The iron and steel industry of the Southeast, however, has drawn primarily upon the deposits in Alabama for coking coal, and a more detailed examination of estimates is desirable. A number of estimates are available which, in total, agree quite closely with Young.

The earliest estimate of Alabama coal reserves was made by Butts (*Iron Ores Fuels and Fluxes of the Birmingham District*) in 1910 and was based upon the Mary Lee group, the Pratt bed, and the Brookwood groups of the Warrior field. He placed the total coking reserves of these coal seams at 4.19 billion tons and assumed that 80 per cent, or 3.36 billion tons would be recovered.

In 1925, Forbes[9] made a study of the percentages of recovery of several of the important Alabama seams. He estimated the ultimate coal recovery for the Pratt Seam as 87.6 per cent, for the Mary Lee as 60.85 per cent,

[8] H. J. Bryson, *Mining Industry in North Carolina*, pp. 61-62.

[9] J. J. Forbes, *Coal Losses in Alabama*, p. 10.

for the Black Creek as 61.25 per cent, for the Thompson as 48.7 per cent, and for the Jagger as 55.3 per cent. The average for all of the above seams was 67.8 per cent.

In 1932, E. F. Burchard[10] prepared an estimate of the coal reserves of the Warrior, Coosa, and Cahaba fields. These estimates are presented in Table 10.

Young's estimate for January 1, 1946 was 66.58 billion tons. Additional tonnage for northeastern Alabama would probably bring Burchard's 1932 figures closely in line with Young's.

Table 10
Area and Estimated Original Tonnage of Principal Alabama Coal Fields

Field	Square miles	Original tonnage (thousands of net tons)
Warrior field	3,500	59,826,968
Coosa basin	260	2,396,160
Cahaba basin	325	2,994,200
Total	4,085	65,217,468

Source: E. F. Burchard, "The Birmingham District, Alabama," p. 123.

In this same report, Burchard states that it is estimated that in the three best beds of coking coal in the Warrior field, nearly 4 billion tons still remain unmined and that 75 per cent of it might be recovered. Although he includes no coal from the Coosa and Cahaba basins in this estimate, it is known that coke can be made from these coals, should the occasion demand it. Coals north and west of the Warrior River were not included. These coals are largely used for steam and similar purposes, but could very probably be made into coke, if needed. In addition, coals of the Tennessee

fields have been, and are being, used in making coke.

A comparison of the coal reserves in the Southeast (with the depletion through production and loss from mining) indicates abundant supplies insofar as the quantity of coal in the ground is concerned. Young estimated the total depletion in the Southeast for 17 years as 413.7 million tons, or an average of 24.3 million tons per year, compared to total reserves of 92.84 billion tons. For Alabama, he estimated total depletion for the 17 years as 301.98 million tons, or an average of 17.76 million tons per year, compared to total reserves of 66.59 billion tons.

Conclusion

In general, it may be said that the Southeast has numerous coal deposits and that the tonnages of several of these deposist are quite large. From the point of view of the basic iron and steel industry, however, dependence has been largely on the Warrior field, and particularly on the Pratt and the Mary Lee groups, for coking coal. Coke has been made in the past from the coals of other deposits, and it is very probable that fields other than the Warrior will be supplementary sources of importance. After washing, the quality of southern coal is good. The chief problems arise from the physical conditions under which the deposits occur. Most of the mining must be done underground. The seams are relatively thin and often are badly folded and faulted. The presence of partings and irregularities in the seams also make for higher costs. In other words, the coal is there, but it is not easy to recover.

10 E. F. Burchard, "The Birmingham District, Alabama," p. 123.

CHAPTER VII

OTHER RAW MATERIAL RESOURCES OF THE SOUTHEAST FOR THE PRODUCTION OF IRON AND STEEL

Iron ore and coal for coke are commonly looked upon as the principal minerals needed for the production of iron and steel. Other materials are required also: limestone and dolomite for fluxes; manganese as a reducing agent and as an alloying material; such metals as chromite, molybdenum, nickel, tungsten, and vanadium (if special types of alloy steel are produced); and supplementary sources of ferrous materials. In this last category, iron and steel scrap is the most important, but included also are the by-products of operations such as those that use pyrite as a raw material. This chapter will describe the resources of the Southeast with respect to these materials.

Limestone and Dolomite

Large deposits of both limestone and dolomite (see Map 8) are available near deposits of iron ore and coal, and are found in a region that extends from the northern border of Tennessee to a point south of the iron ore deposits of Alabama. The deposits of limestone and dolomite of value to the iron and steel industry in the Southeast are to be found in the Paleozoic era of geological time and range from the Cambrian to, and including, the Mississippian rocks. Starting with the oldest, the Conasauga (or Coosa) limestone and dolomite, they include the Ketona dolomite, the Knox dolomite, the Newala limestone, the Chickamauga (Pelham) limestone, the Warsaw limestone, the St. Louis limestone, and the Bangor limestone.

Conasauga (or Coosa) limestone and dolomite occur as beds of considerable thickness in the Birmingham valley, the Lookout Mountain region, the Cahaba region, and the Coosa valley. The Ketona dolomites are found in the Birmingham valley and Lookout Mountain. Knox dolomite occurs in northwest Georgia and Missionary Ridge, extending northeast across Tennessee. It is not separated into the Ketona, as is the case in the Birmingham district. Chickamauga limestone is found in the Birmingham, the Lookout Mountain, the northwest Georgia and the eastern Tennessee areas. A deposit of Warsaw limestone, a pure limestone, is located in the Birmingham district about 300 feet above the iron ore of the Big Seam. Warsaw limestone also occurs in the Cahaba, Lookout Mountain, and Cumberland Plateau areas. St. Louis limestone is found in the Highland Rim area of Tennessee. Bangor limestone occurs in northern Alabama near Russellville (where it has been quarried for building stone) as well as in eastern Tennessee.

Limestone for blast furnace use should be under 3 per cent in silica, but for open hearth use, under 1.0 per cent is preferred. Alumina under 1.0 per cent is acceptable in the blast furnace, but under 0.5 per cent is desirable for the open hearth. Phosphorus is usually low and seldom exceeds 0.03 per cent; in the open hearth, however, under 0.01 per cent is used. Iron is seldom above 0.5 per cent, but can be higher as it adds to the iron recovered. Magnesium carbonate is ordinarily under 5 per cent and often below 1.0 per cent; moisture accounts for less than 1.0 per cent; and calcium carbonate makes up the balance of the aggregate.

While Pennsylvania and Michigan are reported to supply 65 per cent of the metallurgical limestone, Alabama has more high grade limestone close to the blast furnace plants than any other locality. A typical analysis of high-grade Alabama Warsaw metallurgical limestone from the Muscoda Number 5 mine is:

silica, 0.62; alumina, 0.27; calcium carbonate, 98.42; and magnesium carbonate, 0.22 per cent.

Dolomite is not generally used in northern blast furnaces, but high grade deposits are readily accessible to the blast furnaces in the Birmingham district where it is largely used instead of limestone as a blast furnace stone. A representative analysis of southern dolomite shows: silica, 1.00; iron, 0.15; phosphorus, 0.03; alumina, 0.45; magnesium carbonate, 36.22; calcium carbonate, 56.16 per cent; and a small amount of moisture. Another typical high grade dolomite from Dolonah quarry in the Birmingham district has the following composition: silica, 1.09; alumina, 0.60; magnesium carbonate, 42.00; and calcium carbonate, 55.78 per cent.

In general, it can be said that limestone and dolomite are abundant in quantity, occur in close proximity to the coal and ore deposits of the Birmingham district, are of excellent quality, and can be quarried or mined readily.

Manganese

There are deposits of manganese ore in North Carolina, South Carolina, Georgia, Tennessee, and in a number of locations in Alabama. Arkansas, however, is the southeastern state which has the largest deposits. There are two well-defined fields in the state. The first, known as the Batesville district, is located in the northern part of Independence County, for the most part, but extends into Izard and Sharp counties. The second field extends from the Pulaski County line to the western boundary of the state.[1]

Table 11 presents the statistics on the production of metallurgical manganese ore, ferruginous manganese ore, and manganiferous iron ore in the Southeastern states.

The 1945 *Minerals Yearbook* mentions production in the following locations: Cobalt

[1] H. M. Payne, *Undeveloped Mineral Resources*, pp. 122-125.

Table 11

Metallurgical Manganese Ore, Ferruginous Manganese Ore, and Manganiferous Iron Ore
Shipped from Mines in the Southeastern States, 1941-1947

(in net tons)

Kind of ore and state where mined	1941	1942	1943	1944	1945	1946	1947
Metallurgical manganese ore							
Alabama	....	26	....	49	32	....	....
Arkansas	5,015	4,132	5,319	7,109	6,663	1,101	841
Georgia	4,893	4,890	2,467	1,135	1,056	....	....
North Carolina	35	....	140				
Oklahoma	40	31	265	....	....	....	....
South Carolina	....	....	312	1,400	41	78	....
Tennessee	4,394	2,247	2,501	418	....	....	39
Ferruginous manganese ore							
Alabama	....	206	....				
Arkansas	3,381	14,067	8,207	14,755	14,806	1,964	2,094
Georgia	6,715	10,514	5,835	2,232	....	....	....
North Carolina	174	....	115				
Oklahoma	56	....					
South Carolina	....	....	155	171			
Tennessee	1,865	916	803	6,779	1,000	....	....
Manganiferous iron ore							
Alabama	....	162					
Georgia	1,192	....					

Source: *Minerals Yearbook*, 1945, 1946, and 1947.

Hill, Cherokee County, Alabama; Independence County, Arkansas; Lincoln County and Bartow County, Georgia; and McCormick County, South Carolina. Shipments from the mines in these locations to the Birmingham district also are frequently mentioned. In the 1947 *Minerals Yearbook,* mention is made only of Independence County, Arkansas and Bradley County, Tennessee.

Compared with the quantities consumed in the iron and steel industry, domestic production of manganese ore, both in the Southeast and the nation as a whole, is small. The greater part of the requirements are obtained by imports from foreign countries. In this respect the Birmingham district is well located to receive its supplies through the port of Mobile.

Alloying Metals for Special Steels

Of the metals commonly used as alloys in the production of special steels, only chromite is known to occur in the Southeast in deposits of sufficient size to be of any significance. Jackson County and Yancey County, North Carolina, are reported to have deposits that are of good quality and quantity.[2] There are also prospects of ore in Buncombe County and Mitchell County of that state. Molybdenum is not reported in any southeastern state. The tungsten deposits in North Carolina and Alabama and the nickel in North Carolina, South Carolina, Georgia, and Tennessee apparently have little or no commercial significance.

These alloying materials seldom occur in close proximity to blast furnaces and steel works. They are used in relatively small quantities, and their unit values are high compared to weight. Consequently, the geographic location of their source, in normal times, exercises relatively little influence on the location of steel plants. While the general dependence on imports for adequate supplies of many of these materials may present a serious problem for the nation, there is little reason to think that plants in the Southeast, when compared to those in

2 Payne, pp. 118-119.

other American locations, are at any special disadvantage in this respect.

Iron from Copper and Iron Sulphide Ores

In the extreme southeast corner of Tennessee near Ducktown, there are a number of mines which produce sulphide ores of copper and iron, or pyrites. After these ores are mined, they are roasted and the sulphur oxidized to form sulphur dioxide. By the use of a catalyzer, the sulphur dioxide is oxidized to sulphur trioxide, which, with water, forms sulphuric acid. The roasted ore is leached with some of the sulphuric acid, and the copper is dissolved and removed. The residue, after washing, is sintered—the sinter constituting a high grade iron concentrate which is used as a supplemental iron ore. Another source of supply is in Carroll County, Virginia. There are other pyrite deposits in the Southeast (such as those at Pyriton, Alabama) which could be used in this manner, but the cheaper supply of pure sulphur deposits in south Texas and Louisiana has limited the use of these sulphides as sources of sulphuric acid. Consequently, there has been only a small increase in the mining of pyrites and the production of iron sinter, a by-product. In 1950 and 1951, questions concerning the adequacy of the reserves of sulphur in the Gulf Coast area led to renewed exploration in pyrites, but the prospect of new domes seems to have lessened the interest.

Iron and Steel Scrap

Aside from iron ore and coal, iron and steel scrap is perhaps the most important raw material for steel production. Scrap originates from three sources: (1) *home scrap,* in the steel plant itself, where between 25 per cent and 30 per cent of the ingot steel produced becomes scrap in the finishing operations involved in the manufacture of steel mill products; (2) *industrial scrap,* from large processing and fabricating plants in the form of turnings, clippings, chips and other pieces removed from stock in shaping a product; and (3) *country scrap,* which results from the junking of industrial, agricultural, and domestic items made mostly from steel. The United States Bureau of Mines uses a two-division classification in reporting the statistics on the consumption of iron and steel scrap—home scrap and purchased scrap. The latter class includes both industrial and country.

IMPORTANCE OF IRON AND STEEL SCRAP

Iron and steel scrap is a principal component of the charge of the furnaces which are used in foundries and in the basic iron and steel industries. To a very large extent, scrap and pig iron may be substituted for each other. For that reason, the prices of pig iron and scrap and the relative amounts of each used in the melting charges at any particular time are closely interrelated. Since use in steel-making processes constitutes such a large proportion of the total consumption of scrap, the demand for scrap, and hence its price, is very sensitive to variations in the quantities of steel produced.

The importance of the place occupied by scrap as a raw material in the iron and steel industries of the United States is shown by the data presented in Table 12 and Chart 5. The use of scrap varies considerably with the type of furnace. If the total of pig iron and scrap

CHART 5

COMPARATIVE USE OF SCRAP IRON AND STEEL AND PIG IRON IN OPEN HEARTH FURNACES AND CUPOLA FURNACES IN THE UNITED STATES AND THE SOUTH, 1938-1948

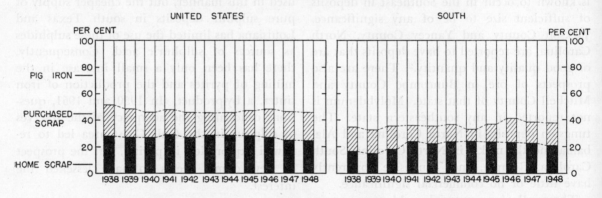

OPEN HEARTH FURNACES

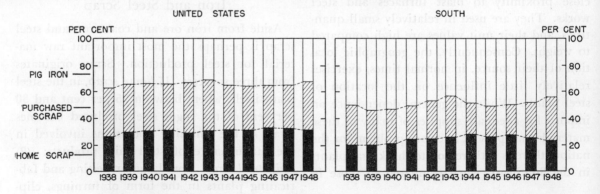

CUPOLA FURNACES

SOURCE: BUREAU OF MINES, U.S. DEPARTMENT OF THE INTERIOR.

is taken as 100 per cent, the proportion of the total charge of open-hearth furnaces represented by scrap varied, during the twelve year period covered by the statistics in the table, from a high of 51.5 per cent in 1938 to a low of 45.8 per cent in 1944. Corresponding percentages for the other types of furnaces were: for Bessemer converters—highest, 6.5 per cent

Table 12

Consumption of Iron and Steel Scrap and Pig Iron in the United States
by Kind of Furnace, 1937-1948

Kind of furnace and year	Consumption in net tons				Per cent of total charge			
	Scrap			Pig iron	Scrap			Pig iron
	Home	Purchased	All scrap		Home	Purchased	All scrap	
Open-hearth furnaces								
1937	15,632,533	13,951,188	29,583,721	28,132,402	27.1	24.2	51.3	48.7
1938	8,910,889	7,449,657	16,360,546	15,376,896	28.1	23.4	51.5	48.5
1939	14,272,346	11,258,540	25,530,886	26,826,173	27.3	21.5	48.8	51.2
1940	18,320,111	12,687,633	31,007,744	36,297,250	27.2	18.9	46.1	53.9
1941	24,002,629	15,920,857	39,923,486	42,481,404	29.1	19.3	48.4	51.6
1942	23,445,884	16,114,069	39,559,953	45,538,846	27.6	18.9	46.5	53.5
1943	25,442,119	14,771,599	40,213,718	47,107,608	29.1	16.9	46.0	54.0
1944	26,006,327	14,801,730	40,808,057	48,281,168	29.2	16.6	45.8	54.2
1945	22,628,604	15,127,687	37,756,291	41,682,581	28.5	19.0	47.5	52.5
1946	18,145,617	14,295,908	32,441,525	34,608,053	27.1	21.3	48.4	51.6
1947	21,727,939	17,560,105	39,288,044	45,338,462	25.7	20.7	46.4	53.6
1948	22,107,617	18,515,530	40,623,147	47,267,334	25.1	21.1	46.2	53.8
Bessemer converters								
1937	248,035	10,128	258,163	4,130,935	5.7	.2	5.9	94.1
1938	125,161	4,138	129,299	2,179,574	5.4	.2	5.6	94.4
1939	213,157	6,972	220,129	3,603,199	5.6	.2	5.8	94.2
1940	248,868	9,322	258,190	3,828,978	6.1	.2	6.3	93.7
1941	320,738	72,506	393,244	5,993,264	5.0	1.2	6.2	93.8
1942	260,025	109,887	369,912	6,131,222	4.0	1.7	5.7	94.3
1943	268,691	112,241	380,932	6,257,927	4.0	1.7	5.7	94.3
1944	274,237	112,359	386,596	5,583,027	4.6	1.9	6.5	93.5
1945	234,034	82,856	316,890	4,750,817	4.6	1.7	6.3	93.7
1946	173,025	69,550	242,575	3,722,756	4.4	1.7	6.1	93.9
1947	212,702	60,261	272,963	4,711,581	4.3	1.2	5.5	94.5
1948	197,890	53,560	251,450	4,778,137	3.9	1.1	5.0	95.0
Electric steel furnaces								
1937	926,304	1,006,617	1,932,921	50,081	46.7	50.8	97.5	2.5
1938	507,759	540,155	1,047,914	17,800	47.6	50.7	98.3	1.7
1939	803,224	869,559	1,672,783	30,542	47.2	51.0	98.2	1.8
1940	1,111,127	1,383,722	2,494,849	46,506	43.7	54.5	98.2	1.8
1941	2,109,839	2,068,318	4,178,157	72,758	49.6	48.7	98.3	1.7
1942	3,025,878	2,880,020	5,905,898	92,878	50.5	48.0	98.5	1.5
1943	3,377,561	3,536,860	6,914,421	393,819	46.2	48.4	94.6	5.4
1944	3,142,304	3,279,550	6,421,854	240,482	47.2	49.2	96.4	3.6
1945	2,374,272	2,709,059	5,083,331	163,457	45.3	51.6	96.9	3.1
1946	1,549,909	2,148,029	3,697,938	113,125	40.7	56.3	97.0	3.0
1947	2,053,278	3,171,083	5,224,361	127,338	38.4	59.2	97.6	2.4
1948	2,384,022	4,321,481	6,705,503	132,314	34.9	63.2	98.1	1.9

Table 12 (cont'd)

Consumption of Iron and Steel Scrap and Pig Iron in the United States by Kind of Furnace, 1937-1948

Kind of furnace and year	Consumption in net tons				Per cent of total charge			
	Scrap			Pig iron	Scrap			Pig iron
	Home	Purchased	All scrap		Home	Pur-chased	All scrap	
Blast furnaces								
1937	1,644,228	1,011,936	2,656,164					
1938	855,492	336,647	1,192,139					
1939	1,125,113	807,840	1,932,953					
1940	1,286,985	793,344	2,080,329					
1941	1,587,866	1,317,072	2,904,938					
1942	1,564,912	1,372,599	2,937,511					
1943	1,417,778	2,150,170	3,567,948					
1944	1,422,118	2,216,342	3,638,460					
1945	1,289,537	2,049,140	3,338,677					
1946	1,168,590	1,104,348	2,272,938					
1947	1,401,162	1,290,937	2,692,099					
1948	1,449,910	1,481,598	2,931,508					
Cupola furnaces								
1937	3,223,803	4,064,567	7,288,370	4,698,662	26.9	33.9	60.8	39.2
1938	1,949,570	2,745,360	4,694,930	2,693,193	26.4	37.1	63.5	36.5
1939	2,856,956	3,557,738	6,414,694	3,349,198	29.3	36.4	65.7	34.3
1940	3,657,048	4,372,777	8,029,825	4,106,119	30.2	36.0	66.2	33.8
1941	5,004,864	5,559,273	10,564,137	5,388,747	31.4	34.8	66.2	33.8
1942	3,936,643	5,117,922	9,054,565	4,490,532	29.0	37.8	66.8	33.2
1943	3,540,327	4,463,659	8,003,986	3,602,918	30.5	38.5	69.0	31.0
1944	3,654,301	3,888,691	7,542,992	3,941,159	31.8	33.9	65.7	34.3
1945	3,614,006	3,729,761	7,343,767	4,084,091	31.6	32.7	64.3	35.7
1946	4,329,283	4,229,939	8,559,222	4,612,704	32.9	32.1	65.0	35.0
1947	5,240,692	5,316,947	10,557,639	5,438,727	32.8	33.2	66.0	34.0
1948	5,323,049	6,143,958	11,467,007	5,280,957	31.8	36.7	68.5	31.5
Total all furnaces								
1935	14,948,362	14,636,807	29,585,169	23,094,919	28.4	27.8	56.2	43.8
1936	21,169,556	19,551,553	40,721,109	33,710,470	28.4	26.3	54.7	45.3
1937	22,255,557	20,311,468	42,567,025	38,143,310	27.6	25.1	52.7	47.3
1938	12,679,902	11,226,424	23,906,326	20,724,871	28.4	25.2	53.6	46.4
1939	19,621,896	16,704,640	36,326,536	35,232,699	27.4	23.4	50.8	49.2
1940	25,047,723	19,481,948	44,529,671	46,185,828	27.6	21.5	49.1	50.9
1941	33,904,680	25,311,576	59,216,256	56,185,472	29.4	21.9	51.3	48.7
1942	33,129,372	27,135,779	60,265,151	59,042,883	27.8	22.7	50.5	49.5
1943	35,037,088	26,613,868	61,650,956	60,315,159	28.7	21.8	50.5	49.5
1944	35,426,349	25,922,852	61,349,201	60,951,621	29.0	21.2	50.2	49.8
1945	30,960,704	25,230,381	56,191,085	53,187,177	28.3	23.1	51.4	48.6
1946	26,134,163	23,349,948	49,484,111	45,071,630	27.6	24.7	52.3	47.7
1947	31,578,942	29,285,419	60,864,361	58,290,755	26.5	24.6	51.1	48.9
1948	32,419,643	32,544,232	64,963,875	60,026,404	25.9	26.1	52.0	48.0

Source: *Minerals Yearbook*, 1935-1948.

in 1944, and lowest, 5.0 per cent in 1948; for electric steel furnaces—highest, 98.5 per cent in 1942, and lowest, 94.6 per cent in 1943; for cupola furnaces—highest, 69.0 per cent in 1943, and lowest, 60.8 per cent in 1937. It can be said that scrap is the predominant ferrous material for electric steel furnaces and that it constitutes approximately two-thirds of the charge for cupola and one-half the charge for open-hearth furnaces. The Bessemer process uses little scrap, and almost all of that which it does consume is home scrap, or, in other words, materials that are recycled through the process.

Throughout the period covered by Table 12, the quantity of home scrap consumed by the open-hearth furnaces exceeded the correspond-

ing quantities of purchased scrap. The war period saw the percentage of scrap in the total decline somewhat compared with an increase in the pig iron percentage. This change was accounted for almost entirely by the decline in the relative position of purchased scrap, which did not increase fast enough to keep pace with the large increase in steel production. In electric furnaces, quantities of purchased scrap have exceeded those of home scrap in all but two years, although usually the differences have not been great. In contrast with the open-hearth situation, the proportion of scrap in the total charge of cupola furnaces tended to be somewhat higher during the war than during the immediate prewar years. This probably arose from difficulty in securing pig iron for

Table 13

Percentage of Total Consumption of Iron and Steel Scrap in the United States Accounted for by the Several Uses, 1939, 1945, 1948

Year and kind of use	Per cent of total consumption		
	Home scrap	Purchased scrap	All scrap
1939			
Open hearth furnaces	72.7	67.4	70.3
Bessemer converters	1.1	.04	.6
Electric steel furnaces	4.1	5.2	4.6
Blast furnaces	5.7	4.9	5.3
Cupola furnaces	14.6	21.3	17.7
Other uses	1.8	1.2	1.5
Total	100.0	100.0	100.0
1945			
Open hearth furnaces	73.1	60.0	67.2
Bessemer converters	.7	.3	.6
Electric steel furnaces	7.7	10.7	9.0
Blast furnaces	4.2	8.1	5.9
Cupola furnaces	11.7	14.8	13.1
Other uses	2.6	6.1	4.2
Total	100.0	100.0	100.0
1948			
Open hearth furnaces	68.2	56.9	62.5
Bessemer converters	0.6	0.2	0.4
Electric steel furnaces	7.4	13.3	10.3
Blast furnaces	4.5	4.5	4.5
Cupola furnaces	16.4	18.9	17.7
Other uses	2.9	6.2	4.6
Total	100.0	100.0	100.0

Sources: *Minerals Yearbook*, 1939, 1945, and 1948.

foundry use. Also, the quantity of purchased scrap was somewhat greater than that of home scrap in the melt of the cupolas.

Scrap iron also constitutes a part of the charge of blast furnaces. Since the content is almost pure iron, the consumption of scrap by blast furnaces may be compared with the production of pig iron on the assumption that scrap charged into a blast furnace is recovered, without appreciable loss, as pig iron. On this basis, the percentages of pig iron production that originated from scrap ranged from 6.3 per cent in 1945 to 4.5 per cent in 1940.

The uses of scrap iron and steel by the various types of furnaces in the United States has been briefly described to provide a background for the discussion of the scrap situation in the South. Two other general points need to be mentioned: the first, to point out the relative importance of the various uses; the second, to mention some of the important considerations with regard to the supply of scrap.

As is shown by Table 13, open-hearth furnaces are by far the greatest consumers of scrap iron and steel, consuming around 70 per cent of the total. Cupola furnaces are the second largest consumers. Electric furnaces and blast furnaces were approximately equal to each other in 1939, but war demands stimulated the production of steel in electric furnaces, and, as a result, this process consumed a considerably larger quantity of scrap in 1945 than blast furnaces did. This situation existed also in 1946, 1947, and 1948.

POTENTIAL SOURCES OF SCRAP

The tendency for the potential supply to accumulate rather than to be depleted is a distinctive feature of the scrap situation. This is in contrast to the case in ore reserves. Iron and steel products are durable in character; the loss of ferrous materials from wear or deterioration is slow and, during the economic life of most of the products, is relatively small. It has been estimated that the steel which is unrecoverable due to corrosion, export, sealing in masonry structures, and other causes is approximately 25 per cent of the new iron and steel in products distributed at any one time. A comparison of purchased scrap that has been used in the various types of furnaces with new products indicates that there must be, each year, a large addition to the potential supply of scrap in the country in the iron and steel in equipment, structures, and other forms.

The iron and steel going into use consists largely of the hot rolled iron and steel products and of the products of foundries. The calculation below gives a fair approximation of these quantities and compares the total with the consumption of purchased scrap for the corresponding period.

If it is assumed that 75 per cent of the iron and steel going into use is recoverable, it seems clear that the quantity of purchased scrap consumed has been far below that level. These figures are approximations, and, for careful estimates, many refinements in the calculations would be needed. Also, it should be mentioned that much of the production during the war was destroyed or sent out of the country and hence is not recoverable to any great extent. Still, despite these qualifications, the data serve to indicate the relative size of the quantities involved.

	Total for period 1937-1940 (Short tons)	Total for period 1941-1945 (Short tons)	Total for period 1937-1945 (Short tons)
Total cupola charge	41,274,991	64,016,894	105,291,885
Less home scrap consumed	11,687,377	19,750,141	31,437,518
Net foundry products	29,587,614	44,266,753	73,854,367
Hot rolled iron and steel products	152,475,229	313,678,422	466,153,651
Total hot rolled and net foundry products going into use	182,062,843	357,945,175	540,008,018
Total purchased scrap consumed	67,724,480	130,214,456	197,938,936
Per cent of total rolled and foundry products	37.2	36.4	36.7

In discussing the importance of secondary ferrous metals, a report of the Bureau of Statistics of the Interstate Commerce Commission makes the following pertinent comments:

Estimates of the reserves of iron and steel represented in products in use in the United States in 1936 aggregated in excess of one billion tons or more than 17,800 pounds per capita. From 1900 to 1930 the amount of steel in use grew steadily at an average rate of about 440 pounds per capita per year. During the depression there was a substantial decrease in this rate of accumulation and in fact in 1932 there was a net decline. After that year, however, the increase was resumed at the lower rate of 300 pounds per capita per annum, although in 1935 it was 507 pounds.* By 5 year periods, 1903-1937 iron ore consumption per ton of steel produced has declined uninterruptedly from 1.5305 tons in the first quinquennium to .9353 tons in the last.** In the five years 1910-1914 the percentage ratio of the consumption of iron and steel scrap to steel production never rose as high as 52 per cent. Between 1920 and 1937 the ratio has never been below 60 per cent, and between 1925 and 1937 never below 65 per cent, and between 1931 and 1937 never below 70 per cent.*** The Bureau of Mines reported to the Military Affairs Committee of the Senate in 1937 that the reservoir of iron in use in this country from which our annual scrap supply is withdrawn, is enormous. Moreover, the amount of metal added to the reservoir in that year (1937) was considerably more than that withdrawn. It may be conservatively estimated that, in 1937, 35,000,000 tons of steel products were added to the store of metal in use, whereas the total scrap withdrawn for domestic consumption and for export probably did not exceed 25,000,000 tons. Thus, in a year of unprecedented scrap exports, our reservoir of potential scrap was actually increased by 10,000,000 tons.

*Steel Facts, April 1936, p. 5, and May 1937, p. 4.

**Report of the Interstate Commerce Commission to the President of the United States on Certain Aspects of the Proposed Lake Erie-Ohio River Canal, 235 I.C.C., p. 798, Table 5.

***Table 6, ibid., p. 799.[3]

Iron and steel scrap, therefore, is an important source of raw material for the basic indus-

[3] W. H. S. Stevens, G. M. Saharov, and E. C. Bryant, Distribution of Natural Resources, pp. II, 18-19.

tries, and the potential reserves from which scrap can be drawn are accumulating at a rapid rate. These have an important bearing on future developments in a region in which industrialization is taking place at a rapid rate.

IRON AND STEEL SCRAP IN SOUTH

As shown by Table 14, the pattern of consumption of iron and steel scrap in the South is quite different from that of the country as a whole. During the period covered by the statistics, the proportion of the total charge of the open-hearth furnaces that was represented by scrap varied between 41.7 per cent in 1946 and 33.3 per cent in 1939. The range of variation for the nation, for the same period, was between 51.5 per cent in 1938 and 45.8 per cent in 1944. Likewise, the proportion of scrap in the charge of cupola furnaces in the South varied between 57.2 per cent in 1948 and 46.5 per cent in 1939. In the nation, the range was between 69.0 per cent in 1943 and 60.8 per cent in 1937. In these two important types of furnaces, a considerably lower percentage of scrap and a higher percentage of pig iron were used in the melt in the South than in the United States as a whole.

In the South, the proportions of both home and purchased scrap in the mix for open-hearth and cupolas generally are low compared with similar figures for the United States. For the most part, the larger differences in these two types of furnaces are associated with purchased scrap. The total figures for all kinds of furnaces also show that the South makes a smaller use of scrap in the melting charge than is the practice for the nation as a whole, but the ratio between home and purchased scrap is more nearly like that for the entire country.

At least two conditions can be cited to account for this situation. In the first place, the Southeast has long been a producer of cheap pig iron, and, at first, the low degree of industrialization made relatively little scrap available. As a result, the pattern of consumption was based largely on the use of pig iron in steel works and foundries. In the second place, the largest steel producer in the region operates

Table 14

Consumption of Iron and Steel Scrap and Pig Iron in the South by Kind of Furnace, 1938-1948

Kind of furnace and year	Consumption of				Total scrap and pig iron consumed
	Scrap			Pig iron	
	Home	Purchased	All scrap		
Open hearth furnaces—consumption in net tons					
1938	310,750	329,105	639,856	1,178,171	1,818,027
1939	421,297	475,896	897,193	1,800,804	2,697,997
1940	610,261	605,627	1,215,888	2,140,677	3,356,565
1941	900,518	446,342	1,346,860	2,305,697	3,652,557
1942	943,265	551,063	1,494,328	2,624,876	4,119,204
1943	1,032,829	559,898	1,592,727	2,653,035	4,245,762
1944	1,110,591	413,506	1,524,097	2,959,583	4,483,680
1945	1,000,125	535,268	1,535,393	2,540,135	4,075,528
1946	806,002	597,063	1,403,065	1,961,338	3,364,403
1947	978,954	685,418	1,664,372	2,608,298	4,272,670
1948	1,037,510	762,506	1,800,016	2,889,501	4,689,517
Open hearth furnaces—per cent of total consumption					
1938	17.1	18.1	35.2	64.8	100.0
1939	15.6	17.6	33.2	66.8	100.0
1940	18.2	18.0	36.2	63.8	100.0
1941	24.7	12.2	36.9	63.1	100.0
1942	22.9	13.4	36.3	63.7	100.0
1943	24.3	13.2	37.5	62.5	100.0
1944	24.8	9.2	34.0	66.0	100.0
1945	24.6	13.1	37.7	62.3	100.0
1946	24.0	17.7	41.7	58.3	100.0
1947	22.9	16.1	39.0	61.0	100.0
1948	22.1	16.3	38.4	61.6	100.0
Electric furnaces—consumption in net tons†					
1938	26,196	24,399	50,595	344	50,939
1939	31,333	25,850	57,183	550	57,733
1940	33,950	62,835	96,785	902	97,687
1941	54,654	96,836	151,490	1,185	152,675
1942	76,503	130,962	207,465	1,947	209,412
1943	124,211	147,256	271,467	5,892	277,359
1944	120,782	131,426	252,208	4,449	256,657
1945	82,657	96,286	178,943	2,992	181,935
1946	54,926	58,790	113,716	1,504	115,220
1947	59,033	79,109	138,142	1,673	139,815
1948	68,580	93,595	162,175	2,466	164,641
Electric furnaces—per cent of total consumption†					
1938	51.4	47.9	99.3	0.7	100.0
1939	54.3	44.8	99.1	0.9	100.0
1940	34.8	64.3	99.1	0.9	100.0
1941	35.8	63.4	99.2	0.8	100.0
1942	36.5	62.6	99.1	0.9	100.0
1943	44.8	53.1	97.9	2.1	100.0
1944	47.1	51.2	98.3	1.7	100.0
1945	45.5	52.9	98.4	1.6	100.0
1946	47.7	51.0	98.7	1.3	100.0
1947	42.2	56.6	98.8	1.2	100.0
1948	41.7	56.8	98.5	1.5	100.0
Cupola furnaces—consumption in net tons					
1938	221,581	317,588	539,169	535,557	1,074,726

Table 14 (cont'd)

Consumption of Iron and Steel Scrap and Pig Iron in the South by Kind of Furnace, 1938-1948

Kind of furnace and year	Consumption of				Total scrap and pig iron consumed
	Scrap			Pig iron	
	Home	Purchased	All scrap		
Cupola furnaces—consumption in net tons—*continued*					
1939	289,998	376,079	666,077	765,891	1,431,968
1940	346,198	427,464	773,662	846,441	1,620,103
1941	562,860	553,311	1,116,171	1,116,267	2,232,438
1942	521,086	595,415	1,116,501	962,474	2,078,975
1943	385,686	442,894	828,580	620,653	1,449,233
1944	385,596	318,858	704,454	645,788	1,350,242
1945	393,393	324,729	718,122	729,300	1,447,422
1946	509,512	394,200	903,712	875,769	1,779,481
1947	596,276	597,625	1,193,901	1,081,976	2,275,877
1948	616,548	828,862	1,445,410	1,095,956	2,541,366
Cupola furnaces—per cent of total consumption					
1938	20.6	29.6	50.2	49.8	100.0
1939	20.2	26.3	46.5	53.5	100.0
1940	21.4	26.4	47.8	52.2	100.0
1941	25.2	24.8	50.0	50.0	100.0
1942	25.1	28.6	53.7	46.3	100.0
1943	26.6	30.6	57.2	42.8	100.0
1944	28.6	23.6	52.2	47.8	100.0
1945	27.2	22.4	49.6	50.4	100.0
1946	28.6	22.2	50.8	49.2	100.0
1947	26.2	26.3	52.5	47.5	100.0
1948	24.3	32.6	56.9	43.1	100.0
All furnaces—consumption in net tons†					
1938	745,176	773,549	1,518,725	1,754,185	3,272,910
1939	962,595	1,028,835	1,991,430	2,612,034	4,603,464
1940	1,212,596	1,279,686	2,492,282	3,068,100	5,560,382
1941	1,787,684	1,340,120	3,127,804	3,511,702	6,639,506
1942	1,794,099	1,615,657	3,409,756	3,684,222	7,093,978
1943	1,773,850	1,425,465	3,199,315	3,371,103	6,570,418
1944	1,852,423	1,203,033	3,055,456	3,699,023	6,754,479
1945	1,685,819	1,305,404	2,991,223	3,360,847	6,352,070
1946	1,599,005	1,321,427	2,920,432	2,926,729	5,847,161
1947	1,944,303	1,746,042	3,690,345	3,813,427	7,503,772
1948	2,047,362	2,121,751	4,169,113	4,075,146	8,244,259
All furnaces—per cent of total consumption†					
1938	22.8	23.6	46.4	53.6	100.0
1939	20.9	22.4	43.3	56.7	100.0
1940	21.8	23.0	44.8	55.2	100.0
1941	26.9	20.2	47.1	52.9	100.0
1942	25.3	22.8	48.1	51.9	100.0
1943	27.0	21.7	48.7	51.3	100.0
1944	27.4	17.8	45.2	54.8	100.0
1945	26.5	20.6	47.1	52.9	100.0
1946	27.4	22.6	50.0	50.0	100.0
1947	25.9	23.3	49.2	50.8	100.0
1948	24.8	25.8	50.6	49.4	100.0

Source: *Minerals Yearbook*, 1938-1948.
†Includes Virginia.

one of its two steel plants on the duplex steel process. This method consumes little scrap but makes steel almost entirely from pig iron. The finishing departments using steel from this plant produce a large amount of home scrap which is used by the second steel plant of the company. Thus, this large producer operates almost entirely on home scrap and buys little from the outside. Other steel producers use purchased scrap to a much greater extent, but they have too small a percentage of the total capacity to bring the Southeast totals in line with those of the nation as a whole.

In earlier years, the fact that the South was predominantly rural and agricultural meant that iron and steel in use in the form of products was both small in quantity and widely scattered. This situation was accentuated by the fact that its agriculture typically called for little in the way of machinery and equipment. Its lack of industry meant that there were few places where scrap was produced in quantity. This situation, however, has been changing with the industrialization that has been taking place during the last three or four decades. Records of steel consumption by states are non-existent, but fairly reliable estimates for certain years can be made. It has been estimated that in 1939 shipments of steel mill products to destinations in the Southeast totaled 1,786,400 tons and into the Southwest, 1,456,100, or a total of 3,242,500 tons for the entire South.[4]

[4] See Chapter XXIII, page 325.

Table 15

Prices of No. 2 Heavy Melting Iron and Steel Scrap in Birmingham and Pittsburgh, by Months, 1930-1949

(dollars per gross ton delivered to consumer)

	1930	1931	1932	1933	1934	1935	1936	1937	1938	1939
Birmingham										
January	13.25	10.00	8.75	7.75	10.00	9.00	9.75	12.75	16.25	13.25
February	13.25	10.75	7.75	7.75	10.00	9.25	9.75	12.75	11.75	13.25
March	13.25	10.75	7.75	7.25	10.00	9.25	11.25	15.25	11.75	13.25
April	13.25	10.75	7.75	7.25	10.00	9.25	11.25	16.50	11.75	13.25
May	13.25	9.75	7.75	7.25	10.00	9.25	11.25	16.50	11.75	13.25
June	12.00	9.75	7.75	8.25	10.00	9.25	11.25	16.00	11.75	13.25
July	12.00	9.75	7.25	9.75	10.00	9.25	11.25	16.25	12.25	13.00
August	12.00	8.75	7.25	10.25	10.00	9.25	11.25	16.25	12.25	13.00
September	12.00	8.75	7.25	11.00	10.00	7.75	11.50	16.25	13.25	13.00
October	12.00	8.75	7.75	10.25	8.50	7.75	11.50	16.25	13.25	13.00
November	10.50	8.75	*	10.25	9.00	7.75	11.50	16.25	13.25	18.00
December	10.00	8.75	7.75	10.00	9.00	9.75	12.75	16.75	13.25	17.00
Pittsburgh										
January	15.25	10.75	9.25	7.25	11.25	11.75	12.75	17.75	12.75	14.50
February	14.75	11.25	9.25	7.50	11.75	12.25	13.25	17.50	13.25	14.50
March	14.75	11.50	9.25	7.50	12.75	11.75	14.25	18.75	12.75	14.50
April	14.25	11.25	8.87	7.75	13.50	10.75	14.25	20.25	11.75	14.50
May	13.75	10.00	8.25	10.25	12.25	10.00	13.25	16.75	10.75	13.25
June	13.25	9.50	8.00	10.25	10.75	10.25	12.50	16.75	9.75	13.00
July	13.25	9.50	6.75	10.75	10.75	10.25	12.62	16.25	11.75	13.75
August	12.75	9.75	6.75	11.75	10.75	11.25	14.25	18.75	14.25	14.00
September	12.75	9.75	8.25	11.75	9.75	12.25	16.00	19.25	14.25	14.75
October	12.75	9.25	8.25	11.25	9.25	12.25	16.50	15.75	14.00	22.25
November	10.75	9.25	7.50	10.75	9.75	12.00	15.50	13.25	13.75	21.25
December	10.75	9.25	7.50	10.50	10.75	12.75	15.50	11.75	14.50	17.25

*Price for November 3 not given; prices for November 10, $7.75.

In 1947 the total for the South was estimated as 7.02 million tons. In addition, this region receives large tonnages of steel in the form of automobiles, refrigerators, textile machinery, agricultural implements, machine tools, and numerous other articles made chiefly from steel which is not fabricated in this region. Thus there is in process a flow of materials which is creating a reservoir from which a large supply of iron and steel scrap can be drawn. The region continues to have certain disadvantages in this respect in that products in use are widely scattered and areas of concentration are still relatively few. Also, a very large proportion of the potential supply is in the form of consumers' durable goods or country scrap rather than the more desirable industrial scrap.

Despite the limitations of the South with respect to the accumulation of products from which a supply of scrap can be drawn, it has been, for many years, a surplus scrap market. In other words, the demand for scrap by the metal industries of the South has not been sufficient to absorb the scrap that is produced. Several bits of evidence confirming this situation may be cited. Table 15 and Chart 6 give the comparative prices by months for Number 2 heavy melting scrap in Pittsburgh and Birmingham. The consistently lower price in Birmingham indicates the greater availability of scrap in the southern districts in comparison to the demand.

Available statistics that give state or regional breakdowns on traffic movements of iron and

Table 15 (cont'd)

Prices of No. 2 Heavy Melting Iron and Steel Scrap in Birmingham and Pittsburgh, by Months, 1930-1949

(dollars per gross ton delivered to consumer)

	1940	1941	1942	1943	1944	1945	1946	1947	1948	1949
Birmingham										
January	16.00	18.00	17.00	17.00	17.00	17.00	17.00	27.25	37.50	40.00
February	15.00	17.00	17.00	17.00	17.00	17.00	17.00	27.75	38.00	35.00
March	14.00	17.00	17.00	17.00	17.00	17.00	17.00	33.00	38.00	32.50
April	14.00	17.00	17.00	17.00	17.00	17.00	17.00	33.00	38.00	25.00
May	13.50	16.00	17.00	17.00	17.00	17.00	17.00	29.00	37.50	20.00
June	15.00	16.00	17.00	17.00	17.00	17.00	17.00	27.00	37.50	20.00
July	15.50	16.00	17.00	17.00	17.00	17.00	17.00	30.75	37.50	18.00
August	15.50	16.00	17.00	17.00	17.00	17.00	17.00	35.75	40.00	
September	15.00	16.00	17.00	17.00	17.00	17.00	17.00	34.50	40.00	
October	17.00	16.00	17.00	17.00	14.75	17.00	17.00	34.50	40.00	
November	17.00	16.00	17.00	17.00	14.75	17.00	17.00	37.50	40.00	
December	18.00	16.00	17.00	17.00	14.75	17.00	22.25	37.50	40.00	
Pittsburgh										
January	17.00	21.75	20.00	20.00	20.00	20.00	20.00	32.25	40.00	42.75
February	16.75	19.75	20.00	20.00	20.00	20.00	20.00	33.25	40.50	38.75
March	15.50	20.00	20.00	20.00	20.00	20.00	20.00	37.85	40.25	36.75
April	14.75	20.00	20.00	20.00	20.00	20.00	20.00	39.00	40.25	27.50
May	15.25	19.00	20.00	20.00	20.00	20.00	20.00	29.75	40.25	21.75
June	17.75	19.00	20.00	20.00	20.00	20.00	20.00	32.25	40.25	20.75
July	18.25	19.00	20.00	20.00	20.00	20.00	20.00	35.75	40.25	18.75
August	17.25	19.00	20.00	20.00	20.00	20.00	20.00	42.75	42.75	
September	17.75	19.00	20.00	20.00	19.75	20.00	20.00	37.75	42.75	
October	19.50	19.00	20.00	20.00	15.75	20.00	20.00	37.75	42.75	
November	20.00	19.00	20.00	20.00	14.00	20.00	20.00	42.50	42.75	
December	20.25	19.00	20.00	20.00	18.75	20.00	25.25	40.00	42.75	

Source: *The Iron Age,* first issue each month of years 1930 through 1949.

From May 1941 to November 1946 the prices shown are U.S. Government ceiling prices except for September, October, and December, 1944 when going prices as obtained from the trade by *Iron Age* are given.

steel scrap are sketchy and incomplete, but such as could be found indicate net movements away from the South. Since 1940, the Interstate Commerce Commission has been publishing figures on tonnages of commodities originating and terminating in the several states which are shipped on Class I railroads. In the case of iron and steel scrap, these data indicate a net movement away from the South; that is, originations greatly exceed terminations. These statistics are presented in Table 16.

The statistics on inland waterways shipments collected by the United States Corps of Engineers likewise indicate, on the Mississippi River and the Ohio River, substantial movements which must have their origins in the South. The items of most significance in this connection are the upbound shipments on these rivers. The classes that are of interest are: on the Mississippi, the outbound-up—traffic that originates in the designated section of the river and

moves out of that section; on the Ohio, the inbound-up—traffic that moves into the Ohio from another source and terminates somewhere

Table 16

Originations and Terminations of Iron and Steel Scrap in the South, as Revenue Freight in Carload Lots on Class I Steam Railroads, 1940-1948

Year	Total originations (in tons)	Total terminations (in tons)
1940	1,419,657	1,024,093
1941	1,831,633	978,541
1942	2,648,550	1,136,005
1943	1,628,909	753,443
1944	1,433,607	736,267
1945	1,541,069	861,798
1946	1,292,273	780,605
1947	2,426,373	1,183,632
1948	2,940,985	1,544,020

Source: Interstate Commerce Commission, Bureau of Transportation Economics and Statistics.

CHART 6

PRICE PER TON OF NUMBER 2 HEAVY MELTING STEEL SCRAP IN BIRMINGHAM AND PITTSBURGH, 1930-1948

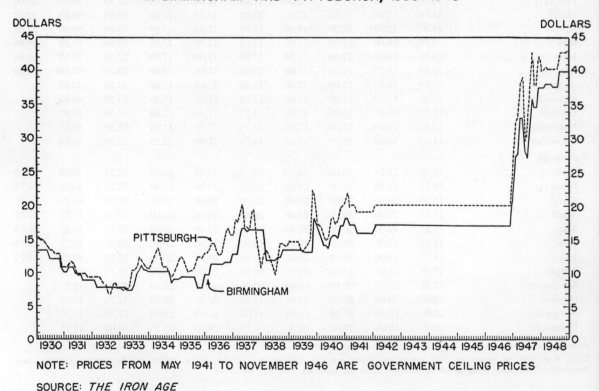

NOTE: PRICES FROM MAY 1941 TO NOVEMBER 1946 ARE GOVERNMENT CEILING PRICES

SOURCE: *THE IRON AGE*

on the Ohio; on both the Ohio and the Mississippi, the "through" shipments—shipments that came from another waterway or section of a waterway and pass through to still a different one. The general course of these movements is up the Mississippi into the Ohio, either for delivery to points along that river or to continue the journey to other streams such as the Monongahela and Allegheny. Figures on scrap iron and steel for 1947 and 1948 are as follows:

Waterway and movement	1947 (Net tons)	1948 (Net tons)
Mississippi River— mouth of Ohio to but not including Baton Rouge		
Outbound—up	166,564	184,738
Through—up	57,908	82,288
Ohio River		
Inbound—up	118,229	129,411
Through—up	82,355	86,303

Before the war, there was a substantial export of iron and steel scrap from the United States to Japan, Italy, and other foreign countries. A large part of this movement was through southern ports. Iron and steel scrap that left the country through Gulf and South Atlantic ports must have originated largely in the South, and it is entirely possible that much of the scrap which passed through the North Atlantic ports also had a southern origin. The size of the shipments is indicated by the data in Tables 17 and 18.

Table 18

Exports of Iron and Steel Scrap Through the Mobile Customs District, 1927-1940
(in gross tons)

Year	Exports
1927	301
1928	5,139
1929	9,454
1930	3,468
1931	3,074
1932	6,015
1933	25,163
1934	59,739
1935	40,040
1936	55,486
1937	123,970
1938	103,159
1939	66,882
1940	65,603

Source: *Foreign Commerce and Navigation of the United States,* 1927-1940.

These data indicate that there is a considerable quantity of secondary iron and steel in the South and that it is not being fully used within the region. The logic of the situation supports the conclusion that the potential supply of such materials will accumulate and should serve as a very important source of raw materials for the metals industries. This does not mean that the utilization of scrap resources can be attained without the difficulties attendant on economical collection, proper classification, and the assembly of uniform materials in quantities sufficiently large to make use feasible.

Table 17

Ferrous Scrap Exported from the United States, 1934-1940
(in gross tons)

Year	Total ferrous scrap exported	Ferrous scrap exported from			
		Atlantic Coast ports	Gulf of Mexico ports	Pacific Coast ports	Other customs districts
1934	1,835,170				
1935	2,103,959				
1936	1,936,132				
1937	4,101,549	2,221,689	1,389,828	342,707	147,325
1938	2,998,591	1,769,611	779,613	368,842	80,525
1939	3,584,439	2,000,940	876,976	544,554	161,969
1940	2,820,789	1,338,250	800,614	391,021	290,904

Source: *Minerals Yearbook,* 1937-1940.

CHAPTER VIII

AVAILABILITY OF RAW MATERIALS FROM OUTSIDE THE SOUTHEAST AND GENERAL CONCLUSIONS CONCERNING RAW MATERIALS

While the review of ore, coal, and limestone resources of the Southeast indicates ample supplies for many years to come, there are problems with regard to raw materials that are of sufficient importance to warrant a survey of the availability of raw materials from sources that lie beyond the boundaries of the region. As already pointed out, the iron ore of the Southeast is relatively low in iron content, it contains sufficient phosphorus to create difficulties, and the only large mass of ore requires underground mining. The coal is excellent in quality after cleaning, but the seams are thin, faulted, and irregular, and the coal—as mined —contains much foreign material that must be removed. These are characteristics which tend to produce high costs per ton in term of man-hours. With increasing wages and other expenditures, attention very naturally is directed toward other sources of supply which offer the chance of securing the desired raw materials on a lower cost basis. If ore and coal can be secured from outside at prices which compare favorably with the production costs of locally produced materials, the industry has a strong incentive to look to the outside for at least a part of its supplies. Also, it may be desirable to use outside sources to supplement the local minerals in order to secure qualities (for instance, low phosphorus iron ore) that would not otherwise be available.

In the discussion of outside sources, a brief statement will be given concerning materials that may be obtained from other parts of the United States. Attention, however, will be centered on foreign countries as sources of supply. As pointed out in the preceding chapter, manganese and most of the alloying materials must be obtained largely from abroad.

The southern industry, however, has no special problems in this connection that require attention now, and so the discussion will have to do primarily with iron ore.

Raw Materials from Other Parts of the United States

It is not probable that the blast furnaces and steel works of the Southeast will make any great use of iron ore from the North or East, but the possibility should not be entirely overlooked. As a matter of fact, emergency supplies of ore were obtained in 1945 and 1946 from the Lake Superior region because of the difficulty of securing local ore rapidly enough, even though a large reserve was close at hand. Small quantities of ore were also received during these years from Missouri, Arkansas, and Texas. The coal fields of Kentucky and West Virginia are conveniently located for barge shipments on the Ohio, Tennessee, and Mississippi rivers. The costs of mining are relatively low. Consequently it is always possible that it may be economical to use coals from these fields instead of Alabama coal. This may be the case even though shipment is made by rail.

Foreign Ore as a Source

Since the war, a very active interest has developed in the importation of foreign ores. In part, this has been stimulated by the depletion of the deposits of high grade ores in the Lake Superior region together with a gradual decline in the quality of these ores from an average of over 60 per cent iron content to about 50.3 per cent. This decline is all the more marked because the ores in recent years include a considerable quantity of concentrates. A second factor, and one of longer standing, is the successful operation of the Sparrows Point, Maryland, plant of the Bethlehem Steel Corporation. This plant is located on Atlantic tidewater and depends for ore largely on foreign imports—at first from Cuba and Morocco, but in more recent years from Chile and Sweden.

As a first step in an examination of foreign deposits as sources of ore, it is well to consider

Table 19

United States Production, Imports, and Exports of Iron Ore, 1920-1949
(in thousands of gross tons)

Year	Iron ore produced in the United States	Imports of iron ore and concentrates	Exports of iron ore and concentrates
1920	67,604	1,273	1,145
1921	29,491	316	440
1922	47,129	1,135	602
1923	69,351	2,768	1,117
1924	54,267	2,047	595
1925	61,908	2,191	631
1926	67,623	2,555	869
1927	61,741	2,621	899
1928	62,197	2,453	1,282
1929	73,028	3,139	1,304
1930	58,409	2,775	752
1931	31,132	1,466	436
1932	9,847	582	83
1933	17,553	861	155
1934	24,588	1,428	609
1935	30,540	1,492	661
1936	48,789	2,232	645
1937	72,094	2,442	1,264
1938	28,447	2,123	592
1939	51,732	2,413	1,057
1940	73,696	2,479	1,386
1941	92,410	2,321	1,908
1942	105,526	731	2,515
1943	101,248	399	2,425
1944	94,118	464	2,158
1945	88,376	1,198	2,063
1946	70,843	2,754	1,507
1947	93,092	4,896	2,811
1948	101,003	6,109	3,081
1949	84,937	7,402	2,425

Source: Iron ore producted, American Iron and Steel Institute, *Annual Statistical Report*, 1920-1949; Imports, Foreign Commerce *and Navigation of the United States*, 1920-1944; *Minerals Yearbook*, 1945-1949.

the record of the past. Tables 19 to 22 present the statistics of imports of iron ore into the United States from 1920 to 1949. No attempt will be made to discuss the details disclosed by these data, but the more outstanding facts will be summarized.

If imports are compared with domestic production and exports of iron ore in the United States, it is easily seen that there is no year of the period from 1920 to 1949 when any large proportion of the iron ore consumed in the nation was furnished by net imports. The largest tonnage of imports, 7.4 million tons, occurred in 1949. This compares with a domestic production in the same year of 84.9 million tons and exports of 2.4 million tons. The largest prewar year was 1929, when 3.1 million tons were imported, compared to a domestic production of 73 million tons and exports of 1.3 million tons. There were two periods during which imports were sustained at rather high levels. These occurred from 1923 to 1930, inclusive, and from 1936 to 1941, inclusive. The annual imports during these two periods varied between 2 million and 3.1 million tons. Although demand for iron ore was urgent during the war, the shortage of shipping brought about a sharp decline in imports. Following the cessation of hostilities, the tremendous postwar demand for steel stimulated a sharp increase in ore imports which, in 1948 and 1949, reached unprecedented levels. Exports were made largely to Canada.

The data on the countries which have furnished iron ore to American iron makers show that substantial tonnages have been imported at one time or other from Spain, the U.S.S.R., Brazil, and the Philippines, but the countries from which imports have most consistently been derived are Norway and Sweden, Canada, Cuba, Chile, and some countries in Africa. By far the largest quantities have come from Chile and have been connected with the operations of the Bethlehem Steel Corporation. Prior to World War II, the imports from Cuba and Norway and Sweden were about the same size. The largest, in any one year, of the period from 1920 to 1940, was 890,000 tons for Cuba

Table 20—Imports of Iron Ore into the United States by Country of Origin, 1920-1949
(in gross tons)

| Year | Total imports of iron ore into United States | Europe | | | | | North America | | | | | South America | | | Africa | Asia | Philippines, Australia, East Indies, Oceania |
		Norway and Sweden	Spain	U.S.S.R.	United Kingdom	All other Europe	Canada*	Newfoundland and Labrador	Mexico	Cuba	All other North American	Chile	Brazil	All other South American			
1920	1,273,456	65,689	69,915		315	4,381	34,084		124	889,852	802			11,649	193,829	2,815	1
1921	315,768	143,234	5,602		152	2,192	4,213			123,222		8,000			28,696	457	
1922	1,135,156	317,539	47,111		580	2,906	2,840	1		381,746	5	259,547		1,400	121,456	25	
1923	2,768,430	754,696	214,891		399	32,509	24,710	33,240		692,979		634,600	70	19,000	358,367	2,969	
1924	2,047,055	317,742	70,645		370	23,478	4,122			285,288		1,144,775	206	6,700	193,714	15	
1925	2,190,697	149,238	144,421		714	41,705	7,829			546,130		1,113,900	600		186,020		140
1926	2,555,441	71,918	83,608		105	20,339	16,984	119,544		539,000	2,000	1,364,400	3,708		333,835		
1927	2,620,717	261,066	27,165		947	10,512	26,079	61,030		392,113		1,369,200	8,905		458,700	2	5,000
1928	2,452,646	26,558	37,420		5,915	2,553	13,309	37,048		369,256	81	1,434,890	31,805		473,940	1,756	18,115
1929	3,139,334	310,406	48,885		916	13,295	3,542	76,340		641,350		1,699,066	46,050	1	249,685	8,000	41,798
1930	2,775,124	202,748	81,012	63,412	145	295	395	48,771	157	190,654		1,689,071	24,507		244,361	9,670	219,926
1931	1,465,613	156,636	38,191	278,612	470	141	1,490	22,920	1,456	89,000		750,702	25		85,980	8	39,982
1932	582,498	106,948	245	162,740	822	150	807		281	77,000		218,492			10,000		5,012
1933	861,153	62,336	900	135,840	241	709	90		148	143,150		467,650	3,600		43,790	2,699	
1934	1,427,521	108,784	1,159	100,605	5,525	189	11,126		1,618	154,500		938,376			55,950		49,689
1935	1,492,435	167,780	946	113,840	561	149	20,453		2,105	221,010		788,725			13,900	2,950	160,016
1936	2,232,229	324,494	198	7,750	570	11	83,911	11,300	3,687	444,500		1,264,130	6,102	1	12,293		73,281
1937	2,442,069	402,890		5,100	516		5,046	45,080	4,183	441,500		1,438,886	11,000		3,700	4,230	79,938
1938	2,122,516	289,241			228	55	936			148,701		1,577,750	9,650		7,480	5,648	82,827
1939	2,412,781	464,319			356		23,541	14,450	1,722	269,866		1,586,625	16,700		18,540	120	16,542
1940	2,483,234	210,804	11,010		393	10	221,846	23,320	3,590	219,653		1,682,600	99,165		7,190	3,653	
1941	2,343,983		7,292		546		280,236	57,026	4,445	180,088		1,685,780	118,870				9,700
1942	731,325				538		256,265		2,418	41,165		383,330	47,600				9
1943	399,117				313		279,222		16,740						102,840		2
1944	463,532				266		255,431		62,630	96	7			10	145,092		
1945	1,197,925		4		706		708,582		37,782	145		214,670			236,027		
1946	2,754,216	232,887			335	32,127	1,102,852	15,500	789	158,268		1,095,627	3		115,806		
1947	4,895,652	1,315,142	600		600		1,553,245		54,966	153,050		1,662,241	85,534		68,635	1,500	1,500
1948	6,108,754	1,467,578	6,449		351	18,494	985,846		163,149	34,500		2,631,997	295,926		497,304	3,000	4,160
1949	7,402,157	2,047,343	9,200		302	7,114	1,603,106		169,823	11,589		2,627,007	354,509	20	565,394	1,500	5,250

*Imports from Canada include pyrite cinder.

Source: *Foreign Commerce and Navigation of the United States, 1920-1944; Minerals Yearbook, 1944-1949.*

Table 21

Imports of Iron Ore into the United States by Groups of Customs Districts,* 1920-1949
(in gross tons)

Year	Total imports of iron ore**	Groups of customs districts					
		Northeastern (except Maryland)	Maryland	Northern	South-eastern	South-western	Western
1920	1,273,456	406,275	826,338	32,874	6,828	......	1,141
1921	315,768	68,195	242,461	3,247	577	......	1,288
1922	1,135,151	841,188	281,350	1,596	9,747	......	1,270
1923	2,768,430	1,427,996	1,290,661	7,327	38,984	......	3,462
1924	2,047,055	1,144,939	885,922	1,537	11,579	......	3,078
1925	2,190,697	922,963	1,258,547	3,554	1,556	52	4,025
1926	2,555,441	933,194	1,595,593	1,347	18,715	......	6,592
1927	2,620,717	941,702	1,624,313	2,016	28,780	31	23,875
1928	2,452,646	880,539	1,461,318	2,339	97,892	......	10,558
1929	3,139,334	974,096	2,112,898	3,334	48,894	......	112
1930	2,775,124	779,850	1,982,848	192	12,029	202	3
1931	1,465,613	568,743	886,361	1,139	8,000	1,346	24
1932	582,498	66,494	504,430	616	10,000	281	677
1933	861,153	76,720	780,454	126	3,678	175	......
1934	1,427,521	238,736	1,136,550	43,867	6,750	1,618	......
1935	1,492,435	184,652	1,225,986	71,300	8,200	2,132	165
1936	2,232,229	334,058	1,764,792	129,105	198	3,699	377
1937	2,442,069	352,490	1,961,798	122,323	......	4,263	1,195
1938	2,122,516	61,267	1,981,384	79,798	30	10	27
1939	2,412,781	168,640	2,182,708	59,669	......	1,732	32
1940	2,483,234	97,720	2,161,344	220,563	17	3,590	......
1941	2,343,983	70,015	1,989,280	280,147	9	4,490	42
1942	731,325	826	471,730	255,910	391	2,468	......
1943	399,117	91,560	11,728	279,035	......	16,792	2
1944	463,532	115,742	28,675	254,948	96	62,250	1,821
1945	1,197,925	158,717	293,704	703,559	445	37,782	3,718
1946	2,754,216	83,661	1,524,398	1,140,512	1,155	789	3,701
1947	4,895,652	120,401	3,067,027	1,648,777	61	55,666	3,720
1948	6,108,754	594,473	4,045,632	1,086,958	210,273	163,876	7,542
1949	7,398,879	783,047	4,448,015	1,747,537	234,579	173,434	12,267

*Customs districts are grouped as follows: Northeastern (except Maryland)—Virginia, Vermont, Massachusetts, New York, and Philadelphia; Northern—Buffalo, Michigan, Chicago, Ohio, St. Lawrence, Minnesota, Duluth and Superior, Pittsburgh, and St. Louis; Southeastern—Mobile, North Carolina, South Carolina, Georgia, New Orleans, and Florida; Southwestern—Galveston, San Antonio and Laredo; Western—San Francisco, Washington, Los Angeles, Montana and Idaho, Dakota, and Oregon.

**Total imports are for the continental United States and do not include Puerto Rico.

Source: *Foreign Commerce and Navigation of the United States,* 1920-1944, and special tabulation for 1945-1949 from U. S. Bureau of the Census.

Table 22

Imports of Iron Ore into the United States by Country of Origin and Groups of Customs Districts, 1938, 1943, and 1946

(in gross tons)

Year and country of origin	Total imports of iron ore into United States	Groups of customs districts					
		North-eastern (except Maryland)	Maryland	Northern	South-eastern	South-western	Western
1938							
Norway and Sweden	289,241	22,458	187,692	79,091	...	...	...
Spain	...	...	...	...	...	...	...
U.S.S.R.	...	...	...	...	...	...	...
United Kingdom	228	115	30	43	30	10	...
All other Europe	55	55	...	...	...	...	...
Canada	875	245	...	603	...	...	27
Newfoundland and Labrador	...	...	...	...			
Mexico	...	...	...	...			
Cuba	148,701	1	148,700				
All other North America	...	...	...				
Chile	1,577,750	22,250	1,555,500	...			
Brazil	9,650	...	9,650				
All other South America	...	...	...				
Africa	7,480	...	7,480	...	...		
Asia	5,648	5,635	13	...			
Philippines, Australia and Oceania	82,827	10,508	72,319	...	...	...	...
Total	2,122,455	61,267	1,981,384	79,737	30	10	27
1943							
Norway and Sweden	...	...	...	...	...	...	...
Spain	...	...	...	...	...	...	...
U.S.S.R.	...	...	...	...	...	...	...
United Kingdom	313	313	...	...	...	...	...
All other Europe	...	...	...	...	...	...	...
Canada	279,047	135	...	278,860	...	52	...
Newfoundland and Labrador	...	...	...	...			
Mexico	16,740	...	...	...	...	16,740	...
Cuba	...	...	...				
All other North America	...	...	...	...			
Chile	...	...	...	...			
Brazil	...	...	...	...			
All other South America	...	...	...	...			
Africa	102,840	91,112	11,728	...	...		
Asia	...	...	...	...			
Philippines, Australia and Oceania	2	...	...	...	...	...	2
Total	398,942	91,560	11,728	278,860	...	16,792	2
1946							
Norway and Sweden	257,345	1	211,805	45,539	...	...	...
Spain	4	...	...	4	...	...	...
U.S.S.R.	...	...	...	...	...	...	...
United Kingdom	334	334	...	...	...	...	...
All other Europe	7,669	7,669	...	...	...	...	...
Canada	1,095,236	2,041	...	1,093,195	...	...	...
Newfoundland and Labrador	15,500	15,500	...	...	...	...	...

Table 22 (cont'd)

Imports of Iron Ore into the United States by Country of Origin and Groups
of Customs Districts, 1938, 1943, and 1946
(in gross tons)

Year and country of origin	Total imports of iron ore into United States	Groups of customs districts					
		North-eastern (except Maryland)	Maryland	Northern	South-eastern	South-western	Western
Mexico	789	...	...	...	...	789	...
Cuba	158,268	...	158,113	...	155	...	...
All other North America	...	...	...	...	...	...	...
Chile	1,095,627	...	1,095,627	...	...	...	...
Brazil	3	3	...	...	...	...	...
All other South America	18	18	...	...	...	...	...
Africa	116,306	56,453	58,853	...	1,000	...	...
Asia	...	...	...	...	...	...	...
Philippines, Australia and Oceania	...	...	...	...	...	...	...
Total	2,747,099	82,019	1,524,398	1,138,738	1,155	789	...

Source: U. S. Bureau of the Census, special tabulation. Totals given for the three years differ slightly from those shown in Tables 20 and 21. Groups of customs districts same as Table 21.

in 1920 and 755,000 tons for Norway and Sweden in 1923. In several years, the imports from each of these two sources dropped below one hundred thousand tons. In 1947, however, imports from Norway and Sweden exceeded one million tons and in 1949 were slightly more than 2 million tons. Postwar imports from Cuba were small, declining to only 11,000 tons in 1949. The imports from Africa during the nineteen twenties were above one hundred thousand tons in each year except 1921. But, after 1930, a figure that large was not reached again until 1943. The Canadian imports were relatively small until 1940, but during the war averaged about a quarter of a million tons per year and increased sharply in the postwar years to reach one and a half million tons in 1947. Mexico was of practically no significance until 1943 and then was quite small. Receipts from Brazil were intermittent and not large. The largest for any one year was 354,509 tons in 1949, the second largest year was 1948 with 295,926 tons, the third largest was 1941 with 118,870 tons, and the fourth largest was 1940 with 99,165 tons. Chile, Cuba, Norway, and Sweden have been the chief sources of foreign ores in the past.

At present, most of the major companies have programs of exploration under way.[1] The Bethlehem Steel Corporation is developing a high grade iron ore deposit at El Pao near the Orinoco River in Venezuela. The United States Steel Corporation is also engaged in exploring ore deposits in Venezuela and has options on the ore of a large area. The deep rock deposits of Canada are being exploited. An active program is underway to explore and utilize the large deposits that are known to exist in Labrador and Newfoundland.[2] Attention is also being given to Brazil, Mexico, and other countries south of the United States. The Republic Steel Corporation has purchased an interest in a company which is developing ore properties in Liberia, Africa.[3] It seems,

[1] A. H. Hubbell, "The Problem of Iron Ore and How It Will Be Solved," Engineering and Mining Journal (July 1949), pp. 84-91.

[2] See Iron Age (November 4, 1948), p. 155; (December 1, 1949), p. 109; (August 31, 1950), p. 71; (October 19, 1950), p. 93; (February 8, 1951), p. 83. Also see John Bartlow Martin, "North to Find Iron," Harpers (December 1951), pp. 33-43 and (January 1952), pp. 79-88.

[3] See "New Ore for Republic," Engineering and Mining Journal (July 1949), p. 91 and "Republic Gets First Liberian Ore," Iron Age (June 28, 1951), p. 93.

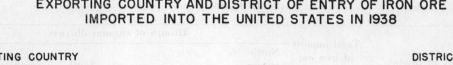

CHART 7

EXPORTING COUNTRY AND DISTRICT OF ENTRY OF IRON ORE
IMPORTED INTO THE UNITED STATES IN 1938

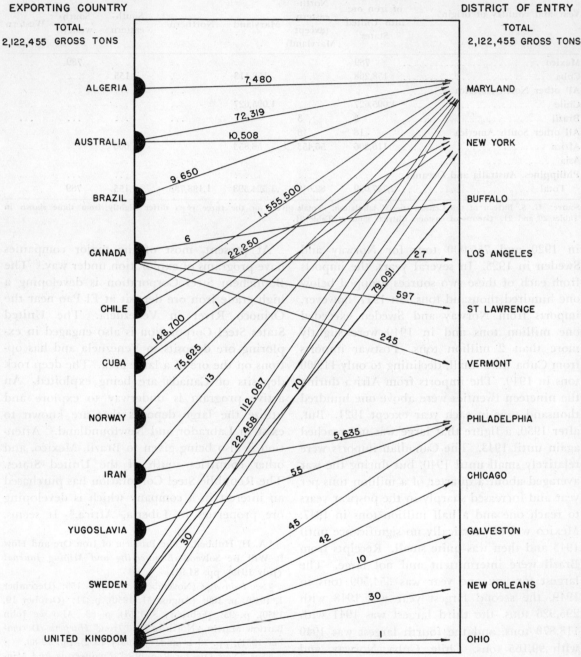

EXPORTING COUNTRY

TOTAL
2,122,455 GROSS TONS

ALGERIA

AUSTRALIA

BRAZIL

CANADA

CHILE

CUBA

NORWAY

IRAN

YUGOSLAVIA

SWEDEN

UNITED KINGDOM

DISTRICT OF ENTRY

TOTAL
2,122,455 GROSS TONS

MARYLAND

NEW YORK

BUFFALO

LOS ANGELES

ST LAWRENCE

VERMONT

PHILADELPHIA

CHICAGO

GALVESTON

NEW ORLEANS

OHIO

7,480

72,319

10,508

9,650

1,555,500

6

22,250

27

79,091

597

148,700

75,625

1

13

112,067

70

22,458

245

5,635

55

45

42

10

30

30

1

SOURCE: BUREAU OF THE CENSUS, SPECIAL TABULATION.

CHART 8

EXPORTING COUNTRY AND DISTRICT OF ENTRY OF IRON ORE
IMPORTED INTO THE UNITED STATES IN 1946

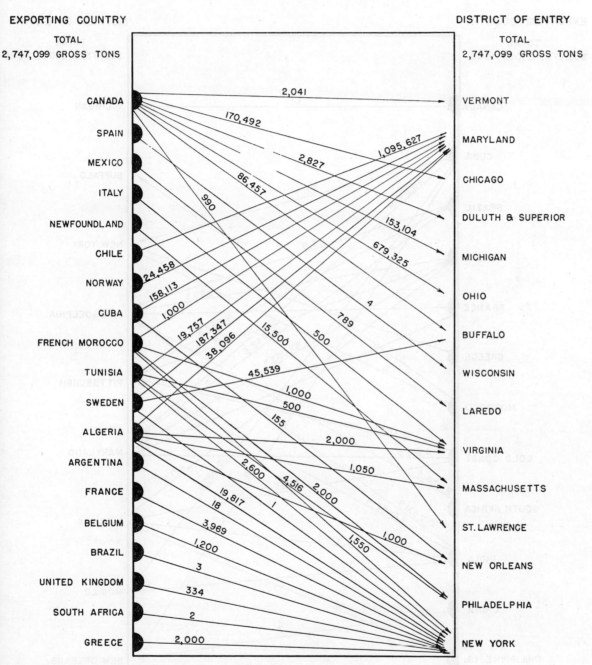

EXPORTING COUNTRY

TOTAL
2,747,099 GROSS TONS

DISTRICT OF ENTRY

TOTAL
2,747,099 GROSS TONS

CANADA
SPAIN
MEXICO
ITALY
NEWFOUNDLAND
CHILE
NORWAY
CUBA
FRENCH MOROCCO
TUNISIA
SWEDEN
ALGERIA
ARGENTINA
FRANCE
BELGIUM
BRAZIL
UNITED KINGDOM
SOUTH AFRICA
GREECE

VERMONT
MARYLAND
CHICAGO
DULUTH & SUPERIOR
MICHIGAN
OHIO
BUFFALO
WISCONSIN
LAREDO
VIRGINIA
MASSACHUSETTS
ST. LAWRENCE
NEW ORLEANS
PHILADELPHIA
NEW YORK

2,041
170,492
1,095,627
2,827
86,457
153,104
990
679,325
24,458
158,113
1,000
4
789
19,757
187,347
15,500
500
38,096
45,539
1,000
500
155
2,000
2,600
1,050
4,516
2,000
19,817
1
18
1,000
3,969
1,550
1,000
1,200
3
334
2
2,000

SOURCE: BUREAU OF THE CENSUS, SPECIAL TABULATION.

CHART 9

EXPORTING COUNTRY AND DISTRICT OF ENTRY OF MANGANESE ORE
IMPORTED INTO THE UNITED STATES IN 1938

GROSS TONS OF ORE CONTAINING 35 PER CENT AND OVER MANGANESE

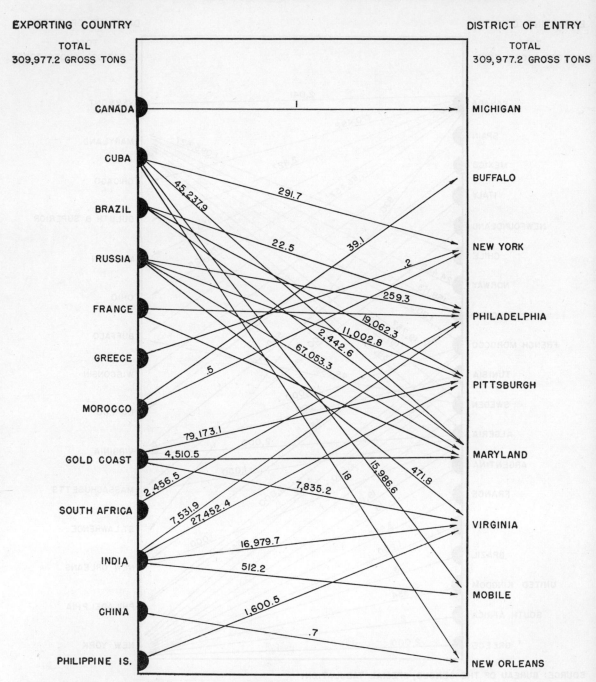

SOURCE: BUREAU OF THE CENSUS, SPECIAL TABULATION.

CHART 10

EXPORTING COUNTRY AND DISTRICT OF ENTRY OF MANGANESE ORE IMPORTED INTO THE UNITED STATES IN 1946

GROSS TONS OF ORE CONTAINING 35 PER CENT AND OVER MANGANESE

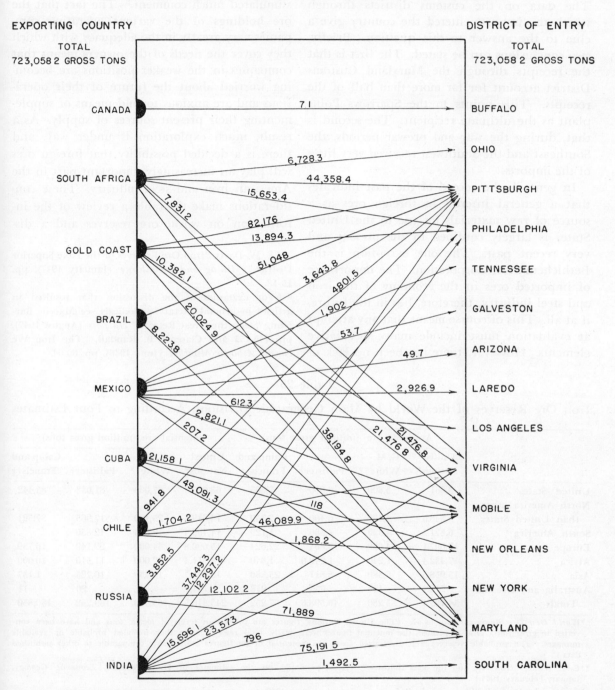

SOURCE BUREAU OF THE CENSUS, SPECIAL TABULATION

therefore, that imported iron ores in the future will probably play a much more important part in the economy of the American iron and steel industry than they have in the past.

The final point has to do with the regions of the nation which have used foreign ore. The data on the customs districts through which the imports entered the country give a clue to the answer to this question. Briefly, two conclusions can be stated. The first is that the receipts through the Maryland Customs District account for far more than half of the receipts. This points to the Sparrows Point plant as the ultimate recipient. The second is that, during the war and prewar periods, the Southeast and the Southwest received very little of the imports.

In general, the record of the past indicates that a general interest in foreign ores as a source of raw materials for use in the United States is largely confined to the present and very recent past. The one exception is the Bethlehem Steel Corporation. The importance of imported ores in the economy of the iron and steel industry, therefore, lies in the future, if at all. This of course means that any attempt at evaluation must include many speculative elements. However, there has been no lack of

interest since 1945. A report by E. W. Davis,[4] Director of the U.S. Mines Experiment Station in Minnesota, on the depletion of the resources of high grade ore of the Mesabi Range and other statements on this same subject have attracted a great deal of popular attention and stimulated much comment.[5] The fact that the ore holdings of the various operating companies vary greatly in the adequacy with which they cover the needs of the owners means that companies in the weaker positions are becoming worried about the future of their operations and are anxious to find means of supplementing their present sources of supply. As a result, much exploration is under way, and there is a decided possibility that foreign ores will play an increasingly important part in the American iron and steel industry. These considerations make desirable a review of the information on world ore reserves and a dis-

4 E. W. Davis, "Iron Ore Reserves of the Lake Superior District," Mining and Metallurgy (January 1947), pp. 15-18.

5 For examples of the discussion that resulted in articles in general literary periodicals see Marvin Barloon, "Steel: the Great Retreat," Harpers (August 1947), pp. 145-155 and Clarence B. Randall, "The Iron We Need," Atlantic Monthly (June 1948), pp. 60-64.

Table 23

Iron Ore Reserves of the World by Main Geographic Divisions, According to Four Estimates

	Available ore (million gross tons)				Potential ore (million gross tons)			
	United Nations*	C. M. White**	Pallister†	Camp and Francis††	United Nations*	C. M. White**	Pallister†	Camp and Francis††
United States	3,861	3,800	6,010	7,805	68,075.3	67,000	81,033	85,442
North America other than United States	5,346.5	4,450	6,400	7,759	14,649.4	25,100	17,965	37,521
South America	6,871.5	4,320	4,580	1,126	14,459.4	12,035	12,850	.....
Europe	17,097.1	14,670	18,894	22,624	15,690.8	34,000	29,149	16,739
Africa	7,432.4	1,240	1,248.6	1,340	113,911.4	12,000	11,510	10,000
Asia	13,958.5	6,380	8,811	25,680	16,375.7	15,435	16,725	1,137
Australia and Oceania	216.4	420	655	918	154.4	.....	20	11
Totals	54,783.4	35,280	46,598.6	67,252	243,316.5	165,570	169,252	150,850

*World Iron Ore Resources, pp. 66-67. (The United Nations' figures are printed in terms of metric tons and have been converted to gross tons. Also as printed, the potential figures were really total reserves since they included probable or available tonnages. The probable reserves were subtracted from the potential to get figures more nearly comparable to other published data.)

**C.M. White, "Iron Ore and the Steel Industry." (Based primarily on the estimates of Harry Mikami, Economic Geology, January-February 1944.)

†Prepared by H. D. Pallister after detailed examination of sources, 1948.

††J. M. Camp and C. B. Francis, The Making, Shaping and Treating of Steel, pp. 66-68. (Estimates as of 1935.)

cussion of those deposits most likely to be of interest to the South.

Reserves of Iron Ore in the World

A number of summary tables of the reserves of iron ore in the world have been published. The estimates thus presented vary widely in the quantities shown for the several countries. After a detailed examination of various sources, H. D. Pallister, as a member of the staff making this study, constructed a table of estimates, using the quantities that seemed best supported by published information as of 1948. In 1950, the Department of Economic Affairs of the United Nations published a report on world iron ore resources and their utilization, giving estimates of reserves which differed in several countries quite decidedly from those that had previously been accepted by Pallister. These differences are particularly large in the case of available (or probable) ore in the United States and in the estimates for a number of underdeveloped areas, especially in Africa. Table 23 presents a summary of estimates from four sources: The United Nations; C. M. White, President, Republic Steel Corporation; J. M. Camp and C. B. Francis; and Pallister.[6]

It must be emphasized that iron is a very common element in the world's composition and that ore occurs in many places. Deposits are often very inaccessible and are distant from the present areas of concentrated population and economic activity. Also, the question as to whether a deposit is usable depends, to a considerable extent, on economic considerations. An ore may have an iron content that makes it submarginal in one country, but, in another, with nearby coal deposits or a lack of richer ore deposits, an ore with the same iron content may be the basis for a going iron industry. These conditions, along with the continual explorations that are being made and the difficulty of measuring the quantity of an ore body that is located primarily underground, mean that any figures must be highly tentative. Consequently, the differences that appear in Table 23 are not too surprising. The statistics that are presented serve to indicate the general order of magnitude of the reserves.

A survey of the world iron ore resources serves to show how widely scattered the deposits are. Also it discloses the very large tonnages that apparently are in existence and may come into use if economic factors permit. From the point of view of availability for import into the United States, a number of factors are of importance. In the first place, countries with highly developed industrial systems, large populations, and large available supplies of coal probably will not favor the export of their iron ore resources. In the underdeveloped countries, strong movements have developed for the building of iron and steel plants to provide at least part of the country's needs. In part, this has been due to the difficulty, in war and postwar years, of getting steel from the countries that formerly were the suppliers, and, in part, it is a phase of the general movement toward nationalism. The United States Government has taken active steps in a number of cases to aid the Latin American countries in their projects. The United Nations also has had a part in developing plans for such projects, while cooperative arrangements have been worked out between American iron and steel companies and the government of the country possessing desirable deposits which provide for a sharing in the results to be obtained by exploiting that country's resources.[7] This means that any com-

[6] A special survey was made by the Department of Economic Affairs of the United Nations and published as *World Iron Ore Resources and Their Utilization, With Special Reference to the Use of Iron Ore in Underdeveloped Areas* (Lake Success, New York: 1950). C. M. White made an address before the American Institute of Mining and Metallurgical Engineers on March 17, 1947, entitled "Iron Ore and the Steel Industry," which was based largely on a table by Harry Mikami in *Economic Geology* (January-February 1944). Also see J. M. Camp and C. B. Francis, *The Making, Shaping, and Treating of Steel.*

[7] See Ted Metaxes, "Renaissance of Steel in South America," *Iron Age* (September 28, 1950), pp. 92-93; United Nations, *World Iron Ore Resources;* and John N. Dorr, "How Much Iron Ore in Brazil," *Iron Age* (August 17, 1950), pp. 81-84 and (August 24, 1950), pp. 79-82. The latter is a report on a long-term study made jointly by the U. S. Geological Survey and the Brazilian Government.

pany entering a foreign country probably will be required to make concessions beyond paying fixed royalties or other monetary settlements. Another factor of importance is that many of the large deposits are in locations which can be made accessible only by the expenditures of great sums of money on the construction of the proper kinds of mining and transportation facilities. Furthermore the great distance of many of the deposits from American ports makes them less likely to be sources of ore than those which are much nearer. While any of the deposits may affect the prospects of the southern iron and steel industry, if they are used in making products which will come in direct competition with those of the southern industry, the principal interest in this chapter is in those which are most available for importation into the South.

Foreign Sources and the Southeast

The ocean hauls from the countries touching the Gulf of Mexico or the Caribbean Sea to the Gulf ports of the United States compare favorably in length with those to east coast American ports. This fact tends to direct attention to those regions. A similar situation with respect to ocean distances exists with respect to the west coast of South America, but the necessity of passage through the Panama Canal, with the attendant payment of tolls, places these areas in a less advantageous position. On the other hand, the deposits in Brazil[8] are shipped from ports that are south of the so-called "hump" of the east coast of South America and are much nearer to Europe and the North Atlantic ports than to the Gulf ports of the South.

Canada, Newfoundland, and Labrador have been receiving much attention in recent years. The deposits of high grade ore in Labrador[9] have been undergoing systematic exploration

and, at the end of 1948, over 300 million tons of ore containing over 55 per cent iron had been proven. By 1951 the figure had been raised to 417 million tons, and the deposits are estimated by some authorities to contain 2 billion tons of reserves.[10] Such large quantities of high grade ore may well have a tremendous impact on the American iron and steel industry, but the users will probably be the plants in the northern and eastern sections of the nation. The interest of the southern industry is indirect.

Imports from Europe, Africa, and Asia may well come to southern ports, but there seems little reason to think that ores from these countries have an especial interest or are likely to exercise much influence on the industry of the South.[11] For these reasons the following paragraphs will be confined to developing in greater detail the situation with respect to the countries bordering the Gulf of Mexico and the Caribbean Sea and to those on the west coast of South America.

MEXICO

Imports from Mexico should be of interest to the southeastern states, as they can come from Mexican east coast points by water to Mobile, and, especially in wartime, such shipments are less hazardous than those from South America. The ore can also be shipped by rail in an emergency. Mexico has long been looked on as a source of precious and semiprecious metals, and it has only been in recent years that her iron ores have been considered worthy of note. Deposits of iron ore are scattered throughout the country, but the lack of an abundance of coal has been a handicap to local development.

---

8 See A. Maozemoff, "The United Nations' Newest Source of Iron," *Engineering and Mining Journal* (December 1942), pp. 55-59 and January 1943, pp. 56-59.

9 J. A. Retty, "Labrador, North America's Newest Iron Ore Field," *Mining and Metallurgy* (September 1948), pp. 480-483.

10 See "Foreign Sources of Iron Ore," *Mineral World* (October 1951), pp. 36-41 and "Labrador Ore Sooner Than You Think," *Iron Age* (August 31, 1950), p. 71.

11 A situation which may lead to developments contrary to this conclusion arises from the fact that the Republic Steel Corporation has steel producing properties in the South, is generally considered to be in a relatively weak position with respect to iron ore in the South, and is reported to be developing ore deposits in Liberia.

The large deposit of iron ore called Cerro de Mercado[12] near Durango has been mined and shipped to the iron and steel plant at Monterrey where coke made from Coahuila coal has been used in producing iron and steel. This plant is operated by the Cia Fundidora de Fierro y Cicero de Monterrey, a Mexican subsidiary of the Armco Steel Corporation. Also, a blast furnace at Monclova is operated by Altos Hornos de Mexico. The total Mexican pig iron capacity is approximately 400 thousand tons a year. Both companies have steel works and rolling mills.[13] The Bethlehem Steel Corporation controls deposits not far from the West Coast. The Republic Steel Corporation also has holdings inland from Vera Cruz and has shipped some of this ore to its Alabama furnaces for test runs. It is said, however, that the deposits are not accessible by railroad, and large-scale developments must await adequate transportation facilities.

CENTRAL AMERICA AND THE CARIBBEAN

Central America and the islands of the West Indies other than Cuba have iron deposits which would be convenient to Gulf ports. Puerto Rico is said to have nearly a half billion tons of limonite reserves ranging from 35 to 45 per cent iron while a mining company was reported in 1951 to be operating a mine in the Hunkas district and to be making regular shipments to the United States.[14] Panama, Honduras, Nicaragua, and the Dominican Republic[15] have reserves estimated in the tens of million tons. Little has been done to develop these reserves, and therefore they can be considered only as potential sources of ore for Gulf ports in the United States.

VENEZUELA

Extending from the Orinoco River southward, dipping under the Amazon and reappearing in the Minas Geraes region of Brazil, occurs the Imataca formation in which iron ores occur. Much of this area is unexplored. Outcrops of iron ore of good quality are visible at a number of places south of the Orinoco River.[16]

The deposit at El Pao was one of the first to attract attention. This location is 30 miles south of San Félix, a town at the junction of the Caroni and Orinoco Rivers. The ore averages 65 per cent iron and is low in phosphorus and silica. It is said that some one hundred million tons can be recovered by open-pit mining. In addition, there are large reserves which necessitate heavy stripping or underground mining.

The Bethlehem Steel Corporation has been exploring and developing the property since 1939. Transportation has been a major problem. The Orinoco River has numerous channels through its delta, and the one which is most commonly used is partly closed by two sand bars. This condition prevents ocean-going ore boats from reaching San Félix. It is reported that the company originally had expected to barge the ore down the Orinoco and through the Gulf of Paria to Trinidad for trans-shipment to large ocean-going ships for delivery to the Sparrows Point furnaces. However, this arrangement was not satisfactory to the Venezuelan government, which refused to dredge the channel and asked that the Bethlehem Steel Corporation either dredge the river channel or transship at a Venezuelan point on the coast. The latter course has been adopted. In addition to the problem of water transportation facilities, it was necessary to provide for moving the ore from the mines to a terminal on the river.[17]

The first shipments of iron ore from Venezuela have been received by the Bethlehem Steel Company at Sparrows Point.[18] The high grade massive deposit of hematite, 63 to 66 per cent iron, is being mined by open-pit methods.

[12] See Alberto Terrone Benitez, "Cerro de Mercado, Mexico's Iron Mountain," *Engineering and Mining Journal* (September 1944), pp. 88-89.

[13] *World Iron Ore Resources*, pp. 20, 30.

[14] "Foreign Sources of Iron Ore," *Mining World* (October 1951), pp. 36-41.

[15] *Minerals Yearbook*, 1949.

[16] "Venezuelan Iron Ore," *Mining Congress Journal* (April 1951), pp. 118-121, 124.

[17] Bethlehem Steel Corporation *Annual Report*, (1947, 1949, 1950).

[18] "Bethlehem Ship Comes in at Sparrows Point," *Iron Age* (March 29, 1951), p. 107.

The ore is hauled in large dump trucks from the mine to a crusher and then to cars for hauling from El Pao. It is then shipped over 30 miles of railroad, built by the company, to a loading dock at Palua on the Orinoco River where hundreds of thousands of tons can be stored and where barges of 4,500 tons capacity can be loaded. A dock with modern loading equipment is provided, and the barges, when loaded, proceed to the Gulf of Paria where a transfer station named Puerto de Hierro is located. The barges are unloaded, and the ore is then loaded on ocean-going ore ships of 26,000 tons capacity for hauling to Sparrows Point. Anticipated annual production is estimated at 3 million tons per year.

After two years of extensive survey and exploration, the U. S. Steel Corporation has recently announced the discovery of very rich and extensive iron ore deposits in the Orinoco region. Preliminary reports in late 1949 indicated 500 million gross tons of low phosphorus ores containing over 60 per cent iron in the "Cerro Bolívar" deposit. Other deposits in the same vicinity are also being explored. These ore bodies seem to be so valuable that leases and royalty details have been arranged with the Venezuelan government and plans are underway to begin shipping 10 million tons annually by 1953.[19]

"Cerro Bolívar" is about 100 miles southwest of the El Pao discovery of the Bethlehem Steel Corporation. It is about 90 miles from the Orinoco River and 275 miles from the nearest Caribbean port of Barcelona. Late in 1951 it was reported that the United States Steel Corporation and the Venezuelan government had reached an agreement which provided for the dredging of the Orinoco and Macareo rivers by the Corporation.[20] Movement of 10 million

tons of ore or more per year will require the construction of a railroad, docks, and ore bins at a river terminal, of large ore carrying vessels of 40,000 tons capacity, and of docks and storage depots at Mobile or other ports of entry. The importance of these developments is emphasized by the action taken by the United States Steel Corporation in the purchase of terminal facilities at Mobile, Alabama, which are to be converted into a modern ore terminal, and the building of an entirely new integrated steel plant near Trenton, New Jersey.

It is further reported that the Republic Steel Corporation has acquired another property in Venezuela not far from the Bethlehem and U. S. Steel Corporation's mines. If this property is developed, Republic very probably will ship at least a part of the ore to their Alabama furnaces.[21]

CUBA

Cuban ores are readily accessible to Mobile and other Gulf ports. They have been shipped to Atlantic coast ports but, in recent years, in decreasing quantities. Directly, this seems to be due to the exhaustion of the reserves of ore for which there has been a demand by American companies.[22] There is said to be about 3 billion tons of hematite ore reserves ranging from 35 to 65 per cent in iron content. The potential reserves of magnetite ore have been variously estimated to be as high as thirteen billion tons, containing up to 2 per cent chrome and 1 per cent nickel. The latter ore is not in demand by furnacemen, as the nickel and chrome cannot be removed in smelting by the ore treatment and furnace practices in current use, and this fact limits the use of the ore.

COLOMBIA AND PERU

Colombia and Peru are reported to have iron ore and coal deposits of some importance, but in neither country have these resources been developed to any great extent. Both have plans

19 T. W. Lippert, "Cerro Bolívar," Journal of Metals (February 1950), pp. 222-236; "Cerro Bolívar—Saga of an Iron Ore Crisis Averted," Mining Engineering (February 1950), pp. 178-192 M. C. Lake, "Cerro Bolívar, U. S. Steel's New Iron Ore Bonanza," Engineering and Mining Journal (August 1950), pp. 72-83.

20 See Iron Age (September 27, 1951), pp. 37-38 and an Associated Press story bearing New York dateline in Birmingham Post-Herald (November 23, 1951), p. 6, col. 1.

21 "Republic, Hanna Seek Venezuelan Ore," Iron Age (January 11, 1951), p. 84.

22 Minerals Yearbook, 1947, p. 622.

for building iron and steel plants.[23] The project in Colombia involves building the integrated Plaz de Rio steel plant at Boyacá with an annual capacity of 100 thousand tons. Iron ore, coal, and limestone are said to be available near the location.[24] Peru, in 1943, had a project for an integrated steel plant of 110 thousand tons annual capacity,[25] but the United Nations survey of 1950 only mentioned preliminary plans. While there are no present indications that either of these countries will become important suppliers of iron ore to the United States, the geographic locations of the countries and the fact that deposits are known to exist make them potential sources.

CHILE

The large scale development of Chilean ore was begun at El Tofo in 1913, but it was not until 1922 that shipping to Sparrows Point, Maryland, really began. The Bethlehem Steel Corporation uses its own cargo vessels of 22,000 tons capacity. Even though handicapped by the great distance from the iron and steel centers and by the payment of freight and Panama Canal tolls, ore shipments have been maintained in large volume except during submarine trouble in World War II. El Tofo ore analyzes about 60 per cent iron and is mainly hematite and martite. Reserves are said to be large.

The same company owns the nearby Romeral mine, with estimated reserves of 18 million tons.[26] Although plans for development (including port facilities) are on paper, this property is being held in reserve until needed. There are also five or six other interesting potential deposits of large size in the neighborhood which average about 60 per cent iron, 0.03 to 0.06 per cent phosphorus, and 0.02 to 0.03 per cent sulphur. The reserves for Chile would doubtless total over a half billion tons. Chilean coal reserves possibly total over three billion tons.

Chile, also, is taking active steps to develop an iron and steel industry. The Valdivia iron and steel plant at Corral, Chile, produces about 48,000 tons of steel, annually, from pig iron mixed with scrap, but this operation supplies only a small part of the country's requirements. The pig iron is produced from iron ore from the El Tofo mine and from Chilean coke. A new integrated steel plant with an annual capacity of 180,000 tons on San Vincente Bay was completed in 1950. This was a project of the government's Corporation de Fomento (Company for Industrial Development). In 1951 plans were being made to expand the capacity to 280,000 tons. This plant is operated by the Cia de Acero del Pacifico.[26] The project, financed in part by the Export-Import Bank, includes a coking plant; a blast furnace; Bessemer converters; electric furnaces; an open-hearth furnace; and mills for structural steel, rails, rods and bars, plate, sheet wire, and iron pipe. The Bethlehem Chile Iron Mines Company has agreed to supply the new Chilean steel works with ore for twenty years.[27] This arrangement is not expected to interfere with supplying the parent company, the Bethlehem Steel Corporation, with from one to one and a half million tons of iron ore per annum.

CONCLUSIONS CONCERNING IMPORTED ORE

The discussion presented above shows that the development of a foreign ore deposit is a large scale operation that requires mining in excess of a million tons of ore—possibly as much as four or five million—annually. In any of the likely ore locations, this involves transportation from the mine to a water terminal (probably on a river), shipment on barge or light draft vessel, trans-shipment to ocean-going vessels, and a long ocean voyage. Except for the Bethlehem Steel Corporation's Chilean project, such facilities were not in existence in

23 *World Iron Ore Resources*, p. 21.

24 Ted Metaxes, "Renaissance of Steel in South America," *Iron Age* (September 28, 1950), pp. 92-93.

25 Charles M. Parker, *Steel in Action*, p. 161.

26 *World Iron Ore Resources*, p. 27; Ted Metaxes, "Renaissance of Steel in South America" *Iron Age* (September 28, 1950), pp. 92-93, "Chilean or for U. S." *Iron Age* (December 20, 1951), p. 57.

27 *Minerals Yearbook*, 1949.

1945 and so had to be built by the corporation undertaking the enterprise. Furthermore, a company which risked as much capital as would be required for such a venture would scarcely wish to be dependent upon someone else for ocean transportation and hence would probably feel compelled to own its own vessels. Generally speaking, capital invested in iron ore mining is recovered rather slowly. To these considerations must be added the political instability of many of the Latin American countries. As a result, it can be concluded that the large amount of capital required and the risk involved make the development of a Latin American ore deposit a project to be undertaken only by one of the major corporations. At present, it seems that Venezuela holds the center of the stage so far as any projects that may affect the future of the iron and steel industry of the Southeast are concerned.

Much has been said of the possibility of erecting a steel plant on the Gulf Coast (probably Mobile) that would operate in much the same manner as Sparrows Point does in the East. Many factors must be considered before any conclusions founded on fact and reason can be reached concerning the feasibility of such a project, and a full discussion is postponed until problems of operations and markets can be examined.

General Conclusions Concerning Raw Materials

The examination of the various phases of the raw materials situation as affecting the iron and steel industry in the Southeast support the following conclusions:

1. The information on iron ore, coal, and limestone indicate that reserves in the Southeast are sufficient to support operations at the present or even on a much increased scale for a long period.

2. Deposits of both coal and iron ore present problems. Mining of each is made more difficult by the irregularities in the beds. Coal beds are thin and contain much extraneous material which must be removed by washing. However,

the quality of the cleaned coal is good. The red hematite ore has a low iron content and enough phosphorus to be troublesome, but much of it has sufficient lime to be self-fluxing. With the exception of the Big Seam, the ore beds do not lend themselves readily to large-scale mining. The brown ore occurs in deposits whose extent is difficult to predict. The pieces of ore are so mixed with extraneous materials that large quantities must be handled to get acceptable shipping ore.

3. The close proximity of the chief deposits of iron ore, coal, and limestone is a distinctive feature and is highly significant.

4. The many deposits of brown ore and red hematite ore can serve as supplementary sources to the Red Mountain deposits. Furthermore, future exploration may disclose reserves that may become important additional supplementary sources, or, with changes in the relative costs, demands, and availability of ore, may become primary sources of supply. An example is the probable westward extension of the Red Mountain formation under the Warrior basin. Furthermore, the small deposits should not be dismissed too lightly, because new techniques of producing iron may make the exploitation of small deposits more feasible than at present.

5. The low iron content of the red hematite ore makes beneficiation a very important problem. The presence of large quantities of easily mined ferruginous sandstone immediately adjacent to the Big Seam adds interest to the research and to the experimentation with beneficiation. The development of practical methods could add tremendously to the effective reserves.

6. The South has only small deposits of manganese and the various alloying metals, but, in this respect, the region does not differ greatly from the rest of the nation.

7. There are a number of factors which indicate that the iron and steel industry may expand without throwing a proportionately heavier burden on the mineral resources of the area.

(a) The South has accumulated a very considerable reserve of secondary ferrous materials, and this reserve can be expected to increase with further industrialization and urbanization.

(b) It is quite feasible to supplement the southern ores with ores imported from foreign countries. Birmingham, the chief southern steel center, can be reached readily by imports through Mobile. Houston is even more accessible, and the establishment of iron and steel mills at Mobile is a distinct possibility.

(c) The use of coal for purposes other than producing metallurgical coke has been decreasing, and this tends to increase the supply available for coking. Furthermore, coal could probably be brought to the southern mills from Kentucky and from other northern fields at no greater transportation costs than several of the steel centers in the North and East must bear.

(d) Increase in the iron content of the ore charged into the blast furnaces, either by concentration of southern ores or by blending with foreign ores, is a distinct possibility. If accomplished, such an increase will decrease the coke required per ton of pig iron produced.

In general, it may be concluded that the raw material resources available to southern iron and steel makers at least are not unfavorable to further development. There are problems, and some are quite serious, but it seems that the balance tends to be on the favorable side.

PART III

THE BASIC IRON AND STEEL INDUSTRIES OF THE SOUTHEAST

INTRODUCTION

The chapters of Part III deal with the problems of making pig iron and steel in the South and are concerned primarily with the mining of ore and coal and the operation of the coke oven plants, blast furnaces, and steel works and rolling mills of the region.

The first two chapters (IX and X) provide a general survey of the development of the basic industries in the Southeast. Both are, in a sense, historical in nature, although the second is based on statistical material to a much greater extent than the first. The first of these two chapters reviews the history of iron and steel in the Southeast during the nineteenth century and the early years of the twentieth century. The second deals with trends since 1900.

The next four chapters (XI, XII, XIII and XIV) describe the operations and discuss the problems that are encountered by the basic industries in the South. The first chapter in this group gives a brief description of the operating companies and their properties. This chapter is followed by one that develops the general features of the problems involved in mining ore and coal and in operating the manufacturing plants of the basic industries. One of the remaining chapters is devoted to the problems of ore mining and ore preparation in the South, and the other gives a similar treatment of the problems of mining coal and producing coke.

Chapter XV attempts to reduce the diverse factors influencing the basic operations to a common denominator—the cost of assembling raw materials at the blast furnace—and to compare the costs at the Southern iron and steel centers with the costs at important centers in other parts of the United States. The final chapter of Part III, Chapter XVI, discusses the influence that special technical problems have had on the basic iron and steel industries of the Southeast and offers a number of suggestions concerning technical developments which may affect the future of the Southern industry.

The general plan is to proceed from an examination of the historical background of the industry to a consideration of the conditions and problems which face the operators at present or are likely to become important in the future.

CHAPTER IX

IRON AND STEEL IN THE SOUTH DURING THE NINETEENTH CENTURY

In the eighteenth century, before the commencement of the Revolutionary War, all the colonies except Georgia engaged in the manufacture of iron. Iron works were established in North Carolina about 1725 and in South Carolina about 1773. Georgia had no colonial iron industry, its first iron enterprise having been established about 1790.[1] By 1800, iron works were in existence in Rockingham, Stokes, Surry, Wilkes, Guilford, Rowan, Lincoln, Burke, and Cleveland counties in North Carolina, and in the vicinity of Kings Mountain and in York County in South Carolina.[2]

The First Era, 1790 to 1860

The period from 1790 to 1860 may be considered as encompassing the first era in the development of the iron and steel industry of the Southeast. It might well be characterized as the charcoal-iron period. Steel making was an art still confined to the more metallurgically mature regions of Europe and to a few northern states—and only in an embryonic stage even there. Likewise, the use of coke for smelting iron ore had not been introduced into the South, although experiments had been made both in Europe and in Pennsylvania. Still, this early period saw many developments which provided a basis for the later expansion of iron making and for the introduction of steel.

The early trans-Appalachian pioneers, who pushed west and southwest into Tennessee and Alabama from the escarpments of the Appalachian plateaus, brought with them bar iron, which, in many ways, was the most essential

of supplies for their frontier life. Work animals had to be shod; wagons repaired; farm tools fashioned; and household items, such as pots and kettles and the like, provided. The small bars and billets, so laboriously hauled over the mountains, had been secured from England or were the products of the early bog-iron workings and forges along the Atlantic Coast.

The pioneers did not permit this situation to continue long. Among the migrants of the 1790's were many blacksmiths and mechanics who had experience, either in England or in the eastern coastal settlements, in the art of smelting ore and in the operation of bloomeries, foundries, and forges. These men recognized the presence of iron ore in the region, and they soon began to produce their own iron. The beginnings were primitive. Small furnaces were built of stone and usually were located so that water power could be used to furnish the air-blast. These furnaces sprang up over a fairly wide area in the mineral belt of the Southeast. The ore which was almost universally used was limonite or "brown" ore. This ore was to be found in many places in the region and often occurred in pocket deposits at, or near, the surface of the ground—a condition which made for easy mining. The flux was taken from quarries of limestone, which were abundant. The fuel used was charcoal, which could be produced readily, since most of the area was covered with suitable forests.

The records of this early period are inconclusive, but it appears likely that the first settlers of Tennessee erected iron works within the state soon after the close of the Revolution.

[1] *Mineral Resources of the United States, 1886,* p. 23.
[2] J. L. Bishop, *American Manufacture,* I, pp. 611-612; 619-621.

A bloomery was built in 1790 at Emeryville,[3] in Washington County. Other bloomeries were built in east Tennessee in 1795 and 1797. In west Tennessee, the Cumberland furnace was erected in Dickson County some time between 1790 and 1795.

The first blast furnace[4] of record in Alabama was one built in the latter part of 1818 near Russellville in Franklin County and was known as the Old Cedar Creek Furnace. Another early venture was the erection in 1830 in Tuscaloosa County of the Roupes Valley Iron Works, known later as the Old Tannehill Furnace. A furnace was built at Polksville, in Calhoun County in 1843 and the Shelby furnace, at Shelby, in Shelby County was built in 1848. By 1856 about seventeen forges and bloomeries had been erected in Alabama, of which half were still in operation and producing about 250 tons of blooms and bars.

Most of the forges and furnaces of this early period followed a similar pattern of existence and operation. Accounts of the pioneer period indicate that early efforts in iron making in the Southeast were designed to meet the requirements of local, and often isolated, areas struggling to develop and maintain an agrarian economy. Furnace capacity seldom exceeded three tons. The furnaces and forges were usually operated as a part of a combination of enterprises under one management and included iron works, grist mills, and sawmills. As steel was practically unknown, the products were wrought iron forgings or gray iron castings.

The raw materials for iron making were close at hand in this early period, and production was relatively easy, but any attempt to expand beyond local needs brought almost insolvable problems in transportation. The wagon trails were wretched, the first railroads were still largely on the east coast, and the waterways were somewhat inflexible as to destinations. There was almost no commercial business until the later years of the period. In the 1840's and 1850's, some bar iron, produced at points on or very near to navigable rivers, found its way to river and Gulf coast towns where it was made into small castings, hollow ware, and farm tools. Railroad building in the Southeast during the 1850's provided a small business in making strap iron rails. By 1860 the total trackage in the nine southeastern states had reached 6,963 miles of the nation's total of 30,626, or 22.7 per cent.[5]

Despite the scattered and rather halting development of the iron industry in the Southeast, the growth of population and the increased knowledge of the mineral resources of the region were two factors of very great importance. In 1820, the reported population of the nine southeastern states was 2,276,411 persons. In 1860, the population of the same area had trebled to reach a total of 6,902,799. The overwhelming majority of the population was engaged in agricultural pursuits, but towns in the area had begun to grow and these centers attracted the workers and craftsmen necessary to the foundation of industry.

There is evidence that the various states by 1860 were conscious of their mineral wealth. As pointed out previously, the modern iron and steel industry is based upon two great mineral deposits: one, the red hematite ore that outcrops in Jefferson county, Alabama; the other, the coking coal of the Warrior River Basin. Red Mountain ore was used by the Indians as a dye rock, and most of the early white settlers considered the red ore as good for dyeing clothes but of little further use. One man, however — Baylis E. Grace — recognized the dye rock as iron ore, and, in the 1840's, sent some of the ore to a forge in Bibb county where it was made into wrought iron and blooms.[6] Nothing more was done with the red ore until after 1860.

Coal outcroppings were found in Alabama by the earliest white settlers, and, in the 1820's, coal was mined along the Warrior River.[7] During the next few years coal was found over

[3] Bishop, I, pp. 613-614.
[4] Ethel Armes, *Coal and Iron in Alabama*, pp. 27-31; 58-59.

[5] *Statistical Abstract of the United States, 1948*, p. 521.
[6] Armes, p. 46.
[7] Armes, p. 50.

a wide area in Alabama and, although some was used in forges, it was mined primarily for domestic use. In 1854, the first coke was made in Alabama[8] and was sold for foundry use. The seams that were discovered in this early period, however, did not yield a satisfactory quality of coking coal, and important developments in the coal mining industry did not take place until later.

The early attempts at exploitations were accompanied by much more systematic exploration. As early as 1827, surveys of mineral resources were made in North Carolina. Similar

8 Armes, p. 68.

surveys were made in 1830 in Tennessee and in 1849 in Alabama. Thus, an inventory was being taken upon which future developments, especially in iron and coal, might be based.

Despite these early beginnings and the growth in population, the iron industries made comparatively little progress. The *Census of Manufacturers* of 1860 indicates that the industrial development of the nine states of the Southeast lagged behind the rest of the country. The area had approximately 22.0 per cent of the population of the nation compared with 6.5 per cent of the capital invested in manufacturing enterprises, 5.4 per cent of the workers employed, and 5.2 per cent of the value of

Table 24

Iron Manufactures in the Southeast and the United States
Compared with Population and All Manufactures, 1860

Item	Southeast	United States	Per cent Southeast of United States
Population 1860	6,902,799	31,443,321	22.0
All manufactures			
Number of establishments	14,263	140,433	10.2
Capital invested (dollars)	65,767,175	1,009,855,715	6.5
Number of hands employed	71,068	1,311,246	5.4
Value of product (dollars)	98,305,960	1,885,861,676	5.2
Iron blooms			
Number of establishments	3	97	3.1
Capital invested (dollars)	88,000	2,135,600	4.1
Number of hands employed	112	1,746	6.4
Value of product (dollars)	251,580	2,623,178	9.6
Tons produced	4,486	51,290	8.7
Pig iron			
Number of establishments	23	286	8.0
Capital invested (dollars)	1,317,675	24,672,824	5.3
Number of hands employed	1,206	15,927	7.6
Value of product (dollars)	645,730	20,870,120	3.1
Tons produced	25,144	987,559	2.5
Bar, sheet, and railroad iron			
Number of establishments	64	256	25.0
Capital invested (dollars)	585,285	19,924,473	2.9
Number of hands employed	627	19,262	3.3
Value of product (dollars)	791,234	31,888,705	2.5
Tons produced	8,363	509,084	1.6
Iron castings—general			
Number of establishments	42	955	4.4
Capital invested (dollars)	479,500	13,890,512	3.5
Number of hands employed	602	15,225	4.0
Value of product (dollars)	801,565	20,000,267	4.0

Source: *Census of Manufactures, 1860.*

product. For the most part, the participation of the Southeast in the iron industries was considerably below its share in all manufacturing. In terms of per cent of the national totals of tons produced and value of product, the region made the best showing in iron blooms but made a much weaker showing in pig iron; bar, sheet, and railroad iron; and iron castings. The statistics compiled from the report of the census are given in Table 24. A further indication of lack of progress is provided by the fact that the value of production of the pig iron industry in the Southeast declined 27.1 per cent from 1850 to 1860, while the value for the nation increased 54.7 per cent. A similar situation is shown for the value of production of bar, sheet, and railroad iron. In the Southeast there was a decrease of 15.8 per cent and in the nation an increase of 100.1 per cent.

Why this drop in production should have occurred is a question which naturally arises. A number of reasons have been advanced. For one thing, the old industry was largely established on the basis of using bloomeries or refining forges to process the iron into shapes for use.[9] These processes were destined to be largely replaced by puddling furnaces and rolling mills, which proved to be much cheaper. Also, the older furnaces used charcoal as a fuel. The production of charcoal was a slow process and soon destroyed the supply of suitable kinds of trees in the vicinity of a furnace. Anthracite coal and coke were being developed as more satisfactory fuels. The southern operators clung to the old methods, while the northern industry, adopting the newer techniques, was able to undersell the southern producers in their own markets. Also, the attention of the South was increasingly given to agricultural pursuits, and its wealthier and more influential men were not interested in the development of manufacturing.

The Civil War and the Southern Iron Industry

The Civil War brought both boom and destruction to the South's iron industry. Gun

forging works and arsenals were built at a number of sites from Selma, Alabama, to Richmond, Virginia. The resulting demand for iron stimulated a marked expansion in the mining and smelting of ores and in the production of pig iron. With the financial assistance of the Confederate Government, the Oxmoor plant of the Red Mountain Iron Company was constructed. This was the first attempt to use the Alabama red ore in quantity, and in this plant, from 1863 to 1865, much of the pig iron used at the Confederate Arsenal at Selma was made.[10] In the South as a whole, it is estimated that several hundred thousand tons of iron ore were smelted into pig iron during the war years.

The Oxmoor furnaces were destroyed by Federal raiders, and the same fate was shared by many of the other iron-making facilities of the Confederacy. The end of the war found virtually every southern iron works in ruins.

Reconstruction and the Rebuilding of the Iron Industry, 1865 to 1883

Following the end of hostilities between the states, there was an almost immediate revival of iron making in the mineral belt of Tennessee and Alabama. At first, the revived industry continued the use of charcoal as the fuel and depended in large part on the brown ores scattered throughout the area. Had these two constituents been the only basis upon which the revival rested, it would probably have been short lived because of the far-reaching effects of the revolutionary changes which were taking place in Pittsburgh and the Great Lakes area. Four events occurred during this period, however, which completely changed the character of the southern iron industry. The first was the discovery and exploitation of large deposits of coking coal in Tennessee and Alabama; the second was the substitution of coke for charcoal in the southern blast furnaces; the third was the use, in quantity, of the red ores of Alabama and the establishment of the iron industry in the Birmingham district; and the fourth was the invention of the two processes that made cheap steel possible—the Bessemer

[9] *Mineral Resources of the United States, 1886,* pp. 32-33.

[10] Armes, p. 160.

process, about 1857, and the Siemens-Martin (or open-hearth process), about 1866.

The first pig iron made in the South using coke as a fuel was produced in 1867 by the Roane Iron Company at Rockwood, Tennessee. In the 1870's, local coal of the Chattanooga area proved suitable for coking. Chattanooga, already a manufacturing town of some local importance before the Civil War, came into prominence as an iron-making center in 1874 when the furnace of the Chattanooga Iron Company went into blast. Other furnaces and iron works were immediately established in the same vicinity, and by 1877, citizens of Chattanooga spoke of their town as the Pittsburgh of the South.[11] The Tennessee Coal, Iron and Railroad Company, chartered in 1860, had begun to widen its activity in this vicinity and was recognized as the dominant corporation in the area.[12] By 1880, several hundred coke ovens were in operation in Tennessee, and coke was shipped as far as East St. Louis.[13] In 1885, there were nine furnaces in or near Chattanooga, together with some seventeen foundries and machine shops.[14]

Birmingham, Alabama, was conceived as an industrial center by its founders. Enough was known of the mineral resources of the area to stimulate interest, but little could be accomplished without the building of a considerable network of railroads to link the ore and coal and to gain access to markets. The construction of the various rail lines that now form parts of the Louisville and Nashville and the Alabama and Great Southern Railroad Systems were undertakings involving devious political intrigue and extending over a period of years.[15]

But the roads were built, and in 1871 the town of Birmingham was founded.

About 1874, a seam of coal of superior coking quality was discovered in the Warrior field. This seam was later named the Pratt seam.[16] In 1878, the Pratt Coal and Coke Company was organized to develop and exploit the large coal field in the Warrior Basin. It was the first big coal company to be formed in Alabama. The first coke pig iron was produced in Alabama in 1876. As pointed out above, the red ores of the Red Mountain seams had been used in quantity during the Civil War, and so the stage was set for the development of the Birmingham district.

The production of coke pig iron, although not an immediate commercial success, served as a stimulant to the industrial development of Birmingham and its mineral area. The Pratt Coal and Coke Company provided a base for the further development of coal for power and for coke. Within a short time, several new enterprises were started, including the Birmingham rolling mills, Alice Furnace Company, Sloss Furnace Company, Pratt Coal and Iron Company, Cahaba Coal Mining Company, Williamson Furnace Company, Woodward Iron Company, and Mary Pratt Furnace Company.[17]

It must not be supposed that the developments around Chattanooga and the rise of the Birmingham district tell the whole story of the development of the iron industry in the Southeast. Between these two centers lay a considerable expanse of the southeastern mineral belt in which iron making had been carried on in a primitive pioneering way before the Civil War.[18] The northeastern Alabama counties of Calhoun and Cherokee and the northwestern Georgia counties of Cass and Fannin had been local centers of iron production before the war. Although there was no revival of antebellum

---

11 Victor S. Clark, *Manufactures in the United States,* II, p. 213, cites *Bulletin,* American Iron and Steel Association (June 4, 1874); (November 12, 1874); (August 1, 1877); (October 3, 1877).

12 For a detailed discussion of the early days of the Tennessee Coal, Iron and Railroad Company, see Ethel Armes, *Coal and Iron in Alabama,* Chapter XIII.

13 Clark, II, p. 213, cites *Bulletin,* American Iron and Steel Association (December 24 and 31, 1879).

14 Clark, II, p. 213, cites *Manufactures Record,* VII, 680 (July 11, 1885).

15 For an interesting discussion, see Ethel Armes, *Coal and Iron in Alabama,* particularly Chapter VIII.

16 Armes, pp. 260, 273.

17 Armes, p. 283.

18 The 1860 *Census of Manufactures* shows pig iron establishments in Calhoun, Cherokee, Bibb, and Shelby counties, Alabama and Cass (now Bartow) County, Georgia, and bar iron producers in Bibb and Shelby counties, Alabama, and Fannin and Fulton counties, Georgia.

furnaces, new iron-making enterprises gradually developed, and the Cahaba coal field was brought into production. The principal iron-making centers were Anniston, where the Woodstock Iron Company was founded in 1872, and Gadsden and Talladega, where furnaces were built in the eighties.

The plants in this mineral region continued, for the most part, the use of the rich brown ores from Bibb, Shelby, Talladega, and Calhoun counties. They did not develop a steel industry, as the Birmingham district did later, but continued to expand their iron production, including charcoal iron, and to manufacture car wheels, wrought-iron bar and plate, and iron-cut nails. These enterprises were on a comparatively small scale and suffered from financial difficulties and the lack of experienced labor.

Despite this promise and progress, the industry did not make a continuously sustained advance through the 35 years following the end of the Civil War. The South had been stripped of most of its wealth. Capital with which to build up the industrial economy of the region was not available in sufficient amount. Most of the early revival in the iron industry was based on local funds or on capital that was contributed in relatively small amounts by individual northern investors who had recognized the possibilities for a southern iron industry while serving in the invading federal armies. But the initial investments were not enough and, for the most part, were swept away in the panic of 1873.

The leaders of the industry would not give up; new capital, mainly from the north and from England, was obtained for investment in the southern enterprises. Companies were merged and expanded. The coal industry was developed on a broad scale to provide both coke and industrial power. Railroad systems joining the various areas in the region with each other and with the more industrially mature states of the North were organized. The Birmingham area was given special assistance by the Louisville and Nashville Railroad management. They provided large sums of capital with which to develop iron and coal resources. More important, they revised the freight tariffs of the Louisville and Nashville Railroad so that low rates on coal and pig iron enabled these items to reach wider and more profitable market areas.

The development of the pig-iron industry, considerable though it was, did not assure the South the industrial expansion and well-being that it sought. As late as 1883, in a widely publicized statement a prominent Alabama producer could say, "You can go into the history of iron making in Alabama for the past twelve years and find it strewn with the wrecks of shattered hopes of the men who built or leased the furnaces. In Georgia the record is the same. . . . Those of Tennessee have not fared much, if any, better, even when backed by millions of English capital and the skilled management from that country. . . . The great trouble is, we do not have home markets. . . . The whole state of Alabama cannot take the product of a single blast furnace for a month. We depend entirely on the North and great West to keep our furnaces going."[19]

The truth of this description of the plight of the southern iron industry can be supported by facts. The whole vast region of the South was still engaged in cotton and range-cattle production. Only one of the fifteen southern cities which enumerated over 100,000 persons in the census of 1940 contained as many as 40,000 people in 1880. There were no large industrial centers in the area. Furthermore, the machine economy of the nation was turning toward steel, and steel was not made in quantity in the South until after 1898.[20]

Cast Iron Pipe and the Modern Iron Industry of the South

The development of the use of cast iron pipe by the large cities for the distribution of water and gas and for the disposal of sewage was one of the chief factors in providing a quantity market for the pig iron of the Southeast. Con-

19 Armes, pp. 302-303.
20 Armes, p. 464.

sequently, the growth of the cast iron pipe industry has a very direct connection with the development of the southern iron industry.

Conduit made from cast iron came into use in Europe as early as the fifteenth century. By the middle of the seventeenth century, many of the major European cities, including London, had replaced the lead and bored-log conduits with cast iron pipe. By 1817, the first major installation of cast iron pipe for the carriage of water had been made in the United States at Philadelphia. The pipe had been imported from England. Likewise, cast iron pipe was considered the proper conduit for use in gas systems. By 1819, the water and gas companies were seeking cast iron pipe of American make.[21]

As more of the nation's large cities adopted cast iron pipe for their water and gas lines, the enlarged consumption of pipe gave rise to a new industry. The first cast iron pipe in the United States was made at the bar iron furnaces of New Jersey in 1819, but the growing demand resulted in building, in New Jersey and Pennsylvania, foundries especially designed to make pipe. It was not until 1867 that cast iron pipe was manufactured in the South. In that year a small foundry located in Nashville, Tennessee, produced some cast iron pipe for local consumption. In 1877, the first real pipe shop in the South was built in Chattanooga, and, in 1884, this plant was enlarged.

The year 1883 marked the beginning of a period of growth in the cast iron pipe industry. The need for water works and sewerage installations mounted with the increase in urbanization which accompanied the nation's industrial expansion during the eighties and early nineties. From 1883 until the panic of 1893, some 36 new shops began casting pressure and soil pipe to meet the demand. It is in this period that the trend of the industry toward southern locations became apparent. From 1883 through 1891, four plants were established in Alabama, at Birmingham, Anniston, Bessemer, and Bridgeport.

That the South, and especially Alabama, should become an important center of the rapidly growing cast iron pipe industry is not surprising. In 1883, No. 1 foundry pig iron was made in Tennessee and Alabama at a cost of less than $10.50 a ton.[22] Southern pig iron proved to be a satisfactory foundry iron and was produced in such quantity that the supply was in excess of the local demand for iron and steel manufactures.[23] Inasmuch as cast iron pipe had been placed in the same freight classification as pig iron, the low rates which made the movement of southern pig to northern markets so attractive also served to open the large urban centers of the North as market areas for southern pipe.

The panic of 1893 interrupted the expansion of the cast iron pipe industry. The seven-year period, 1893 to 1900, was a period of keen competition marked by the formation of selling pools by the major pipe companies in order to preserve their markets. This device was abandoned upon court order in a suit known as the Addyston Pipe Case.[24] Following this decision, a concentration movement began with the consolidation of many of the major pipe producers. In 1898, the pipe shops at Chattanooga, South Pittsburg, Anniston, and Bessemer were consolidated as the American Pipe and Foundry Company. The following year, 1899, saw the formation of the United States Cast Iron Pipe and Foundry Company, a consolidation of the American Pipe and Foundry Company and plants located in six central and northern states.[25]

After 1900, activity in the pipe industry was resumed, and in the period from 1900 to 1914, almost the entire growth of the industry took place in the South, with Alabama leading as the center of development. Of the twelve new plants built in the United States over the fourteen-year period, two were located in Ohio, one

21 Henry Jeffers Noble, *Cast Iron Pressure Pipe Industry*, pp. 11-12.

22 Clark, II, p. 217.

23 In 1886, the South made over 875,000 tons of pig iron, a figure attained but once by the whole country prior to the Civil War. Clark, II, p. 217.

24 Clark, II, pp. 127-128.

25 Noble, p. 78.

each in Pennsylvania, Virginia, and Georgia, and seven in Alabama. In 1913, more than a million tons of cast iron pipe and fittings were made in the United States. The leading producing state on a tonnage basis was Alabama.[26]

The Beginnings of Steel Production

While pig iron was being produced in quantity in the South by 1883, it had certain properties which imposed definite restrictions on its use. It was considered as being a suitable foundry iron, especially for such products as cast iron pipe. As shown in the preceding paragraphs, pig iron was finding an expanding use for such purposes. However, production could easily be pushed more rapidly than the existing demand would warrant, and there were definite limitations on other outlets because the iron was so high in phosphorus that it was useless for many kinds of gray iron castings. In 1887, a member of the International Association of Metallurgists and Mineralogists, which was meeting in Birmingham, is reported to have remarked that Birmingham iron contained so many impurities and was so brittle that it had to be shipped on sawdust to prevent its being broken.[27] The phosphorus content of the iron created a serious problem in another respect, since it was present in proportions that made the iron unsuitable for use in acid lined Bessemer converters of the steel-making process then in use. Since it was becoming increasingly evident that steel was to provide a great, if not the most important, use for iron, the iron makers of the South directed a large part of their efforts toward finding ways of entering that field.

The meeting referred to in the preceding paragraph brought to Birmingham James Henderson, who owned a patented process for the manufacture of steel in the open hearth. When he became convinced that steel could be made from Birmingham pig iron, a company was organized to build a furnace and demonstrate the Henderson process. As a result of this experiment, a ton of steel was produced in March, 1883, which was reported to have met the requirements for high grade steel. A new plant was built and was recognized as a mechanical success, but the high cost of manufacture apparently kept it from being successful commercially.[28]

In the latter part of 1891, an experiment took place that proved to be an important step in preparing the way for steel making in Birmingham. It resulted in making the first low silicon, or basic, iron produced from red ore. In July, 1895, basic pig iron was produced on a commercial scale for the first time in Alabama. A leading iron maker of the day pointed out the significance of this event as follows:

> Unfortunately the local ore contained too much phosphorus to be made into steel by either the Bessemer or Open Hearth acid process, and not enough for the Basic Bessemer process, which were those then commonly in use elsewhere. . . . About this time the basic Open Hearth process began to come to the fore and for this southern pig iron would be suitable, providing the percentage of silicon and sulphur could be kept sufficiently low.[29]

This objective was accomplished in the production of basic pig iron which, by October, 1895, was being sold in considerable quantities by the Tennessee Coal, Iron and Railroad Company to Carnegie and to the Illinois Steel Company.[30]

In March, 1896, a T.C.I. representative, after a tour of northern steel mills, reported that Alabama basic pig iron was being made into steel at the Homestead Works of the Carnegie Company. This report naturally directed renewed attention to the possibility of producing steel in Birmingham, where two small open-hearth furnaces, intended to be run on scrap, were under construction. As a result, steel was produced in July, 1897, by the Birmingham rolling mill, but it was not until November 30, 1898, that basic open-hearth steel was produced on a commercial scale at the Ensley plant of the T.C.I.[31]

26 Clark, II, p. 128.
27 Armes, p. 407.

28 Armes, pp. 407-410.
29 Armes, p. 433.
30 Armes, pp. 433-435.
31 Armes, p. 462.

There remained one serious problem. While steel can be produced from pig iron and iron ore in the basic open-hearth furnace, it is not economical. In the North, scrap had accumulated and, when combined with pig iron in the charge, made it possible for the open-hearth furnaces to produce cheap steel. The problem was finally solved by the introduction of the duplex process by which Bessemer converters were used in the first stages of the steel-making process and basic open-hearth furnaces in the later stages. The rebuilding of the Ensley plant, in 1906 and 1907, incorporated this process and marks the final step in ushering in the modern steel industry in the Birmingham district. A new era began with the acquisition, in 1907, of the capital stock of the Tennessee Coal, Iron and Railroad Company by the United States Steel Corporation, which put the financial strength of that corporation behind the Alabama operation. Also a new source of engineering and technical skill became available through transfer of experienced personnel from other mills of the combination.

Early Manufacture of Iron and Steel Products

The manufacture of iron products was fairly common in the pre-Civil War period, and the armament needs of the Confederate Government stimulated much activity during the war. The forge, blacksmith shop, and small machine shop that made iron products on order seem most typical, and the iron manufacturer who stood ready to make almost any product that a customer might desire continued into the later period. In fact, the machine shop of the present might well be considered a direct descendant of the early general iron works. Ethel Armes mentions[32] that during the Civil War, C. B. Churchill and Company carried on a general foundry and machine business making chilled rolls, furnace thimbles, pinions and boxes, bridge housings, railroad chair plates, and some cast-iron fence work. Between 1884 and 1887, Samuel Noble and his associates built

four blast furnaces, and the engines, machinery, and all iron work for these furnaces were produced by the Noble brothers in their Anniston shops.[33]

At the same time, specialized plants were being built and operated. Immediately after the close of the Civil War, Hamilton T. Beggs built a small foundry and manufactured stoves for several years.[34] In 1882, a nail plant was built at Brierfield. This plant was handicapped by the scarcity of skilled labor, but, when operatives were imported from the North, a sizable operation was carried on for several years. The shift from iron-cut nails to steel-cut nails destroyed the market, and the company failed.[35] The lists of companies operating during the 80's show many whose names indicate special lines of manufactures. In Birmingham, such companies include the Southern Bridge Company, Birmingham Bridge and Bolt Works, Smith Sons Gin and Machine Company, Birmingham Chain Works, and Birmingham Axe and Tool Company. In Decatur, Alabama, were located the Decatur Iron Bridge and Construction Company, Ives and Sons Steam Engine and Iron-Working Plant, and the Consolidated Car Construction and Repair Shop of the L. and N. Railroad Company, said to be the largest shop of its kind south of the Ohio River.

In 1900, the Alabama Steel and Wire Company had in operation a plant capable of using 300 tons of billets a month. Also, the Southern Car and Foundry Company, an amalgamation of several works, erected a plant at Birmingham with a capacity of 10 wooden and 10 pressed-steel cars a day.[36]

In the field of shaping iron or steel by the rolling process, there were a number of small mills which produced iron bars, plates, and sheets. In 1879, construction began on the Birmingham Rolling Mill.[37] The plant, the first in that city, was in operation the next year.

32 Armes, p. 143.

33 Armes, p. 316.
34 Armes, p. 143.
35 Armes, p. 326.
36 Clark, II, pp. 50, 138.
37 Armes, p. 284.

The idea of the promoters was, first, to have a merchant mill for the manufacture of bars, sheet, plate, and guide mill irons, and, later, to follow with a steel mill. However, as has already been mentioned, steel was not produced in Birmingham in quantity until 1897. At that time, it is reported that steel plates were rolled which were used to equip a U. S. gunboat. In 1900, the Tennessee Coal, Iron and Railroad Company[38] constructed a continuous billet and rail mill, and, by 1902, the company was operating its rail mill successfully.

The appearance of plants to produce or use by-products associated with iron and steel making is another significant development. In 1898, the Semet-Solvay Corporation erected its first by-product coke ovens at the Ensley furnace of the T.C.I. In 1900, the Birmingham Cement Company was consuming between 100 and 200 tons of blast-furnace slag a day, and the Ensley Brick Company was manufacturing brick on a large scale from the shale underlying the company's coal.[39]

The operations which have been mentioned are not intended to provide a complete list or to bring out all of the lines of activities that were attempted. Neither do they serve to indicate the importance of the results obtained. They merely serve as examples of the efforts that were being made to establish an industry in a limited local market and, in a rough fashion, trace the development of those efforts.

The Struggle for Markets

That the Southern iron makers were very conscious of the cramping effect of lack of markets upon the expansion of the industry has been indicated already in the preceding paragraphs. In 1883, Robert P. Porter,[40] after a careful and extended study of the Southern iron industry, stated in his report:

The men who have gone into the iron business with any hope of making iron cheaper than England, and making nothing else, have lost their money. . . . The $55,000,000 of capital which has gone into Southern indus-

try during the first four months of this year (1883) has been invested in cotton and woolen mills, flour mills, saw mills, furniture factories, agricultural implement works, oil mills, and a variety of other industries that will tend to create a home market for the products of the heavy mining and pig-iron industries.

. . . That iron can be made cheaper in the South than in any Northern state is undoubtedly true. To imagine, however, that the six Southern iron producing districts can make pig iron, and nothing else, paying the same price for less effective labor, and from three dollars to five dollars per ton to carry their product to market and grow rich out of this one industry, requires a greater amount of faith in Southern possibilities than I possess.

This quotation indicates two highly significant factors: one, the inability of the nearby, or home, market to take any large proportion of the potential production of the blast furnaces, and the second, the tendency of the iron makers to look to far-away markets. Mr. Porter's advocacy of diversified industries at home sixty-seven years ago has a very up-to-date sound.

Clark, in his *History of Manufacturers* in the United States, quotes a practical iron maker as saying just before outbreak of the first World War:

Up to 1907 no steel maker in the South had made a great financial success. The industry was considered a precarious one. Many problems had to be solved before cheap steel could be produced here. A tremendous investment of capital was required. To make steel cheap it must be made on a very large scale. . . . If the large output exists, a large demand is required to consume it. This consumption in the South did not exist before 1907, and does not exist today. . . . The Tennessee Coal, Iron and Railroad Company before 1907 . . . had no working capital to spare. . . . It had to receive the highest prices for its products to subsist. Its mills were small and old fashioned. . . . It did not produce large tonnage. Its customers were comparatively few and were small buyers. It made a small range of steel products. The flurry of 1907 was too great a financial strain for such a weak company.[41]

38 Clark, II, p. 51.
39 Clark, II, pp. 49-50.
40 Armes, p. 303.

41 Clark, II, p. 52.

The characteristics of the South largely explain the limited home market for Southern-made iron, but the nature of the iron produced in the South was also an important factor that limited the development of the local market. The high phosphorus pig iron was suitable for low grade iron castings, such as pipe and stove iron. It could not be used to produce many of the common gray iron castings made in foundries. Most gray iron specifications have a maximum of 0.20 per cent phosphorus, while the southern pig iron contained about 0.80 per cent. This factor greatly restricted the markets outside the region and also limited the development of a well-rounded gray iron industry in the South which would have greatly strengthened local demand.

Although conscious of the weakness of nearby markets, the emphasis of the southern iron and steel companies in their efforts to secure markets seems to have been largely on gaining a place in distant markets. It is scarcely necessary to seek long for the reason. To build home markets was a slow process, while the distant markets already existed and, if tapped, promised immediate profits. This type of outlet, however, had its difficulties because such markets could be reached only if costs of production and transportation charges were low enough to permit delivery at competitive prices. The attack on the problem followed three lines. One, attempts were made to develop export trade; two, a great deal of attention was given to the making of products which might be sold out of the South; and three, freight tariffs were sought that encouraged the movement of southern iron.

During the 1890's, exports of Birmingham iron and steel assumed important proportions. In 1894, 10,000 tons of cast-iron pipe were shipped to Japan from Birmingham, and this was followed by much larger shipments to the same country the following year.[42] In 1896, it was reported that iron could be shipped from Birmingham, Alabama, to Liverpool at less cost than to New York, and shipments

of 10,000 to 11,000 tons a week during the active season were made from Birmingham to Europe.[43] By 1897, the larger iron companies of the Birmingham district were selling more iron abroad than they were at home, and their foreign markets were widely distributed, including England, Italy, Germany, Holland, Belgium, Canada, Japan, Austria, and Mexico.[44] In 1898, Birmingham was said to be the third largest point of export of pig iron of the world—Middlesborough, England, being the first, and Glasgow, Scotland, second. Between 1895 and 1898, the annual foreign sales of iron by the Tennessee Coal, Iron and Railroad Company had risen from 25 tons to over 190,000 tons; those of the Sloss Iron Company had risen during the same interval from 100 tons to 67,000 tons.[45] The anticipation of a foreign market for steel was one of the strong arguments advanced to the board of directors of the Tennessee Coal, Iron and Railroad Company in favor of building a steel plant in 1898. After 1900, however, the effect of competition of English, and particularly of German, iron and steel, made foreign markets less desirable, and exports declined in relative importance.

The important place that cast-iron pipe early took in the iron industries of the South has already been discussed. In part, this was due to the adaptability of southern pig iron to this particular use, but a second important reason was that pipe provided a means of marketing iron in a form that could be distributed widely from the South. The market influence was also a powerful motivating force in the development of a steel-producing industry in the South. The market for foundry iron was not enough to absorb the product of existing blast furnaces, to say nothing of expansion. The demand for steel was increasing. The logic of the situation was expressed in the report of the president of the Tennessee Coal, Iron and Railroad Company in 1894:

Our ownership of a well-equipped steel plant would furnish a welcome and profitable mar-

42 Clark, II, p. 24.

43 Clark, II, p. 109.
44 Clark, II, p. 111.
45 Clark, II, p. 112.

ket for a large part of our iron, thus enabling us to obtain a readier sale and better prices for such pig iron as we might desire to dispose of on the general market.[46]

The problem continued troublesome after the building and successful operation of a steel works. The construction of a mill to roll steel railroad rails was due, in part, to the fact that it offered a quantity market for steel in a form that could readily be moved in bulk for long distances. The much more recent establishment of a tin plate mill arose from the fact that the large Pacific Coast market provided by the canning industry could be reached readily from Birmingham.

Early in the development of iron making in the South, freight rates favorable to the shipment of pig iron to the North and West were established by many of the railroads. It is said that, in effect, the management of the Louisville and Nashville Railroad assured those who were building furnaces in the Birmingham area that the railroad would move the iron at rates that would enable them to compete on the market. The situation with regard to iron and steel is, of course, only a part of the general freight rate structure of the South which has provided relatively low rates for bulky basic commodities such as pig iron, steel, raw cotton, and lumber. In connection with iron from the South, a decision of the Interstate Commerce Commission in 1914 is of importance.[47] Between 1881 and 1907, the freight rate on pig iron from Birmingham and Chattanooga to Louisville and other northern points was based on a sliding scale varying with its market price. In 1907, a flat rate was established and maintained independently of the price of pig iron. In 1914, the Interstate Commerce Commission lowered these rates appreciably, not only for iron and steel from Alabama but also from Virginia, thereby extending the area of profitable marketing of these districts farther north along the Atlantic Coast and also farther west than it had been for many years.

46 Clark, II, p. 48.
47 Clark, II, p. 26.

Summary

The history of iron and steel making in the Southeast brings out a number of important points which aid greatly in understanding present day problems. These may be summarized briefly as follows:

1. The iron industry had its beginnings in the Southeast as much as 150 years ago. By the Civil War, blast furnaces had been built in numerous places and systematic exploration of ore and coal deposits had been attempted. Production of iron, therefore, is not a young industry in the Southeast.

2. The old industry was based on numerous small establishments using brown iron ore and charcoal. These establishments were scattered widely over the Southeast. In more recent years, the industry has become one that consists largely of the large furnaces that use coke and red ore and are located in Birmingham and Gadsden, Alabama. In the pre-Civil War years, the southern industry was slow in making the transition to newer methods and made little progress.

3. The industry had the advantage of two factors which were favorable to low operating costs. These were cheap labor and low transportation costs in assembling raw materials, due to the occurrence of the principal raw materials in close proximity to the furnaces. On the other hand, the history of the industry is a long story of struggle against adverse conditions.

(a) The industry was almost completely destroyed by the Civil War, and the rebuilding had to be done in an area that was impoverished by the war and upset by reconstruction policies.

(b) The industry was beset by difficult technical problems. The physical conditions under which iron ore and coal occur created serious mining and handling problems. The iron content of the ore was low, while the high phosphorus content of the ore had the greatest hampering effect. The pig iron produced was not suitable for many kinds of cast iron products. Even more important, southern pig iron could not be used in making steel in the Bessemer furnaces which were used largely in the earlier steel industry of the country. Even with the development of the basic open-hearth process, which could handle the phosphorus problem, the lack of iron and steel scrap created a handicap. Thus, steel making in Pennsylvania and other locations in the North was well established before the development of the duplex process opened the way for large scale production in the South.

(c) The limited market in the South was extremely discouraging and influenced the iron and steel producers to seek means of reaching distant markets. The development of the cast iron pipe industry in the South can be largely explained as providing a form in which cheap southern pig iron could be marketed at distant points. Later, the emphasis on steel rails in southern rolling mills arose from the need for finding products which had wide markets. In still more recent years, tin plate production, likewise, was based upon the possibility of getting a large outlet for steel in a distant market.

(d) Securing the capital required to finance adequately the large scale operations essential to success was difficult. Even the largest company, the Tennessee Coal, Iron and Railroad Company was not on secure financial grounds until after its absorption by the United States Steel Corporation.

It is in these conditions that the reasons for the relatively low development of the iron and steel industry of the Southeast in the early years of the twentieth century are largely to be found.

CHAPTER X

TRENDS IN THE BASIC IRON AND STEEL INDUSTRIES
OF THE SOUTH SINCE 1900

It is the purpose of this chapter to examine the trends which can be discerned in the basic iron and steel industries of the South. Attention will be directed especially to the period extending from 1900 to 1948, although in particular instances modifications in the period will have to be made because of variations in the years for which comparable data may be available. The analysis will be based on information drawn from several sources. The *Census of Manufactures* provides information (collected each five years from 1900 to 1919, each two years from 1919 to 1939, and in 1947) on the more or less standard items. The data include number of production workers (or wage earners), wages paid, value of products, and value added by manufacture. The *Annual Statistical Report* of the American Iron and Steel Institute and *The Directory of the Iron and Steel Works of the United States and Canada* of the same organization provide data on the production of pig iron, steel ingots, and hot rolled iron and steel products, together with the capacity of blast furnaces and steelworks. The Bureau of Mines publishes information on iron ore and coke. While there are serious problems with respect to the data, the basic industries are relatively well-covered compared to the processing and fabricating industries. The most troublesome problems are those that arise from the undisclosed figures for states or areas. This situation results from the application of the disclosure rules under which the fact-gathering agencies operate.

Before beginning a discussion of the trends in the blast furnace products and the steelworks and rolling mills industries, a brief statement will be made concerning the position of the three basic iron and steel industries in the manufacturing economy of the South in 1947.

Also, the outstanding general characteristics of the period covered by the analysis will be reviewed briefly in order to give the reader a background for the study of the changes shown by the several statistical series.

Position of the Basic Industries
in the South in 1947

The general statistics of the blast furnace products, the steelworks and rolling mills and the electrometallurgical products industries in the South for 1947 are presented in Table 25.

For the most part, the figures speak for themselves, but attention may be drawn to certain relationships. The general position of the three basic iron and steel industries in the total manufacturing structure may be seen by representing the particular industry as a percentage of the total for all industries. Such measures for the South and the United States for 1947 are shown by the following tabulation:

	United States Total all industries in U. S. = 100 per cent	South Total all industries in South = 100 per cent
Number of production workers		
Blast furnace	0.27	0.19
Steelworks and rolling mills	3.68	1.22
Electrometallurgical products	.07	.05
Total basic iron and steel	4.02	1.46
Wages paid		
Blast furnace	0.31	0.24
Steelworks and rolling mills	4.42	1.64
Electrometallurgical products	.08	.06
Total basic iron and steel	4.81	1.94
Value added by manufacture		
Blast furnaces	0.44	0.38
Steelworks and rolling mills	3.06	0.93
Electrometallurgical products	.07	.07
Total basic iron and steel	3.57	1.38

The above percentages indicate that, relative to total manufacturing in the respective areas, the blast furnace products industry and the electrometallurgical products industry occupy about the same position in the South as they do in the nation as a whole. On the other hand, the steelworks and rolling mills industry in the South has a much weaker relative position than it occupies in the national structure of manufacturing.

Table 25 shows that the South occupies a much stronger relative position in the blast furnace industry of the nation than it does in the steelworks and rolling mills industry. In the case of the former industry, the South had approximately 10 per cent of the production workers, 8.6 per cent of the wages, and 10.4 per cent of the value added. These percentages compare with 4.8 per cent, 4.1 per cent, and 3.6 per cent, respectively, for steelworks. The electrometallurgical industry is much smaller than either of the other two basic industries, but the relative position of the South in this industry is approximately the same as in the blast furnace industry.

General Characteristics of the Period from 1900 to 1948

While the general characteristics of the economic development in the United States during the first half of the twentieth century are well known and need no elaborate description in this report, iron and steel are so intimately related to economic change that the tables, charts, and other information that do form the basis for analysis can scarcely be appraised or interpreted unless the general conditions prevailing at various points of time are kept in mind. For these reasons, a brief resumé is given.

One of the most outstanding features of the period was that it was one of very great industrial growth. While the upsurge seemed halted during the nineteen thirties, and there was much talk of overcapacity and a mature econ-

Table 25

Basic Iron and Steel Industries in the South Compared with the United States, 1947

	The United States	The South	Per cent South of the United States
Blast furnaces			
Number of establishments	86	12	14.0
Number of production workers	32,697	3,238	9.9
Wages ($1,000)	93,598	8,048	8.6
Value added by manufacture ($1,000)	328,060	33,987	10.4
Steelworks and rolling mills			
Number of establishments	215	13	6.0
Number of production workers	438,088	21,100	4.8
Wages ($1,000)	1,337,938	55,050	4.1
Value added by manufacture ($1,000)	2,275,697	82,994	3.6
Electrometallurgical products			
Number of establishments	19	4	21.1
Number of production workers	8,175	865	10.6
Wages ($1,000)	23,449	1,980	8.4
Value added by manufacture ($1,000)	55,493	6,601	11.9
Total of basic industries			
Number of establishments	320	29	9.1
Number of production workers	478,960	25,203	5.3
Wages ($1,000)	1,454,985	65,078	4.5
Value added by manufacture ($1,000)	2,659,250	123,582	4.6

Source: *Census of Manufactures, 1947,* and special tabulation, U. S. Bureau of the Census.

omy, the war and immediate postwar period of the forties have been marked by a resumption of the pressure for expansion. A measure of the general industrial growth is furnished by the estimates made by Fabricant[1] in 1937. According to his estimates, the output of manufacturing in 1913 was practically double that of 1899. In 1917, it was two and one-half times, and in 1937, three and three-fourths times the 1899 output.

The period was also marked by a number of pronounced cyclical fluctuations which are of great significance in the study of an industry as responsive to cyclical changes as iron and steel is. Starting from the low levels of the mid-nineties, business by 1900 was entering on a long period of expansion and general prosperity which was punctuated by the relatively mild recession of 1903-04 and by the much sharper and more serious depressions of 1907-08 and 1913-14. World War I induced, during the war and immediate postwar years, a boom condition which is one of the outstanding features of the entire period. The sharp, but relatively brief, readjustment of 1921 and 1922 was followed by the prosperity of the twenties, which saw a number of lines of activity reach, or exceed, their wartime peaks, while others, particularly agriculture, were languishing. The year 1929, or an average of a period from 1923 or 1924 to 1929, set levels of comparison for the decade that followed. The depression reached its lowest depths in 1932, but the recovery was slow and halting and was not complete until the stimulus resulting from the outbreak of the second world war began to be felt. The general features of the war and immediate postwar years scarcely need special description.

Trends in Wage Earners, Wages, and Value Added, 1900 to 1939

The reports of the Census of Manufactures make available a considerable amount of data on the blast furnace products and steelworks and rolling mills industries, but, unfortunately,

[1] Solomon Fabricant, *The Output of Manufacturing Industries.*

figures are not published for some of the states in several of the years. Consequently it is not possible to derive totals for the South that are based upon published statistics. Furthermore, the statistics for 1947, as published in the state and industry reports of the 1947 Census of Manufactures, make direct comparisons of the blast furnaces and steelworks and rolling mills industries with the years preceding 1939 almost impossible. Consequently, the data for the period 1900 to 1939 will be examined first, and the changes from 1939 to 1947 will be discussed later. Of the various measures used by the Census of Manufactures, three were selected to form the basis for the 1900 to 1939 analysis: number of wage earners, wages paid, and value added by manufacture. Tables 26 and 27 present the available figures.

Statistics for Alabama are relatively complete, and the fact that this state represents a very high percentage of the total of the South makes it possible to trace the record reasonably well. The census statistics, however, must be used with considerable caution in making comparisons between two widely separated years. Concepts of what constitute the items being measured have necessarily changed. Also, changes in price and wage levels account for at least a part of the changes in the items which are expressed in monetary units, and it is difficult to approximate the effect of these factors because of the long and technical analysis that is required for a careful study. Consequently, comments will be confined largely to the general changes that have taken place in the number of wage earners and in the percentages of the United States totals that are accounted for by southern states.

The statistics make it quite apparent that a decided decline in the number of wage earners in the blast furnace products industry took place after 1919 in both the United States and the South. In both areas the numbers reported in 1900 are approximately equal to those for 1919. In 1900, the number of wage earners in the United States was almost exactly twice that of 1939; in 1919, the figure was slightly more than twice the 1939 level. In the South, the

Table 26

Blast Furnace Products Industry in the Southern States as Compared with the United States, 1880-1939

	Quantities				Per cent of United States		
	United States	Alabama	Georgia	Tennessee	Alabama	Georgia	Tennessee
Number of wage earners (average for year)							
1880	41,695	1,566	754	1,579	3.8	1.8	3.8
1890	33,415	3,989	254	1,012	11.9	.8	3.0
1900	39,358	5,034	194	1,763	12.8	.5	4.5
1904	35,078	4,954	303	1,358	14.1	.9	3.9
1909	38,429	3,783		1,143	9.8		3.0
1914	29,356	3,547		503	12.1		1.7
1919	41,660	5,214		884	12.5		2.1
1921	18,698	2,625		73	14.0		.4
1923	36,712	5,343		910	14.6		2.5
1925	29,188	4,861		380	16.7		1.3
1927	27,958	4,157		339	14.9		1.2
1929	24,960	2,398		450	9.6		1.8
1931	13,572	1,468			10.8		
1933	12,098	964			8.0		
1935	15,178	1,342			8.8		
1937	23,075	1,831			7.9		
1939	19,537	2,224			11.4		
Wages paid (dollars)							
1880	12,655,428	553,713	77,415	261,897	4.4	.6	2.1
1890	14,614,458	1,521,304	45,501	438,376	10.4	.3	3.0
1900	18,500,462	1,382,017	48,391	438,929	7.5	.3	2.4
1904	18,935,000	1,939,208	112,698	545,861	10.2	.6	2.9
1909	24,606,530	2,077,477		519,274	8.4		2.1
1914	22,781,000	1,985,000		233,000	8.7		1.0
1919	73,769,395	7,177,159		882,634	9.7		1.2
1921	29,369,685	3,376,406		64,521	11.5		.2
1923	58,935,384	6,048,576		883,624	10.3		1.5
1925	45,312,168	5,024,708		272,230	11.1		.6
1927	44,258,499	4,574,023		347,824	10.3		.8
1929	41,958,569	2,897,066		338,412	6.9		.8
1931	19,258,799	1,480,871			7.7		
1933	11,564,000	706,000			6.1		
1935	18,915,554	1,244,458			6.6		
1937	38,001,438	2,551,864			6.7		
1939	28,312,336	2,675,923			9.5		
Value added by manufacture (dollars)							
1880	30,695,827	829,683	225,094	350,582	2.7	.7	1.1
1890	35,544,538	3,821,807	101,586	915,582	10.8	.3	2.6
1900	75,286,778	5,877,499	154,178	1,524,634	7.8	.2	2.0
1904	52,881,000	5,633,560	222,368	818,892	10.7	.4	1.5
1909	70,791,394	5,758,623		1,272,459	8.1		1.8
1914	53,074,000	6,175,000		563,000	11.6		1.1
1919	173,180,062	12,147,093		1,651,277	7.0		1.0
1921	58,721,728	4,826,331		167,661	8.2		.3
1923	179,983,675	16,219,260		1,907,880	9.0		1.1
1925	147,869,349	18,233,389		592,697	12.3		.4
1927	129,349,202	13,897,794		1,024,974	10.7		.8
1929	161,131,773	12,060,000		898,993	7.5		.6

Table 26 (cont'd)

Blast Furnace Products Industry in the Southern States as Compared with the United States, 1880-1939

	Quantities			Per cent of United States		
	United States	Alabama	Georgia	Tennessee	Alabama	Georgia	Tennessee
1931	52,239,544	4,842,656			9.3		
1933	29,729,000	2,125,000			7.1		
1935	74,003,790	4,173,122			5.6		
1937	127,644,430	11,310,428			8.9		
1939	87,082,842	8,908,226			10.2		

Source: Data for 1880, 1890, and 1900: *Census of Manufactures, 1900*, X, Part 4.
　　　Data for 1904, 1909: *Census of Manufactures, 1910*. U. S. figures and Census of Manufactures Bulletins state figures for 1904.
　　　Data for 1914 and 1919: *Census of Manufactures, 1920*.
　　　Data for 1921, 1923, 1925, 1927, 1931, 1933, 1935, and 1937: *Biennial Census of Manufactures*.
　　　Data for 1929: *Census of Manufactures, 1930*.
　　　Data for 1939: *Census of Manufactures, 1940*.

Table 27

Steelworks and Rolling Mills in the United States and Alabama, 1880-1939

Year	Number of wage earners (average for year)			Wages paid (dollars)			Value added by manufacture (dollars)		
	United States	Alabama	Per cent Alabama of U.S.	United States	Alabama	Per cent Alabama of U.S.	United States	Alabama	Per cent Alabama of U.S.
1880	96,164	60	.1	41,880,687	18,000	..	73,169,549	22,100	..
1890	137,295	1,696	1.2	74,460,433	681,660	0.9	115,591,850	1,297,076	1.1
1900	183,023	2,204	1.2	102,238,692	1,072,384	1.0	206,121,167	1,452,890	0.7
1904	207,562	3,636	1.8	122,491,993	1,508,681	1.2	232,760,594	3,006,376	1.3
1919	375,088	8,121	2.2	637,637,430	9,331,613	1.5	1,148,326,618	15,645,679	1.4
1921	235,515	4,094	1.7	324,987,239	5,106,300	1.6	476,533,898	7,580,449	1.6
1923	388,201	6,927	1.8	637,825,137	8,969,974	1.4	1,109,926,433	17,835,103	1.6
1925	370,726	7,669	2.1	614,984,982	10,283,309	1.7	1,134,107,013	22,807,570	2.0
1927	361,312	7,473	2.1	601,275,499	11,010,770	1.8	1,090,184,943	25,709,650	2.4
1929	394,574	9,253	2.3	689,015,541	12,199,977	1.8	1,461,705,648	34,726,234	2.4
1939	368,904	13,496	3.7	569,724,280	*	..	1,147,548,010	*	..

*Not available.

Source: Data for 1880, 1890, and 1900: *Census of Manufactures, 1900*, X, Part 4.
　　　Data for 1904: *Census of Manufactures, 1910*.
　　　Data for 1919: *Census of Manufactures, 1920*.
　　　Data for 1921, 1923, 1925, and 1927: *Biennial Census of Manufactures*.
　　　Data for 1929: *Census of Manufactures, 1930*.
　　　Data for 1939: *Census of Manufactures, 1940*.

only data available for 1939 are those for Alabama. There was one small establishment in Tennessee which probably did not employ more than 100 wage earners. If 2,325 is assumed to represent the total wage earners in the blast furnace industry in the South in 1939, this figure would compare with 6,991 in 1900 and 6,098 in 1919. Although 1929 was a year of general prosperity, the number employed in the blast furnace industry in the nation was approximately 60 per cent of that of 1919 and in the South was only 47 per cent. In neither the nation nor the region did employment return, in 1939, to the 1929 level.

While the record is incomplete and the available figures show considerable fluctuations, it seems that the South's relative position in the blast furnace industry (measured in wage earners, wages, and value added by manufacture) did not become stronger; if anything, it weakened. In 1900, the combined participation of Alabama, Georgia, and Tennessee was 17.8 per cent of the national total of wage earners, 10.2 per cent of wages, and 10.0 per cent of value added. By 1919, Georgia had been eliminated,

and the total shares reported for Alabama and Tennessee, combined, for the three measures were 14.6 per cent, 10.9 per cent, and 8.0 per cent respectively. In 1929, the corresponding percentages were 11.4, 7.7, and 8.1. In 1939 only Alabama reported, and the percentages for that state were 11.4, 9.5, and 10.2, respectively.

In the case of the steelworks and rolling mills industry, a different picture is presented. While the industry nationally did not reach as high a figure in 1939 as that of 1929, the difference was not great, and 1929 represented a peak somewhat above 1919 and 1923. It would seem, therefore, that the steel industry was not one of shrinking employment, at least not to a degree comparable to the blast furnace industry. During the earlier years, a fairly sizable operation was reported in Tennessee, and in the latter years, one establishment operated in Georgia. The only continuous data, however, are for Alabama, and even there the record after 1929 consists only of a figure for the number of wage earners in 1939. The Alabama figures support the conclusion that

Table 28

The Basic Iron and Steel Industries in the South and United States, 1939 and 1947

	The South			United States			Per cent South of U.S.	
	1939	1947	Per cent increase	1939	1947	Per cent increase	1939	1947
Number of establishments								
Blast furnaces....................	8	12		81	86			
Steelworks and rolling mills........	13	13		253	215			
Electrometallurgical products.......	2	4		18	19			
Total..........................	23	29		352	320			
Number of production workers (average for year)								
Blast furnaces....................	2,302	3,238	40.7	19,537	32,697	67.4	11.8	9.9
Steelworks and rolling mills and electrometallurgical products.......	15,377	21,965	42.8	371,678	446,263	20.1	4.1	4.9
Total..........................	17,679	25,203	42.6	391,215	478,960	22.4	4.5	5.3
Value added by manufacture ($1,000)								
Blast furnaces....................	8,994	33,987	277.9	87,083	328,060	276.7	10.3	10.4
Steelworks and rolling mills and electrometallurgical products.......	53,941	89,595	66.1	1,163,416	2,331,190	100.4	4.6	3.8
Total..........................	62,935	123,582	96.4	1,250,499	2,659,250	112.7	5.0	4.6

Source: *Census of Manufacturers, 1947,* summary statistics; those for the South, special tabulation for 1939 and 1947 by the Bureau of the Census.

the industry in that state was expanding steadily. In 1900 the number of wage earners was reported as 2,204; in 1919 the number was 8,121; in 1929, 9,253; and in 1939, 13,496. These changes are in contrast to the smaller percentage increases in the United States during the early part of the period and the more stabilized condition represented by national figures for 1939 as compared with 1929.

The per cent share of Alabama in the national total of the steelworks and rolling mills industry is small, being a maximum of 3.7 for the number of wage earners in 1939, but there is considerable evidence of a tendency to improve. Trends in the steelworks and rolling mills industry, insofar as they can be measured by the Census of Manufactures data, are decidedly more favorable than are those of the blast furnace products industry. The southern steelworks and rolling mills industry in 1939, however, had not reached a position in relation to the blast furnace industry that was comparable to that which existed in the nation as a whole.

Changes in the Basic Iron and Steel Industries, 1939 to 1947

Special tabulations provided by the U. S. Bureau of the Census furnish information on a comparable basis for 1939 and 1947 on the number of establishments, the number of production workers, and the value added by manufacture. This information can be used for analyzing changes in the basic industries in the South when compared with the nation as a whole. These data are presented in Table 28.

The statistics indicate little change in the number of establishments in the three basic industries. In fact, the only change of any significance was a decrease in the number of establishments reported in the steelworks and rolling mills industry in the United States. On the other hand, large increases occurred in the number of production workers and the value added by manufacture. Of course, the large percentage increases in the value added figures are due, in part, to the general rise in prices. For the basic industries as a group, the South

had a larger per cent of increase in the number of production workers than did the United States, 42.6 per cent compared to 22.4, and its percentage of the nation's total increased from 4.5 per cent to 5.3 per cent. This change was the resultant, primarily, of the increase in steelworks and rolling mills, since the region's increase in the blast furnace industry was considerably smaller, percentagewise, than that of the nation. On the other hand, the South failed to increase the value added by manufacture in its basic iron and steel industries to as great a degree as the country did as a whole. Again, the changes in the steelworks and rolling mills seem to be the decisive factor. With the number of production workers increasing at a more rapid rate than that for the United States, the failure to increase the value added, at least as fast as the nation, raises a question as to what may be the underlying cause. One explanation is that the South did not participate in the increase in the products that have a high value added per production worker.

The fact that World War II occurred between the two census years places much interest

Table 29

Estimates of Employment in Blast Furnaces and Steelworks in Alabama, Third Quarter 1939, and Third Quarter and Annual Average, 1943-1949

Year	Average number employed (1,000 employees)		Indexes, third quarter 1939 equals 100	
	Third quarter	Annual average	Third quarter	Annual average
1939	21.2	*	100.0	100.0
1943	24.3	24.6	114.6	116.0
1944	22.1	22.1	104.2	104.2
1945	20.7	21.0	97.6	99.1
1946	24.5	22.5	115.6	106.1
1947	25.4	25.0	119.8	117.9
1948	27.2	26.5	128.3	125.0
1949	26.1	24.0	123.1	113.2

*Not available.

Note: Changes were made in industry classifications which raise questions concerning the comparability of the 1947-1949 estimates with those of former years, but it does not seem that the blast furnace and steelworks estimates were materially affected by the change.

Source: Estimates by U. S. Bureau of Labor Statistics and Alabama Department of Industrial Relations.

on the reaction of the basic industries in the South during the intervening years. The reports of the unemployment compensation agencies on the number of workers on payrolls constitute a valuable source of information on industrial developments, but unfortunately the available statistics are for broad general industry groups. In Alabama, however, estimates of employment have been made by the U. S. Bureau of Labor Statistics and the Alabama Department of Industrial Relations, and these estimates, because of the concentration of the basic iron and steel industries of the South in Alabama, provide a means of tracing the tendencies of the war and immediate postwar years. The data indicate a level in 1943 some 15 per cent above the 1939 level. The years that followed saw some declines from the 1943 figure, and in 1945 employment seems to have been at about the 1939 level. In 1947, however, activity returned to a point as high as, or somewhat higher than, in 1943 and continued high in 1948. Work stoppages, particularly in coal mining, resulted in a decline in 1949.

Trends in Iron Ore, Coke, Pig Iron, and Steel Produced in South, 1900 to 1947

A second type of measure of developments in the basic iron and steel industries in the South consists of the series representing the quantities of important raw materials and commodities produced. From the available data, five series were chosen as the most complete and as sufficiently representative to provide quantitative measures to compare with the statistics derived from the *Census of Manufactures*. These five series were: production of iron ore, production of coke, production of pig iron, production of steel ingots and castings, and production of hot rolled iron and steel products. The order in which these items are named follows the order in which they occur in the manufacturing process. The data are presented in detail by the accompanying tables and graphs. In the text discussion, the outstanding features of the changes during the period will be summarized, but no detailed recital of the year-to-year changes will be attempted.

One of the outstanding tendencies brought out by an examination of available figures by states is the gradual elimination of the states of Tennessee, Georgia, and North Carolina, from iron ore, coke, and pig iron production, and the concurrent concentration of these activities in Alabama. During the early part of the twentieth century, the three states produced around one million tons of iron ore compared with three to four times that quantity in Alabama. After 1921, the three states together never produced in excess of one-half of a million tons and usually not more than one hundred thousand tons. During World War II, however, there was a revival of iron ore mining in Georgia which reached a peak in 1943 of 413,468 tons. A rather similar record is shown for coke and pig iron, except that there was no revival of note in Tennessee or Georgia. The steel industry from the beginning was largely concentrated in Alabama, and the industry in Tennessee has not been a significant factor. A small but active industry has been in operation in Georgia for a number of years, but is not large enough to exercise much influence upon regional totals.

A second interesting development has been the emergence of a sizable iron and steel industry in Texas during the war period. The quantities produced are small compared with those reported for Alabama, but a beginning was made, and the future of these ventures certainly will bear watching.

Since the primary interest of this study of the basic iron and steel industries is in the Southeast, and since the data show that the operations are concentrated in Alabama, it follows that a study of the trends in that state will give a reasonably adequate indication of the trends in the basic industries of the South. It happens, also, that the statistics for Alabama are fairly complete and comparable for the period, while the record for the other states is quite spotty. For these reasons, the more detailed analysis will be based upon Alabama alone.

In general, all five series indicate quite a considerable tendency to increase during the period. The depression of the thirties, of course, constituted a sharp interruption, but the war period that followed saw increases that appeared to restore former trends. Also, the five series showed very definite and pronounced reactions to the cyclical fluctuations which characterized business activity during the period.

A number of different approaches may be used in a study of trends during a period. Since the immediate purpose does not require exact measurement, the more mathematical procedures were not applied, although the Bureau of Business Research of the University of Alabama has made a number of special studies dealing with trends of several of the series.

The results of these analyses will be cited. A reasonably good indication of trend characteristics can be obtained by an examination of the reaction of a given series to the stimulation of periods of prosperity or to the depressing effects of periods of declining general activity. Tables 30 and 31 present summaries of this type which compare the behavior of the five selected series in Alabama and in the United States.

REACTION TO BUSINESS CYCLES

To serve as representative of periods of high activity, the years 1913, 1917, 1920, 1926, 1929,

Table 30

Reaction of the Production of Iron Ore, Coke, Pig Iron, Steel Ingots, and Hot Rolled Iron and Steel Products to Periods of Prosperity: Alabama and the United States

Period of comparison	Per cent change				
	Iron ore	Coke	Pig iron	Steel ingots	Hot rolled products
1900 to 1913					
Alabama	+ 89.1	+ 57.5	+ 73.8	......	+655.1
United States	+124.9	+125.5	+124.6	+202.9	+161.3
1913 to 1917					
Alabama	+ 34.9	+ 47.2	+ 43.5	+ 52.6	+ 63.7
United States	+ 21.5	+ 20.1	+ 24.7	+ 44.1	+ 33.4
1913 to 1920					
Alabama	+ 13.0	+ 20.8	+ 16.3	+ 46.3	+ 66.0
United States	+ 9.1	+ 10.9	+ 19.2	+ 35.0	+ 30.5
1913 to 1926					
Alabama	+ 31.3	+ 43.8	+ 43.5	+111.3	+138.3
United States	+ 9.1	+ 22.8	+ 27.1	+ 55.0	+ 43.2
1913 to 1929					
Alabama	+ 23.7	+ 43.0	+ 31.7	+108.5	+125.2
United States	+ 17.8	+ 29.3	+ 37.6	+ 81.1	+65.7
1929 to 1937					
Alabama	− 2.3	− 10.4	− 4.8	+ 9.2	+ 4.3
United States	− 1.3	− 12.5	− 12.9	− 8.3	− 10.5
1929 to 1939					
Alabama	− 7.6	− 18.9	− 3.3	+ 23.4	+ 22.3
United States	− 29.2	− 26.0	− 25.2	− 14.5	− 15.1
1929 to War Peak (highest war year)					
Alabama	+ 37.2	+ 20.5	+ 34.5	+ 91.6	+ 97.7
United States	+ 44.5	+ 23.6	+ 31.7	+ 47.3	+ 43.1
1939 to War Peak (highest war year)					
Alabama	+ 48.5	+ 48.6	+ 39.0	+ 55.3	+ 61.7
United States	+104.0	+ 67.0	+ 75.9	+ 69.9	+ 68.4

Source: Computed from statistics derived from following sources: iron ore and coke, U.S. Bureau of Mines; pig iron, steel ingots (U.S.), and hot rolled products, American Iron and Steel Ingots; steel ingots for Alabama, confidential figures furnished to Bureau of Business Research, University of Alabama.

1937, 1939, and the peak year of war production were chosen, and the percentage changes from a number of different base points were calculated for each of the five series, both for Alabama and for the United States. These percentages are given in Table 30, and the results can be summarized as follows:

1900-1913—Alabama's percentages of increase were not nearly as great as those of the United States for iron ore, coke, and pig iron; no data are available for Alabama for steel ingot production; the percentage of increase for the tonnage of hot rolled products is very much larger for Alabama than for the nation. It should be pointed out, however, that the beginning quantity of hot rolled products for the state is small, and the percentage increase is not highly significant.

1913-1917—Alabama's percentage increases are much larger than those of the United States for each of the five series.

1913-1920—Alabama's percentage increases were greater than the nation's, except for pig iron (an increase of 16.3 per cent compared to 19.2 per cent) but the quantities produced in 1920 were smaller than in 1917, except for steel ingots and hot rolled products in Alabama.

1913-1926—Alabama's percentage increases were much greater than those of the United States for each of the five series.

1913-1929—Alabama's percentage increases were higher than those of the United States for each measure except pig iron. In the United States, 1929 was a year of higher production in each of the selected lines than 1926, while the reverse was true in Alabama.

1929-1937—Generally, the level of production shown by the five measures failed to reach the quantities recorded in 1929. Iron ore production in the United States approached the 1929 level but remained somewhat below it, and the Alabama record was not quite as favorable as that of the nation. However, steel ingots and hot rolled products in Alabama exceeded 1929, indicating a strong recovery in these lines in the state.

1937-1939—Alabama was at a higher level in 1939 than in 1937 in pig iron, steel ingots, and hot rolled products. The reverse was true for all five items for the United States and for ore and coke in Alabama.

The peak year of the war. The wartime peak, or war year with the largest production, occurred at different times in different series and also varied as between Alabama and the nation as a whole. When compared to those of 1929, Alabama's percentages of increase were greater than those of the United States for pig iron, steel ingots, and hot rolled iron and steel products, but not so large as the national increases for ore and coke. A comparison with 1939 shows that the state's expansion in ore, coke, and pig iron was definitely smaller than the nation's, and fell somewhat short in steel and hot rolled products. In other words, Alabama's position with regard to the earlier peaks was strong, but its record in making a large and sudden expansion during the war emergency did not come up to the national average. Undoubtedly, underground mining was a contributing factor.

In general, this summary of the reaction to the stimulus of prosperity indicates that Alabama industries were characterized by larger percentage increases than the nation as a whole. The tendency seems particularly strong for steel ingots and hot rolled iron and steel products. Another feature is the tendency for Alabama's production to exceed preceding highs and move on to establish new high records.

To indicate reaction to the depressing effects of a recession in activity, the following periods were chosen: 1913 to 1914; 1917 to 1919; 1920 to 1921; 1929 to 1932; 1937 to 1938; 1944 to 1946. The data on the changes in the five series during these six periods are given in Table 31. The percentage declines vary widely for the several periods, but an analysis of the comparative degrees of change for the state and the nation shows that Alabama's per cent of decline was the smaller in all except six of the thirty cases. Four of these exceptions occurred in the first three periods.

Since the analysis indicates that the Alabama industry reacted more strongly to periods of prosperity and was more successful in resisting downward adjustments, the general conclusion is that the basic industries in Alabama have been growing and have exhibited a great deal of vitality in the past. However, the tendency to increase has been stronger in the products produced by the steelworks and rolling mills industry than in the blast furnace products industry.

LONG TERM TRENDS

For a number of years, the Bureau of Business Research of the University of Alabama has studied trends in Alabama industries. Certain of the findings of these studies have a bearing on the present problem. W. M. Adamson, in *Industrial Activity in Alabama, 1913-1932*,[2] found that the production of pig iron during the period under study showed a relatively slow growth, but that the increase was slightly greater in Alabama than in the United States. Based on a straight line trend, fitted by the method of least squares to the data from 1914

[2] W. M. Adamson, *Industrial Activity in Alabama.*

to 1930, the annual growth increment was 1.36 per cent of the calculated normal for the central year, 1922. The corresponding figure for the United States was 1.24 per cent. In the case of steel ingots, the growth was much faster. The growth increment of a straight line, fitted by the same methods and for the same period, was 4.76 per cent of the normal for the central year for the state and 2.55 per cent for the United States. This indicates a faster growth in Alabama than in the United States. A second measure used by Adamson gives further support to the conclusion drawn from the trend line analysis. This procedure was to compare the average annual production of the last half of the entire period with that of the first half.

In *The Coke Industry in Alabama,* Mable Mills points out:

A very natural question that arises in connection with trend is whether this industry in Alabama has been growing as fast as in the country as a whole. There are several approaches to answering this question. One

Table 31

Reaction of the Production of Iron Ore, Coke, Pig Iron, Steel Ingots, and Hot Rolled Iron and Steel Products to Periods of Declining Activity: Alabama and the United States

Period of comparison	Per cent of decline				
	Iron ore	Coke	Pig iron	Steel ingots	Hot rolled products
1913 to 1914					
Alabama	7.2	7.2	11.2	32.5	23.4
United States	33.1	25.4	24.7	24.6	25.9
1917 to 1919					
Alabama	28.2	30.9	27.9	12.1	19.8
United States	19.0	20.5	19.7	22.8	24.1
1920 to 1921					
Alabama	51.2	36.9	49.5	37.7	38.5
United States	56.4	50.7	54.8	53.0	54.3
1929 to 1932					
Alabama	78.7	70.5	75.6	71.3	69.8
United States	86.5	63.4	79.2	75.5	74.6
1937 to 1938					
Alabama	31.8	20.7	21.6	23.2	21.1
United States	60.5	38.0	48.6	43.9	42.9
1944 to 1946					
Alabama	31.8	18.5	20.6	25.3	24.5
United States	60.5	21.0	26.5	25.7	22.6

Source: Same as Table 30.

is to take the yearly increment of trend and express it as a per cent of the year of origin. In this case, the Alabama increment for the 1880-1946 trend period was 2.5 per cent of 1913, the year of origin, and the United States increment was 2.65 per cent of 1913.

Another approach is to take Alabama's contribution to the national total, as is presented in Table VII, and compare over the period from 1880 to 1946. Alabama coke amounted to only 1.8 per cent of the national total in 1880 and this percentage increased to 12.5 per cent in 1892. After 1903, however, Alabama's contribution fell below 10 per cent and did not rise to 10 per cent again until 1921. In 1922 and in 1924, Alabama production was slightly above 10 per cent of the nation total, but from 1926 to 1930 was only a little more than 8 per cent. In 1935, Alabama production dropped to 5.7 per cent of the national total, but rose again to 10.4 per cent in 1938. Since 1938, Alabama has accounted for around 8 per cent of the United States output. Thus it would appear that the Alabama industry grew faster than the national industry in the early years, 1880-1900, but slowed down after 1900 and kept a steady pace with the na-

tional industry except for occasional spurts or drops.[3]

The quotation given above summarizes Miss Mills' analysis of the changes in the share of the nation's production of coke that is accounted for by the Alabama industry. A similar check of trends can be made for the production of iron ore, pig iron, and hot rolled iron and steel products. The Alabama production is shown in detail in Charts 11, 12, and 13.

The averages for the two decades from 1920 to 1929 and from 1930 to 1939, as given in Table 32, indicate a somewhat larger share in the total production of iron ore for Alabama than in the two earlier periods, 1900 to 1909 and 1910 to 1919, but this gain was lost during the war period—apparently due to the inability of the Alabama metal mining industry to expand as rapidly as the rest of the country. In the case of pig iron, relatively little change in the state's share is indicated except that the lowest percentage appears for the six year period from 1940 to 1945. The averages for

[3] Mable D. Mills, *Coke Industry in Alabama,* pp. 17-20.

Table 32

Production of Iron Ore, Pig Iron, Hot Rolled Iron and Steel Products, Alabama and the United States, and Per Cent Alabama of United States; Averages Per Year for Selected Periods, 1900-1948

	1900 to 1909 (Average per year)	1910 to 1919 (Average per year)	1920 to 1929 (Average per year)	1930 to 1939 (Average per year)	1940 to 1945 (Average per year)	1946 to 1948 (Average per year)
Production of Iron Ore—thousand gross tons						
United States	38,393	59,607	59,434	37,312	92,438	87,803
Alabama	3,639	5,315	6,093	3,923	7,506	7,090
Per cent Alabama of United States	9.5	8.9	10.3	10.5	8.1	8.1
Production of Pig Iron—thousand net tons						
United States	22,154	35,058	38,753	25,647	57,591	56,181
Alabama	1,683	2,451	2,826	1,941	3,751	3,697
Per cent Alabama of United States	7.6	7.0	7.3	7.6	6.5	6.6
Production of Hot Rolled Iron and Steel Products—thousand net tons						
United States	16,662	28,513	35,328	27,467	60,390	62,110
Alabama	229	676	1,153	992	2,427	2,394
Per cent Alabama of United States	1.4	2.4	3.3	3.6	4.0	3.9

Source: *Minerals Yearbook,* 1900-1948, and American Iron and Steel Institute, *Annual Statistical Report,* 1900-1948.

CHART II

PRODUCTION OF IRON ORE IN ALABAMA, 1900 — 1948
QUANTITY PRODUCED

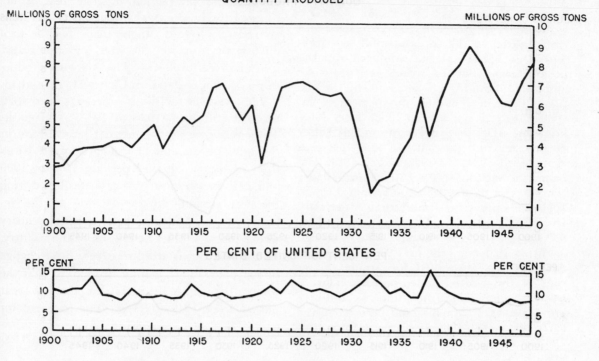

PRODUCTION OF COKE IN ALABAMA, 1900 — 1948
QUANTITY PRODUCED

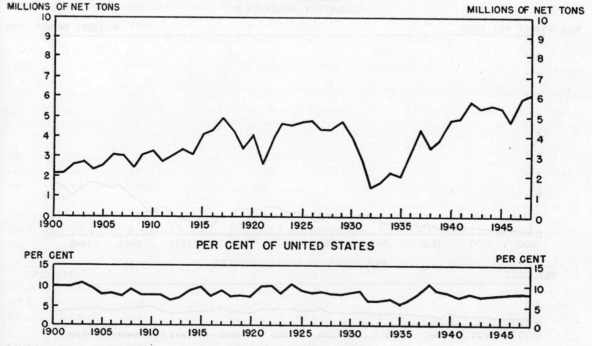

SOURCE: BUREAU OF MINES, U.S. DEPARTMENT OF THE INTERIOR

CHART 12

PRODUCTION OF PIG IRON IN ALABAMA, 1900—1948
QUANTITY PRODUCED

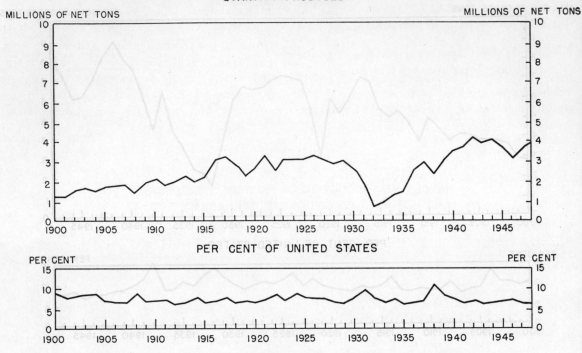

PRODUCTION OF HOT ROLLED IRON AND STEEL PRODUCTS
IN ALABAMA, 1900—1948
QUANTITY PRODUCED

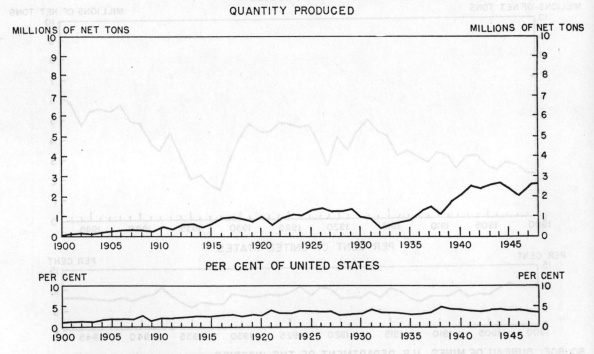

SOURCE: AMERICAN IRON AND STEEL INSTITUTE.

hot rolled iron and steel products give further support to the conclusion that the Alabama steel works and rolling mill industry was increasing more rapidly than the country as a whole, and hence the state's share in the national total showed significant increases.

Trends in Capacity and Location of Blast Furnaces in the South

The ten-year period prior to 1890 saw the establishment of most of the present blast furnaces of Alabama and Tennessee, or their predecessors. The greater proportion of the furnaces of that period were located in Alabama and Tennessee, with the former outranking the latter more than two to one. Other southern states in which blast furnaces have been located are Georgia, North Carolina, Mississippi, and Texas.

In 1890, the South accounted for slightly over three million tons of the blast furnace capacity. The principal contributing states

CHART 13

INDICES OF PRODUCTION OF PIG IRON, STEEL INGOTS, AND HOT ROLLED PRODUCTS IN ALABAMA, 1900–48

1935-1939 AVERAGE EQUALS 100

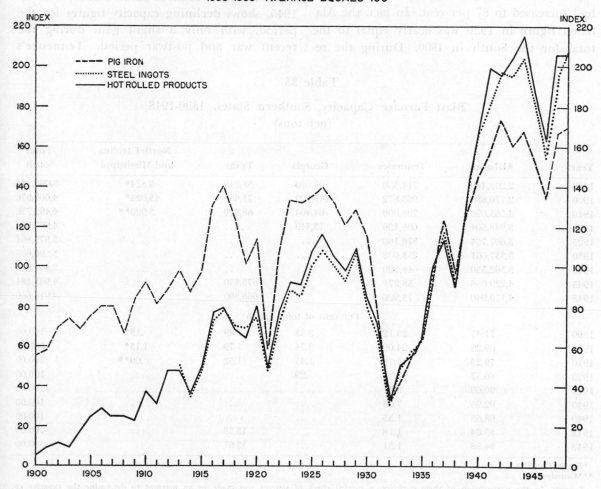

SOURCE: AMERICAN IRON AND STEEL INSTITUTE AND UNIVERSITY OF ALABAMA BUREAU OF BUSINESS RESEARCH.

were Alabama and Tennessee. The remaining states—Georgia, Texas, and North Carolina—made up only 5 per cent of the total. By 1920 North Carolina and Texas had dropped out of the blast furnace picture and Georgia showed a blast furnace capacity of only 13,440 tons. One blast furnace was built in Mississippi about 1910 but was soon abandoned. This left the field open to Alabama and Tennessee, which were the only southern states showing blast furnace activity until 1945, when Texas came back into the picture. Blast furnace capacity for the South reached a peak of nearly five million tons in 1945.

Alabama plays the leading role. In 1890, this state contributed some two-thirds of the capacity in the South and, by 1920, its share had increased to 87 per cent. In fact, the Alabama figure in 1920 was nearly equal to the total for the South in 1900. During the re-cession year of 1930, Alabama's share rose to 93 per cent and increased to 99 per cent in 1940. However, the pressure of war demands led to the revamping of old plants and the building of new ones. Consequently, in 1945 Alabama, still the leading southern state by far, was contributing only 85 per cent of the southern capacity. Until World War II, Alabama's highest blast furnace capacity had been reached during the period of World War I, the reported capacity at that time being 3,988,504 tons. Since then, the state's blast furnace capacity has never dropped below 3.3 million tons, even during the depression of the thirties, and, in 1945, the reported capacity was 4,229,056 tons. The reported figure for January 1, 1948, was slightly lower, being 4,170,940 tons.

Tennessee, with three plants still reported in 1945, shows declining capacity figures for the period, with only a slight gain during the recent war and postwar period. Tennessee's

Table 33

Blast Furnace Capacity, Southern States, 1890-1948

(net tons)

Year	Alabama	Tennessee	Georgia	Texas	North Carolina and Mississippi	Total South
1890	2,208,480	714,560	103,040	58,240	5,824*	3,090,144
1900	2,770,880	963,872	149,520	71,680	45,024*	4,000,976
1910	3,565,096	798,000	64,400	68,320	3,920**	4,499,736
1920	3,988,504	605,136	13,440	....	....	4,607,080
1925	3,607,704	370,160	....	....	....	3,977,864
1930	3,337,661	253,008	....	....	....	3,590,669
1940	3,562,350	48,720	....	....	....	3,611,070
1945	4,229,056	58,278	....	673,850	....	4,961,184
1948	4,170,940	73,920	....	668,800	....	4,913,660
Per cent of total South						
1890	71.47	23.12	3.33	1.89	.19*	100.00
1900	69.25	24.09	3.74	1.79	1.13*	100.00
1910	79.23	17.73	1.43	1.52	.09**	100.00
1920	86.57	13.14	.29	....	....	100.00
1925	90.69	9.31	....	....	....	100.00
1930	92.95	7.05	....	....	....	100.00
1940	98.65	1.35	....	....	....	100.00
1945	85.24	1.18	....	13.58	....	100.00
1948	84.88	1.51	....	13.61	....	100.00

*North Carolina.

**Mississippi.

Source: In the preparation of these statistics, a careful check of sources was made in an attempt to determine the capacity of furnaces after eliminating those that were out of service. The *Directory of Iron and Steel Works of the United States and Canada* was a basic source.

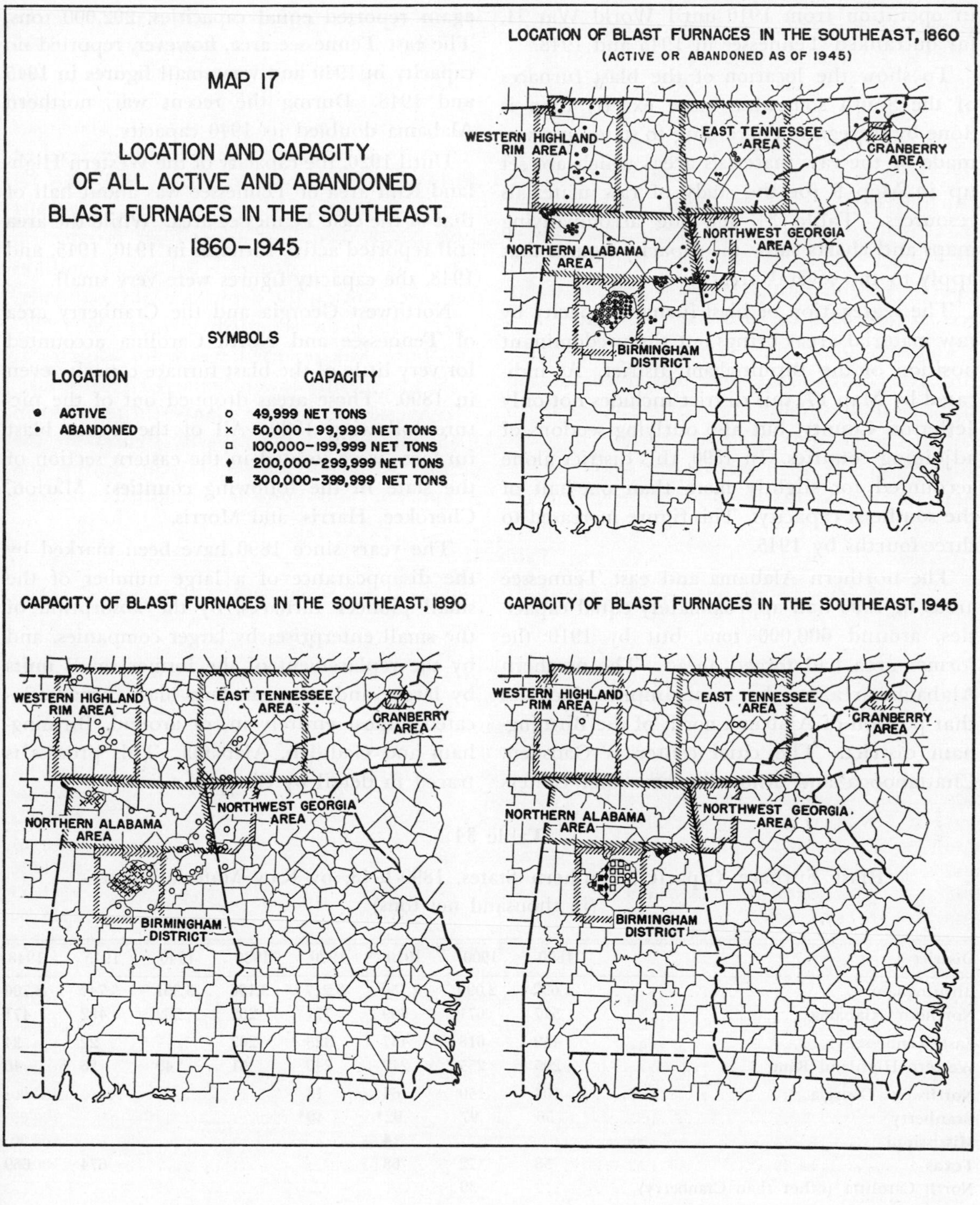

MAP 17

LOCATION AND CAPACITY
OF ALL ACTIVE AND ABANDONED
BLAST FURNACES IN THE SOUTHEAST,
1860–1945

SYMBOLS

LOCATION		CAPACITY	
● ACTIVE		○	49,999 NET TONS
● ABANDONED		✕	50,000–99,999 NET TONS
		□	100,000–199,999 NET TONS
		◆	200,000–299,999 NET TONS
		■	300,000–399,999 NET TONS

LOCATION OF BLAST FURNACES IN THE SOUTHEAST, 1860
(ACTIVE OR ABANDONED AS OF 1945)

WESTERN HIGHLAND RIM AREA
EAST TENNESSEE AREA
CRANBERRY AREA
NORTHERN ALABAMA AREA
NORTHWEST GEORGIA AREA
BIRMINGHAM DISTRICT

CAPACITY OF BLAST FURNACES IN THE SOUTHEAST, 1890

WESTERN HIGHLAND RIM AREA
EAST TENNESSEE AREA
CRANBERRY AREA
NORTHERN ALABAMA AREA
NORTHWEST GEORGIA AREA
BIRMINGHAM DISTRICT

CAPACITY OF BLAST FURNACES IN THE SOUTHEAST, 1945

WESTERN HIGHLAND RIM AREA
EAST TENNESSEE AREA
CRANBERRY AREA
NORTHERN ALABAMA AREA
NORTHWEST GEORGIA AREA
BIRMINGHAM DISTRICT

highest capacity of 963,872 net tons was reached in 1900. In 1948, capacity for this state was only 73,920 tons. Texas, with no blast furnaces in operation from 1910 until World War II, far outranked Tennessee in 1945 and 1948.

To show the location of the blast furnaces of the South somewhat more exactly than is done by segregation according to states, use was made of the raw materials areas which are set up in Map 9 for the study of raw materials resources. Table 34 and the accompanying maps and charts show the capacity figures that apply to the several areas.

The segregation of blast furnace capacity by raw material areas brings out the predominant position of the Birmingham district. As indicated by Map 17, this district includes not only Jefferson County, but also outlying sections of adjoining counties. In 1890, this district alone accounted for slightly more than one-half of the southern capacity. This figure increased to three-fourths by 1945.

The northern Alabama and east Tennessee areas in 1900 had approximately equal capacities, around 600,000 tons, but by 1910 the former area had forged ahead. The northern Alabama area, as the name implies, includes that portion of Alabama north of the Birmingham district. The chief center is Gadsden. Chattanooga and Knoxville are chief centers of the east Tennessee area. In 1920, northern Alabama had four times the capacity of the east Tennessee area. In 1930, the two areas again reported equal capacities, 202,000 tons. The east Tennessee area, however, reported no capacity in 1940 and very small figures in 1945 and 1948. During the recent war, northern Alabama doubled its 1940 capacity.

Until 1920, the capacity of the Western Highland Rim area of Tennessee was about half of that of the east Tennessee area. While the area still reported active furnaces in 1940, 1945, and 1948, the capacity figures were very small.

Northwest Georgia and the Cranberry area of Tennessee and North Carolina accounted for very little of the blast furnace capacity even in 1890. These areas dropped out of the picture following 1920. All of the Texas blast furnaces were located in the eastern section of the state in the following counties: Marion, Cherokee, Harris, and Morris.

The years since 1890 have been marked by the disappearance of a large number of the small pioneer furnaces, by the absorption of the small enterprises by larger companies, and by the replacement of the former small units by larger and more modern blast furnaces located almost entirely in, or around, Birmingham and Gadsden, Alabama. This process is traced in detail by Chart 14.

Table 34

Blast Furnace Capacity, Southern States, 1890-1948, by Raw Material Areas
(in thousand net tons)

District	1890	1900	1910	1920	1930	1940	1945	1948
Birmingham	1,692	2,099	2,756	3,217	3,136	3,361	3,747	3,700
Northern Alabama	517	671	809	771	202	202	482	471
East Tennessee	459	618	457	325	202	....	22	34
Western Highland Rim	205	255	249	240	51	49	36	40
Northwest Georgia	103	150	64	13	....	....	....	....
Cranberry	56	97	92*	40*	....	....	....	....
Mississippi	....	....	4	....	....	....	....	....
Texas	58	72	68	....	....	....	674	669
North Carolina (other than Cranberry)	....	39	....	....	....	....	....	....
Total South	3,090	4,001	4,499	4,606	3,591	3,611	4,961	4,914

Source: Same as Table 33.   *In Tennessee only.

CHART 14

RECORD OF BLAST FURNACES IN OPERATION IN THE SOUTHERN STATES, 1870-1947

SHOWING RECORD OF INDIVIDUAL BLAST FURNACES

SYMBOLS

\ REBUILT   / ENLARGED   ∿∿ INTERMITTENT   = ALTERNATE   * ABANDONED

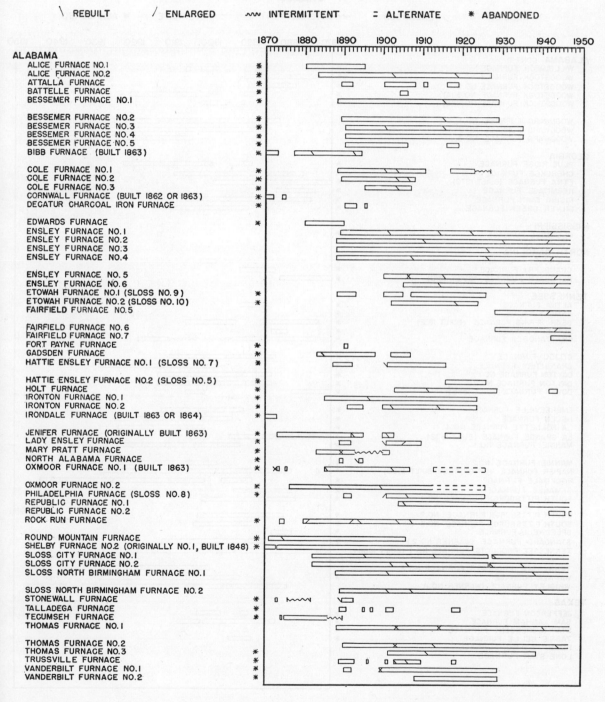

CHART 14 CONT'D.

RECORD OF BLAST FURNACES IN OPERATION IN THE SOUTHERN STATES, 1870—1947

SHOWING RECORD OF INDIVIDUAL BLAST FURNACES

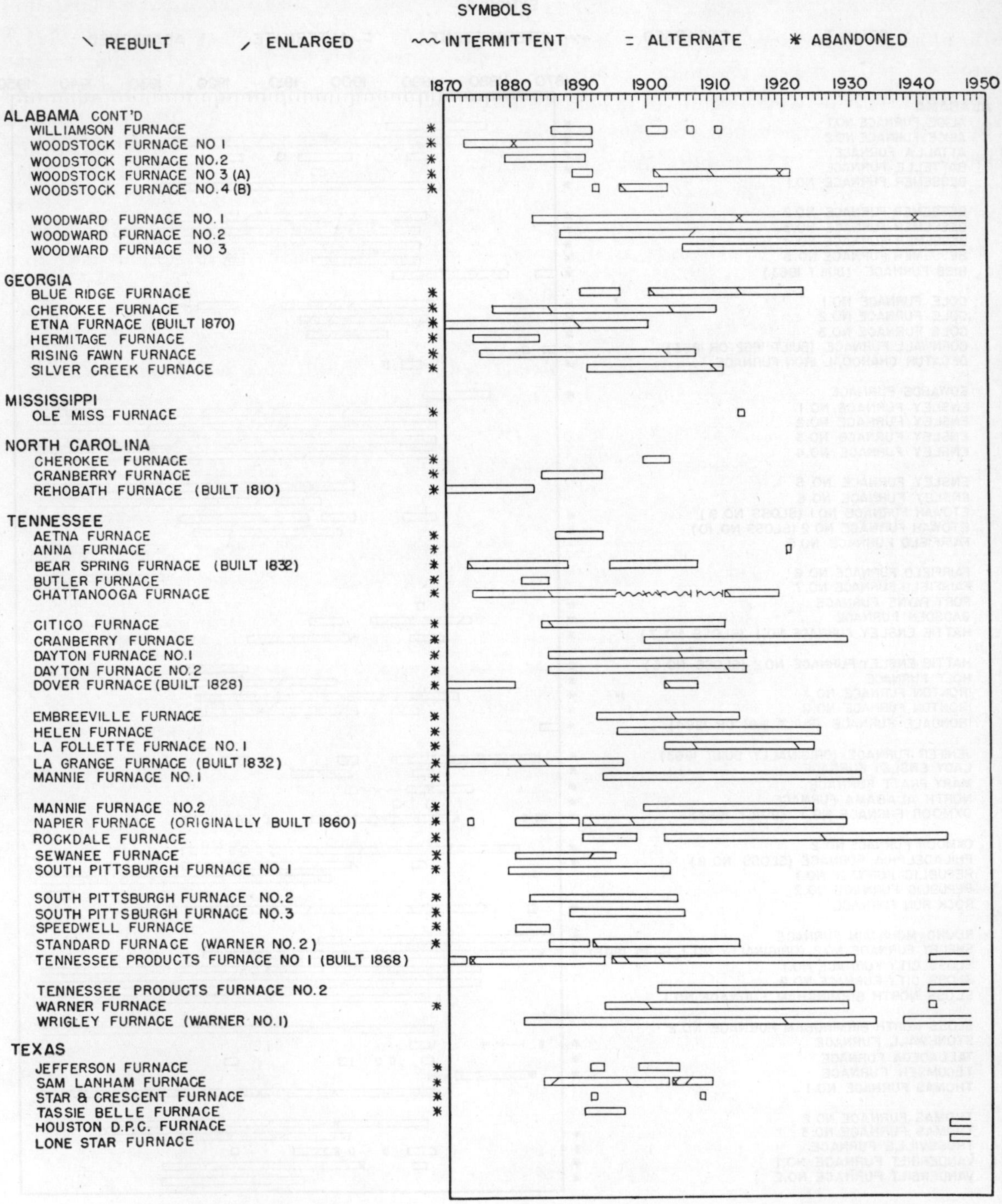

SYMBOLS

\ REBUILT   / ENLARGED   ∿ INTERMITTENT   = ALTERNATE   ✳ ABANDONED

	1870	1880	1890	1900	1910	1920	1930	1940	1950

ALABAMA CONT'D
WILLIAMSON FURNACE
WOODSTOCK FURNACE NO 1
WOODSTOCK FURNACE NO.2
WOODSTOCK FURNACE NO 3 (A)
WOODSTOCK FURNACE NO.4 (B)

WOODWARD FURNACE NO.1
WOODWARD FURNACE NO.2
WOODWARD FURNACE NO 3

GEORGIA
BLUE RIDGE FURNACE
CHEROKEE FURNACE
ETNA FURNACE (BUILT 1870)
HERMITAGE FURNACE
RISING FAWN FURNACE
SILVER CREEK FURNACE

MISSISSIPPI
OLE MISS FURNACE

NORTH CAROLINA
CHEROKEE FURNACE
CRANBERRY FURNACE
REHOBATH FURNACE (BUILT 1810)

TENNESSEE
AETNA FURNACE
ANNA FURNACE
BEAR SPRING FURNACE (BUILT 1832)
BUTLER FURNACE
CHATTANOOGA FURNACE

CITICO FURNACE
CRANBERRY FURNACE
DAYTON FURNACE NO.1
DAYTON FURNACE NO.2
DOVER FURNACE (BUILT 1828)

EMBREEVILLE FURNACE
HELEN FURNACE
LA FOLLETTE FURNACE NO.1
LA GRANGE FURNACE (BUILT 1832)
MANNIE FURNACE NO.1

MANNIE FURNACE NO.2
NAPIER FURNACE (ORIGINALLY BUILT 1860)
ROCKDALE FURNACE
SEWANEE FURNACE
SOUTH PITTSBURGH FURNACE NO 1

SOUTH PITTSBURGH FURNACE NO.2
SOUTH PITTSBURGH FURNACE NO.3
SPEEDWELL FURNACE
STANDARD FURNACE (WARNER NO.2)
TENNESSEE PRODUCTS FURNACE NO 1 (BUILT 1868)

TENNESSEE PRODUCTS FURNACE NO.2
WARNER FURNACE
WRIGLEY FURNACE (WARNER NO.1)

TEXAS
JEFFERSON FURNACE
SAM LANHAM FURNACE
STAR & CRESCENT FURNACE
TASSIE BELLE FURNACE
HOUSTON D.P.C. FURNACE
LONE STAR FURNACE

Trends in Capacity to Produce Steel Ingots and Casting

The rated capacity of the several types of furnaces which produce steel provide another measure of the steel industry. With the exception of a relatively small quantity produced in electric furnaces, southern steel is produced by open-hearth furnaces. In the Ensley plant in Birmingham, Alabama, Bessemer converters are used as one step in the duplex process, but the final stage involves the use of open-hearth furnaces and, consequently, no Bessemer capacity is reported in the South. Also, there is no production of crucible steel.

In 1915, steelmaking capacity was concentrated in Alabama, with Georgia as the only other southern state in which steel was produced. No capacity for electric furnaces was reported, and the total capacity of the open-hearth furnaces of the South comprised 3.9 per cent of the open-hearth capacity of the United States and 2.6 per cent of the total steelmaking capacity. By 1930, the total capacity of the South had increased from 1,164,800 net tons in 1915, to 2,437,680 net tons, a gain of 109 per cent. This compares with a gain in the total capacity of the nation of 63 per cent. As a result of the faster growth, the South's share of the national total increased from 2.6 per cent in 1915 to 3.5 per cent in 1930. From 1930 to 1940, the South continued to increase at a faster rate than the nation—an increase of 27 per cent as compared with 15 per cent—and

Table 35

Annual Capacity for Production of Steel Ingots in the South and the United States, January 1, 1915-1949 (in net tons)

Furnace and year	Southeast	Southwest	Total South	United States	Per cent South of United States
Open-hearth furnaces					
1915	1,164,800	....	1,164,800	29,886,472	3.9
1920	1,575,840	....	1,575,840	45,164,213	3.5
1930	2,378,880	50,400	2,429,280	60,181,710	4.0
1940	3,013,965	56,000	3,069,965	73,343,547	4.2
1945	3,571,000	520,000	4,091,000	83,835,460	4.9
1947	3,696,000	520,000	4,216,000	80,715,630	5.2
1949	3,653,000	630,000	4,283,000	84,572,160	5.1
Electric furnaces					
1915	....	....	....	97,888	....
1920	21,504	1,344*	22,848	875,078	2.6
1930	....	8,400	8,400	866,757	1.0
1940	30,240	3,293	33,533	1,592,080	2.1
1945	116,000	35,110	151,110	5,233,810	2.9
1947	116,000	17,660	133,660	5,032,530	2.7
*1949	98,000	17,660	115,660	5,899,490	2.0
Total capacity					
1915	1,164,800	....	1,164,800	44,265,984	2.6
1920	1,597,344	....	1,597,344	59,576,614	2.7
1930	2,378,880	58,800	2,437,680	70,635,652	3.5
1940	3,044,205	59,293	3,103,498	70,635,652	3.8
1945	3,687,000	555,110	4,242,110	80,950,901	4.5
1947	3,812,000	537,660	4,349,660	94,947,070	4.8
1949	3,751,000	647,660	4,398,660	90,902,180	4.6

*Includes Louisiana.

Source: American Iron and Steel Institute, *Annual Statistical Report*, 1915-1949. As originally reported, the figures shown here for January 1, 1915, 1920, 1930, and 1940 were dated December 31 of the preceding year.

its share in the total rose to 3.8 per cent. The war saw quite decided increases in steel capacity and, again, the gain was greater percentagewise in the South. During the five-year period, it was 37 per cent for the region and 17 per cent for the United States. As a result, the South's participation rose to 4.5 per cent in 1945. The postwar years have shown further increases in open-hearth capacity in the South, but declines in the capacity of the electric furnace. In 1947, the region's share of total capacity had increased to 4.8 per cent but 1949 showed a lower figure of 4.6 per cent.

As indicated by Table 35, the capacity of the South in 1914 was entirely in open-hearth plants while the capacity of electric furnaces was negligible until World War II. Even in 1945 and 1947, the electric furnace capacity was only 151,000 and 134,000 tons, respectively, or a small fraction of the total capacity. Also, the Southeast had almost all of the steelmaking capacity of the region until World War II, at which time a program of building steel plants was initiated in Texas. This raised the total capacity of the Southwest to 555,110 net tons in 1945 and 647,660 in 1949. The Texas development made up a substantial portion of the gain in the South, but, even so, the capacity in the Southwest in 1949 was only about 17 per cent of that of the Southeast. It is of interest also to note that, up to 1947, steelmaking capacity in the Southeast gained slightly faster on a percentage basis than the country did as a whole and that the percentage share of the Southeast in the total increased from 3.8 per cent in 1939 to 3.9 per cent in 1945 and to 4.2 per cent in 1947. In 1949, however, the participation of the Southeast fell to 3.9 per cent.

Table 36

Annual Capacity for Production of Steel Ingots in the South and the United States,
January 1, 1915-1949
(in net tons)

Type of furnace and year	1915	1930	1940	1947	1949
Open-hearth furnaces					
Alabama	1,097,600	2,275,840	2,860,480	3,542,000	3,488,000
Georgia	67,200	103,040	153,485	154,000	165,000
Tennessee	......	......	......	......	......
Oklahoma	......	50,400	56,000	54,000	54,000
Texas	......	......	......	466,000	576,000
Total South	1,164,800	2,429,280	3,069,965	4,216,000	4,283,000
Electric furnaces					
Alabama	......	......	30,240	78,000	60,000
Georgia	......	......	......	......	......
Tennessee	......	......	......	38,000	38,000
Oklahoma	......	......	......	......	......
Texas	......	8,400	3,293	17,660	17,660
Total South	......	8,400	33,533	133,660	115,660
Total capacity					
Alabama	1,097,600	2,275,840	2,890,720	3,620,000	3,548,000
Georgia	67,200	103,040	153,485	154,000	165,000
Tennessee	......	......	......	38,000	38,000
Oklahoma	......	50,400	56,000	54,000	54,000
Texas	......	8,400	3,293	483,660	593,660
Total South	1,164,800	2,437,680	3,103,498	4,349,660	4,398,660

Source: American Iron and Steel Institute, *Annual Statistical Report,* 1915-1949. As original reported, the figures shown here for January 1, 1915, 1930, and 1940 were dated December 31 of the preceding year.

The distribution of the steelmaking capacity by states is given in Table 36 for the years 1914, 1929, 1939, and 1947. Steelmaking is characterized by large-scale production and, consequently, plants occur only in a few places. In 1947, seven open-hearth plants were reported in the South. Two of these, and by far the largest and most important, are located in Birmingham or its environs. One is in Gadsden, Alabama; one, in Anniston, Alabama; one, in Atlanta, Georgia; one, in Houston, Texas; and one, in Sand Springs, Oklahoma. In the same year, there were five steel plants in the South with electric furnaces. These were located in Birmingham, Alabama; Anniston, Alabama; Knoxville, Tennessee; Fort Worth, Texas; and Beaumont, Texas. The predominant place held by Birmingham in southern steel is shown by the fact that its ingot capacity in 1947 was approximately 2.7 million tons, or more than 60 per cent of the total for the South. Gadsden and Anniston are located at relatively short distances from Birmingham and can almost be considered as constituting a part of that district.

The data on steelmaking capacity adds to the evidence that the steel industry of the South has been increasing more rapidly than that of the country as a whole and that it has had a much faster growth than the blast furnace products industry.

Capacity to Produce Rolled Iron and Steel Products

The measurement of the capacity of a plant to produce rolled iron and steel products presents a difficult problem because of the great variety of products and the differences in the requirements of the different kinds. Also, the finishing departments of a rolling mill are usually equipped to turn out a greater volume of finished products than can be maintained by the steelmaking and preliminary processing departments of the plant. As a result, the capacity for producing finished products has been calculated at different times by at least two different methods. One is known as the balanced production method and the other as the maximum production method. The first

assumes that the available steel will be rolled into products according to a balanced program. The second calculates the maximum for each product on the assumption that the steel will always be on hand to keep the finishing process going. Detailed statistics are available, by products and by states, only for 1935, 1938, 1945, and 1948. The figures for 1945 are on a basis that does not make them comparable to those of the other three years and consequently were not used in the analysis that follows.

The capacity in 1948 of the rolling mills of the Southeast and the Southwest to produce the various classes of iron and steel products and the percentage shares in the nation's capacity are presented in Table 37. These data serve to show the South's present position with respect to the kinds of products that its mills are equipped to produce and also point out the kinds of products in which the region had no capacity in 1948.

An examination of the capacity statistics for the production of the various classes of steel mill products shows that there were eight in which the southern mills had 15 per cent or more of the total capacity of the United States. These were: standard railroad rails (over 60 pounds); concrete reinforcing bars from new billets; rerolled concrete reinforcing bars; nails and staples; bale ties; chemically treated black plate; hoops, cotton ties, and baling bands; and strip for cold reduced black and tin plate. Of these, only the first two and the last named classes rank among the top uses of steel in the nation. In seven classes, the South's share ranged from 10 per cent to 14.4 per cent. Included in this group were: joint or splice bars and tie plates; track spikes, bolts, nuts, rivets, and washers; galvanized wire; barbed wire; woven fence; hot dipped tin and terne plate; and galvanized sheets. Several of these are important products, but it is of interest to note that they are largely connected with railroads, wire products (largely for agriculture), and materials used by the container industry. The five classes in which the region's per cent of the nation's total ranged from 5 to 9.2 were: sheared plates, wire rods, plain wire, electricweld pipe, and electrolytic tin plate. Finally, there were ten classes in which the South had some capacity, but with a share of less than 5 per cent. These were: heavy structural shapes; light structural shapes; light rails; universal plates; steel skelp; hot rolled sheets; hot rolled strip; galvanized strip; steel bars (other than concrete reinforcing); and ingots, blooms, and billets for forging.

Capacity to produce the various kinds of steel mill products was reported on the same basis (on the balanced production assumption) in 1935, 1938, and 1948, and the published statistics should be reasonably comparable. The appearance of new products and changes in product classifications, however, present difficulties that prevent ascribing a high degree of

precision to the percentage changes derived from the published figures. Still, the data presented in Table 38 serve to show the changes that took place.

In general, the changes that occurred in the South compare quite favorably with those for the nation as a whole. For all finished hot rolled products, the percentages of increase for the South were 6.8 per cent, from 1935 to 1938, and 82.5 per cent, from 1938 to 1948. These percentages compare with 6.3 per cent and 30.0 per cent, respectively, for the two periods for the United States.

The changes in capacity in the United States from 1935 to 1938, as indicated by Table 38, suggest a considerable readjustment. Of the thirty-nine products (not counting group sub-

Table 37

Capacity to Produce Steel Mill Products, United States, Southeast, Southwest, and South, 1948
(quantities in short tons)

	Capacity to produce steel products				Per cent of the United States		
	United States	Southeast	Southwest	Total South	Southeast	Southwest	South
Total all finished hot rolled products							
Steel	73,872,430	3,422,600	521,700	3,944,300	4.6	0.7	5.3
Iron	452,300	......	......	......	...	...	...
Total	74,324,730	3,422,600	521,700	3,944,300	4.6	0.7	5.3
Rails							
Standard (over 60 lbs. per yard)	2,705,600	470,000	......	470,000	17.4	...	17.4
60 lbs. or less per yard	292,800	3,600	......	3,600	1.2	...	1.2
Total	2,998,400	473,600	......	473,600	15.8	...	15.8
Joint or splice bars and tie plates	1,154,000	166,600	......	166,600	14.4	...	14.4
Structural shapes							
Heavy	5,236,930	180,000	71,000	251,000	3.4	1.4	4.8
Light	1,058,470	38,000	11,200	49,200	3.6	1.0	4.6
Total	6,295,400	218,000	82,200	300,200	3.5	1.3	4.8
Steel piling	247,400	......	......	......	...	...	...
Plates							
Sheared	5,811,400	400,000	104,000	504,000	6.9	1.8	8.7
Universal	1,371,300	18,000	......	18,000	1.3	...	1.3
Strip mill	683,000	......	......	......	...	...	...
Total	7,865,700	418,000	104,000	522,000	5.3	1.3	6.6
Hoops, cotton ties, and baling bands	108,300	75,900	......	75,900	70.1	...	70.1
Hot rolled strip	3,527,590	53,700	......	53,700	1.5	...	1.5
Strip for cold reduced black and tin plate	4,114,300	624,000	......	624,000	15.2	...	15.2
Bars, other than concrete reinforcement							
Steel	12,008,260	363,550	77,900	441,450	3.0	0.7	3.7
Iron	142,300	......	......	......	...	...	...
Total	12,150,560	363,550	77,900	441,450	3.0	0.6	3.6

Table 37 (cont'd)

Capacity to Produce Steel Mill Products, United States, Southeast, Southwest, and South, 1948
(quantities in short tons)

	Capacity to produce steel products				Per cent of the United States		
	United States	South-east	South-west	Total South	South-east	South-west	South
Concrete reinforcing bars							
New billets	1,124,100	96,900	106,900	203,800	8.6	9.5	18.1
Rerolled	388,700	75,000	36,000	111,000	19.3	9.3	28.6
Total	1,512,800	171,900	142,900	314,800	11.4	9.4	20.8
Wire rods	6,195,170	397,750	98,100	495,850	6.4	1.6	8.0
Skelp							
Iron	310,000	......	......	......	...	...	...
Steel	4,095,900	105,000	......	105,000	2.6	...	2.6
Total	4,405,900	105,000	......	105,000	2.4	...	2.4
Blanks or pierced billets for seamless tubes....	3,285,040	......	......	......	...	...	...
Wheels and axles (rolled)	404,050	......	......	......	...	...	...
Ingots, blooms, and billets for forging	806,590	11,600	7,600	19,200	1.4	1.0	2.4
Miscellaneous hot rolled products	305,960	......	......	......	...	...	...
Cold finished bars	3,217,260	......	......	......	...	...	...
Buttweld pipe	2,502,320	......	......	......	...	...	...
Lapweld pipe	669,200	......	......	......	...	...	...
Seamless pipe and tubes	3,462,800	......	......	......	...	...	...
Electricweld pipe	2,025,400	175,000	......	175,000	8.6	...	8.6
Spiralweld pipe	114,000	......	......	......	...	...	...
Gasweld pipe	5,000	......	......	......	...	...	...
Galvanized pipe	1,266,000	......	......	......	...	...	...
Conduit	167,500	......	......	......	...	...	...
Boiler tubes	338,400	......	......	......	...	...	...
Mechanical tubing	1,173,800	......	......	......	...	...	...
Plain wire	5,805,340	482,200	52,400	534,600	8.3	0.9	9.2
Wire and wire products							
Galvanized	1,802,070	197,760	24,000	221,760	11.0	1.3	12.3
Nails and staples	1,179,140	212,600	23,000	235,600	18.0	2.0	20.0
Barbed wire	561,875	69,040	9,000	78,040	12.3	1.6	13.9
Woven fence	1,071,130	139,740	8,000	147,740	13.0	0.8	13.8
Bale ties	162,880	28,500	......	28,500	17.5	...	17.5
Total	4,777,095	647,640	64,000	711,640	13.6	1.3	14.9
Sheets							
Hot rolled	18,947,570	343,000	9,000	352,000	1.8	0.1	1.9
Cold rolled	8,758,845	......	......	......	...	...	...
Galvanized	2,791,620	323,000	......	323,000	11.6	...	11.6
Long terne	227,700	......	......	......	...	...	...
Black plate, ordinary	473,000	......	......	......	...	...	...
Chemically treated black plate	117,500	23,500	......	23,500	20.0	...	20.0
Hot dipped tin and terne plate	3,714,150	415,000	......	415,000	11.2	...	11.2
Electrolytic tin plate	2,176,100	188,000	......	188,000	8.6	...	8.6
Cold rolled strip	2,654,940	......	......	......	...	...	...
Galvanized strip	386,550	13,140	......	13,140	3.4	...	3.4
Track spikes, bolts, nuts, rivets, and washers..	636,580	69,180	......	69,180	10.9	...	10.9

Source: *Directory of Iron and Steel Works of the United States and Canada, 1948.*

Table 38

Change in Capacity of Steelworks to Produce Steel Mill Products, South Compared with the United States, Per Cent Changes, 1935-1938 and 1938-1948

	Per cent change 1935 to 1938		Per cent change 1938 to 1948	
	South	U.S.	South	U.S.
Total finished hot rolled products				
Steel	+ 6.81	+ 6.31	+ 82.50	+ 29.98
Iron	N. C.	—43.93	*	+ 5.41
Total	+ 6.79	+ 5.60	+ 81.95	+ 29.80
Rails				
60 lbs. or less per yard	—16.67	— 1.61	+ 20.00	— 14.64
Standard (over 60 lbs.)[1]	—53.13	—15.71	+108.89	+ 2.10
Total	—52.85	—14.31	+107.72	+ 0.18
Joint or splice bars and tie plates	—66.50	—24.05	+250.00	+ 12.84
Structural shapes				
Heavy	+ 8.33	—17.32	+175.82	+ 42.80
Light	N. C.	+35.29	+278.46	— 24.15
Total	+ 7.22	— 7.40	+188.65	+ 24.34
Steel piling[2]	# †	— 9.62	† *	+ 5.28
Plates				
Sheared	+81 26	+ 6.68	+109.22	+ 33.41
Universal	—50.83	—27.35	+ 52.54	+ 19.37
Strip mill	# †	# †	† *	†
Total	+61.06	— 2.82	+106.57	+ 42.89
Hot rolled sheets[3]	+56.92	+48.06	+ 10.07	+ 77.68
Hoops, cotton ties, and baling bands	+ 5.19	—37.14	— 46.55	— 28.52
Hot rolled strip	+19.20	+ 1.81	+ 20.13	— 17.70
Strip for cold reduced black plate and tin plate	....	....	+175.13	+ 99.26
Bars—other than concrete reinforcement				
Steel	— 1.72	— 7.00	+ 49.87	+ 30.89
Iron	N. C.	—33.46	*	— 45.04
Total	— 1.68	— 8.00	+ 46.69	+ 28.81
Bars—concrete reinforcement				
New billet	#	#	+ 40.36	+ 1.14
Rerolled	#	#	+ 52.05	— 9.08
Total	+12.59	— 0.42	+ 44.27	— 1.70
Wire rods	+ 3.49	+ 1.26	+ 88.11	+ 42.14
Skelp				
Steel	# †	—12.08	† *	+ 43.19
Iron	# †	—51.47	† *	+134.85
Total	# †	—15.12	† *	+ 47.23
Blanks or pierced billets for seamless tubes	# †	+27.73	† *	+ 11.34
Wheels and axles (rolled)[4]	# †	— 5.82	† *	+ 37.88
Ingots, blooms, and billets for forging purposes	N. C.	+22.17	— 1.03	— 27.14
Miscellaneous finished hot rolled products	# †	+ 9.77	† *	— 34.72
Cold finished bars[5]	#	+15.25	*	+109.30
Buttweld pipe	# †	— 2.81	† *	+ 18.02
Lapweld pipe	# †	—29.75	† *	— 50.44
Seamless pipe and tubes	# †	+23.54	† *	+ 10.84
Electricweld pipe and tubes	# †	—16.00	†	+158.84
Spiralweld pipe	# †	# †	† *	†
Gasweld pipe	# †	# †	† *	†
Galvanized pipe	# †	— 3.96	† *	+ 43.72

Table 38 (cont'd)

Change in Capacity of Steelworks to Produce Steel Mill Products, South Compared with the United States, Per Cent Changes, 1935-1938 and 1938-1948

	Per cent change 1935 to 1938		Per cent change 1938 to 1948	
	South	U.S.	South	U.S.
Conduit	# †	# †	† •	†
Boiler tubes	# †	# †	† •	†
Mechanical tubes	# †	# †	† •	†
Plain wire	+35.20	+11.89	+ 58.17	+ 29.15
Galvanized wire	—32.66	— 7.33	+138.97	+ 36.92
Nails and staples	+10.14	+ 2.51	+ 46.52	+ 3.51
Barbed wire	—31.23	— 5.74	+ 40.61	+ 15.33
Woven fence	— 2.88	+ 0.03	+ 51.06	+ 46.58
Bale ties	# †	# †	†	†
Cold rolled sheets	# †	+60.51	† •	+ 58.13
Galvanized sheets	+20.89	+ 7.24	+ 48.85	+ 37.01
Long terne sheets	# †	+13.14	† •	+ 10.76
Black plate[6]	# †	—22.62	†	— 72.34
Tin and terne plate[7]	#	+37.02	+201.50	+ 61.35
Cold rolled strip	# †	+ 4.11	† •	+ 84.72
Bolts, nuts, spikes, rivets, etc.[8]	—18.52	— 7.23	+ 74.70	— 15.90

Explanatory Notes:

No report of capacity 1935; † No report of capacity 1938; • No report of capacity 1948.
N.C. No change.

1 Called "All other" in 1935 and 1938 directories.
2 Called "Sheet piling" in 1935 and 1938 directories.
3 Total of "Hot rolled black sheets" and "Hot rolled annealed black sheets" in 1935 and 1938.
4 "Rolled wheels" in 1935 directory.
5 "Cold drawn bars" in 1935 directory.
6 Total of "ordinary black plate," and "chemically treated black plate" in 1948; "Hot rolled black plate (including black plate for tinning)" in 1938; "Black plate (including black plate for tinning)" in 1935.
7 Total of "Hot dipped tin and terne plate" and "Electrolytic tin plate" in 1948; total of "Hot reduced tin and terne plate" and "Cold reduced tin and terne plate" in 1938; and terne and tin plate in 1935.
8 Includes "Track spikes" in 1948 to make comparable with 1938 and 1935.
Source: American Iron and Steel Institute, *Directory of Iron and Steel Works of the United State and Canada*, 1935, 1938 and 1948.

totals) on which percentage changes could be calculated, twenty-one showed decreases, several quite large. The South had no representation either in 1935 or 1938 in nine of these products. For the remaining twelve products, the South showed increases instead of decreases for three, no change for one, and decreases that were smaller, percentagewise, than the national decrease for one, and larger than the national for seven. In the products that made a weak showing nationally, it would seem, therefore, that the adjustment was felt quite strongly in the South. The eighteen products which increased nationally represent the other side of

the readjustment. In these, the South made quite a favorable showing. There were six of the eighteen products in which the South had no representation either in 1935 or 1938. Of the remaining and twelve, the South had larger increases, percentagewise, than the United States in seven products. In addition, there were two products in which the South had no representation in 1935 but for which capacity was reported in 1938.

The period from 1938 to 1948 was characterized by increases in capacity. The changes in capacity can be summarized as follows:

Degree of change in capacity nationally	Number of products	No capacity in the South 1938 or 1948	Change in South	
			More favorable than U.S.	Less favorable than U.S.
Increase 40 per cent or more	13	5	6	2
Increase 20 per cent to 39.9 per cent	6	1	5	
Increase 10 per cent to 19.9 per cent	7	4	3	
Increase less than 10 per cent	4	1	3	
Decrease	11	2	7	2
Total	41	13	24	4

On the assumption that a larger percentage of increase, or a smaller percentage of decrease, than the nation is favorable, the summary of the data indicates that, in those products in which it had representation, the South made a strong showing between 1938 and 1948. The failure to secure representation in more of the different kinds of products presents the most serious question concerning the developments of the period.

The data on the capacity of southern mills to produce steel products suggest that quite a variety is being produced, and in sizable tonnages, and that there are a number of products in which the southern mills hold a very important place in the nation's production. However, it can readily be seen that the mills are largely based on a relatively small number of basic demands: agriculture, railroads, containers, and building construction. The twenty-one classes in which the South, in 1948, had no capacity indicate important weaknesses. The most conspicuous one was the absence of capacity to produce any of the many varieties of pipe or tubes, and this in face of the fact that the South is one of the nation's great markets for products of this type. The South did not produce cold finished bars, cold rolled sheets, or steel piling, and was limited in the varieties of rolled shapes that were produced. Thus, many of the products desired for industrial purposes were not being produced. Since the end of the war, active steps have been taken to remove some of the deficiencies by developing pipe plants in Gadsden and Houston and a cold reducing mill in Birmingham.

Conclusions

One characteristic of the basic iron and steel industries of the South during the first half of the twentieth century was the tendency toward concentration of production in a few large units in, and around, Birmingham, Alabama. The appearance of blast furnaces and steelworks in Texas during, and following, World War II was the only significant exception.

Generally, the evidence indicates substantial growth in the basic industries, particularly in the production of steel and finished rolled products. Employment in blast furnaces has tended to decline, but this evidently has been due to technological changes, since production of pig iron has had a sustained, though slow, upward trend. Employment in steelworks and rolling mills, on the other hand, has increased greatly, along with the increases in production and capacity. The production series indicate that the southern industries have responded strongly to prosperity and have resisted the depressing effects of the downward swings of the cycles to a greater degree than the nation as a whole. Increases in capacity and an increasing variety of products indicate strength and healthy growth.

It must not be assumed, however, that all of the developments have been favorable. Compared with the situation in the nation as a whole, the steelworks and rolling mill industry of the South is still underdeveloped when measured in terms of its position in the total manufacturing structure of the region and in its relationship to the blast furnace industry. This last situation suggests that the blast furnace industry of the South must find an outlet for its pig iron in uses other than steelmaking to a greater extent than the industry does generally.

Another serious weakness is the lack of facilities to produce many of the kinds of steel products required by the metal fabricating industries or used in an industrialized economy. Some of the more important steel products that are not made in southern steel mills are: line pipe for oil and gas transmission, oil country pipe for drilling and producing oil, standard pipe for domestic and industrial purposes, power piping and boiler tubes for chemical and power plants, alloy steel tubing for oil refineries and for textile and paper plants, cold drawn mechanical tubing, conduit tubing for electrical work, cold rolled sheets, wide hot rolled sheets, cold rolled strip, steel piling, bridge flooring, industrial floor plates, cold drawn bars, and wire rope. No doubt, the scattered, and small, markets in the South have been factors that help account for the absence of plant capacity, but there are some lines, particularly in pipe, where this is scarcely a sufficient explanation.

CHAPTER XI

THE COMPANIES COMPRISING THE BASIC IRON AND STEEL INDUSTRY OF THE SOUTH

Having reviewed the early history of iron and steel in the South and having examined the more important trends of the basic industries for the last 30 or 40 years, the next step in developing a well-rounded statement of the facts concerning the industry is to give a description of the operating companies. These include the Tennessee Coal, Iron and Railroad Company, the Republic Steel Corporation, the Sloss-Sheffield Steel and Iron Company, the Woodward Iron Company, the Connors Steel Company, and the J. I. Case Company (formerly the Kilby Steel Company), in Alabama; the Atlantic Steel Company, in Georgia; the Knoxville Iron Works and the Tennessee Products Corporation, in Tennessee; and the Sheffield Steel Corporation, the Lone Star Steel Company, the Valencia Iron and Chemical Company, the Texas Steel Company, and the Beaumont Iron Works, in Texas and Oklahoma. Of these, the Tennessee Coal, Iron and Railroad Company, a subsidiary of the United States Steel Corporation, is the giant. Three of the companies are integrated concerns; that is, they produce pig iron, steel ingots, and finished steel products. These are the Tennessee Coal, Iron and Railroad Company, the Republic Steel Corporation, and the Sheffield Steel Corporation. The Sloss-Sheffield Steel and Iron Company and the Woodward Iron Company are producers of merchant pig iron but do not produce steel, and the Tennessee Products Corporation does not carry its iron operations beyond the blast furnace. The Atlantic Steel Company and the plant of the former Kilby Steel Company have open-hearth steel furnaces and produce rolled steel products but own no blast furnaces. The Connors Steel Company,[1] the Knoxville Iron Company, the Texas Steel Company, and the Beaumont Iron Works are

relatively small concerns that produce rolled steel products and also small quantities of steel in electric furnaces. The Lone Star Steel Company and the McCrossin Engineering Company were engaged in the development of new plants in Texas during the war. Since the war, the blast furnace properties of the McCrossin Engineering Company have been acquired by the Valencia Iron and Chemical Company.

The Alabama Companies

The Tennessee Coal, Iron and Railroad Company is, by far, the most important single operator in the South. The company was incorporated in 1860 as the Tennessee Coal and Railroad Company; changed its name to the Tennessee Coal, Iron and Railroad Company in 1881; acquired the properties of the Pratt Coal and Iron Company in 1886; consolidated the properties of three important companies in 1892, namely the Tennessee Company, the De-Bardeleben Coal and Iron Company, the Cahaba Coal Mining Company; in later years took over the Robinson Mining Company, the Sheffield Coal, Iron and Steel Company, the Smith Company, and the Bessemer Rolling Mill Company; and, in 1907, became a subsidiary of the United States Steel Corporation. By this series of consolidations the company came into possession of reserves of iron ore and coal that certainly exceed the total holdings of all the other southern iron and steel operators.

---

[1] The Connors Steel Company was bought by the H. K. Porter Co., Inc., Pittsburgh, in the fall of 1950. The plant is being operated as the Connors Steel Co. Division of H. K. Porter Co., Inc. See *Alabama Today and Tomorrow* (Montgomery, Alabama: Alabama State Chamber of Commerce, October 1950). A two million dollar program to expand capacity was announced in *Iron Age* (March 29, 1951).

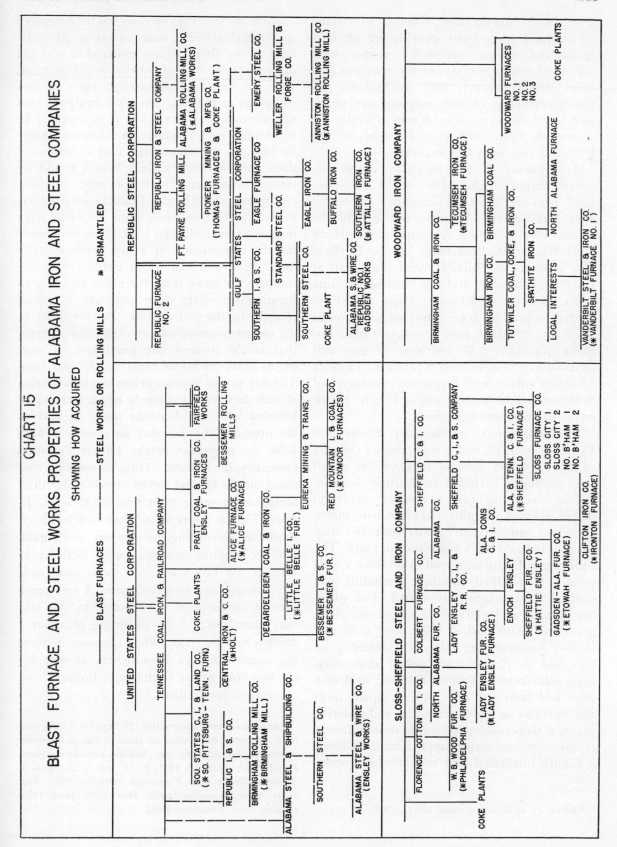

CHART 15

BLAST FURNACE AND STEEL WORKS PROPERTIES OF ALABAMA IRON AND STEEL COMPANIES

SHOWING HOW ACQUIRED

——— BLAST FURNACES ——— STEEL WORKS OR ROLLING MILLS * DISMANTLED

The plants thus acquired, together with those which have been built, provide for an integrated and balanced production of the widest variety of products of any of the southern concerns. On January 1, 1952, the separate corporate existence of the company was terminated and the operation became officially the Tennessee Coal and Iron Division of the United States Steel Corporation.

As of January 1, 1948, the iron and steel producing manufacturing plants of the Tennessee Coal, Iron and Railroad Company,[2] all located near Birmingham, Alabama, consisted of the Ensley Works, Ensley, Alabama; the Fairfield Steel Works, Fairfield Sheet Works, Fairfield Tin Works, and Fairfield Wire Works, all at Fairfield, Alabama; and the Bessemer Rolling Mills, Bessemer, Alabama. These plants included by-product coke plants with 572 ovens (capacity, 2,939,350 tons of coke); 9 blast furnaces (capacity, 2,374,500 tons of iron and ferro-alloys); 21 open-hearth furnaces (capacity 2,850,000 tons of steel ingots and castings); and 3 Bessemer converters, which supply blown metal to open-hearth furnaces.

The rolling mills at Bessemer, Ensley, and Fairfield, in 1948, had a total annual capacity of 2,954,700 net tons of finished hot rolled steel products. Included are facilities for producing rails and rail accessories, structural shapes, sheared and universal plate, bars, sheets, hoop and cotton tie strip, wire rods, and strip for cold reduced black plate and tin plate. The finishing mills are equipped to produce a wide variety of finished products, including galvanized sheets; chemically treated black plate; hot dipped and electrolytic tin plate; plain, galvanized, and barbed wire; wire nails and staples; woven fence; bale ties; finished splice bars and tie plates; track spikes; axles; forgings; cold formed sections; culverts; steel castings; and bolts and nuts. The company owns and operates an ore-conditioning and sintering plant, a slag-crushing plant, its own railroads, repair shop, and water supply system. It forms a highly integrated and self-contained operation.

2 *Directory of Iron and Steel Works, 1948.*

Since the war, the company has been engaged in an improvement and expansion program. One of the first projects undertaken was the opening of the Concord coal mine. This mine, with the new coal preparation plant, is said to be one of the most modernly equipped coal operations in the world and is expected to be the largest coal producer in Alabama. Early in 1948, it was announced that a hot rolled sheet mill at the Fairfield Works would be converted to a cold reduction mill, thus providing one of the kinds of rolled steel products that had not previously been available from southern steel mills. In 1949, plans were made for the construction of a new modern office building in Fairfield which would enable the company to move from the office building in Birmingham where space previously had been rented. In the fall of 1950, the president of the company announced an expansion program that would increase the production of steel ingots from 2,850,000 tons to 3,350,000 tons. The key to this expansion was the importation of rich ores from Venezuela which were to be blended with the Alabama ores. As part of the program, the company purchased, in May 1950, the properties of the Turner Terminal Company in Mobile. These properties consisted of docks and other terminal facilities located on a water front tract of 32 acres. In April, 1951, it was reported that work had been started on converting the property into a modern ore-handling terminal with facilities to transfer the ore from ships to railroad cars, river barges, and into stockpiles. A vice president of the company was reported to have said that plans call for the importing of about 3 million tons per year. The expansion involves the construction in Birmingham of new by-product coke ovens, open-hearth furnaces, and other auxiliary facilities.[3]

3 Announcements concerning the expansion programs have appeared from time to time in the daily newspapers of Birmingham and Mobile (see *Birmingham Post-Herald,* April 17, 1951, p. 14, col. 4) and also in *Alabama Today and Tomorrow* (October 1947; February 1948; December 1949; May 1950; June 1950; October 1950; November 1950).

The Republic Steel Corporation, or rather its predecessor, the Republic Iron and Steel Company, first entered the South by acquiring what are commonly called the Thomas Furnaces in 1899. Originally, there were three of these furnaces, but No. 3, built in 1901-02, was dismantled in 1939. The Pioneer Mining and Manufacturing Company built Furnace No. 1 in 1886-1888 and Furnace No. 2 in 1889-1890. The two furnaces had an annual capacity in 1948 of 376,000 net tons.[4] The Thomas Works has a by-product coke plant with a capacity of 235,000 net tons of coke. In 1937, the corporation acquired the properties of the Gulf States Steel Corporation which, since that year, have been operated as the Gulf Steel District of Republic. The blast furnaces, coke plant, and steel works of this unit are located in Gadsden, Alabama. There are two blast furnaces with a total capacity of 471,000 tons. The first of these was built in 1902-03 by the Alabama Steel and Wire Company and was involved in a series of reorganizations by the owner-companies. These reorganizations finally resulted in the establishment of the Gulf States Steel Corporation in 1913. The second blast furnace was built in 1942. The Gadsden plant includes by-product coke ovens with a capacity of 565,-000 tons of coke per year, eight open-hearth furnaces with an annual capacity of 650,000 net tons of steel ingots, and rolling mills with total capacity of 515,000 net tons of hot rolled steel products. The principal finished products include sheets, bars, plates, wire products, and bolts and nuts. In 1948, the corporation added an electric fusion weld pipe mill which is producing large diameter welded-steel pipe. During the war, it engaged rather extensively in ore beneficiation, and it has a plant for that purpose in Birmingham. The Corporation has considerable ore and coal reserves, but, in the Birmingham district, it is generally considered to be in a relatively weak position in this respect. This directs considerable interest toward the Corporation's explorations in Mexico and Liberia, and, most recently, in Venezuela.[5] In

past years, its Thomas Furnaces were largely used to produce merchant pig iron, but it seems that much of the product now is being used in the Gadsden steel furnaces.

The Sloss-Sheffield Steel and Iron Company was formed in August, 1899, by a consolidation of the Sloss Iron and Steel Company with twelve smaller concerns. These included the Lady Ensley Coal, Iron and Railroad Company; the Franklin Mining Company; the Lady Ensley Furnace Company; the American Coal and Coke Company; the Loss Creek Coal Company; the Walker County Coal Company; the Russellville Ore Company; the Hamilton Creek Ore Company; the Colbert Iron Company; the Philadelphia Furnace Company; Miss Emma Ore Mining Company; and the North American Furnace Company.[6] The Sloss Furnace Company, the original of the Sloss Iron and Steel Company, was formed in 1881. Of the four furnaces presently operated, Sloss City No. 1 and Sloss City No. 2 were completed in 1882. These two furnaces have the distinction of being the oldest blast furnaces still in operation in Alabama. The remaining two furnaces built by the Sloss Iron and Steel Company, Sloss North Birmingham No. 3 and No. 4, were completed in 1888 and 1889. With the reorganization of 1899, three North Alabama blast furnaces were acquired. These were the Lady Ensley, the Hattie Ensley, and the Philadelphia Furnace.

In 1923, five more blast furnaces were acquired when the Cole Furnaces (only one of the original three was then standing), the Etowah Furnaces, and the Clifton Furnaces were taken over. Since the founding of the Sloss Company in 1881 that company has owned a total of twelve blast furnaces in Alabama, a number equaled only by the Tennessee Coal, Iron and Railroad Company. Due to the high cost of assembling the raw materials, the Sloss-Sheffield Steel and Iron Company has now abandoned and dismantled all its blast furnaces except the four in the Birmingham district.[7]

These four furnaces have been rebuilt a number of times, and in 1948 the City Fur-

4 Directory of Iron and Steel Works, 1948.

5 "Republic, Hanna Seek Venezuelan Ore," Iron Age (January 11, 1951), p. 84.

6 Ethel Armes, Coal and Iron in Alabama, p. 451.

7 Woodward Iron Company, Alabama Blast Furnaces, p. 130.

naces Nos. 1 and 2 had a combined annual capacity of 281,230 net tons pig iron, while the North Birmingham Furnaces Nos. 3 and 4 had an annual capacity of 105,240 net tons of pig iron and 36,800 net tons of ferro-manganese. The company also owned two coke plants, one at Lewisburg, Alabama, with 94 beehive ovens, and one at North Birmingham with 120 Semet-Solvay ovens. Early in 1951, the company announced plans for an addition to their by-product coke plant. Their raw material properties consist of iron ore mines, coal mines, and a dolomite quarry, all in Alabama. The company is generally considered to be in a relatively weak position with respect to ore reserves.

The controlling interest in the capital stock of the company is now in the hands of the same interests that control the United States Cast Iron Pipe Company, and it is generally supposed that the steel and iron company serves, to an extent, as a source of pig iron for the pipe company.

The fourth iron producer in the Birmingham district is the Woodward Iron Company, which operates three blast furnaces known as Woodward Furnaces Nos. 1, 2, and 3. The company's first furnace went into blast in 1883. Four years later, the second furnace went into operation. Furnace No. 3 was built in 1903 and blown in during June, 1905. Furnace No. 1 has been rebuilt twice and its size increased, while No. 2 has been enlarged once. In 1948, these three furnaces had a combined annual capacity of 526,170 net tons of pig iron. "A very low cost on pig iron was possible at Woodward because of the proximity of raw materials and low cost assembly of materials over the company's railroad."[8] The company's coal and ore mines are located within a few miles of the furnaces.

With the purchase of the Birmingham Coal and Iron Company in 1912, the company added the two Vanderbilt Furnaces, coal and ore mines, and coke ovens. "However, the most important feature of the purchase was acquisition of immense coal reserves."[9] The Vander-

bilt Furnaces were operated until 1929, when they were blown out. They were sold for scrap in 1935.

In 1939, this company installed the country's first modern de-humidifying system for controlling the moisture content of the air blown into the furnace, an installation which has proved signally successful.

Since the first small, hand-filled furnace went into blast in August 1883, the Woodward Iron Company has produced more than 12,500,000 tons of pig iron. The company has ore and coal reserves adequate to operate its three blast furnaces at peak capacity for more than a century. The Woodward Iron Company ranks today as the largest independent and completely integrated manufacturer of merchant pig iron in the United States.[10]

In December, 1951, the company announced the completion of a new blast furnace with a capacity of 650 tons daily. The cost of the project was estimated as 415 million dollars.

The two other companies in the basic iron and steel industry in Alabama are the Connors Steel Company, Division of H. K. Porter Company, Inc., whose plant is in Birmingham, and the Anniston plant of J. I. Case Company, formerly the Kilby Steel Company. The former rolls quite a variety of lighter shapes, such as cotton ties, strip steel reinforcing bars, and concrete construction accessories. To a large extent the company depends on reheated ingots or scrap, an important item being scrap railroad rails. In addition, it has two electric arc furnaces with a rated capacity in 1945 of 60,000 net tons. The Kilby Steel Company had two basic open-hearth furnaces and two electric arc furnaces with a combined capacity in 1945 of 74,400 net tons. In 1947, the plant of this company was acquired by the J. I. Case Company and is being used in the manufacture of tractors and other agricultural implements.

The Tennessee and Georgia Companies

There were eighteen blast furnaces in Tenneccssee in 1890 but the number steadily declined until, at present, only three are reported. These are now owned by the Tennessee Prod-

---

8 *Alabama Blast Furnaces*, p. 156.
9 *Alabama Blast Furnaces*, p. 158.

10 *Alabama Blast Furnaces*, p. 158.

ucts and Chemical Corporation. Its predecessor was incorporated in 1917 as the Bon Air Coal and Iron Company. This company owned two pig iron blast furnaces at Allen's Creek, Wayne County, Tennessee, and one furnace at Goodrich, the latter having been purchased from the Standard Iron Company. The Bon Air Coal and Iron Company also owned a charcoal pig iron furnace at Lyles-Wrigley which was completed in 1920. These furnaces, along with coal, iron ore, and timber lands, were the property of the Bon Air Coal and Iron Corporation in 1926 when it was consolidated with the Chattanooga Coke and Gas Company, Inc., and J. J. Gray, Jr., to form the Tennessee Products and Chemical Corporation. The furnaces at Allen's Creek and Goodrich, Tennessee, were dismantled in 1926. The property acquired from J. J. Gray, Jr. consisted of the Rockdale Furnace at Rockdale, Tennessee. This furnace was built in 1890. It was still active in 1938, but stood idle in 1944, and, according to the 1945 *Annual Statistical Report* of the American Iron and Steel Institute, was abandoned in 1945.

The closing of the Rockdale Furnace leaves only three active furnaces in Tennessee. These include the previously mentioned Lyles-Wrigley Furnace built in 1881. In 1948, this furnace had an annual capacity of 40,320 net tons of low-phosphorus charcoal pig iron. The other two furnaces, known as Tennessee Products Nos. 1 and 2, are located at Rockwood, Tennessee. These furnaces, which had been idle for a long period of time, were acquired in 1941 from the Roane Iron Company. They were built in 1893 and 1901, replacing furnaces constructed earlier. They have been rebuilt and enlarged several times. In 1948, Furnace No. 1 was reported as idle and Furnace No. 2 as having a capacity of 33,600 tons of ferro-manganese. The company owns coal and iron ore mines and limestone quarries in Tennessee together with a coke and by-product plant and eight electric furnaces for the manufacture of ferrosilicon at Chattanooga.

In the Southeast, there are two additional plants, both in the steel works and rolling mill industry, and a third which is in the process of organization. Of these, the most important is the Atlantic Steel Company, whose Atlanta plant has three basic open-hearth furnaces with a total capacity, in 1948, of 165,000 net tons. Although limited by a small capacity and by dependence on purchased scrap or pig iron for raw materials, the company has a good record of producing a variety of steel products which include steel bars; concrete reinforcing bars; wire rods; plain and galvanized wire; nails and staples; barbed wire; woven fence; bale ties; hot rolled strip; and bolts, nuts, and rivets. For the year 1950, the company reported[11] the production of 200,830 net tons of steel ingots and the shipment of 172,556 tons of steel and steel products. This tonnage established high records for the company. The Knoxville Iron Works, Knoxville, Tennessee, has two electric arc furnaces with a total capacity of 38,000 net tons and has rolling mill equipment to produce relatively small quantities of hot rolled bars, light structural shapes, and strip, from rerolled rail scrap.

Early in 1951, a new company, the Tennessee Steel Corporation,[12] was incorporated to build a plant at Oneida, Scott County, Tennessee. Two 25 ton top-charge electric furnaces and one smaller unit were planned at that time, but more recent reports indicate that the company will build two 40-ton electric furnaces instead of the two 25-ton furnaces.[13] Finishing facilities are to include a rod mill and strip mill. Annual capacity is to be 100,000 tons, not counting a rail rerolling and slitting mill of 36,000 tons capacity. Finished products are to include bar shapes and sections, household and agricultural pipe, hot rolled strip, merchant and reinforcing bars, mine rails, cross ties, mine and fence posts. *Iron Age* comments that the anticipated cost of the new mill will be

[11] "New Company Records Set by Atlantic Steel," *Alabama Purchasor* (April 1951), p. 15.

[12] "Local Market Mill to be Built in Tennessee," *Iron Age* (January 11, 1951), p. 79.

[13] Letter of Mr. Stefan Robock, Chief, Industrial Economics Branch, Division of Regional Studies, Tennessee Valley Authority, September 25, 1951.

approximately $50 per ton of capacity compared to costs of $200 to $300 per ton for completely integrated new steel capacity. The opinion is also offered that such mills, designed to serve a local market, have the protection of a freight umbrella under an f. o. b. mill pricing system.

The Texas Companies

While the primary interest in this study of the basic iron and steel industry is in the Southeast, Texas and Oklahoma have played such an important part in the market of the iron and steel produced in the Birmingham district that recent developments in the Southwest should be described. The most important operator in this area is the Sheffield Steel Corporation, a subsidiary of the Armco Steel Corporation. It operates six basic open-hearth furnaces (two of which were government built) in connection with a blast furnace at Houston, Texas. The total annual capacity of the open-hearth furnaces of this plant in 1948 was 560,000 net tons. The blast furnace, which was government constructed, had an annual capacity of 274,000 net tons. The company also has a small plant at Sand Springs, Oklahoma, which has one open-hearth furnace with an annual capacity of 54,000 net tons together with a billet and a bar mill. The rolling mills were equipped to produce heavy structural shapes, sheared plates, hot rolled steel bars, concrete reinforcing bars, wire rods, plain, galvanized, and barbed wire, nails and staples, woven fence, and hot rolled sheets.

In 1950, the Sheffield Steel Corporation and the A. O. Smith Corporation acted jointly to build a large diameter electric weld steel pipe at Houston.[14] The plant is designed to have a capacity of 35,000 tons of pipe per month. It is located near the Sheffield Steel Corporation's mill from which it receives its plate. In the same year, the United States Steel Corporation[15] through a subsidiary, the Consolidated Western Steel Corporation, built a similar mill at Orange, Texas, which is expected to produce 100,000 tons of pipe per year. The steel plate to be used by the mill presumably will be shipped by inland waterway from U. S. Steel Corporation's mills, probably largely from Birmingham. This development, along with the mill of the Republic Steel Corporation at Gadsden, Alabama, puts the South definitely into the production of steel pipe.

The other steel works in Texas are not operated in connection with blast furnaces. These are located at Fort Worth and at Beaumont. The steel works located at Fort Worth is owned by Texas Steel Company and consists of two electric arc furnaces with a total capacity of 22,320 net tons. The Beaumont Iron Works Company, Beaumont, Texas, has two electric furnaces, with a combined capacity of 3,600 net tons.

In addition, there are two ventures in Texas in the basic iron and steel industry which had their origin in the World War II production program. One of these was a blast furnace located at Rusk, Texas. It was owned by the McCrossin Engineering Company, which was succeeded January 1, 1948, by the Valencia Iron and Chemical Corporation. The blast furnace was reported in the *Iron and Steel Works Directory, 1948,* as being scheduled for completion in 1948. Its capacity was to be 27,000 tons.[16] The other was the construction, in 1944, of a blast furnace at Daingerfield, Texas. The plant consists of a by-product coke plant of 375,000 ton capacity and a blast furnace with a capacity of 394,800 tons of pig iron. The plant is operated by the Lone Star Steel Company[17] which, after several years of precarious existence, seems to be getting on a sounder basis. The company has built and operates a cast-iron pressure pipe foundry, which has an annual capacity of 80,000 tons of

---

14 "Pipe Production in Houston Plant Stated to Open August 1," *Iron Age* (March 23, 1950), p. 81.

15 "First Pipe Leaves New Twin Mills," *Iron Age* (May 4, 1950), pp. 102-103.

16 A letter from the Rusk Chamber of Commerce in the spring of 1951 stated that the blast furnace had not been completed.

17 "New Lone Star Mill Rated at 500,000 Tons," *Manufacturers Record* (April 1951), p. 42.

pipe, and has a project for building a completely integrated steel mill having an annual capacity of 500,000 tons of ingots. The rolling mills are to be designed principally to produce tubular goods. It is reported that the company has secured approval of a 73 million dollar government loan, and that it has succeeded in raising from private sources the additional capital that was required to qualify for the government loan.

CHAPTER XII

INTRODUCTION TO MINING AND OPERATING PROBLEMS OF THE BASIC IRON AND STEEL INDUSTRIES OF THE SOUTHEAST

The preceding chapter described the development of the companies that are operating the plants which produce pig iron, steel, and steel products in the South. This discussion showed that the productive capacity was located largely in Birmingham, Alabama, and Gadsden, Alabama, and that the operations in these two cities were near enough to each other in distance and were sufficiently interrelated to be considered as belonging in one district, which, for convenience, may be termed the Birmingham district. Earlier chapters presented an analysis of the natural resources of the South that are related to the production of iron and steel and also described the trends that have been developing in production and in capacity to produce. It is the purpose of this chapter to provide the background for the discussion of selected important operating problems which confront the industry in the Southeast.

General Characteristics of the Basic Industries

In approaching the study of operating problems, it is well to have in mind the more important general characteristics of the basic iron and steel industries. The fact that the industry is characterized by large-scale production and that the operation of a fully integrated unit involves large investments of capital was brought out in Chapter II. A review of the properties owned by the four principal companies operating in Birmingham serves to reinforce this point. Even the very sketchy outline presented by Chart 16 of the principal steps involved in a completely integrated unit (such as the Tennessee Coal, Iron and Railroad Company) is sufficient to establish the complexity and the highly technical character of the operations.[1]

LOCATIONS OF THE PROPERTIES OF THE PRINCIPAL COMPANIES

As already mentioned the occurrence of the three most important raw materials—iron ore, fluxing stone, and coal—in close proximity to each other is perhaps the most widely known characteristic of the Birmingham district. The over-all situation in this respect is shown by Maps 10 and 11. To bring out the situation with respect to each of the four leading companies, separate maps are shown. The extensive nature of the properties of the Tennessee Coal, Iron and Railroad Company is shown graphically by Map 18, which also brings out the fact that the properties are quite closely grouped geographically. Of all of the operating concerns, the mines and plants of the Woodward Iron Company are the most compactly located. It can also be said that these two companies own the rights to ore and coal reserves considered the most desirable in the district. The properties of the Republic Steel Corporation and the Sloss-Sheffield Steel and Iron Company are more scattered. The former has blast furnaces in Birmingham, but its largest, most modern blast furnaces and its steel works are in Gadsden. It draws its ore and coal, however, largely from mines in the vicinity of Birmingham. It has had a rather unfortunate experience with its iron-mining

[1] A full description of the operations of the iron and steel makers would require much more space than was considered appropriate in this report and so will not be attempted. Any reader interested in a full description will find a very well prepared statement in *Steel Making at Birmingham*.

CHART 16

PLANTS AND PRODUCTS OF AN INTERGRATED
IRON AND STEEL COMPANY

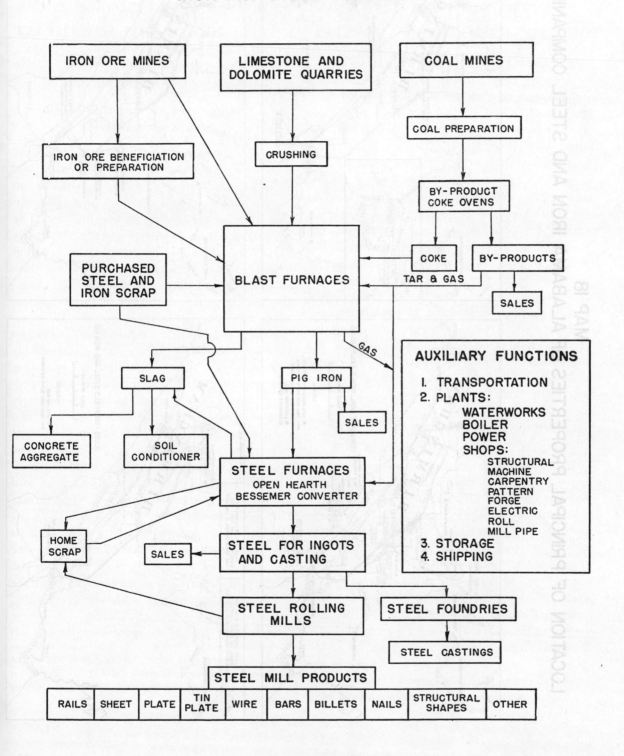

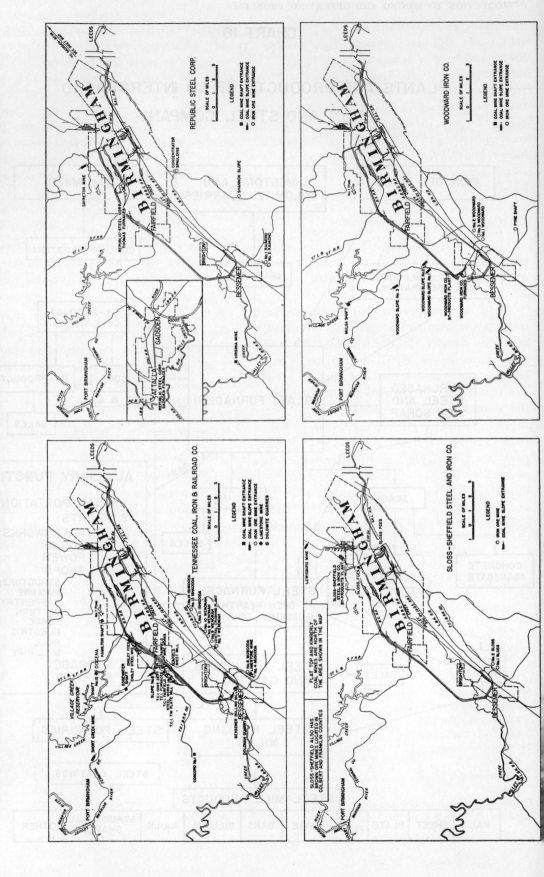

MAP 18

LOCATION OF PRINCIPAL PROPERTIES OF ALABAMA IRON AND STEEL COMPANIES, 1948

operations, since its Raimond mines have been abandoned and its Shannon Mine has never been considered a satisfactory operation. The blast furnaces of the Sloss-Sheffield Steel and Iron Company are divided between two locations, both of which are at considerable distances, for the Birmingham district, from the iron mines. In addition it has brown ore mines and washers in Franklin and Colbert counties that are at least 100 miles from the blast furnaces.

SIZE OF THE PRINCIPAL OPERATION UNITS

The general characteristics and the relative size of the operations of the four companies are indicated by the data presented in Table 39.

These data support several conclusions concerning the companies operating in the Birmingham district. In the first place, they emphasize the diversified facilities of the Tennessee Coal, Iron and Railroad Company as well as its predominant position in the district. In the second place, the statistics on ore mined suggest that the Tennessee Coal, Iron and Railroad Company and the Woodward Iron Company are producing ore in quantities which make them independent of other sources. It should be said in this connection that 1947 and 1948 have seen imports of rather sizable quantities of foreign ore into the Birmingham

district, and that the Tennessee Company not only has been using such ore but plans greater use. It would seem, however, that this is a matter of choice and is not dictated by a lack of available local ore. The third conclusion, which is supported by opinions widely expressed in the district, is that the Republic Steel Corporation and Sloss-Sheffield Steel and Iron Company, finding difficulty in producing enough ore from their Birmingham mines, are in need of supplementing with ores secured from other sources. Purchased ore constitutes a possible source, but the quantities so available are limited by the fact that practically no red ore in the district is produced for the market. Brown ore is produced for the market in Alabama and northwest Georgia, and pyrite sinter from Ducktown, Tennessee, may be obtained. It is understood that Republic and Sloss-Sheffield are the principal purchasers. Furthermore, Republic, as previously pointed out, is much interested in the possibility of using foreign ore.

Transportation Facilities and Problems

The nearness of ore, coal, and fluxing stone to the blast furnaces and the resulting savings in transportation have long been featured as outstanding advantages for Birmingham as an iron-producing center. Consequently, the situa-

Table 39

Production and Employment in Mining Operations and Plant Capacities of the Four Principal Companies in the Birmingham District, 1948

	Tennessee Coal, Iron & Railroad Co.	Republic Steel Corporation	Sloss-Sheffield Steel & Iron Co.	Woodward Iron Company
Mining operations—production in				
Red hematite ore	5.764,199	620,020	361,565	1,423,233
Brown ore	....	....	335,372	....
Coal	3,467,171	899,270	806,557	844,015
Employed in mining				
Red ore	3,327	353	422	821
Brown ore	....	....	142	....
Coal	4,118	1,332	1,276	933
Capacity of blast furnaces (net tons)	2,374,500	847,000	423,270	526,170
Capacity of open hearth furnaces	2,850,000	650,000	....	....

Table 39 (cont'd)

Production and Employment in Mining Operations and Plant Capacities of the Four Principal Companies in the Birmingham District, 1948

	Tennessee Coal, Iron & Railroad Co.	Republic Steel Corporation	Sloss-Sheffield Steel & Iron Co.	Woodward Iron Company
Capacity of rolled products				
Rails	473,600			
Long joint or splice bars and tie plates................	166,600			
Structural shapes—heavy.....................	180,000			
Plates—sheared	400,000			
Plates—universal	18,000			
Skelp		105,000		
Sheets	628,000	75,000		
Hook and cotton tie strip.................	49,900			
Strip	8,200			
Strip for cold reduced black plate and tin plate............	624,000			
Bars—other than concrete reinforcement..................	158,400 ⎱	150,000		
Concrete reinforcement	67,400 ⎰			
Wire rods	169,000	185,000		
Ingots, blooms and billets for forging...............	11,600			
Total	2,954,700	515,000		
Other finished products				
Galvanized sheets........................	21,300	110,000		
Black plate—chemically treated.............	23,500			
Tin plate—hot dipped......................	415,000			
—electrolytic	188,000			
Wire—plain	170,600	200,000		
—galvanized	75,100	80,000		
—barbed	32,900	23,000		
—nails and staples.................	81,700	88,000		
—woven fence	81,700	23,000		
—Bale ties	13,400	9,000		
Finished splice bars and tie plates...............	173,000			
Track spikes	30,000			
Axles	15,500			
Forgings	8,600			
Cold formed sections.....................	7,300			
Culverts	10,000			
Steel castings	12,000			
Iron castings	67,000			
Brass and bronze castings..................	810			
Bolts and nuts.........................	21,600	12,000		
Electric fusion weld pipe.....................		175,000		

Note: Connors Steel Company, a Birmingham concern, (now owned by H. K. Porter, Co., Inc.) reported the following capacities in net tons: 2 electric furnaces, 60,000; hoops, cotton ties and baling bands, 7,600; strip, 14,000; bars other than concrete reinforcement, 7,400 bars concrete reinforcement—new billet steel, 10,000; bars concrete reinforcement—rail steel, 55,000; total capacity for hot rolled products, 94,000.

Source: Mining operations, Alabama Department of Industrial Relations; *Annual Statistical Report, 1948-49;* Iron and steel capacities, *Directory of Iron and Steel Works of 1948.*

tion with regard to transportation facilities should be examined in some detail.

The large volume of materials to be moved from mines to by-product plants and blast furnaces together with the relatively short distances involved undoubtedly are factors which have encouraged the iron and steel companies to acquire ownership of transportation facilities. Where these facilities are not owned, special arrangements are made to use the tracks of interconnecting common carriers for reaching outlying operations. These arrangements place the companies in an independent position, free from outside rail shipping congestion. The following list of railroads serving the Birmingham district, as well as the furnaces near Gadsden, is divided into three classes according to types of transportation.

Railroads Serving the Birmingham District

Common carriers
Louisville and Nashville Railroad
Southern Railway
Illinois Central Railroad
Seaboard Air Line Railway
St. Louis and San Francisco Railway
Central of Georgia Railway
Atlanta, Birmingham and Coast Railroad
Gulf, Mobile, and Ohio

Switching lines
Warrior River Terminal Company
Birmingham Belt Railroad Company

Iron and steel company-owned railroads
Tennessee Coal, Iron and Railroad
    Company
Woodward Iron Company
Republic Steel Company
Sloss-Sheffield Steel and Iron Company
Birmingham Southern Railroad Company

In the Birmingham district, red iron ore is hoisted from the mines, screened, and crushed to the desired size. It is then passed into ore pockets from which it is drawn into hopper bottom cars for transportation by direct short rail haul (usually by company-owned and operated equipment) to the furnace storage bins. In a few cases, in order to reach the com-

pany railroads, it is necessary first to ship over outside-owned railroads. Also, at one mine, the ore is beneficiated before it is transported to the furnaces.

The coal mines are served by company railroads with, in most cases, only a short haul. Some of the mines now are 10 or more miles away from the coke plant, which is usually only a short distance from the furnaces. Company switch engines deliver the coal to the larries which charge coal into the coke ovens. They also spot the coke cars under the ovens that are being discharged and then take the cars to the quenching department where water sprays put out the fire in the coke before it goes to the bin.

Most of the limestone and dolomite quarries are near the furnaces, and their products can be handled by trucks or by railroad cars over company-owned switching tracks.

Imported ores, and other raw materials, ordinarily enter by the port of Mobile and can be shipped by all-rail haul from Mobile[2] or can be brought in barges (one company has its own barges) by the Mobile-Tombigbee-Warrior rivers to Birmingport, and thence by the Warrior River Terminal Company rail line to the furnaces.

Brown iron ores from the Woodstock, the Russellville, the eastern Alabama, or the northwestern Georgia districts are hauled to the washers in large trucks, while the concentrates from the washers are trucked to railroad cars which move over common carriers to the furnaces at Gadsden or Birmingham.

In most cases, the haul of raw and semifinished products is short, and seasonal influences are of minor importance. The close proximity of raw materials to furnaces obviates the need for the stock-piles required at northern plants and lessens the amount of capital tied up in inventories. Also, as a result of

[2] It has been reported that the G. M. and O. Railroad Company has placed orders for 250 new hopper-type cars for ore in anticipation of the movement of Venezuelan ore to Birmingham. See "$2,400,000 Order for Freight Cars Placed by GM&O," *Mobile Register* (August 4, 1951), p. 1, col. 7.

being transported on a company-owned railroad, the hot metal can be taken direct from the blast furnace to the hot metal mixer. From this the molten iron can be drawn, when needed in making steel, without first being cast into pigs and then remelted—a process which adds to production costs.

The contrast of the transportation situation in the South with that in the North, the West, and the Pacific Coast regions is very great. In these regions, seasonal changes, long distances of raw materials from iron and steel plants, the rehandling of ores, and the use of varied methods of transportation are important factors. Huge stockpiles of several hundred thousand tons of coal or ore are a familiar sight at northern plants.

In the North, the lake iron ores from Minnesota, Wisconsin, and Michigan must be mined, loaded on hopper-bottomed cars, and moved from the mine to upper lake ports, either by company-owned railroad or by common carrier. The distance covered is greater than the total movement in the South. At the upper lake ports the iron ore is dumped from the railroad cars into large bins located at shipside. From the bin, the ore is drawn off rapidly through swing chutes (a chute for each hatch) into an ore boat. At the lower lake docks, the ore must be rapidly removed from the vessels by some type of clam shell (the Hulett ore unloader is in common use) and carried into railroad cars for further shipping to other consuming points or to stockpiles from which it is moved to furnace bins when needed.

The movement must take place mainly in the spring, summer, and fall, because the long winter season closes the open-pit mines, halts the lake transportation, and renders handling by rail difficult. Late opening of navigation on the lakes in the spring or sudden early closing in the fall frequently shortens the season and causes a rush to move as much ore as possible in a short season. In order to prevent interruption of operations, huge inventories of all raw materials must be carried. Also, freezing weather causes delay in removing

material from cars. Rail freight, inventory, and handling charges from lower lake ports to inland blast furnaces such as Pittsburgh, Youngstown, Canton, Johnstown, Hamilton, and Granite City range from 97 cents to $3.76 per ton of ore. Furthermore, coal must be hauled long distances to many of the iron and steel producing centers in the North and East.

A recent authoritative study of this subject summarizes the transportation as follows:

> On the basis of Lake Erie base price of Mesabi Non-Bessemer ore, the value of ore at the mouth of the mine is $2.54 per ton, allowing $0.05 per ton to cover interest, marine insurance, and incidentals. The transportation charges from the mouth of mine to inland steel district vary from $2.83 to $4.08. Thus the transportation costs exceed the value of the ore at the mouth of the mine.[3]

These transportation costs are such a factor that many of the steel companies and mining companies have organized lake and rail transportation subsidiaries which are often the most profitable units in the corporation. It is evident that the Southeastern operations are in an advantageous position on transportation costs.

Conditions Favorable to Close Managerial Control

The discussion of transportation facilities and problems points directly to the conclusion that transportation and storage costs in the Birmingham district should be low because of the short hauls and the ease with which year-around operation of mines and facilities can be obtained. The proximity of all the important operations to each other has another implication which should be mentioned. This is that the job of maintaining control over the varied operations that are needed to produce iron and steel is made easier by this situation. The Birmingham companies are perhaps the only ones in the United States where the general management can reach all important operating mines and plants by local telephone or

3 *Economic Analysis of the State of Minnesota*, p. 121.

can at any time visit personally any unit in a matter of minutes. Under such circumstances, it should be possible to obtain a coördination of activities that is unlikely, or even impossible, where operating units are as widely scattered as they are in the North and the West.

The fact that the companies own their own ore and coal reserves and mines and carry on the mining as operating departments should aid greatly in the full integration of production. It should be pointed out, however, that the ownership of reserves has other implications. The distribution of the ownership is such that two of the companies are in a weak position and have not yet been able to secure satisfactory supplementary sources. Also, the complete ownership by the operating companies of the known reserves of commercial red ore in the district tends to preclude an expansion of operations though the establishment of new companies.

Problems Arising from Resource Conditions

The chapters on the natural resources of the district suggested that problems of a serious character face the companies which attempt to exploit ore and coal deposits. The chapters which follow will discuss these problems in detail, and so it is sufficient here to remind the reader that the favorable factors do not tell the whole story. Predominantly, both the iron ore and the coal are so far below the surface that underground mining is required. The

iron ore is low grade; that is, its iron content is low. This means that larger quantities of ore per ton of finished product must be mined, transported, and passed through the furnace than is the case in the northern districts. Also, this characteristic means that it is necessary to use more coke per ton of iron produced. In addition, the presence of a relatively high percentage of phosphorus has influenced the technical practices of the steel works and has imposed limitation on the uses made of products. In the case of coal, the seams are thin and the presence of foreign materials has necessitated elaborate washing procedures. The exploitation of both the ore and coal deposits is made more difficult by the frequent folds, faults, and irregularities of the geological strata.

It can be seen, therefore, that an operating company has a very difficult task to make full use of the favorable factors and to overcome the less favorable ones. The following chapters will take up, in the order indicated, these topics:

Problems of mining and preparation of iron ore

Problems of mining and preparation of coal and production of by-product coke

Costs of assembling raw materials for pig iron in Birmingham compared to costs in other iron-producing centers

Metallurgical and other technical problems

Conclusions with regard to raw materials, resources, and operating problems in the basic industries.

CHAPTER XIII

IRON ORE MINING AND ORE PREPARATION IN THE SOUTHEAST

It is the purpose of this chapter to discuss the problems involved in iron ore mining and in the preparation of ore for the blast furnaces in the Southeast—particularly in Alabama. Detailed descriptions of the technical methods involved in operations will not be attempted, but a general knowledge of mining technology is essential to an understanding of the business and economic problems. Consequently, the first section of the chapter will give a summary of fundamental operations.

Fundamental Operations in Iron Ore Mining

Before ore can be mined, a means of getting access to the mineral mass must be provided. The ore seldom is directly exposed, for it usually lies under a cover of soil, rock, and other materials. In case the cover, or overburden, is relatively thin, it may be removed or stripped, usually by power shovels, and the ore exposed. Operations of this kind are classed as open-pit mining. If the ore bed lies too deep below the surface for stripping, the approach is to provide a passageway from the surface to the ore. In general, this is accomplished either by a shaft (vertical well) or a slope (tunnel) which is dug at an incline with varying degrees of steepness depending upon the location of the ore bed with reference to the surface. The term "underground mining" is applied to this method. In the case of underground mining, an intricate system of tunnels or passageways must also be provided, leading from the main shafts or slopes to the working areas where the ore is being removed. Preliminary either to the removal of overburden for open-pit mining or to digging shafts, slopes, or other approaches, much exploratory work must be done. As a result, a mining company

has a very large investment in a mine before the removal of ore can be begun.

A second requirement for mining is to have a means of breaking workable quantities of ore loose from the ore mass. This is usually accomplished by drilling holes into the ore at desired places. These holes are loaded with an explosive which, when detonated, breaks a quantity of the ore. Since some of the ores are quite soft, breaking down the ore is easy. On the other hand, the hard ores present a much more difficult problem. Also, open-pit mines present a situation which makes drilling and blasting much easier and less dangerous than is the case with underground operations.

A third general task is to get the ore to the surface or to the mouth of the mine. In the case of open-pit mines, the power shovels which dig the ore from its original position load it directly on cars or on motor trucks to be hauled out of the pit. In the case of underground mines, at least two operations are involved: loading and hauling. The loading into cars or skips may be done either by hand labor or by machine. In large mines, haulage often involves more than one stage. The ore may be hauled by one type of car from the working spaces to the main passageway, slope, or shaft, and then transferred to other cars or skips for the remainder of the trip to the surface. Often, storage is provided at these transfer points, and a very common practice is to plan these storage spaces or pockets in such a manner that loading on the next set of cars can be done by gravity through chutes.

A fourth general type of operation that is required in most ore mines involves crushing the ore to desired size, removing undesirable materials, and providing storage until the ore is needed for transportation to the blast furnaces. If concentration or beneficiation is undertaken, the plant for this purpose is usually associated closely with the mining operation.

Finally, the operations that have to do directly with the recovery of the ore require the use of a wide variety of auxiliary facilities. Ventilation must be provided, both to get oxygen to the workers and to remove noxious or unpleasant gases; the roof of the mine must have adequate support to afford protection from falling rock and from caving; and power and supplies must be gotten to working places. In both underground and open-pit mines, water is almost certain to be a problem, and usually powerful pumps and a system of pipes or waterways must be provided to keep the mine dry enough to be worked.

These are some of the general characteristics of iron ore mines, and the preceding summary has been given to introduce the description that follows of the mines and mining practices in the Southeast.

Iron Ore Mines in the Southeast

The chapter on iron ore deposits established the fact that there are numerous locations in the Southeast where red ore, brown ore, or carbonate ore occur. At one time or another, many of these deposits have been worked, but for the last twenty or twenty-five years significant operations have been confined to the red ore mines near Birmingham and the brown ore mines of Alabama and northwest Georgia. Therefore, attention for the present will be restricted to these locations.

As indicated by Map 11 and described in Chapter V, the red ore mines are located in a section of Red Mountain which extends from Birmingham to a point opposite Bessemer, Alabama. The brown ore mines are more scattered, occurring in Franklin, Tuscaloosa, Bibb, Colbert, Shelby, Cherokee, Etowah, and St. Clair counties in Alabama and in Bartow and Polk counties in Georgia. Table 40 is derived from data in the annual report of the Alabama Department of Industrial Relations for the fiscal year ending September 30, 1949, and gives an indication of the sizes of the various operations in Alabama.

The data in Table 40 calls attention to the fact that a large portion of the ore production is concentrated in the Ishkooda, Muscoda, and Wenonah mines of the Tennessee Coal, Iron and Railroad Company and in the Pyne Shaft of the Woodward Iron Company. Also, the small size of the mining operations in recovery of brown ore is thrown in sharp relief by the scale of operations that characterize the red ore mines. Still another point of contrast is that the red iron ore mines are almost entirely operated by companies which also operate blast furnaces, while the majority of the brown ore mines are in the hands of firms that have to market the ore after it is produced.

In addition to the mines listed above, there are a number of small mines, such as the Old Jap red ore mine near Gadsden, Alabama, that are operated occasionally. Operations have been suspended or abandoned in the Raimond and the Shannon mines of the Republic Steel Corporation. The largest and most important mines not specifically listed above are the brown ore mines in northwest Georgia, one of which is said to be the largest brown ore mine in the Southeast.

Having reviewed the location and size of iron ore mines in the Southeast, the study of ore mining in the region will be continued by a section on methods of mining red ore in the Southeast and one on mining brown ore in the Southeast. The purpose of these discussions is not to give a full presentation of the technical processes and problems, but rather to summarize in nontechnical language enough of the methods of operation to provide a basis for discussing later the economic problems faced by those who attempt to produce iron ore in the region.

Red Ore Mining in the Southeast

The chapter on iron ore resources of the Southeast developed the characteristics of the ore deposits of the Red Mountain area which determine the conditions that control the exploitation of these ores. The bed that has been of primary importance is the one known as the Big Seam. This bed outcrops along the northwestern face of Red Mountain and slopes down and to the south and east from the outcrop with a dip of some 20 degrees. It has been found, however, that the dip of the seam flattens somewhat as the workings get farther away from the outcrop. The ore is a red hematite which is hard compared with the high-grade Mesabi ores, but not nearly as hard as the low-grade taconites of Minnesota. In general, the strata immediately above and below the Big Seam provide a good roof and floor for mining operations. Also, the thickness of the seam and the quantities of ore that are available in the area are great enough to permit large-scale operations for a long period of time.

The features of the ore bed that impose problems must be faced. In the first place, the location of the Big Seam with reference to the surface is such that recovery of ore must be by underground mining, except for relatively short distances back from the outcrop. The irregularities in structure often make special procedures necessary or impose serious limitations on the extent to which the ore can be recovered. Most serious of these are the difficulties that arise from folding and faulting of the strata and from the separation of the Big Seam into the Upper Bench and the Lower Bench by partings which vary from a few inches to several feet in thickness. The low iron content of the ore and the variations in lime and silica content are also important factors in determining where to mine and how much of the ore body to remove. As pointed out previously, these variations are much more

Table 40

Number of Employees and Production of Iron Ore Mines in Alabama

Fiscal Year (Oct. 1-Sept. 30) 1948-1949

Mine	Seam	County	Employees		Production (gross tons)
			Surface	Under-ground	
Red Hematite					
Edwards	Big	Jefferson	33	147	285,089
Spaulding	Big	Jefferson	97	76	334,931
Sloss Red ore	Big	Jefferson	66	300	354,285
Gadsden Red Ore	Shinbone	Etowah	8	48	7,280
Ishkooda	Big	Jefferson	61	907	1,921,007
Muscoda	Big	Jefferson	104	875	1,766.986
Wenonah	Big	Jefferson	110	1,270	2,076,206
Pyne	Big	Jefferson	95	465	1,068,119
Red ore	Big	Jefferson	48	52	77,714
Songo	Big	Jefferson	47	114	277,400
Brown Ore					
Arrington Mining Co.	Arrington	Cherokee	20		33,624
Erwin Mining Co.	Erwin	Cherokee	12		10,693
Shook & Fletcher	Tait's Gap	Blount	21		25,000
Shook & Fletcher	Adkins	Bibb	47		200,000
Shook & Fletcher	Auxford	Franklin	40		56,571
Shook & Fletcher	Warner	Franklin	40		153,457
Sloss-Sheffield	#14	Franklin	77		131,246
Sloss-Sheffield	La Grange	Colbert	65		7,474
Sloss-Sheffield	1 miscl. oper.)	Bibb			4,739
Sloss-Sheffield	1 miscl. oper.)	Blount			28,143
Sloss-Sheffield	4 miscl. oper.)	Calhoun			17,388
Sloss-Sheffield	6 miscl. oper.)	Cherokee			5,034
Sloss-Sheffield	1 miscl. oper.)	Cleburne			91,660
Sloss-Sheffield	2 miscl. oper.)	Franklin			3,689
Sloss-Sheffield	1 miscl. oper.)	St. Clair			2,931
Sloss-Sheffield	1 miscl. oper.)	Shelby			6,413
Sloss-Sheffield	2 miscl. oper.)	Talladega			36,655

Source: *Annual Statistical Report, 1948-49.* Alabama Department of Industrial Relations.

pronounced when comparisons are made between places along the seam from north to south than down the dip. The most desirable ore has a lime content sufficient to make it self-fluxing. On the other hand, much of the ore is high in silica. The costs of eliminating this element, combined with low iron content, have meant that, in many places, it has not been profitable to remove all of the available ore.

The methods used in the various underground red ore mines in the Birmingham district have many similar features.[1] With the exception of two shafts which have been sunk to the Big Seam on the east side of Red Mountain in Shades Valley, all the mines are developed by main passageways, or slopes, driven downward from the Jones (or Birmingham) Valley side of Red Mountain just below the crest. These slopes are on the dip in the ore or may be driven about 10 feet below the ore seam to allow for dumping ore into cars or skips that operate on tracks laid on the floor of the slope.

At intervals of 100 to 250 feet along the main slopes, secondary or branch passageways—commonly called drifts—are driven into the ore seam to the right and left from the slope. The distance between the drifts depends on the method of loading the ore in the working places. The drifts are so driven that they rise at a slight angle above the horizontal, thus allowing mine waters to drain back to the main slope.

The ore between drifts, or levels as they are called, is mined up the dip by breaking out

[1] For a description of mining methods in the Birmingham District, with illustrations and in nontechnical language, see *Steel Making at Birmingham*, pp. 5-12. More technical discussions of particular operations are given in the following: E. F. Burchard and Charles Butts, *Iron Ores, Fuels and Fluxes*, pp. 134-142; W. R. Crane, *Iron Ore (Hematite) Mining Practice in the Birmingham District, Alabama*; W. R. Crane, *Development, Mining, and Handling of Ore, Birmingham District, Alabama*; T. C. De Sollar, "Red Iron Mines of the Woodward Iron Company at Bessemer, Alabama," pp. 67-77; E. M. Hall and A. W. Beck, "Iron Mining in Muscoda Number 6;" N. E. Thompson, "Red Ore from Raimund," pp. 29-32.

the ore to form working areas, or stopes, which extend from the lower drift or level to the one next above. Pillars of ore are left on either side of the main slope to support the top and protect the main haulageway. Other pillars are left between stopes at regular intervals. The size of the pillars necessarily varies with the depth of the seam below the surface. These drifts and stopes continue to the boundaries of the property along the strike—the direction of the horizontal line in the bed of the seam. As the work advances, about 50 per cent of the ore is left in the pillars. The ore in these pillars is recovered only after the other ore in the area has been mined. The pillars are mined as the workers retreat from the area. The main slope pillars are left to protect the haulageway until the mines is to be abondoned, and then they are removed from the bottom of the slope retreating toward the surface.

Heavy steel rails are laid in the main slopes to provide for a main haulageway for the mine. Formerly, four or five cars holding about two tons each were coupled together and pulled up the slope by means of a rope and hoisting engine to a rotary dump where the ore was quickly dumped without detaching the cars. This procedure has been supplanted, except at one slope, by the use of skips of 10 to 12 ton capacity. Rails are also laid in the drifts or secondary passageways to provide for hauling ore from the working space to the main haulageways. In this case, electric locomotives are used to pull trains of two or more cars, and the ore is dumped into pockets from which it can be loaded, usually by gravity, into the skips of the main slope.

The main haulage slopes could be continued indefinitely down the dip were it not for the fact that the dip gradually flattens as the bottom of the basin is approached. When this occurs, the skips will not go farther by gravity, and it is necessary to use gathering electric motors to haul the ore from the drifts and stopes to the bottom of the incline and dump it into pockets for loading the skips on the main haulageway.

Faults or breaks in the strata are frequently nearly parallel with the strike of the seam and cause varying degrees of displacement of the ore seam. If the ore seam drops down on the lower side of the fault, it is often possible to continue the main haulage for a short distance by means of a rock slope until the seam is encountered again and development can proceed as before. Where the ore seam on the down dip side of the fault has been raised by the earth movement above the working seam, an underground auxiliary hoisting system is installed. This can consist of a haulage slope with drifts and stopes on the part of the seam below the fault. A separate skip is installed on this slope, dumping the ore into a pocket placed above the lower end of the main slope. The ore can then be drawn from the pocket

into the skip on the main haulage slope and conveyed to the surface. In addition to the problem of establishing connections between haulageways, the fault may have created a serious water hazard or may have shattered the strata to such an extent that special care must be taken to make the passageway through the fault safe. Such conditions tend to add to mining costs.

The two exceptions to the use of slopes as the means of approach to the ore body are the Shannon shaft of the Republic Steel Corporation and the Pyne shaft of the Woodward Iron Company. In the case of the former, the shaft is at a 60 degree angle with the horizontal and has never been considered as a satisfactory

CHART 17

DIAGRAM ILLUSTRATING LAYOUT OF HAULAGEWAYS (SLOPES AND DRIFTS)
AND WORKING SPACES (STOPES) OF AN UNDERGROUND SLOPE MINE

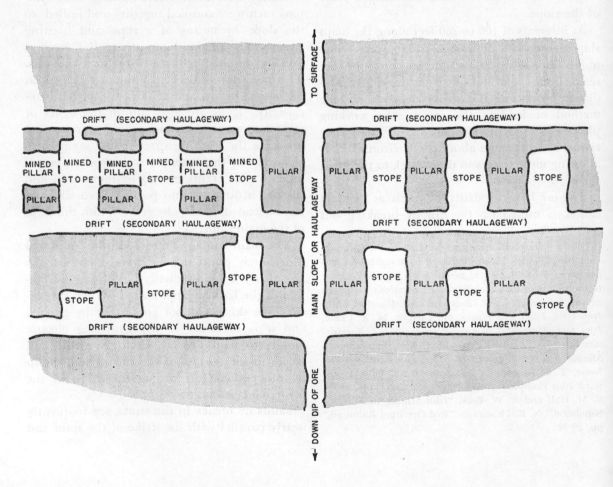

mine. The latter is a vertical shaft and has been very successful. The mine layout is very similar to a coal mine, with the ore being hoisted to the surface by counterbalanced hoisting equipment. The fact that this mine is considered as one of the lowest-cost operations in the district may raise the question as to whether the vertical shaft approach may not have advantages as the workings progress farther down the dip of the seam and long hauls up the inclined slope become necessary.

In driving the stope, or working place, upward from the drift, the miners drill holes in the ore face with pneumatic drills, which fre-

quently are mounted on tripods. The holes are drilled in such a way that the first holes will leave free faces for the second and succeeding rounds of shots to provide the most effective breaking of ore for the amount of explosive used. The holes are loaded with a special type of explosive containing a high percentage of nitroglycerine which gives off relatively small quantities of offensive gases. The charges are shot by delayed action electric detonators to give the proper rotation of firing for repetitive charges.

In the early days of red ore mining, the ore was loaded into the cars by hand, but for many

CHART 18

HYPOTHETICAL PROFILE SHOWING ADJUSTMENT OF HAULAGE SLOPE THROUGH FAULTED SECTION

VERTICAL SCALE EXAGGERATED

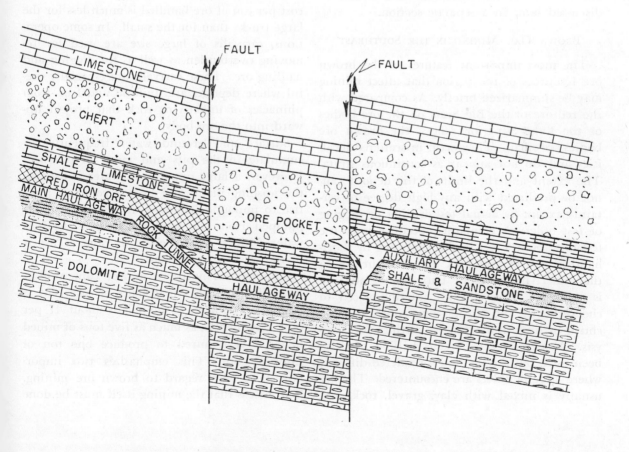

years the cars have been loaded mechanically. At present, over 90 per cent of the red ore is loaded by mechanical loaders. The most popular type is the scraper loader. Manufacturers, however, are busy with the production and selling of other types of loaders.

As suggested, a variety of servicing operations are necessary to maintain proper working conditions. For ventilation, airways are driven downward from the surface and parallel to the main slope to intersect the drifts near the limits of the workings. Ventilator fans have been utilized to force in air and provide the conditions required for men working underground. Also, the drifts and stopes have to be planned to provide drainage, and, at proper locations, powerful pumps are installed to remove the water from the mine.

The final stages of the work at a mine involve the crushing and storage of the ore until such time as it is needed for transportation to the blast furnaces. If beneficiation is undertaken, it is done in connection with these operations. The beneficiation problem, however, is one of such great importance that it will be discussed later in a separate section.

BROWN ORE MINING IN THE SOUTHEAST

The most important features of the brown ore resources of the region that affect mining may be summarized briefly. As compared with the red ore of the Big Seam or the ore bodies of the Lake Superior ranges, the brown ore bodies are small. They occur in scattered localities and do not appear as continuous strata. The extent and the limits of the deposit cannot be predicted with any high degree of certainty except by actual test drilling or digging of test holes. A common procedure is to use test pits about 3 feet in diameter, dug by short-handled shovel and pick from the surface to the underlying rock, or until high grade ore is assured. These pits are usually placed to checkerboard the area. Some operators use churn drilling and save the cuttings for analysis. A special type of core drilling has also been used, but the method is rendered difficult where large boulders are encountered. The ore usually is mixed with clay, gravel, rock, and

other foreign materials. As a result, brown ore mining operations tend to be relatively small in scale.

After the operator has satisfied himself that sufficient ore is available, he moves in his mining equipment, which usually consists of a power shovel, trucks, and some device for washing the ore. The power shovel is usually mounted on caterpillar treads, which make it more flexible since it can move itself from place to place as needed. A shovel with a drag-line mounted scraper bucket is more flexible than the dipper equipped unit.

After the overburden has been removed from a sufficient area, the operator proceeds to use the power shovel to dig the ore itself and place it in trucks to be hauled to the washer. There are usually areas of ore that are left in the pit by working around them, because the ore is so low in grade that it overloads the washer and costs more to handle than the value of the product recovered. In recent years, there has been a tendency to use larger trucks, and many units of 15-ton capacity or more are in use. It has been found that the maintenance cost per ton of ore handled is much less for the large trucks than for the small. In some operations, carryalls of large size are used for removing overburden as well as for digging and hauling ore. These carryalls are especially useful where deposits are uniform and free from pinnacles of underlying rock that project upward into the ore body.

Surface and ground water frequently accumulate in the pits and must be pumped. However, a large quantity of water is used in the washing plant, and so it is common practice to impound behind a dirt dam the water pumped from the working area, as well as water drained from the washer, and to use it in the washing operations.

Shipping ore must have an iron content of at least 40 per cent, and usually 50 per cent is desired. The average analysis is about 47 per cent. Frequently, as much as five tons of mined material is required to produce one ton of shipping ore. This emphasizes two important facts with regard to brown ore mining. The first is that the mining itself must be done cheaply, and the second is that the operations which remove the undesirable portions, namely the washing or beneficiating of the ore, are very important.

A number of different methods are in use, but in general the mined materials must be crushed or broken up into pieces small enough to permit efficient separation and then passed through a washer, which by the difference in the weights of the constituents and the action of water separates the iron bearing materials.[2]

Trends in Employment and Production In Iron Ore Mining

The methods used in mining the red and the brown ores in the Southeast having been

[2] For a more detailed description of brown ore mining, see Charles Morgan, *Prospecting, Mining and Washing the Brown Ores of Alabama.*

described briefly, attention will next be given to an analysis of the trends in iron ore mining in the United States and Alabama as reflected in the data on tons produced, number of persons employed, and tons produced per man-hour, as presented in Table 41. This analysis brings us immediately to grips with some of the most important of the problems of ore mining, since it makes necessary an examination of the more important developments in mining methods and technology and their effects. The differences that appear when Alabama is compared with the United States require explanation, and an understanding of the tendencies in the nation and the state provides the basis for conclusions concerning the prospects for the future.

To bring out some of the outstanding facts presented in Table 41, an abbreviated statement is presented at the bottom of this page.

	United States	Alabama	
	Quantity	Quantity	Per Cent of U.S.
Peak of World War I (1917)			
Number of employees in iron mines	60,594	8,887	14.7
Man-hours	153,585,171	25,076,020	16.3
Tons of merchandisable ore	75,288,851	7,037,707	9.3
Tons per man-hour	0.490	.281	57.3
Peak of World War II (1943)			
Number of employees in iron mines	33,280	7,308	22.0
Man-hours	76,627,434	16,479,125	21.5
Tons of merchandisable ore	100,595,322	8,478,736	8.4
Tons per man-hour	1.313	0.515	39.2
Change between the two peak years (1917 to 1943)			
In number of employees (per cent)	− 45.08	−17.77	
In man-hours (per cent)	− 50.11	−34.28	
In tons of merchandisable ore (per cent)	+ 33.6	+20.48	
In tons of ore mined per man-hour (per cent)	+167.96	+83.27	
Average period from 1915-1924			
Number of employees	46,724	7,132	15.3
Man-hours	115,245,360	20,128,836	17.5
Tons of merchandisable ore	60,444,954	5,766,410	9.5
Tons per man-hour	0.531	0.297	55.9
Average period from 1936-1945			
Number of employees (9 years)	27,100	5.516	20.4
Man-hours	54,548,989	11,907,709	21.8
Tons of merchandisable ore	75,635,552	6,615,963	8.7
Tons per man-hour	1.363	0.611	44.8
Change (per cent) between the averages of 1915-24 and 1936-45			
In number of employees (per cent)	42.0	− 22.7	
In man-hours (per cent)	− 52.6	− 40.8	
In tons of merchandisable ore (per cent)	+ 25.1	+ 14.7	
In tons per man-hour (per cent)	+156.7	+105.7	

Table 41

Production of Merchantable Ore and Average Number of Men Employed, United States and Alabama, 1880-1945

Year	United States Merchantable Ore Gross Tons	United States Merchantable Ore Per Cent Iron Content	United States Employment Average No. of Men Employed	United States Employment Total Man Hours	Alabama Merchantable Ore Gross Tons	Alabama Merchantable Ore Per Cent Iron Content	Alabama Employment Average No. of Men Employed	Alabama Employment Total Man-Hours	Merchantable Ore United States Per Man Per Shift Gross Tons	Merchantable Ore United States Per Man-Hour Gross Tons	Merchantable Ore Alabama Per Man Per Shift Gross Tons	Merchantable Ore Alabama Per Man-Hour Gross Tons
1880	7,120,362	51.23	35,000	**	171,139	50.68	750	**	0.882	**	1,316	**
1889	14,518,041	51.27	36,341	**	1,570,319	**	3,019	**	1.613	**	2,187	**
1902	35,554,135	**	44,800	**	3,574,474	**	**	**	3.052	**	2,450	**
1915	55,526,490	**	43,385	105,528,377	5,309,354	**	5,074	13,651,011	4.702	0.526	3,889	0.389
1916	75,167,672	**	57,049	140,753,166	6,747,901	**	7,253	21,524,718	4.807	.534	3,135	.313
1917	75,288,851	**	60,594	153,585,171	7,037,707	**	8,887	25,076,020	4.437	.490	2,807	.281
1918	69,658,278	**	55,674	148,605,632	5,754,624	**	7,999	25,605,998	4.273	.469	2,247	.225
1919	60,965,418	**	51,780	131,067,892	5,033,035	**	8,348	25,097,753	4.211	.465	2,013	.201
1920	67,604,465	**	50,590	133,452,211	5,894,011	**	7,257	21,860,954	4.650	.507	2,696	.270
1921	29,490,978	**	32,348	61,146,846	2,876,141	**	4,864	8,471,135	4.369	.482	3,395	.340
1922	47,128,527	**	35,758	79,438,561	5,234,568	**	6,390	16,511,214	5.263	.593	3,120	.317
1923	69,351,442	50.42	41,294	107,551,244	6,783,146	37.23	7,710	23,303,607	5.878	.645	2,996	.291
1924	54,267,419	49.91	38,765	91,324,498	6,993,613	36.95	7,534	20,185,952	5.319	.594	3,460	.346
1925	61,907,997	50.22	35,757	86,340,684	7,093,250	37.10	7,155	21,115,364	6.405	.717	3,359	.336
1926	67,623,000	50.43	34,399	84,225,524	6,847,789	37.27	6,460	19,340,090	7.197	.803	3,686	.354
1927	61,741,100	50.02	34,755	82,004,761	6,445,464	37.00	6,172	17,547,854	6.727	.753	3,820	.367
1928	62,197,088	50.08	30,238	71,403,631	6,307,844	37.37	5,979	15,822,084	7.766	.871	4,068	.399
1929	73,027,720	50.17	30,763	77,111,086	6,453,075	37.47	5,498	14,595,242	8.454	.947	4,423	.442
1930	58,408,664	50.28	30,975	71,620,115	5,738,478	37.48	5,139	12,876,652	7.267	.816	4,345	.446
1931	31,131,502	50.19	22,867	40,928,283	3,615,144	37.23	3,672	6,926,226	6.773	.761	5,002	.522
1932	9,846,916	50.25	12,649	16,427,009	1,374,534	37.37	2,882	2,960,020	5.387	.599	4,506	.464
1933	17,553,188	50.01	15,125	17,931,489	2,133,457	37.46	2,940	4,485,588	8.274	.979	4,232	.476
1934	24,587,616	50.37	16,513	25,478,440	2,343,819	37.61	2,927	4,638,936	7.717	.965	4,042	.505
1935	30,540,252	50.30	14,987	26,281,693	3,277,535	36.63	3,264	5,538,167	9.317	1.162	4,743	.592
1936	48,788,745	50.59	20,306	37,246,583	4,179,967	37.29	4,063	7,028,402	10.566	1.310	4,834	.595
1937	72,093,548	50.50	25,945	51,416,193	6,307,581	36.75	4,906	10,024,673	11.270	1.402	5,076	.629
1938	28,447,282	49.55	.....	30,388,000	4,303,329	36.36	.....	11,137,408	.....	.936	.....	.657
1939	51,731,730	50.28	21,859	39,055,362	5,960,507	36.42	4,902	9,094,637	10.642	1.325	5,325	.655
1940	73,695,899	50.64	25,128	48,731,997	7,316,127	36.43	5,593	11,137,408	12.155	1.512	5,343	.657
1941	92,409,579	50.93	28,587	60,369,336	7,884,851	37.15	6,159	13,208,120	12.222	1.531	4,881	.597
1942	104,883,184	51.00	32,774	75,216,291	8,850,534	36.77	6,867	17,268,918	11.468	1.394	4,531	.513
1943	100,595,322	51.00	33,280	76,627,434*	8,478,736*	36.61	7,308*	16,479,125*	10.550	1.313	4,193*	.515*
1944	94,654,177	50.69	29,244	65,639,530	6,829,437	36.18	5,191	12,482,059	11.579	1.442	4,420	.547
1945	89,056,050	51.27	26,777	60,799,166	6,048,562	35.87	4,654	11,216,339	11.778	1.465	4,368	.539

Source: 1880-1938—N. Yaworski and others, Technology, Employment, and Output per Man in Iron Mining, pp. 206, 212; 1938-1945—Minerals Yearbook, 1938-45.

For the United States as a whole, there has been a very large decrease in the number of persons employed in iron ore mining and a still larger per cent of decrease in the number of man-hours. This is true whether measured from the peak war years or between the annual averages for the ten-year periods from 1915 to 1924 and 1936 to 1945. In contrast, there was a substantial increase in the number of tons of merchandisable ore produced. The result of these changes was a large increase in the tons of ore produced per man-hour. In the case of Alabama, the changes have been in the same direction as in the nation, but the percentages of change were smaller: the number of employees and man-hours did not decline as greatly, and production in terms of tons of ore did not increase as much. As a result, the productivity of mining as measured in terms of tons per man-hour did not improve as much in Alabama as in the nation as a whole. Coupled to this situation is the fact that the production per man-hour is relatively low in Alabama as compared with the national ratio: 0.297 tons per man-hour in Alabama for the average of 1915-1924 as compared with 0.531 tons for the United States; for the period 1936-1945 the figures are 0.611 tons and 1.363 tons respectively. These data point to one of the serious problems of ore mining in Alabama—namely, the low productivity in terms of labor. The fact that the southern mines have been losing in relative position rather than gaining in this respect makes the problem even more serious. A further study of this situation involves an analysis of the conditions under which mining is carried on and of the methods used.

As pointed out above, the two basic types of mining are open-pit and underground. The differences in the labor requirements for recovering iron ore by these two methods are of basic importance in a study of mining costs. Generally speaking, the production in tons per man-hour is much higher in open-pit than in underground mining and the improvement over the years has been much more rapid. Ore recovered by underground methods forms a relatively large proportion of the Alabama production—88 per cent of usable ore. In contrast, the Lake Superior area, from which the northern ore is largely taken, has been worked principally by open-pit methods, as 85 per cent of the Lake ore is produced from open pits.

Table 42

Tons of Ore Produced per Man-Hour by Open Pit and Underground Mines in the United States and Alabama, 1915-1938

| | Tons Produced Per Man Hour | | | |
| | United States | | Alabama | |
Year	Open-Pit Mines	Under-ground Mines	Open-Pit Mines	Under-ground Mines
1915	1.121	0.389	0.247	0.442
1916	1.104	0.369	0.228	0.339
1917	0.912	0.347	0.203	0.302
1918	0.832	0.321	0.154	0.242
1919	1.062	0.313	0.162	0.208
1920	0.966	0.351	0.177	0.291
1921	0.762	0.364	0.259	0.349
1922	1.087	0.395	0.181	0.352
1923	1.171	0.408	0.208	0.308
1924	0.989	0.438	0.202	0.371
1925	1.393	0.493	0.214	0.356
1926	1.784	0.510	0.204	0.383
1927	1.591	0.493	0.274	0.380
1928	1.815	0.548	0.272	0.421
1929	1.837	0.589	0.304	0.465
1930	1.496	0.563	0.324	0.466
1931	1.212	0.583	0.315	0.548
1932	0.931	0.503	0.364	0.468
1933	1.993	0.508	0.401	0.485
1934	1.791	0.598	0.322	0.550
1935	2.470	0.663	0.238	0.674
1936	2.665	0.701	0.304	0.672
1937	3.005	0.692	0.386	0.676
1938	1.795	0.642	....	....

Source: N. Yaworski, *Technology, Employment and Output per Man in Iron Mining.*

The data presented in Table 42 provide a comparison of the productivity per man-hour in Alabama with the nation as a whole for both open-pit and underground iron ore mining. For both classes, the Alabama productivity is much lower than the national averages. Also, the Alabama figures depart from the situation which holds for the nation with reference to the comparative productivity of the two methods of mining. Generally, open-pit mining is represented by lower figures for tons per man-hour than those for underground mining, but in Alabama the reverse is true. This arises from the fact that the open-pit mines in Alabama have to do with brown ore, are scattered and relatively small, and have not been able to use large-scale methods. Furthermore, the character of the ore requires the handling of large quantities of extraneous materials to get the usable ore.

While the Alabama figures in Table 42 demonstrate that open-pit operations are not always more efficient than underground mining, a brief consideration of the fundamental mining operations suggests that the former method has many points of advantage. Reaching the ore is more direct, transportation takes place under more favorable conditions, and many of the facilitating activities that are required for underground mining are either easier to provide or are unnecessary. On the other hand, large-scale production methods are important in mining, and it is entirely possible for a large-scale underground mine to operate more efficiently than a small open-pit mine.

The tendency for the productivity figures to increase is very evident, both for the United States and for Alabama. As a result, it is important to examine the reasons for the improvements. Yaworski and Kiessling[3] have listed factors which are summarized below:

1. *The growth of open-pit mining in the United States*. The percentage of the total output produced by open-pit mines increased from 40 per cent in 1915 to 66 per cent in 1937, despite the gradual depletion of the most accessible ore deposits.

2. *The concentration of production in larger mines*. This has permitted labor economies. In 1880, almost two-thirds of the total production came from mines with an annual output of less than 50,000 tons each. Now the production from mines of this size is

negligible. Whereas in 1880 not a single mine produced more than 1,000,000 tons, from 40 to 50 per cent of the total output in the immediate pre-war years was from mines of this size. Furthermore, the average output per worker is much higher at the large mines than at the small ones.

3. *Technological advances which have reduced labor requirements*. Important factors are:

(a) The progressive substitution of mechanical power for manual labor.

(b) Constant improvements in equipment whereby machine output is increased while the labor necessary to maintain and operate it is reduced.

(c) The more skillful use of equipment and a more systematic ordering of work.

In the case of open-pit operations, the spectacular improvements in power shovels and the development of large motor-driven trucks have been important. In underground mining, there have been important improvements in methods of drilling and blasting, underground transportation, and underground loading.

The improvements in equipment and methods have affected each of the essential classes of operations. Often the developments have been gradual, and the continuous character of the changes and their adoption in practice has been an outstanding feature of mining technology. As a result, the output of iron mines has been increased despite the use of smaller numbers of employees and the depletion of the more accessible ore deposits.

Barger and Schurr[4] have pointed out a significant characteristic of the application of the newer techniques. In the earlier mining methods, dependence was placed primarily upon the ability of the individual miner to reach, break the mineral, and separate it from the waste. The emphasis was on quality of the product and the skill of the miner. The introduction of the newer and larger-scale methods led to what is spoken of as nonselective mining, and had two results: a decline in the grade of

3 N. Yaworski [and others], *Technology, Employment, and Output per Man in Iron Mining*.

4 Harold Barger and S. H. Schurr, *The Mining Industries, 1899-1939*, p. 452.

ore mined and the elaboration of techniques of ore concentration. In other words, mining of ore and separation of waste materials tended to become separate operations. The emphasis changed from the skill of the miner to the skill of the engineer because, in non-selective mining, costs depend largely on how carefully the engineer has determined the geological structure and chemical nature of the ore deposits prior to working out suitable techniques and how well he has designed mining and beneficiating operations on the basis of his geological data.

Trend Toward Beneficiation of Iron Ore

An important factor in the development of iron ore mining technology is the one suggested above, namely, the increased use of beneficiation or methods of improving the grade of mined ore by mechanical or chemical means before delivery to blast furnaces. Table 43 shows that there has been a persistent tendency for beneficiated ores to account for an increasing percentage of the total quantity of iron ore shipped from mines during the period from 1914 to 1946.

Beneficiation of Iron Ore in the Southeast

The beneficiating[5] of iron ore is the use of any processing method for the purpose of improving the physical structure or the chemical composition of the ore. The physical structure may be improved by breaking coarse lumps into smaller particles or by agglomerating fine particles into coarser lumps. When the chemical composition is improved, the term "concentration" is used to describe the process. The ore is separated into two or more parts, of which one, at least, is of greater value per ton than the original ore, and the more valuable parts are saved while the others are rejected.

Beneficiation is accomplished by any one, or a combination, of several methods. In cases where several methods are used, the name used to described the process is the name of

[5] Yaworski, p. 279.

the most important of the various processes used by the plant. The more important methods are summarized below:

1. *Crushing and sizing.* This involves breaking the ore to convenient maximum size, followed by screening the crushed ore to eliminate fine dust, which may be agglomerated, and sorting the screened ore into desirable sizes for smelting operations.

Table 43

Beneficiation of Iron Ore Shipped from Mines in the United States 1914-1946 (excludes ore containing 5 per cent or more manganese)

Year	Beneficiated (1,000 long tons)	Total (1,000 long tons)	Percentage Beneficiated of Total
1914	4,130	39,714	10.4
1915	5,581	55,493	10.1
1916	8,105	77,871	10.4
1917	8,167	75,573	10.8
1918	7,882	72,021	10.9
1919	7,356	56,373	13.0
1920	8,515	69,281	12.3
1921	3,728	26,653	14.0
1922	6,623	50,613	13.1
1923	10,687	69,811	15.3
1924	7,093	52,083	13.6
1925	8,736	63,925	13.7
1926	8,372	69,293	12.1
1927	8,115	61,232	13.3
1928	8,621	63,433	13.6
1929	9,424	75,603	12.5
1930	8,974	55,201	16.3
1931	4,676	28,516	16.4
1932	407	5,331	7.6
1933	3,556	24,624	14.4
1934	4,146	25,793	16.1
1935	6,067	33,426	18.1
1936	9,659	51,466	18.8
1937	12,350	72,348	17.1
1938	4,836	26,431	18.3
1939	9,426	54,827	17.2
1940	12,926	75,198	17.2
1941	19,376	93,054	20.8
1942	23,105*	105,314*	21.9
1943	20,118*	98,817*	20.4
1944	20,303*	94,545*	21.5
1945	19,587*	87,581*	22.4
1946	15,589	69,494	22.4

*Includes ores for paint.

Source: 1914-1940——Barger and Schurr, *The Mining Industry, 1899-1939.* And *Minerals Yearbook, 1940-1946*

2. *Washing, spraying and logwashing.* The purpose is to remove fine sand and clay particles from coarse lumps of good ore. This method is useful, particularly on brown ores where the iron material often occurs in hard lumps or nodules.

3. *Jigging.* This method makes use of a pulsating water bath wherein heavier mineral particles sink, and finer, lighter clays and sand float off the top.

4. *Classifying.* This is a hydraulic method wherein finer and lighter particles are overflowed and large heavy particles sink.

5. *Heavy media or sink float.* Immersion of the ore in a selected liquid medium whose specific gravity is greater than that of clay and sand causing these to float. As the specific gravity of the medium is less than that of the ore minerals, the minerals sink.

6. *Froth flotation.* The addition of chemical reagents to finely ground ore pulps, wherein the reagent "wets" the ore mineral selectively, causing it to float to the surface, where it is held in a frothy scum produced by the use of air and frothing agents. The gangue minerals are not floated.

7. *Magnetic concentration.* In cases where the ore particles are naturally magnetic, or may be rendered so by roasting, effective concentration may be accomplished by passing the crushed ore, either wet or dry, over magnetic separators.

The methods described under items 2, 3, 4, 5, and 6 have all been developed for non-ferrous ores such as gold, silver, lead, copper, zinc, and nickel. Many of these ores occur in nature as sulphides of high specific gravity (usually over 6) which makes them more amenable to gravity separation than iron ores, whose gravity is about 6. The sulphide minerals are also specifically susceptible to wetting by flotation reagents, whereas oxide minerals, typical of iron ores, are not. Except for the flotation process, none of the gravity separation methods are satisfactory on finely ground ores, under 150 mesh, since the ore particles in this size-range tend to become colloidal and remain suspended indefinitely.

The most immediate result of concentration is that it reduces the bulk of the mineral which must be moved to the blast furnace and increases the iron content of a given number of tons of ore charged into a furnace. In cases where ore must be transported long distances, the saving in freight is important. Perhaps even more important is the improvement in smelting qualities. If economical means can be found to remove, to a substantial degree, materials which otherwise would be eliminated by the use of large amounts of coke and air blast, savings in smelting costs result. The importance of crushing large lumps, particularly of hard, dense ore, to small size and of agglomerating very fine ore into lumps by sintering arises from the fact that the reducibility of an ore depends upon its porosity and the size of the lump, the ores that are both porous and in small pieces being reduced the quickest.

Camp and Francis cite as an example of the effect of improved ore preparation the experience of the Ironton Furnace of Columbia Steel.

> With ore charged as mined, the output of this furnace was between 275 and 350 tons of iron per day, with a coke consumption of 2600 to 2800 pounds per ton of iron; in 1936, the rated capacity was 600 tons per day, with a coke consumption of 1700 to 1800 pounds per ton.[6]

These changes they attribute to a new system of preparing and handling ore which, from the description, seems similar to that now used in the blanding and sintering plant of the Tennessee Coal, Iron and Railroad Company. This company, by crushing and creening red ore into sizes of ¾″ to 2″, ⅜″ to ¾″ and sintering the fine material under ⅜″ size, was able to increase the output of its blast furnaces at least 15 per cent.

Beneficiation is not a new problem nor is it particularly a southern problem. The use of the brown ores has always depended upon some means of eliminating either by hand pick-

6 J. M. Camp and C. B. Francis, *The Making, Shaping and Treating of Steel,* p. 279.

ing or washing a very large part of the material dug out of the pits. The discovery of the high-grade Lake Superior ores almost led to the abandonment of the low grade ores of the eastern states. Then work was started on concentration. Magnetic concentration was found to be effective in cases where the ores were magnetites, and recent years have seen a very large increase in the mining and use of ores from the northeastern states, particularly from the Adirondack region. While a large part of the most accessible Mesabi ore is so high in iron content that it is considered a direct shipping ore, there are portions of the deposit where concentration is necessary in order to produce an ore valuable enough to stand shipping. As a result, washing and jigging have been used in Minnesota for a number of years.

As indicated, the brown ore mined in the Southeast has been washed to produce a merchantable product, and little more needs to be said in that connection. Beneficiation of the red ores of the Birmingham district has been receiving a considerable amount of attention for the last thirty years. Among the early projects that were undertaken, under the cooperative program of the Southern Mine Experiment Station of the United States Bureau of Mines and the School of Mines at the University of Alabama, was a study of concentration of iron ores. This work has been continued and various methods have been tested. The results of this experimental work have been presented in a series of reports.[7] One of the metallurgists associated with the early experiments, Oscar Lee, later became associated with the Republic Steel Corporation and has had a leading part in the efforts of that company to perfect methods for concentrating the ore produced by its Spaulding Mine.

In addition to the experimental work, at least two large-scale and very significant attempts have been made to beneficiate the red ores of Alabama. One of these consists of the iron ore conditioning plant of the Tennessee Coal, Iron and Railroad Company. The other is the concentration plant of the Republic Steel Corporation located at the company's Spaulding Mine. These two plants will be described briefly.

Ore Conditioning Plant, Tennessee Coal, Iron and Railroad Company

In order to furnish a uniform grade of iron ore and to put the ore in a condition that would facilitate its use in the blast furnaces, the Tennessee Coal, Iron and Railroad Company[8] built at Wenonah, during 1939 and 1940, an ore conditioning plant to treat all the iron ore produced by the company's mines on Red Mountain. The plant was designed to crush, screen, and blend the raw ores, and to sinter the fine ore resulting from the crushing and screening processes together with accumulated flue dust.

The raw ore from the mines is crushed so that approximately 75 per cent is less than one inch. The screening process separates the crushed ore into three sizes: plus $3/4$ inches; minus $3/4$ inches but plus $3/8$ inches; and fine, below $3/8$ inches in size. The coarse and medium sizes are moved by conveyors to storage bins or silos and are ready for the blending process. The fine ore goes to the storage bins of the sintering plant. Flue dust and coke breeze are brought from the blast furnace and coke oven plants in drop-bottom cars, and carefully blended mixtures of fine ore, flue dust, and coke breeze are prepared for the sintering plant. The product of the process consists of lumps of porous material which become raw material for the blast furnaces.

Care is taken to keep the ore produced by each mine in separate bins or silos and also to keep each day's product separate. The purpose of this is to enable the practice man who controls the mixtures to know exactly the quan-

[7]For discussions of beneficiation of Alabama red iron ores, see B. W. Gandrud [and others], *Classifications and Tabling of Alabama Red Iron Ores;* F. D. DeVaney [and others], *Gravity Concentration of Alabama Oolitic Iron Ores;* Oscar Lee, "Birmingham's Future Depends on Concentration," pp. 104-106.

[8] A. A. Nelson and Roy Yingling, "Remote Control, a Feature of Ore Conditioning Plant," pp. 74-79.

tities and qualities of the ores that he has available. The object of the plant is to deliver materials as nearly uniform as possible to the blast furnaces, in place of scrambled quantities of ores (from seven or eight mines) differing in quality and varying in size from 3½ inches to dust. This is accomplished by blending the crushed and classified ores under careful control.

The plant is highly mechanized, with belt conveyors, automatic weighing devices, discharge chutes, automatic sampling equipment, and many other devices which, to a large degree, are electrically manipulated from control centers.

CONCENTRATION PLANT, REPUBLIC STEEL CORPORATION

In 1940, the Republic Steel Corporation completed a 1,000-ton pilot plant at its Spaulding Mine, and after two years operation this plant was expanded as a Defense Plant Corporation project. The plant[9] was designed to produce a daily out-put of 1,800 tons of concentrate and was the first large-scale iron ore concentration plant in the Southeast.

Birmingham red ore presents difficult problems for concentration. It has a specific gravity of 3.6, and the iron oxide is amorphous. The lime, alumina, and some of the silica are very finely disseminated through the mass, and coat and bind the silica grains. Normal grinding methods are not applicable because the ore slimes easily, and every precaution is necessary to minimize slimes. The objective of most concentrating plants is to remove as much gangue material as possible in order to secure the maximum improvement in grade. However, with Birmingham red ores, raising the iron content of the concentrates above a certain point is accomplished at the expense of lime. Lime is essential to fluxing silica and alumina in the blast furnace and is already present in the ore. There is no object in grinding finer to increase iron content in the concentrate if this means the removal of lime which must

later be added at the blast furnace. Then, too, the lime present in the sintered concentrate is more efficient as a flux than lime added in the blast furnace in lump form. Therefore, grinding at the Spaulding Plant is limited to minus eight mesh.

The next step is to separate the particles of the ore that are richer in iron from the poorer. This is accomplished by a gravity method. After crushing, the ore is passed over vibrating screens with eight mesh square openings. The undersize product goes to bowl classifiers and the oversize to rod mills. The latter are low-level mills, using light rod loads, and are operated in closed circuits with screens. The purpose is to rescruff or break up the ore particles without the pulverizing effects of grinding. The ore that goes directly to the bowl classifiers is divided into two parts. The overflow is a 150 mesh slime product which is delivered to the thickeners. The remainder, the rake product, is sent to eight cell hydraulic classifiers where it is classified into eight spigot products and delivered to concentrating tables. The overflow of the classifiers, like that of the bowls, goes directly to the thickeners. The materials that pass over the concentrating tables, after being dewatered, are filtered on a small drum type filter. The slimes from the bowls and classifiers, after thickening, are filtered on American-type disk filters.

The final step takes the filter cake to the sintering plant. A Dwight-Lloyd sintering plant was built for the Defense Plant Corporation and adjoins the concentrator. It is a complete plant. The fuel originally used was oil, but facilities to use natural gas have been installed. The sinter made from the table concentrate has a good physical structure and will average over 51 per cent iron, 7.5 per cent lime, and 13 per cent silica. The increase in iron concentrate to sinter is appreciable and is due, of course, to the removal of oxygen, CO_2, and combined water in the process.

Untreated siliceous red ore varies from 32 to 36 per cent iron, 20 to 30 per cent silica, 3 to 4 per cent alumina, 7 to 12 per cent lime (CaO), and 0.25 to 0.58 per cent phosphorus. There

9 Oscar Lee, "Birmingham's Future Depends on Concentration," pp. 104-106.

is also a small quantity of manganese in the ore—normally about 0.2 per cent. The product of the concentrating plant (before sintering) ranges from 50 to 63 per cent of the raw ore delivered to the plant. The concentrate carries 46 to 48 per cent iron, 6 to 8 per cent lime, 9 to 11 per cent silica, and 3 to 3.8 per cent alumnia. The table concentrate makes up 60 per cent of the total mill product and the remainder is slime. Although the table product is higher in iron content than the slime, this is compensated by the higher lime content of the slime.

PROSPECTS OF FURTHER DEVELOPMENTS OF BENEFICIATION IN THE SOUTHEAST

The Tennessee Coal, Iron and Railroad Company is engaged in a careful investigation of the problems of beneficiation and handling of southern ores and the discussion of prospects of further developments may well be introduced by summarizing the report of Mr. E. H. Rose, research engineer of that company. Mr. Rose points out that at least 25 years of research have gone into the effort to find an economically sound process of concentrating the southern red ore and that all but one of the processes that have been attempted have been abandoned.[10] He discusses the technical problems which have caused so much trouble and has a number of suggestions concerning possible developments in the future.

The reason for the lack of success lies in the distribution of the iron and gangue-bearing minerals in the Red Mountain ore. Rose describes the constituents as follows: "The iron mineral in both ores is a soft earthy hematite, which tends to become 'paint' upon the slightest provocation, especially when wet. In the sandstone, the individual silica grains are imbedded in the continuous matrix of non-crystalline, clay-containing hematite."[11] A separation by grinding requires a rubbing or

scuffing action to rub off the iron bearing cement from the silica grains, and no grinding mill is available to do this efficiently. Moreover, the iron mineral so separated is usually smaller than 150 mesh. If the grinding is done dry, a difficult dust-collecting problem arises, while if wet grinding is employed, most of the iron mineral is obtained as slime. This imposes a tremendous dewatering problem for any plant handling thousands of tons of ore per day. A production of 6 million tons of red ore per year will require concentrating plants capable of producing 25,000 tons of concentrate per day.

Rose speculates in his paper regarding the feasibility and cost of subjecting crushed red ores to a magnetic roast and then separating the magnetized iron mineral from the non-magnetic mineral by passing the treated ores over magnetic separators. This is the most efficient and cheapest method of concentrating iron ores and is used with great success wherever the iron occurs in nature as the magnetic oxide Fe_3O_4. A whole industry has been built on this process in New York state, and some 3 million tons of sinter containing over 60 per cent iron are now being produced there from mines which have stood idle since Colonial days.

The adaption of magnetic concentration to the Birmingham ores will involve several steps, all of which add to the cost of the concentrate. These include:

Fine grinding (dry)

Magnetic roast at 1100°F in reducing gas to convert hematite to magnetite

Wet grinding and magnetic separation of magnetite from gangue

Sintering or some agglomeration method of making a suitable blast furnace feed of the concentrate.

Both the magnetic roast and the sintering operation require fuel and special furnace equipment. Laboratory studies of the Bureau of Mines and several ore companies have shown that a concentrate containing up to 55 per cent iron can be made by this process with an iron recovery of 92 per cent of the iron in the low

[10] The Spaulding mill, which was described above, is in operation, but Mr. Rose is not convinced that the cost of operation is low enough to prove definitely the success of the plant.

[11] E. H. Rose, *Address*, pp. 221-242.

grade ore charged. If such a material can be substituted for the 35 per cent iron ore now being smelted, Rose estimates an increase in blast furnace output of 48 per cent, a decrease in coke consumption of 849 pounds of coke per ton of iron produced, a decrease in fluxing stone of 714 pounds per ton, and a decrease in slag volume of 1700 pounds per ton of iron. At present day costs, this improvement in smelting practice is estimated to save nearly $6.00 per ton of iron or about $3.00 per ton of 55 per cent iron concentrate. These large savings should go a long way towards paying for the cost of magnetic concentration of Birmingham ores if the engineering and operating difficulties involved can be overcome.

A pilot plant test of this practice was made several years ago at its Red Mountain Ruffner Mine by Sloss-Sheffield Steel and Iron Company. Although a successful magnetic roast was conducted and a concentrate of satisfactory grade was produced, the output of the plant never reached expectations and difficulty in the operation of the magnetic separators resulted in high costs. This outcome led to the abandonment of the project, but interest in this process is still high in the Birmingham district.

A thorough laboratory investigation of the reduction of iron oxides using the fluo-solids technique is described in the *Yearbook* of the American Iron & Steel Institute for 1951.[12] This work was done over a period of several years at the Illinois Institute of Technology in cooperation with the Inland Steel Company. Six different kinds of iron-bearing materials, including Minnesota taconite, New York State magnetite, Lake Superior hematite, mill scale, and blast furnace flue dust were studied. In the fluo-solids technique, the ores are crushed and floated (fluidized) in a stream of reducing gas and passed through coils in a furnace where the reactants are heated to the desired temperature. Although many different temperatures were used, it was found that in no case was all of the iron bearing material changed to a mag-

netic form, either as Fe_3O_4 or as metallic iron. This carefully conducted investigation demonstrates that ore dressing methods, based on roasting iron ores in such a manner as to produce a magnetic compound which may be separated by magnetic concentration, is an extremely difficult operation to control. This result raises considerable doubt regarding the use of the magnetic roast as a means of concentrating Birmingham iron ores.

At the present, the best prospect for the beneficiation of some of the Southern ores seems to rest on the improvement of the gravity methods employed at the Spaulding concentrater and the feasibility of the flotation process in floating silica out of iron ores too high in silica for economic smelting. The best information available indicates that the hard, high lime, self fluxing ores of the Birmingham district are now being smelted at costs as low as those obtained in northern plants using the present high grade Lake Superior ores. There is need today for more intensive study of beneficiation methods which might be adapted to the beneficiation of the high silica ores of the Birmingham district. This should include the ferruginous sandstones which underlie the Big Seam ores in Red Mountain and the hematitic ores in Talladega county, Alabama.

In the Lake Superior districts, the beneficiation of low grade iron ores is also a vital question in relation to the ore mining industry and to the survival of the northern steel industry. The reserves of direct shipping ores which can be mined in open pits have been rapidly depleted in the past ten years and, if production at present rates continues, most of this cheap ore will be consumed in another ten years, according to existing estimates for reserves. At the present time, ore from open-pit mines costs about $2.75 per gross ton at the mine, whereas ore of equivalent quality costs over $4.00 per ton when obtained from underground mines. Practically all of the Wisconsin and Michigan ore is now gotten from underground mines, and increasing amounts will have to be mined by this method in Minnesota unless new deposits of open-pit ore are developed. In 1948,

12 *Yearbook, 1951,* American Iron and Steel Institute, pp. 208-240.

about 85 per cent of the Lake Superior ore was obtained from open-pit mines. If 50 per cent of the 1948 ore production had been obtained from underground mines, the increase in cost of all the ore used would have been about 45 cents per ton of ore—a cost which would represent about $1.00 per ton in the cost of pig iron.

Geologists have repeatedly estimated that over 72 billion tons of taconite ore, containing 25 per cent to 40 per cent iron, is available in the Lake Superior region. Much of this material is on the surface and may be mined in open pits but it cannot be used in its present condition on account of its low iron and high silica content. The chemical composition of the taconite ores is similar to that of the ferruginous sandstones of the Birmingham district, but the physical character of the taconites is radically different. The taconite ore is much harder, making it more difficult to mine and crush as compared to the softer ores of the Red Mountain deposits. The iron-bearing minerals are also in the form of separate particles, not in the form of the amorphous mud or cement which is so typical of the oölitic ores in the South. This feature results in a better liberation of the iron minerals from the silica in grinding and makes this material more amenable to ordinary ore dressing practices such as classifying, jigging, flotation, or heavy media separation. At the present time, all of these methods are in use on a small scale on borderline ores in Minnesota, but no operation on taconite ore has yet been successful. In recent years, all of the large ore mining companies have organized research staffs to study this tremendous problem, and intensive investigations are under way in numerous research laboratories in the Lake Superior district.

Here again, the main factor of successful ore dressing of taconite entails fine grinding to get a good mechanical separation of the hematite mineral from the silica. The fine grinding of the hard ore is costly and also gives rise to slime conditions which make an unsatisfactory situation for gravity separation of the minerals. As a result, the greatest interest at the present time seems to be in the flotation or magnetic separation methods for processing taconite ores, since these two processes are adapted to the separation of the minerals in finely ground pulps. Rather thorough studies of these two processes have been conducted by the U. S. Bureau of Mines, Minnesota State Mines Experiment Station, and several ore mining companies, both in the laboratory and on a pilot plant basis. The cost of the concentrates produced has always been well above that of direct shipping ores and, as long as these are available, no large-scale installation of hematitic taconite concentrating plants is economically feasible.

It has been estimated that an investment cost of at least $20 per ton of concentrate will be required even for large-scale operations. Twenty year amortization cost alone would amount to $1.00 per ton. If most of the 90 million tons of 50 per cent iron ore now being shipped from the Lake Superior region annually were to be replaced with concentrated ore, the total investment needed would approach two billion dollars. The added cost of grinding, magnetic roasting of hematitic taconite, and sintering would amount to at least $3.00 per ton of concentrate. If the iron content of the taconite concentrate is 50 per cent, the northern steel industry will be faced with an increased cost of $4.00 per ton for a 50 per cent iron concentrate. From this, there will result little saving in shipping costs or smelting costs as compared with the open pit Mesabi ores. A concentrate containing over 60 per cent iron, however, would cause such a large saving in shipping and smelting costs that the savings would partially compensate for the cost of concentration. It is evident that the efficiency of the concentrating process will largely determine the outcome of this important problem. The northern steel plants are, therefore, obviously faced with higher impending iron ore costs, either from more underground mining or beneficiation expense.

Late in 1951, plans[13] were announced for the erection of three large magnetite concentration plants in Minnesota. These three plants will be operated by the Oliver Iron Mining Company of United States Steel Corporation; the Reserve Mining Company, owned jointly by Republic Steel Corporation and Armco Steel Corporation, and the Erie Mining Company, owned mostly by Youngstown Sheet & Tube Company and Bethlehem Steel Corporation. It is significant that all of these plants will process only the taconite ores which contain the iron mineral in the form of magnetite. These ores are amenable to direct magnetic concentration without any preliminary treatment besides fine grinding. The concentrate will be pelletized or sintered. The problem of beneficiation of the huge deposits of hematitic taconite is obviously far from solved, a situation very similar to that which exists in respect to the low grade hematitic ores of Alabama.

Reserve Mining Company is erecting a plant to process about 1,000,000 tons of magnetic taconite per year, yielding about 300,000 tons of 65% iron concentrate which will be pelletized for shipment to blast furnaces. Extensive trials of this product at the plants of the two mining companies has shown it to be a very desirable blast furnace feed. Plans call for expanding the plant to an annual output by 1956 of 2.5 million tons of concentrate with a total investment of $75,000,000. This amounts of $10 per annual ton of raw ore treated or $30 per ton of concentrate produced and indicates the very high investment involved in the erection of iron ore-concentrating plants. It is reasonable to assume that amortization costs per ton will exceed operating costs in this mill.

The Erie Mining Company project is quite similar, but it is still in the development stage. The company has applied for a certificate of

13 *Journal of Metals* (November 1951), p. 969; "Reserve Taconite Interests Acquired by Republic and Armco" *Iron Age* (September 21, 1950), p. 108; "Republic-Armco Push Taconite Program," *Iron Age* (November 9, 1950), p. 107; "Plan 300,000 Ton Taconite Pellet Pilot Plant," *Iron Age* (December 7, 1950), p. 137.

necessity to cover a $300,000,000 plant that would ultimately produce 10.5 million tons of concentrate pellets per year. At this time, no decision has been reached on this proposal. It should be noted that this scheme also anticipates an investment cost of about $30 per annual ton of concentrate. Such a high cost can only be absorbed by a very high grade concentrate (65% iron) such as that which is obtained in the magnetic concentrate of magnetite ores.

In the southern region, the outlook is not entirely gloomy. The district has long operated on ores from underground mines. It has also produced cheap pig iron from 35 per cent iron ores. The introduction of successful beneficiation processes to raise the iron content of the concentrate to 50 per cent would result in such a large saving in smelting costs at the blast furnace that there should be little increase in the over-all cost of pig iron in the district. These factors make the concentration of Birmingham ores particularly attractive. This is especially true if the cost of coal and coke continues to rise to higher levels, since the coke saving in smelting richer ores is the most important item. A successful method of beneficiation of Birmingham iron ores would seem to be a most important objective for the southern pig iron and steel industry.

Summary of Iron Ore Mining and Ore Preparation in the Southeast

The characteristics that have been brought out by the preceding paragraphs provide the background for the consideration of the future prospects of iron ore mining in Alabama and the Southeast. Developments must be viewed in light of the decrease in employees and man-hours and of the very great increase in tons of ore produced per man-hour which has marked the history of the industry for the past 50 years. The region cannot escape the impact of the forces that brought about these changes: the increased use of large open-pit mines, the application of large-scale methods of production, the mechanization of operations, the great increase in underground mining labor wage rates, and the application of new techniques. All of these tendencies have the general effect of placing more emphasis on the engineer and the manager.

The ore deposits of the region have certain limitations which cannot easily be overcome. The brown ore and most of the red deposits occur under conditions which do not permit large-scale operations. The problem of mining such deposits in competition with large mechanized mines becomes more difficult as wage rates become higher. In the case of the Big Seam in the Birmingham district, large-scale operations are the rule, but the ore is low grade, the mining must be done by underground methods, and the physical irregularities induced by folding and faulting impose additional difficulties. The fact that the seam is a bed some 15 feet in thickness that stands at a relatively low per cent of incline from the horizontal, rather than a thick ore mass with great vertical thickness, eliminates the possibility of applying such modern mining techniques as block caving or top slicing and caving. Also, the working places are getting continuously farther underground, and haulage of ore up an incline is getting longer. These are conditions which present problems for the future and suggest the need for reviewing the practices that are in use. For instance, the question may be raised as to whether vertical shafts sunk in Shades Valley may not be more economical than the long underground hauls up a slope.

Depletion of the more accessible and higher-grade ores is making beneficiation increasingly important. The application of beneficiation to southern ores can have important effects. The ores are naturally low grade, and improvements either of their iron content or their smelting properties can have far-reaching results in reducing both the handling costs and the quantities of coke required. Such savings may constitute important offsets to increased labor costs. Beneficiation has important implications from a conservation point of view, because it should bring about a more complete use of resources. For instance, in many mines a large part of the lower bench of the Big Seam is not being used because of its high silica content, although the iron content does not differ greatly from other portions. In addition, it is possible that concentration may make it possible to use ferruginous sandstones which can be very easily mined.

The data that have been presented show that Alabama is at a decided disadvantage so far as productivity per man-hour is concerned. If the data were stated in terms of iron content, this disadvantage becomes even more apparent. The nearness of coal and fluxing materials are offsetting factors, but there can be little question that the industry cannot afford to do other than give the closest attention to mining and ore preparation techniques which will improve the South's relative position.

CHAPTER XIV

COAL MINING AND COKE PREPARATION
AS RELATED TO IRON AND STEEL IN THE SOUTHEAST

Coal Resource Characteristics and Coal Mining in the Southeast

Although the coal resources of the Southeast were described in some detail in a previous chapter, certain of the general characteristics should be reviewed because of the direct bearing upon the problems of mining and coal preparation. Coal deposits occur in many locations in Tennessee and Alabama, but those that have been most extensively used by, and seem to be of greatest significance to, the basic iron and steel industry are the deposits in the Warrior and Cahaba fields. The seams that have been most important are the Pratt, the Mary Lee, and the American, although coke has been made from other seams. While there has been, and continues to be, this concentration on coal mined close to Birmingham in the eastern part of the Warrior basin, the possibility that all the coal resources of northern Alabama and Tennessee may prove to be reserves from which the industry can draw in the future should not be overlooked.

The physical characteristics of the Birmingham area that give rise to serious mining problems are the relatively thin seams; the presence of partings of rock, bone coal, and other materials; and the irregularities arising from folding and faulting of the strata. These characteristics make it difficult for Alabama mines to meet the competition of other coal fields which have more favorable resource conditions. The locations where low costs can be obtained by open-cut or strip mining are relatively few. Underground mining under the conditions mentioned above results in high costs per ton of coal. In contrast the coal seams of Kentucky, West Virginia and Pennsylvania are much thicker and more regular and easier to mine.

Coal Mining Methods in the Southeast

In exploiting the coal resources of the southeastern states, the method of development and of mining depends on the location of the coal seam. Where the coal seam is exposed on a side hill and is reasonably flat, the main horizontal passages or main entries are excavated in the coal seam. After the seam is mined far enough undercover, the side or cross entries are turned right and left from the main entries. These cross entries usually consist of a haulageway and a parallel airway. They are turned at regular intervals and are usually placed at an angle of 90 degrees to the main entries, although in case of heavy grades, the angle between the cross and the main entries may be as low as 45 degrees.

Where the coal seam crops out and dips downward from its exposure, the main entries may be driven down the slope in the coal. The cross entries are then turned off right and left from the main slope entries and are nearly horizontal with the grade in favor of the loads.

Where the coal lies at some distance below the surface, it may be reached by either a slope cut through the overlying rock from the surface or by a vertical shaft. Where a slope is driven in the coal seam or where a slope is driven through the overlying rock, the mine cars are usually pulled up the slope to a rotary dump or to the tipple on the surface by a rope wound on the drum of a hoisting engine.

Practices vary in vertical shaft mines. In some such mines the mine cars are hoisted in a cage to the surface, where the coal is dumped. In other mines, to save the expense of raising and lowering the dead weight of the mine cars to the surface, the coal is discharged from the mine cars into a pocket near the shaft cut out of the rock underlying the coal seam. The coal passes from the pocket through a measuring device which loads the equivalent of three or four cars into a skip (a vertical container traveling on guides in a shaft and so arranged that it automatically discharges its contents at the surface). The skip is hoisted to the surface by a rope which winds on the drum of a hoist fixed on the surface at the spot where the skip is tipped to discharge its contents into a bin. From there a feeder conveys the coal to the washer.

In most operations two drums are used on the hoisting engine. The hoisting rope on one drum winds on the top side of the drum from the skip in one compartment, while the other hoisting rope unwinds from the bottom side of the other drum to the skip in the opposite compartment. In this manner the two skips tend to balance each other in weight, and, in hoisting, the weight of coal and rope and the acceleration of starting constitutes the load on the hoisting engine. This is called balanced hoisting.

The main entries into a coal mine are used for many purposes, such as haulageways, manways, and airways. Theoretically, one passage should be sufficient to handle all the coal from a mine and take care of other uses. However, it is necessary to carry air to workmen in the mine and then carry the used or exhaust air to the surface. In Alabama, the state law requires that each man receive 100 cubic feet of air per minute and each mule 500 cubic feet. The movement of this amount of air into the mine through the mine passages results in friction, especially if the passages are small. In some mines, the main entries may consist of as many as seven parallel passages which distribute the air and reduce the friction. The haulageway and two parallel entries can be used for ingoing air, while the other four parallel passages can be used for the exhaust air, which is drawn out by a fan. Parallel passages are connected by breakthroughs driven for air circulation in working areas. When operations shift to other areas, exhaust and incoming air are separated by sealing the old breakthrough between incoming and outgoing air.

In many of the larger mines, the side entries are turned at intervals of 1,000 feet or more, forming what is called a panel, and between these panel entries, cross entries are run parallel to the main entries. Rooms or working places can be driven from these cross entries, and the pillars between the rooms can be mined on a retreating system as fast as the row of rooms on a cross entry is completed. The cross-entry pillars and, later, the panel-entry pillars can be removed also by the use of the retreating system of mining. In some mines, a modified system of long-wall retreating is being used in order to mine the coal within the panel. In other mines, and especially in thin coal seams, the entire mine is worked on the long-wall system. In these mines, entries are run to the limits of the area and a long-wall face is opened between two entries. The coal is then undercut across this face while timbers are used to protect the workmen. The top is allowed to break or settle as the coal is mined by the retreating method.

Safety Problems in Alabama Mines

The fact that the coal in a great many Alabama coal mines gives off a certain amount of explosive gas (largely methane gas) makes it imperative that every precaution be taken to render this gas non-explosive by dilution with properly arranged ventilating air. A great deal of the coal is undercut before blasting. The undercutting is done by hard steel bits set in a heavy chain which travels around a cutter bar somewhat similar in operation to a band saw. If one of these bits hits a piece of hard rock or an iron sulphur ball, a spark may be made which might fire the coal dust. To avoid this hazard, a water connection is made into the cutter bar. The water spray wets the coal dust as it is made. As a further precaution, the mined coal is sprayed with water while it is on the cars and before it is hoisted. The working places, entries, and main passages are sometimes sprayed with water, but in most cases they are dusted with finely ground limestone dust. This rock dusting, when properly done, makes the coal dust inert. In many mines, miners are required to wear electric cap lamps and safety hats and shoes. Smoking is usually prohibited. Nearly all mines are required to have a fire boss who inspects all working places before the men are allowed to enter.

MECHANIZATION IN ALABAMA MINES

Mechanization of coal mining in Alabama has been in progress for many years. The study of bituminous coal mining that was made by the National Research Project noted that:

> Alabama has been and still is a melting pot of experimentation in mechanical loading. Despite difficult physical conditions, such as pitching beds, impurities, and varying seam thickness, the state loaded about one-sixth of its output by machines in 1937. Mechanization made considerable progress even under low-wage scales.[1]

In 1913, only 23 per cent of Alabama coal was cut by machines compared with the national total of 51 per cent. By 1939, these percentages had risen to 71.4 per cent for Alabama and 88.2 per cent for the United States and, in 1943, to 78.2 per cent and 90.3 per cent, respectively. The per cent of underground coal that was mechanically loaded increased in Alabama from 0.5 per cent in 1929 to 24.3 per cent in 1939. The corresponding percentages for the United States were 7 per cent and 31.0 per

[1] W. E. Hotchkiss [and others], *Mechanization, Employment, and Output per Man in Bituminous Coal Mining,* p. 174.

cent. Recent years have seen further changes. No doubt the shortage of labor and its increased cost have been factors. *The Annual Report,* Alabama Division of Safety and Inspection, for the fiscal year 1948-49 shows that 83 per cent of the product of underground mines was loaded mechanically. Furthermore, strip mining of coal increased from 0.5 per cent of the state's total in 1939 to 7 per cent in 1948-49.

The distribution of the underground mechanically loaded coal for the fiscal years 1945-46, 1946-47, 1947-48, and 1948-49 by type of equipment is given in Table 44. Since 1939, drag scrapers and shaking conveyors have greatly decreased in relative importance and pit car loaders have practically disappeared. On the other hand, use of mobile loaders increased from 42.8 per cent of the total of mechanically loaded coal in 1945-46 to 46.9 per cent in 1946-47, but decreased to 45.2 per cent in 1948-49. Power shovels showed a big increase in 1947-48, but the trend in the last two years seems to be toward belt and chain conveyors. The data indicate that mine operators are continually seeking improved methods.

Preparation of Alabama Coal

Due to the high percentage of undesirable materials, most of the Alabama coals are washed before they are ready for market. Almost all of the coal that is used in the produc-

Table 44

Mechanically-Loaded Coal in Underground Mines of Alabama by Type of Equipment
Fiscal Year Ending September 30, 1946, 1947, 1948, and 1949

Kind of equipment	1945-46		1946-47		1947-48		1948-49	
	Net tons mined	Per cent of total mechanically loaded	Net tons mined	Per cent of total mechanically loaded	Net tons mined	Per cent of total mechanically loaded	Net tons mined	Per cent of total mechanically loaded
Drag scrapers................	548,816	5.9	398,224	3.6	425,768	3.5	138,809	1.2
Belt and chain conveyors.....	1,732,368	18.5	1,867,387	17.0	2,621,654	21.4	3,458,683	31.3
Shaking conveyors............	2,216,274	23.6	2,221,570	20.2	1,972,854	16.1	1,306,821	11.8
Power shovels	866,975	9.2	1,347,447	12.3	1,495,494	12.2	1,162,277	10.5
Mobile loaders...............	4,014,125	42.8	5,157,149	46.9	5,715,968	46.8	4,998,206	45.2
All types of mechanical loaders.......	9,378,558	100.0	10,991,777	100.0	12,231,738	100.0	11,064,796	100.0

Source: Alabama Department of Industrial Relations, *Annual Statistical Report,* 1945-46 to 1948-49.

tion of coke is cleaned in this manner. Generally, the washers are equipped either with crushing rolls or Bradford breakers. The latter breaks and sizes coal in one operation. The coal is then washed, and bone coal and slate are removed in one of the various types of jig. The jig consists of a water-tight compartment with a screen on which the dirty coal can be fed with water so that the water is level with the top of the coal. Next, some means of producing an up and down pulsation of the dirty coal bed is used. The clean coal rises to the top, and the bone coal and slate settle to the bottom. The up and down pulsation is accomplished by means of a series of jigs. The equipment is so designed that accumulated bone and slate is discharged continuously at the same time that clean coal is discharged over the upper rim of the jig compartment.

While jigs are extensively used in Alabama mines, experiments have been made with other methods of coal preparation. At the Virginia mine of the Republic Steel Corporation, the Chance Cone, a heavy medium means of flotation, is being used. At the Praco mine of the Alabama By-Products Corporation, the Simons Carves Deduster is being used to produce clean coal by removing dust. Also, shaking concentration tables are used by a number of the large companies for improving the fine coals or the recrushed bone coal.

Coal Preparation at the New Concord Mine

The new Concord mine of the Tennessee Coal, Iron and Railroad Company is a highly mechanized large-scale operation on which construction was begun in 1946. The mine in 1951 has not yet attained full capacity. One of the distinctive features is that the coal is brought to the surface by means of a conveyor belt that is nearly a mile in over-all length and has a vertical lift of 700 feet. It is said to be capable of delivering 1,000 tons of coal per hour. The coal is from the American Coal Seam, which contains a considerable quantity of rock. To remove the rock and to crush, size, and blend the coal, a large coal preparation plant[2] has been built adjacent to the mouth of the mine.

Mining and handling operations act to crush the coal partly. Some of the larger pieces of rock are removed at the underground dumping station, but further crushing and sizing are necessary. Coal from the mine is discharged from the slope conveyor over screens and into one of two revolving breakers. Inside these breakers, which resemble huge barrels, are steel balls which beat against the coal as the breakers revolve, pounding it to granules and nut-sized lumps. These pass through screens and onto conveyors for further treatment. The larger pieces of rock are removed and hauled away. The coal, still containing a high percentage of crushed rock, is stored in blending bins from which it is removed as needed.

From the bins the coal moves to the top of the preparation building where it is again divided according to size, all pieces larger than one-fourth inch in diameter being fed into one cleaning system, while the smaller material passes to a second.

In order that the larger coal may be separated from the extraneous material, the coal and rock are fed into a cone that contains a mixture of sand and water in constant motion. The coal, being lighter than the sand and water, moves around the top of the cone and flows off over a screen, where the water is drained away. The rock sinks to the bottom of the cone and is automatically released when a sufficient volume has accumulated.

The smaller particles—less than a quarter of an inch in diameter—are mixed with water and fed to vibrating table washers, so tilted that the water (bearing coal and rock) flows down over them, and fuel and refuse are separated from each other and directed to troughs arranged along one side and one end.

Coal Preparation in North and South

The fact that cleaning coal has long been a problem with the southern mine operators

2 "T.C.I.'s Concord Mine Is World's Most Modern," *Alabama Today and Tomorrow* (November 1950), pp. 5-6.

has made them pioneers in methods. In recent years, the percentage of sulphur that is being encountered in many of the northern coals which were formerly used for coke is making washing necessary in the North also, and this may have the effect of removing one of the causes of differences in costs of coking coal between the North and the South.

An indication of the relative importance of mechanical cleaning in coal mines in Alabama is given by Table 45.

Table 45

Proportion of All Coal Mined in Alabama That Was Mechanically Cleaned 1939-1948

Year	Per cent of coal mechanically cleaned	Per cent of raw coal cleaned that was discarded as refuse
1939	82.5	12.2
1940	84.3	12.4
1941	83.0	12.9
1942	81.3	14.1
1943	77.7	14.7
1944	77.1	17.6
1945	75.8	20.9
1946	71.7	23.0
1947	73.1	25.6
1948	71.6	25.9

Source: *Minerals Yearbook*, 1939-48.

Mining Costs and Productivity

As suggested at several points, the coal mines of Alabama tend to be high cost operations. For the period from April to December 1937, the National Bituminous Coal Commission found total producing, administrative, and selling costs to be $2.53 per ton in Alabama, Georgia, and parts of Tennessee compared with $2.19 for parts of West Virginia and Virginia (known as Southern No. 1) and $2.04 for parts of West Virginia, Tennessee, and eastern Kentucky areas (known as Southern No. 2).[3]

The data presented in Tables 46 and 47 indicate a decidedly higher cost in Alabama than in the nation as a whole in terms of the use of human labor. In the past, the lower

[3] Hotchkiss, p. 303.

hourly earnings have been an offsetting factor in the calculation of money costs but the wage differentials have been narrowing in recent years. The data presented in Table 46 provide the basis for an interesting calculation as of 1939. The average hourly earnings are given as 61 cents in Alabama and 79 cents in the United States. The production per man-hour indicates that it required 2.22 man-hours to produce one ton of coal in Alabama and 1.34 hours in the nation as a whole. At the average earning rates the indicated labor costs per ton were $1.35 for Alabama and $1.06 for the nation.

Table 46

Average Hourly Earnings of Wage Earners and Working Proprietors and Production in Tons Per Man-Hour Bituminous Coal Mining, Alabama and the United States, 1939

	Alabama	United States
Average hourly earnings of wage earners and working proprietors	$0.61	$0.79
Production—tons per man-hour		
All mines	0.451	0.745
Underground mines	0.450	0.701
Strip pits	0.635	1.991

Source: *Census of Mineral Industries, 1939*, I, p. 233.

Table 47

Production of Coal Per Man-Day in Alabama and the United States, 1939-1948

Year	Production per man-day (number of tons) Alabama	Production per man-day (number of tons) United States
1939	3.16	5.25
1940	2.98	5.19
1941	2.87	5.20
1942	2.82	5.12
1943	2.92	5.38
1944	3.03	5.67
1945	3.22	5.78
1946	3.77	6.30
1947	3.81	6.42
1948	3.77	6.26

Source: *Minerals Yearbook*, 1939-48.

The cost figures compiled by the Office of Price Administration for commercial mines for the years 1943, 1944, 1945, and 1946 (shown by Table 48) provide additional evidence on comparative costs. Not only were the costs for the Alabama and southern Tennessee district higher than those for the districts selected as being the most direct competitors, but the ratios between the costs tended to become more unfavorable. This is particularly true of mine labor costs. District 13 mine labor costs per ton in 1943 were 57.6 per cent and in 1946, 74.3 per cent higher than those of District 3. The offsetting influence of other costs lessened to some extent the effect of the increased labor costs since total producing, administrative, and selling costs per ton of District 13 were 42.0 per cent higher than those of District 3 in 1943 and 47.9 per cent in 1946.

Coal Mining Operations of the Iron and Steel Companies in the Southeast

Of the companies that comprise the basic iron and steel industry of the Southeast, the small companies — Connors Steel, Knoxville Steel, and Atlantic Steel—buy their coal or coke on the market. The Tennessee Products Corporation has a coke plant but does not operate coal mines. On the other hand, each of the four major companies—the Tennessee Coal, Iron and Railroad Company, Republic Steel Corporation, Woodward Iron Company, and the Sloss-Sheffield Steel and Iron Company —own and operate coal mines which supply all or a major part of their requirements. According to the reports of the Division of Safety and Inspection, Alabama State Department of Industrial Relations, the mines of the iron and steel companies produced 6,277,991 tons of coal

Table 48

Costs Per Ton of Mining Coal by Commercial Mines in District 13
(Alabama and Southern Tennessee Coal Fields) and Other Selected Districts, 1943-1946
(in dollars)

Year and type of cost	Coal mining production districts*			
	No. 13	No. 8	No. 3	No. 2
Mine labor cost				
1943	2.08	1.65	1.32	1.63
1944	2.46	1.86	1.53	1.81
1945	2.68	1.98	1.59	1.92
1946	3.19	2.31	1.83	2.21
Total producing cost				
1943	3.04	2.44	2.07	2.52
1944	3.52	2.68	2.34	2.72
1945	3.81	2.91	2.53	2.91
1946	4.42	3.32	2.91	3.28
Total producing, administrative, and selling costs				
1943	3.21	2.66	2.26	2.64
1944	3.68	2.91	2.54	2.84
1945	3.99	3.14	2.74	3.06
1946	4.63	3.56	3.13	3.41

*Districts include the following areas:
    District 13—Alabama and Southern Tennessee
    District 8—Eastern Kentucky, Northern Tennessee, Southwestern Virginia, and Southwestern West Virginia
    District 3—Northern West Virginia
    District 2—Western Pennsylvania

Source: U. S. Office of Price Administration, *Survey of Commercial Bituminous Coal Mines*, Economic Data Series 15.

in the fiscal year 1947-48 and 6,017,013 tons in 1948-49. This represents 32.8 per cent and 42.0 per cent, respectively, of the total production of the state for these two years.

Table 49 gives the employment and production figures for each of the mines operated by the iron and steel companies. These data, together with other information contained in the annual reports of the Division of Safety and Inspection, indicate the general characteristics of the mines. Generally speaking, they are relatively large-scale operations. All the mines are underground operations and are classed as gassy, but the reports indicate that they rate high with regard to safety measures. With the exception of one of the mines of the Sloss-Sheffield Steel and Iron Company, mining machines are used exclusively to cut the coal. In the one exception, pick and machines are reported. In 1948-49, 96.2 per cent of the coal was reported as mechanically loaded. Of this,

70 per cent was loaded with mobile loaders and over 18 per cent with shaking conveyors. It seems reasonable to conclude that the coal mines of the iron and steel companies[4] employ up-to-date methods and rank among the best in the state so far as management is concerned.

As indicated by Table 51, the products of these mines consist largely of washed or cleaned coal of small size. This is the product required by the by-product plants operated by each of the companies to produce the coke needed for blast furnaces and other operations.

Production of Coke in Southeast as Related to the Basic Iron and Steel Industry

With the exception of the coke plant operated by the Tennessee Products Company,

[4] For a description in popular style and illustrated, see *Steel Making in Birmingham*, pp. 12-18, 21-28.

Table 49

Number of Employees and Production of Mines
Operated by Iron and Steel Companies in Alabama
Fiscal Year (Oct. 1-Sept. 30) 1948-1949

Name of operator and mine	Employees			Production Short tons
	Number outside mine	Number inside mine	Total number	
Republic Steel Corporation				
Sayre	93	248	341	301,262
Sayreton (Nos. 1, 2, and 3)	130	534	664	416,538
Virginia	71	226	297	181,470
Sloss-Sheffield Steel and Iron Company				
Bessie	40	249	289	208,230
Flat Top	61	457	518	298,830
Kimberly	26	79	105	78,291
Lewisburg (No. 2)	60	304	364	221,206
Tennessee Coal, Iron and Railroad Company				
Concord	68	401	469	373,453
Docena	107	818	925	571,924
Edgewater	165	684	849	1,068,832
Hamilton	111	681	792	629,313
Short Creek	99	557	656	632,889
Wylam*	83	344	427	190,760
Woodward Iron Company				
Dolomite	61	362	423	283,257
Mulga	80	430	510	560,758
Total all iron and steel companies	1,255	6,374	7,629	6,017,013

*Closed June 30, 1949.
Source: *Alabama Department of Industrial Relations Annual Statistical Report*, Fiscal Year 1948-49.

all of the plants in the Southeast that have a direct connection with the basic iron and steel industry are located in Alabama. As detailed information is largely limited to the Alabama operations, this discussion consequently will be confined largely to that state.[5]

The first record of the quantity of coke produced in the United States is included in the census report for 1880, the data having been compiled by the United States Geological Survey. The production reported for Alabama in 1880 was 60,781 net tons; only very small quantities had been produced in the state prior to that time. During the next decade, output in the state increased greatly and, by 1890, had reached 1,072,942 tons. In 1946, Alabama's production was 4,665,939 tons, or 8 per cent of the nation's total. The state ranked fifth, its production having been exceeded by Pennsylvania, Ohio, Indiana, and New York, in the order named.

All of the active producers of coke in Alabama are located in three counties: Jefferson,

Table 50

Coal Mined by Iron and Steel Companies in Alabama and Loaded Mechanically, by Kind of Equipment Fiscal Year (Oct. 1-Sept. 30) 1948-1949

Kind of loading equipment	Number of tons loaded	Per cent of total mechanically loaded
Drag scrapers	......	...
Belt and chain conveyors...	408,295	7.0
Shaking conveyors	1,087,109	18.8
Mobile loaders	4,181,166	72.3
Power shovels	110,095	1.9
Total mechanically loaded	5,786,665	100.0
All coal mined by iron and steel companies	6,017,013	
Per cent mechanically loaded		96.2

Source: *Alabama Department of Industrial Relations Annual Statistical Report,* Fiscal Year 1948-49, p. 154.

[5] The following discussion is based largely on Mable Mills, *The Coke Industry of Alabama.*

Table 51

Production of Mines Operated by Iron and Steel Companies in Alabama by Types of Coal, Fiscal Year (Oct. 1-Sept. 30) 1948-1949

Types or kinds of coal	Production Short tons
Egg	
Dry	
Washed	
Nut	
Dry	
Washed	29,598
6" x 0" - 5" x 0"	
Dry	
Washed	
3" x 0" - 2" x 0"	
Dry	
Washed	
1½" x 0" and smaller	
Dry	134,398
Washed	5,125,680
Run of mine	
Dry	17,720
Washed	709,617
Total dry	152,118
Total washed	5,864,895
Grand total	6,017,013

Source: Alabama Department of Industrial Relations, *Annual Statistical Report,* Fiscal Year 1948-49, p. 135.

Etowah, and Tuscaloosa. Jefferson is by far the most important, since Etowah and Tuscaloosa account for only a minor share of the production.

Ownership of the state's coke industry is concentrated in the hands of a relatively small number of enterprisers—in 1948 only six. With the exception of the Alabama By-Products Corporation and the DeBardeleben Coal Company, these owner-operators are iron and steel companies, and the majority of the coke produced is used in blast furnace operations. The number of ovens, the production of coke, and the quantity of coal used in the production of coke by all plants in the state of Alabama and by the plants of the iron and steel companies are shown in Table 52.

The figures presented in Table 52 show that the plants operated by the iron and steel companies account for a very large part of the coke-plant operations of the state. They account for 83 to 90 per cent of the coke during the nine years shown, and the annual average is approximately 85 per cent.

Practically all of the coal used in the manufacture of coke is mined in the state. The five main seams from which this coal has come are the Mary Lee, Pratt, American, Blue Creek, and Black Creek, with more than 50 per cent coming from the Mary Lee alone. Some coal is brought in from West Virginia to blend with the Alabama coals, but this amounts to a small proportion of the total—in 1946, 1.8 per cent.

Since undue proportions of ash, sulphur, or other impurities are to be avoided, the coal used in the manufacture of coke is carefully prepared. The previous discussion points out that a large percentage of coal mined in Alabama is washed. In 1948, it was reported that washed coal comprised 97 per cent of all coal used in the production of coke.

From the data given in Table 53, it can be seen that, in each year from 1937 to 1948 inclusive, the Alabama by-product plants obtained a higher yield of coke from the coal processed than did the nation as a whole. This indicates that the washed Alabama coal is not of inferior grade and also that the Alabama industry has been using modern coking practices.

BEEHIVE VERSUS BY-PRODUCT COKE PRODUCTION

The first by-product coke ovens built in Alabama were constructed in 1895 at the Ensley plant of the Tennessee Coal, Iron and Railroad Company by Semet-Solvay. Since then there has been a shift from the beehive to the by-product ovens. In 1909, beehive ovens accounted for 83 per cent of total coke production in Alabama and 84 per cent in the country as a whole. In 1925, the output of beehive ovens constituted only 1.9 per cent of the total

Table 52

Number of Ovens, Tons of Coke Produced, and Quantity of Coal Used in Manufacture of
Coke in Alabama, All Coke Plants and Coke Plants of Iron and Steel Companies
Fiscal Years 1938-1939 to 1946-1947

Year	Number of ovens		Coke produced (short tons)	Coal used (short tons)
	Beehive	By-product		
All plants				
1938-39		954	3,855,881	5,418,667
1939-40		1,074	4,585,902	6,746,554
1940-41	293	1,254	4,923,741	6,890,443
1941-42	308	1,352	5,424,658	7,750,774
1942-43	94	1,297	5,537,200	7,645,047
1943-44	94	1,366	5,620,769	7,560,420
1944-45		1,246	5,465,813	7,557,265
1945-46		1,250	4,922,509	6,569,257
1946-47		1,248	5,547,721	7,764,891
Plants of iron and steel companies				
1938-39		805	3,472,009	4,882,802
1939-40		925	4,067,498	6,013,966
1940-41	244	1,045	4,371,836	6,126,829
1941-42	244	1,118	4,594,789	6,619,094
1942-43	94	1,063	4,753,115	6,046,275
1943-44	94	1,132	4,798,853	6,450,644
1944-45		1,012	4,604,792	6,372,275
1945-46		1,016	4,100,187	5,467,040
1946-47		1,014	4,671,128	6,651,013

Source: *Alabama Department of Industrial Relations, Annual Statistical Report,* 1943-44 through 1946-47; *Annual Report,* 1938-39
through 1941-42.

Table 53

Yield of Coke from Coal
Alabama and the United States
1937-1948

Year	Beehive ovens		By-product ovens	
	Alabama (per cent)	United States (per cent)	Alabama (per cent)	United States (per cent)
1937		64.2	72.4	70.7
1938		61.6	70.9	69.9
1939		62.9	71.0	70.0
1940		63.7	71.0	70.5
1941	60.7	63.7	71.5	70.8
1942	61.5	64.3	71.7	70.8
1943	59.7	63.8	72.5	70.8
1944		64.2	72.3	71.0
1945		64.1	71.6	70.9
1946		63.7	71.5	70.6
1947		63.8	70.9	70.6
1948		63.7	71.5	70.2

Source: *Minerals Yearbook,* 1937-1946.

Alabama production and 22.1 per cent of the national total. For many years the beehive ovens of Alabama have been idle, except for the years from 1941 through 1943, when a limited number were brought into operation to relieve the emergency demand. However, these ovens accounted for less than two per cent of the state's coke production during these emergency years.

USES OF ALABAMA COKE

The coke produced in Alabama is used largely within the state. The data presented in Table 54 shows that, in 1946, only 12 per cent was shipped outside Alabama. Still, Alabama, with movements going to 30 other states, had the most widespread shipment of any of the coke-producing states. From the standpoint of kind of use, the greater part of Alabama's coke was used by the producer in blast furnaces. Since 1918, at least two-thirds of the total has been so used, the highest percentage having been 90.7 per cent in 1939. In addition to the use in blast furnaces, the fact that the industry can furnish coke for foundries and for industrial purposes, many of which are metallurgical in character, has been, and continues to be, an important factor in the development of the iron and steel industry.

COKE-OVEN BY-PRODUCTS

When coal is heated well above its decomposition temperature in by-product coke ovens, it yields in addition to coke a considerable quantity of gaseous material from which are recovered the principal by-products—gas, tar, ammonia, and crude light oil. These materials have important industrial uses and their value constitutes an important offset against the cost of producing coke.

Coke-oven gas is the most valuable of the four principal by-products, judged either as a source of income or in calorific value. In addition to providing the fuel requirements of the by-product coke ovens from which it is produced, coke-oven gas supplies various other fuel needs. In 1946, 46 per cent of the gas produced in by-product coke ovens in Alabama was used to heat ovens, and the remainder was consumed by affiliated metallurgical works, neighboring industries, and public utilities.

The principal uses of tar are as a raw material for the manufacture of coal-tar products, as a fuel for open-hearth furnaces or other metallurgical operations, and as a fuel under boilers. In 1946, 62.5 per cent of that produced in Alabama was sold, while 36.5 per cent was used by the producer on the premises.

In coal carbonization, ammonia is recovered either as its water solution or as a crystallized ammonium sulfate. In 1946, 91 per cent of the ammonia recovered in the coking process in Alabama was converted to ammonium sulfate and sold as a fertilizer material.

Crude light oil is a term used in the by-product industry to designate the mixture of all those condensible products derived from the coking process, the boiling points of which do not exceed 200 degrees centigrade. It consists of benzol, toluol, and their hemologs. In the Birmingham district, crude light oil is being utilized in the manufacture of motor fuel.

The quantities of the various by-products that were produced in the period from 1939 to 1946 and the disposition made by the producers are shown in Tables 55 to 58. The value of coke produced is compared with the potential value of the by-products and with the value of the sales of the by-products in Table 59. While the method of arriving at the potential value is subject to criticism due to the assumption that the unsold by-products had a unit value equal to the part that was sold, the estimates of the potential values do give some indication of the importance of the by-products either as direct sources of revenue to the producers or

as materials for use in the associated manufacturing processes. The question as to whether the producers are deriving the full advantage from these products is an important one which cannot be examined in this study but might well merit special attention.

An examination of the data in Table 58 serves to emphasize an important characteristic of the price behavior of by-products. The potential value of by-products produced declined from 88.1 per cent of the total value of coke

Table 54

Distribution of Coke Produced in Alabama Which Was Shipped or Used by Producer in 1946, by States and Type of Use (in net tons)

Destination	Coke				
	Furnace use	Foundry use	Other industrial uses	Domestic use	Total coke
Alabama	3,822,221	145,573	123,939	75,298	4,167,031
Arizona		4,070	......	......	4,070
Arkansas		617	34		651
California		13,381	10,513	......	23,894
Florida		2,539	47,041	2,996	52,576
Georgia		17,310	25,267	11,165	53,742
Idaho		162	......	......	162
Illinois		1,058	286	14,819	16,163
Indiana		4,878	701	1,801	7,380
Iowa			37	1,064	1,101
Kansas		1,381	34		1,415
Kentucky		4,939	6,282	677	11,898
Louisiana		7,656	32,244	2,099	41,999
Maryland		144		......	144
Michigan		30,235	......	808	31,043
Mississippi		1,782	955	937	3,674
Missouri		4,224	......	313	4,537
Nebraska			207	216	423
New Mexico		95			95
New York		195			195
North Carolina		9,746	7,469	4,630	21,845
Ohio		18,565	3,690	......	22,255
Oklahoma		765	114	......	879
Oregon		2,518	......	......	2,518
South Carolina		4,120	4,040	7,179	15,339
Tennessee		56,585	23,006	4,103	83,694
Texas		28,038	30,731	......	58,769
Utah		406	......	......	406
Virginia		12,367	2,490		14,857
West Virginia		......	43,102		43,102
Wisconsin		601	......	1,264	1,865
Export		11,109	15,216	......	26,325
Total	3,822,221	385,059	377,398	129,369	4,714,047

Source: U. S. Bureau of Mines, *Distribution of Oven and Beehive Coke in 1946.*

at ovens in 1940 to 40.0 per cent in 1946. Sales of by-products in 1940 amounted to 60.5 per cent of the value of coke; in 1946 sales of by-products were only 27.3 per cent of the value of coke. Although coal and manufacturing costs increased during the war, prices of chemicals remained relatively stable. It would seem that the demand for by-products did not increase in the same manner as did the demand for coke. Since the production of by-products is justified as a means of reducing the cost of the main product and not as a primary source of revenue, the reaction of supply to costs and to price changes is not a very immediate one. This condition is an important factor in the determination of blast furnace costs, as will be shown in the next chapter.

From 1921 to 1938, there was a large increase in the proportion of the by-products that were sold. In 1921, sales of the four principal by-products accounted for 47.7 per cent of the potential value of their total production. In 1938, the corresponding per cent was 74.7. The war-time years saw a decline from this proportion to approximately 68 per cent. Thus a large part of the potential value is being realized by sale. However, there remains the question as to whether both opportunities for sale and realizable values might be improved by the development of more numerous users and new and more varied uses.

Conclusions with Respect to Coal Mining and Coke Production

While the existence of a good grade of coking coal in close proximity to the Big Seam of red ore is a resource condition of the greatest importance, this advantage is counterbalanced by factors which make for high costs in mining, such as thin seams, partings of undesirable materials, and irregular strata. The mines operated by the iron and steel companies are among the best in the region so far as the use of modern methods of mining is concerned. Each of the four major companies is equipped

Table 55

Coke-Oven Gas Produced and Sold in Alabama, 1939-1948

Year	Produced	Used in heating ovens	Surplus sold or used	Wasted
		In M cubic feet		
1939	60,865,445	26,259,841	33,045,531	1,560,073
1940	72,870,639	32,047,398	39,027,507	1,795,734
1941	72,138,690	32,322,941	38,062,387	1,753,362
1942	84,788,995	38,316,744	43,813,596	2,658,655
1943	80,151,439	35,619,752	41,638,986	2,892,701
1944	88,470,186	39,579,100	46,303,486	2,587,600
1945	79,552,354	36,161,661	41,221,472	2,169,221
1946	66,563,169	30,767,881	34,722,316	1,072,972
1947	84,331,666	39,325,816	43,311,093	1,694,757
1948	85,126,822	39,030,349	44,381,147	1,715,326
		Per cent of total produced		
1939	100.0	43.1	54.3	2.6
1940	100.0	44.0	53.5	2.5
1941	100.0	44.8	52.8	2.4
1942	100.0	45.2	51.7	3.1
1943	100.0	44.4	52.0	3.6
1944	100.0	44.7	52.4	2.9
1945	100.0	45.5	51.8	2.7
1946	100.0	46.2	52.2	1.6
1947	100.0	46.6	51.4	2.0
1948	100.0	45.9	52.1	2.0

Source: *Minerals Yearbook*, 1939-48.

to produce its own coke in modern by-product plants. Also, the coal resources of north Alabama and Tennessee, other than those directly exploited by the iron and steel companies, constitute a reserve of coal that should prove adequate for many years to come, provided costs of mining do not become so high that they make it unprofitable to recover the coal. Fur-

Table 56

Coke-Oven Tar Produced, Used by Producer, and Sold in Alabama
1939-1948 (in gallons)

| Year | Produced | Used by producer | | | |
		Total	Fuel under boilers	In open hearth	Otherwise
1939	46,869,260	17,756,884	. . . . . .	17,664,450	92,434
1940	57,101,546	28,052,421	42,516	27,856,894	153,011
1941	56,506,001	21,883,969	536,234	21,078,644	269,091
1942	65,869,866	22,079,097	265,797	21,507,495	305,805
1943	61,306,901	14,969,735	663,470	14,123,700	182,565
1944	65,810,296	23,127,269	279,233	22,716,102	131,934
1945	62,285,739	18,966,684	296,872	18,544,761	125,051
1946	52,021,128	19,010,755	305,724	18,606,374	98,657
1947	64,866,672	29,584,416	693,593	28,716,874	173,949
1948	66,369,414	29,233,550	855,642	28,188,006	189,902

| Year | Sold | | |
	Total	For use as fuel	For refining into tar products
1939	27,927,930	9,902,390	18,025,540
1940	31,395,861	6,658,552	24,737,309
1941	33,710,998	6,546,500	27,164,498
1942	44,596,096	. . . .	44,596,096
1943	43,751,698	9,863,870	33,887,828
1944	40,391,759	. . . .	40,391,759
1945	42,688,330	. . . .	42,688,330
1946	32,517,021	. . . . . .	32,517,021
1947	32,203,562	. . . .	32,203,562
1948	35,863,209	. . . .	35,863,209

Source: *Minerals Yearbook,* 1939-1948.

Table 57

Coke-Oven Ammonia Produced and Sold in Alabama, 1939-1948
(in pounds)

| Year | Sulfate equivalent of all forms | Produced as | | Sold as | |
		Sulfate	Liquor NH_3 content	Sulfate	Liquor NH_3 content
1939	133,436,377	125,977,737	1,864,660	124,387,618	1,810,089
1940	159,802,374	142,256,518	4,386,464	148,289,395	4,387,056
1941	164,301,444	139,381,188	6,230,064	140,170,109	6,183,599
1942	186,939,287	159,143,535	6,948,938	154,513,244	7,056,766
1943	174,423,799	145,434,583	7,247,304	149,481,831	7,198,913
1944	186,541,338	169,917,138	4,156,050	164,698,305	4,221,137
1945	175,135,481	160,227,205	3,727,069	162,362,226	3,672,800
1946	148,228,385	135,458,585	3,192,450	136,731,313	3,204,660
1947	185,824,523	180,020,039	1,451,121	176,337,562	1,500,464
1948	192,858,634	186,195,626	1,665,752	186,068,966	1,675,568

Source: *Minerals Yearbook,* 1939-1948.

thermore, the existence of two by-product coke producers that are not associated with the basic iron and steel industry constitutes a supplementary source of coke for the industry and a source for foundries and other metal-working establishments. The fact that the southeastern coal resources present serious cost problems should call for the use of the best engineering

knowledge and practices available. A final point is that wasteful methods of mining coal are generally considered to have made many tons of Alabama coal unminable that might have been recovered had greater care been exercised. This is a serious loss to the state, and additional losses of this kind should be avoided.

Table 58

Coke-Oven Crude Light Oil Produced in Alabama and Derived Products
Obtained and Sold, 1939-1948 (in gallons)

| Year | Produced | Refined on premises | Derived products obtained and sold | |
			Produced	Sold
1939	16,287,270	16,231,054	14,029,044	13,567,774
1940	19,188,504	18,286,845	16,289,727	15,798,009
1941	*	*	*	*
1942	22,378,246	20,111,009	17,442,896	17,210,861
1943	20,088,217	19,001,294	16,254,319	15,618,576
1944	22,553,373	22,482,885	19,710,704	19,009,315
1945	21,275,658	21,087,679	18,381,092	16,859,290
1946	18,086,578	17,509,374	15,122,047	14,941,494
1947	22,852,138	22,002,834	19,175,866	18,432,998
1948	23,210,383	22,965,327	19,750,054	18,731,681

*Not reported in *Minerals Yearbook* by Bureau of Mines.

Source: *Minerals Yearbook*, 1939-1948.

Table 59

Value of Coke at Ovens; Potential Value of Production and Value of
Quantities Sold of Four Principal By-Products in Alabama
(Coke-Oven Gas, Tar, Ammonia and Crude Light Oil)

Year	Value of coke at ovens (dollars)	Potential value of 4 by-products produced* (dollars)	Value of 4 by-products sold (dollars)	Potential value of 4 by-products as per cent of value of coke at ovens	Value of 4 by-products sold as per cent of value of coke at ovens	Value of 4 by-products sold as per cent of potential value of by-products produced
1939	10,917,559	10,319,499	7,151,669	94.5	65.5	69.3
1940	13,748,837	12,111,367	8,321,169	88.1	60.5	68.7
1941	18,628,534	†	†	. . .	. . .	. . .
1942	26,950,850	15,968,570	11,013,027	59.3	40.9	69.0
1943	27,838,884**	15,361,629	10,863,693	55.2	39.0	70.7
1944	32,057,000	16,996,831	11,631,730	53.0	36.3	68.4
1945	33,448,229	16,037,649	10,876,216	47.9	32.5	67.8
1946	32,669,886	13,069,416	8,915,214	40.0	27.3	68.2

*Potential value arrived at by multiplying total production by average value of that sold. For ammonia and crude light oil for the years 1921 to 1937 the average value of that sold in the United States was used, as data by states was not available.

†Production of crude light oil not available.

**Value of beehive production not included.

Source: Mable D. Mills, *Coke Industry in Alabama*.

CHAPTER XV

RAW MATERIAL ASSEMBLY COSTS AT STEELMAKING POINTS IN THE UNITED STATES

Previous chapters have presented discussions of the location and chief characteristics of the deposits of essential mineral raw materials and the location of iron and steel plants in the United States. Especial attention has been given to the development of the iron and steel industry in the Southeast, to the operating companies and their properties, and to the problems encountered in the mining and preparation of ore and coal. A general conclusion that can be drawn from the information presented in these earlier chapters is that many factors are exercising an influence on the operations of the iron and steel plants and that these various factors form workable combinations which differ with each site and perhaps with each plant. Some of the important elements are distance from ore and coal deposits, quality of ore and coal, readiness with which the ore and coal can be mined, kind of transportation that must be used in getting raw materials from mines to blast furnaces, ownership of mineral reserves, technical factors related to the use of the raw materials and the manufacture of products, and the age and efficiency of plants. The combined effect of all the various factors is registered in the total cost of operation. Facilities were not available to make a complete cost study, but a survey of the cost of assembling the raw materials[1] needed to make pig iron and steel at the leading steelmaking centers of the United States has been made.

[1] The survey of the cost of assembling raw materials at steelmaking points was made by E. C. Wright, Professor of Metallurgy, University of Alabama, formerly Assistant to the President, National Tube Company. Professor Wright prepared the estimates and the text of this chapter.

The Elements of Cost

In analyzing the cost of assembling raw materials for making steel it is necessary to study the cost of bringing each important ingredient to the steel plant. The cost of mining each constituent may vary widely in a given field; hence it becomes necessary to estimate the production costs of a number of producers and to take a weighted average of the whole district. For example, Lake Superior iron ores are obtained from open-pit mines to the extent of about 85 per cent of the total production and 15 per cent from deep underground mines. Some of these ores are then subjected to ore dressing operations to improve their quality to that of blast furnace grade. At the present time, it is reported that nearly 25 per cent of all the Lake ores are being treated by one or more beneficiating processes. A weighted average cost of the Lake ore now being consumed in northern steel plants must include these factors. To this figure is then added the cost of transporting the ore by ship and rail to the steel plant. Only a rough approximation can be thus obtained since the relative cost of underground and open-pit mining in the many different mines can only be guessed. Furthermore, the cost of beneficiation varies depending on the methods used.

A similar situation exists in respect to the cost of coal and coke. The average cost in each district represents a weighted average of all the reporting mines and includes data from strip mines, small wagon mines, and the highly mechanized mines of the larger coal producers.

The cost of blast furnace coke is complicated, depending not only on the cost of the coal charged but also on the value of the by-products of the coke oven. Two of the most important by-products—coke oven gas and tar—are usually consumed as fuels in the steel mills, and their credit value is often calculated on a BTU basis in comparison with the cost of coal at the point of use. At points such as Baltimore and Chicago, where the cost of coal, shipped for long distances, is high, the by-product credit is high; at Birmingham and Pittsburgh, where coal is much cheaper, and in Texas, where natural gas and fuel oil is cheap, the by-product credit for these two items is much lower. This difficult accounting procedure often gives an odd result for the net cost of blast furnace coke.

Early in this survey it was realized that the effect of the greatly increased cost of mining low grade iron ore in the Birmingham district and the rapid depletion of the high grade open-pit ores of the Lake Superior region would have a critical influence on the cost of making steel in both the northern and southern steel districts within the next few years. Consideration of these two problems led to a review of the developments in the concentration of low grade ores in both districts and also to a study of the intensive activities of the major steel companies in the exploration of foreign ore deposits.

PROBABLE EFFECT OF ORE CONCENTRATION ON COSTS

The situation with respect to concentration and the probable effects on costs of ore and pig iron were discussed in some detail in Chapter XIII. It was pointed out that the concentration of the taconites in the Lake Superior region was almost certain to increase the cost per ton of ore at the lake port. This added cost might be as much as three dollars per ton. If the concentration simply brought the iron content up to the present average of the Lake Superior ores, around 50 per cent, no savings in cost of shipping or smelting would result. On the other hand, the southern industry is adjusted to using 35 per cent ore and the introduction of a successful concentration process that would raise the iron content to 50 per cent

would result in a decided reduction in the smelting costs required to produce a ton of pig iron.

COST OF IMPORTING ORE

The difficulties associated with the beneficiation of both Lake Superior and southern iron ores has recently led to greatly increased interest in the development of foreign ore deposits. A study of this phase of the iron ore problem introduces a great difficulty in any cost analysis because of the erratic situation in ocean shipping costs. This is particularly true of vessels sailing under the American flag, as the high labor standards established for American seamen, compared to those prevailing on foreign lines, make the daily operating costs of American vessels much higher than those of foreign competitors. Shipping companies estimate that it costs between $1,500 and $2,000 per day to operate a 10,000 ton freighter. Moreover, the tremendous tonnage of iron ore which must be moved (from two to ten million tons annually) makes it almost necessary for the ore shipper to organize his own shipping line. This factor will almost certainly require a tremendous investment cost in organizing the shipping needed for the movement of large tonnages of foreign ores, and an amortization figure of $1.00 to $3.00 per ton of ore will have to be faced in supplying the mining plant, port facilities, and ships needed for foreign ore development. Such a figure has been included in the mining costs estimated for the foreign districts.

The most interesting foreign iron ore deposits for American steel producers are those in Labrador, Chile, Brazil, Venezuela, Africa, and Mexico. Some of the factors influencing the costs of developing and using the deposits in the first four of these countries will be summarized.

The enormous deposits of high grade iron recently discovered in Labrador,[2] which are now undergoing systematic exploration, have

[2] J. A. Retty, "Labrador—North America's Greatest Iron Ore Field," pp. 480-483.

attracted great interest. Several mining and steel producing companies have organized companies to exploit these deposits. The delivery of these ores to existing steel producing centers will involve mining under difficult climatic conditions, the construction of a railroad 300 miles long to the St. Lawrence River, and the shipment of the ores from a river port by rail (or a combination of rail and boat) to steel plants. A large investment in mining equipment, transportation, and storage depots will be involved in this development, but present estimates indicate that these ores may be delivered to steel plants at a cost only slightly higher than the present delivery cost of Lake Superior ores.

The large and rich ore bodies of Brazil seem to be so unfavorably situated geographically that their use in American steelmaking does not seem at all feasible at present. The ores are located about 300 miles from the nearest Brazilian ocean port and are then at least 4,500 miles from the nearest American steel center. It is estimated that the cost of shipping the ores from the mine to the blast furnace is between $9.00 and $12.00 per ton, a prohibitive figure at this time. In 1950, Brazilian ore of 67 per cent iron content was quoted at 24 cents per iron unit or $16.08 per gross ton. The cost of this ore delivered to Birmingham must be at least 21 cents per unit or $14.07 per gross ton, and since the mining cost should not exceed $1.50 per gross ton, the effect of high transportation cost is obvious. These shipping costs may be greatly reduced by the use of huge ore boats carrying from 20,000 to 40,000 tons.

The Chilean ores have been used for many years by the Bethlehem Steel Company at its Sparrows Point plant near Baltimore; before World War II and since the close of hostilities, about two-thirds of the ores used at this plant originated in Chile. Although the distance is nearly 9,000 miles, the ore deposits are near the coast in Chile and are unloaded directly from the boat to the blast furnace stock-pile at the plant. Ocean shipping costs were reduced by the use of large ore carriers holding over 20,000 tons, and this enabled the company to deliver this high grade ore (62 per cent iron) at quite favorable costs. In 1948, over 2,600,000 tons of Chilean ore were imported.

As pointed out previously, there is, at present, great interest in the ore deposits in the Orinoco River region of Venezuela. The two largest American steel producers are now actively engaged in developing certain of these deposits, and several other companies are exploring other possibilities. The mines are some 300 to 400 miles from the mouth of the Orinoco River and are only about 2,500 miles from such ports as Mobile, Baltimore, or Philadelphia. Estimates of the assembly cost of these ores at Mobile and Birmingham are therefore included, although these data are entirely speculative since no cost information based on actual shipments of the ores could be obtained. Fairly reliable figures are available for the costs of Swedish, Brazilian, and Chilean ores, as considerable tonnages of these ores have been consumed in this country. Lippert's article, previously cited, gives much new information about the status of the Venezuelan ore deposits. The extensive program projected by the two largest steel producers clearly indicates that these ores may be delivered to existing steel plants at a favorable cost. The estimated cost of these rich ores at Birmingham and Mobile (given in Table 60) confirms this assumption.

An interesting speculation as to the origin of iron ores that will be used in the Great Lakes, Pittsburgh, Youngstown, and Ohio Valley steel centers in 1960 is presented by Henning and Braund in the American Iron & Steel Institute *Yearbook, 1950*.[3] The authors estimate that ten years from now these northern plants will be using 10 million tons of taconite concentrate and 20 million tons of imported ores, mostly from Labrador and Venezuela. If the projected increase in foreign ores now prophesied for the Alabama district is added to this, it will be evident that between 30 and 40 per cent of the total iron ore will come either from beneficia-

[3] C. C. Henning and R. W. Braund, "Present and Prospective Sources of Supply of Steel Making Raw Materials," pp. 251-273.

tion plants or from imports. This prophecy is emphasized by the great increase in ore imports since 1945. A recent report states that 8,260,395 tons were imported in 1950.

EFFECT OF INCREASE IN FREIGHT RATES ON COSTS

In compiling the raw material costs, the effect of greatly increased railroad freight rates during the past five years is very evident, and freight rates have become increasingly important to plants which have to haul both coal and iron ore by rail. This applies particularly at locations like Chicago and Baltimore, which are now faced with coal costs of over $10 per ton of pig iron—a situation which is largely due to the much higher rail freight rates.

Table 62 shows the percentage increase in the cost of iron ore, coke, pig iron, and steel in 1950 compared to 1945. Plants which require long distance transportation show a greater cost for assembly of ore and coal which brings out the effects of increased freight rates. The high percentage of increase in coke costs at Birmingham is due to higher coal mining costs. An important contributing factor has been the tendency toward the equalization of mining labor rates in this district with those in other coal mining areas.

The Cost Estimates and Their Limitations

In addition to the complications discussed in the preceding paragraphs, great difficulty was encountered in making the survey because the period July, 1947 to July, 1950 was one of chaotic costs. An example of the wide fluctuations in material cost is exhibited in iron and steel scrap prices; this commodity varied between $20 and $46 per ton during the year of 1949. In addition, freight rates on all raw materials were raised several times, and the cost of mining coal has increased each year as the annual miners' union contract was renewed. Repeated strikes, work stoppages, and slowdowns have also contributed to increased costs of all materials needed for steelmaking. To secure the best information possible, members of the research staff held discussions with large steel producers in the East and South; with railway, barge, and ocean steamship operators; with coal and ore mining companies; and with many trade associations and government bureaus, such as the American Iron and Steel Institute, National Coal Association, state mining institutes, and the United States Bureau of Mines.

In spite of the difficulties, it is believed that a fairly logical estimate of the cost of assembling the basic raw materials (such as coal, coke, fluxing stone, iron ore, and scrap) was obtained for each of the important steelmaking centers of the Southeast and of the eastern and northern districts. The limitations of the estimates must be recognized. The figures finally compiled are composite or average costs for any given district, since the costs of two different companies in any one district may vary considerably. This applies particularly to the cost of mining coal, since the coal costs given in this chapter exhibit the average cost of the district as shown in the tables of the National Coal Association and the United States Bureau of Mines. Also, the cost estimates are based on fully integrated plants, producing at least 1,000,000 tons of steel per year—a tonnage which permits the efficient use of coke oven and blast furnace by-products together with a balanced smelting and finishing plant operation. Furthermore it should be emphasized that the cost figures included in Tables 60 and 61 include only the costs of the more important components entering into the manufacture of pig iron.

CONCLUSIONS WITH RESPECT TO ASSEMBLY COSTS FOR PIG IRON

It is significant that the totals of the estimated costs of raw material assembly in the important eastern and southern steelmaking districts in 1950 do not differ greatly. The variations that do occur in the actual total costs of pig iron at the different locations may well be due to differences in the abilities of the managements in various plants or in the efficient use of by-products. It is quite obvious that the present plants have been located at

Table 60

Assembly Cost of Raw Materials Necessary to Produce a Net Ton of Pig Iron at Various Locations, July 1, 1950 (per net ton)

Location	Ore cost at mine net ton††††	Freight mine to furnace	Iron unit cost of ore****	Tons ore per ton pig iron	Ore cost per ton pig iron	Cost flux per ton pig iron	Cost ore and flux per ton iron	Coal cost at mine per ton	Freight mine to furnace	Tons coal per ton of coke	Tons coal tons coke per ton of pig iron	Coal cost per ton of pig iron	By-product credit on cost of coal	Net cost of coke per ton pig iron	Total cost assembly ton pig iron	Overhead cost above materials	Total††† cost pig iron per net ton
Youngstown, Ohio																	
Lake Ore	$2.62*	$3.88	$0.144	$2.00††	$13.00	$0.80	$13.80	$5.00	$1.85	1.55	Coal 1.40	$9.59	$2.30	$7.29	$21.09	$3.00	$24.09
Pittsburgh Coal....						(0.4 tons)			(Barge & Rail)		Coke 0.90						
Pittsburgh, Pa.																	
Lake Ore	2.62*	4.28	0.153	2.00††	13.80	0.80	14.60	5.00	0.40	1.55	Coal 1.40	7.56	2.16	5.40	20.00	3.00	23.00
Pittsburgh Coal						(0.4 tons)			(Barge)		Coke 0.90						
Pittsburgh, Pa.																	
80% Lake Ore......	2.62*	4.28	0.153)			0.70											
20% New York Ore.	5.32	3.13	0.141)	1.85	13.34	(0.35 tons)	14.04	5.00	0.40	1.55	Coal 1.32	7.13	2.06	5.08	19.12	3.00	22.12
Pittsburgh Coal									(Barge)		Coke 0.85						
Baltimore, Md.																	
20% Lake Ore......	2.62*	5.12	0.172)		2.58												
30% Swedish Ore .			0.140)	1.73	3.65	0.60	13.23	5.11	4.63	1.40	Coal 1.12	10.91	1.21	9.70	22.93	3.00	25.93
50% Chilean Ore...	2.00**	5.35	0.132)		6.40	(0.30 tons)			(Rail)		Coke 0.80						
					12.63												
Lorain, Ohio																	
Lake Ore	2.62*	2.70	0.117	2.00††	10.64	0.52	11.16	5.11	3.54	1.40	Coal 1.26	10.90	1.74	9.56	20.72	3.00	23.72
Ky. & W. Va. Coal..						(0.35 tons)			(Rail)		Coke 0.90						
Chicago, Ill.																	
Lake Ore	2.62*	2.70	0.117	2.00††	10.64	0.52	11.16	5.11	4.24	1.40	Coal 1.26	11.78	1.48	10.30	21.46	3.00	24.46
Ky. & W. Va. Coal..						(0.35 tons)			(Rail)		Coke 0.90						
Birmingham, Ala.																	
100% Red Ore.....	3.75	0.35	0.124	2.70	11.07	0.30	11.37	6.00†	0.40	1.54	Coal 1.85	11.85	2.45	9.40	20.77	3.25	24.02
Alabama Coal						(0.20 tons)					Coke 1.20						

Birmingham, Ala.

50% Ala. Red Ore..	3.75)	0.35	0.124)													
50% Venezuelan Ore	2.50)	5.95	0.128)	2.10	13.19	0.30	13.49	6.00†	0.40	1.54	Coal 1.39	8.90	1.80	7.10	20.59	3.00	23.59
Alabama Coal......				(0.25 tons)							Coke 0.90					

Mobile, Ala.

50% Red Ore.....	3.75)	2.00	0.184)													
50% Venezuelan Ore	2.50)*	4.17	0.115)	2.10	13.04	0.30	13.34	6.00†	1.40	1.54	Coal 1.39	10.28	2.03	8.25	21.59	3.00	24.59
Alabama Coal......				(0.25 tons)							Coke 0.90					

East Texas

Texas Ore........	5.50**	0.60	0.137	2.00	12.20	1.50	13.70	6.00	1.25	1.56	Coal 1.40	10.15	.83	9.32	23.02	3.30	26.32
Oklahoma Coal......				(0.70 tons)							Coke 0.90					

*Average net ton cost of underground and open pit mines.

**Includes cost of mining and amortization of equipment and transport to seaboard.

***Includes prorated estimate of mining, washing, calcining, and sintering per ton of 50 per cent iron concentrate.

****Value of ore per gross ton at assembly point divided by the percentage of iron in the ore.

†Includes mining and washing costs.

††Average analysis of Lake Superior ores shipped 50.3 per cent.

†††Does not include credits for blast furnace by-products such as gas, slag, flue dust.

††††Iron ore figures are converted from long tons to short tons for conversion purposes.

Table 61

Special Coal and Coke Cost Per Net Ton, July, 1950 (per net ton)

	Cost coal per ton at mine*	Freight per ton to furnace	Tons coal per net ton of coke	Cost of coal per net ton of coke	Cost above coke ovens per ton of coke	By-products per ton coke									Total by-products credit	Net cost coke per net ton
						Gas** cu. ft.	Value	Tar*** gallons	Value	Am. sulphate† pounds	Value	Light oil†† gallons	Value	Coke breeze		
Youngstown, Ohio — Pittsburgh Coal	$5.00	$1.85 (Barge & Rail)	1.55	$10.62	$2.15	11,500	$1.37	15.0	$1.50	36	$0.76	5.5	$0.88	$0.20	$4.71	$8.06
Pittsburgh, Pa. — Pittsburgh Coal	5.00	.40 (Barge)	1.55	8.37	2.15	11,500	1.20	15.0	1.50	36	0.76	5.5	0.88	0.20	4.54	5.98
Baltimore, Md. — West Va. Coal	5.11	4.63	1.40	13.64	2.00	9,500	1.78	6.5	0.65	20	0.42	3.0	0.48	0.20	3.53	12.11
Chicago, Ill. — E. Ky. & W. Va. Coal	5.11	4.24	1.40	13.09	2.00	9,500	1.71	7.5	0.75	22	0.46	3.3	0.53	0.20	3.65	11.44
Lorain, Ohio — 40% W. Va. 60% Pennsylvania	5.06	3.54	1.40	12.56	2.05	10,000	1.66	9.5	0.95	25	0.53	4.0	0.64	0.20	3.98	10.63
Birmingham, Ala. — Alabama Coal	6.00	.40	1.54	9.86	2.15	10,900	1.44	12.0	1.20	30	0.63	4.5	0.72	0.20	4.19	7.81
Mobile, Ala. — Alabama Coal	6.00	1.40	1.54	11.42	2.15	10,900	1.66	12.0	1.20	30	0.63	4.5	0.72	0.20	4.41	9.16
East Texas — Oklahoma Coal	6.00	1.25	1.56	11.30	2.15	11,800	0.60	16.0	0.80	28	0.59	5.6	0.89	0.20	3.08	10.37

*Includes mining and washing costs. Estimated as average for mining districts based on National Coal Association and Bureau of Mines figures.

**Gas credit based on 500 BTU gas at value of 1,000,000 BTU at point of use except in E. Texas where coke oven gas competes with natural gas.

***Coal Tar @ 10c per gallon except in E. Texas where tar is credited @ 5c per gallon.

†Ammonium Sulphate @ 2.1c per p.

††Light oil derivatives @ average value of 16c per gallon.

points that are highly competitive as to raw material assembly costs and over-all steelmaking costs for finished steel. However, the importance of raw material assembly cost as a location factor must not be overrated. For example, another important factor in the selection of a location of any steel plant is its relative position to the consuming market for the finished steel produced. This phase of the problem will be discussed later in Part IV.

Of the eight established centers shown in Table 60, East Texas has the highest estimated total assembly cost ($23.02). This compares with Birmingham ($20.77), Lorain ($20.72),

Pittsburgh ($20.00 or $19.12, depending on the kind of ore used), Chicago ($21.46), and Baltimore ($22.93). The great influence of high transportation costs is very evident in the higher cost plants such as Chicago and Baltimore. Pittsburgh, Birmingham, Lorain, and Mobile are highly competitive and this bears out the old adage that it is usually cheaper to bring the ore to the coal fields.

The use of Venezuelan ore alone at Mobile would provide a lower theoretical cost than the mixture of half Alabama ore and half Venezuelan ore shown in the table. If such a charge were to be used at Mobile, it would permit such a low coke consumption (1,400 pounds per ton of pig iron) that very low smelting costs would result. The figure would be $17.22, representing a cost which is $3.00 to $5.00 per ton lower than at any other point. However, it is not believed that such a charge would be satisfactory, as the slag volume per ton of iron might not be sufficient to give adequate control of the sulphur in the pig iron. If the cost of Venezuelan ore is eventually found to be cheaper than the figure estimated, there is no doubt that Mobile would be an attractive location for a steel plant.

Table 62

Percentage of Increase in Costs in 1950 Compared with 1945

	Per cent increase—1945-1950			
	Iron ore	Coke	Pig iron	Steel
Pittsburgh ...	110	32	73	76
Baltimore ...	118	40	94	84
Lorain	104	43	87	76
Chicago	104	44	93	84
Birmingham .	73	58	68	79

Source: Per cent increases based on cost estimates for 1945 and 1950 were prepared by E. C. Wright.

Table 63

Cost of Basic Open-Hearth Ingots Per Net Ton, July 1950
Based on 50 Per Cent Pig Iron and 50 Per Cent Scrap Charge and 90 Per Cent Yield of Metallics Charged

Location	Pig iron cost per net ton	Cost per net ton of open-hearth steel ingots								
		Pig iron	Home* scrap	Pur-chase** scrap	Iron ore	Flux	Addi-tions††	Total cost of mate-rials	Cost above material (fuel,† labor, etc.)	Total cost
Youngstown, Ohio.......	$24.09	$13.40	$8.42	$8.75	$0.58	$0.35	$1.65	$33.15	$6.70	$39.85
Pittsburgh, Pa..........	23.00	12.80	8.12	8.75	0.61	0.35	1.65	32.28	6.70	38.98
Baltimore, Md..........	25.93	14.56	8.93	7.50	0.62	0.35	1.65	33.61	6.70	40.31
Lorain, Ohio...........	23.72	13.35	8.33	7.50	0.50	0.35	1.65	31.68	6.70	38.38
Chicago, Ill...........	24.46	13.75	8.55	7.50	0.50	0.35	1.65	32.30	6.70	39.00
Birmingham, Ala.......	24.02	13.47	8.40	6.50	0.40	0.35	1.65	30.17	6.70	36.87
Mobile, Ala...........	24.59	13.66	8.75	6.50	0.55	0.35	1.65	31.46	6.70	38.16
East Texas............	26.32	14.76	9.06	6.25	0.55	0.35	1.65	32.62	6.70	39.32

*Based on 25 per cent home scrap @ 90 per cent yield. Valued at cost of pig iron + $6.00 per net ton conversion cost.
**Based on 25 per cent purchased scrap @ 90 per cent yield. Valued at average *Iron Age* scrap price, January 1-July 1, 1950.
†Fuel costs fluctuate widely in different districts and are too involved for accurate estimates.
††Based on average additions of ferro-silicon, ferro-manganese and aluminum per ton of ingots.

The breakdown by kinds of raw materials is much more significant. In the case of cost of iron ore per ton of pig iron produced, Birmingham is about on a par with the lake ports of Chicago and Lorain, but is lower than Pittsburgh and Sparrows Point. Its mining cost per ton of ore is high and the number of tons of ore required per ton of pig iron is also high. The very low cost of transporting ore from the mine to the blast furnace is the factor that gives Birmingham its relatively favorable ore cost. While fluxing material cost is relatively unimportant in the total cost, Birmingham does hold a favorable position in that respect. The cost of coke per ton of pig iron at Birmingham, using all red ore, is $9.40. This compares with a much lower cost at Pittsburgh and a somewhat lower cost at Youngstown. The cost at Lorain is about equal to the Birmingham figure, while Chicago and Sparrows Point are much higher. Birmingham's mining cost per ton of coal is relatively high, $6.00 per ton, as compared with $5.00 and $5.11 for the other points. However, Birmingham has a big advantage in coal freight costs over all the other centers except Pittsburgh. This advantage is particularly pronounced in the case of Chicago and Sparrows Point. Birmingham's big disadvantage comes from the larger quantity of coke required to produce a ton of pig iron, 1.20 tons as compared with around .90 tons for the other centers.

The estimates presented in the table serve to bring out two further points of interest. The estimated cost of coke per ton of pig iron for the use of high-grade Venezuelan ore drops to $5.59 compared to $9.40 for the use of Alabama red ores. This bring to the front the possible saving in cost that may be attained by having higher grade ores. Such a result might be obtained by the successful concentration of Alabama ores or by blending the Alabama ores with the high-grade foreign ores.

The use of a 50 per cent mixture of Alabama red ore and Venezuelan ore would have a stimulating effect on southern steel operations for several reasons: (1) it would increase the output of the blast furnace at no increase in fixed costs; (2) it would require less coke per ton of pig iron produced; (3) it would make pig iron (with less than .35 per cent phosphorus) which could be used suitably for most gray iron castings; and (4) it would reduce the amount of scrap needed by foundries, thereby making more scrap available for steel manufacture. The importation of the high grade, low phosphorus Venezuelan ores to the Alabama district will thus have far-reaching technical and economic advantages.

Estimated Cost of Steel

Table 63 exhibits the estimated cost of making steel ingots at selected steel centers. This is based on a 50 per cent pig iron and 50 per cent scrap charge, since this mixture approximates the average charge used in American open-hearth plants; one-half of the scrap consumed consists of the home scrap obtained in the rolling operations of ingots and one-half is scrap purchased from dealers. Although the cost of pig iron is fairly stable, the cost of purchased scrap varies widely. In the first six months of 1950, the price of steel scrap at Pittsburgh varied between $20 and $46 per ton, so an average of these extremes was taken for estimating purposes for this item. Scrap prices have always been higher in the larger steel centers because the great demand, compared with the supply available in the immediate area, tends to set prices which encourage movement of scrap to such centers. Since the South has a surplus of scrap, steel mills in the region can obtain supplies of this vital raw material at lower cost. The cost of open-hearth ingots at Mobile and Birmingham is definitely lower than for any other district in the table.

The estimates seem to confirm the feasibility of an iron and steel center at Mobile so far as the costs of assembling raw materials is concerned. Here again a word of caution is in order. The data presented are estimates and do not pertain to what may be the most important problems—namely, the markets for steel that can be reached from Mobile and the advisability of making the large investment of capital that would be required.

CHAPTER XVI

TECHNICAL PRACTICES AND PROBLEMS AND GENERAL CONCLUSIONS CONCERNING THE BASIC IRON AND STEEL INDUSTRIES OF THE SOUTH

The practices and problems of mining and preparing ore, coal, and coke for use in the blast furnaces of the Southeast have been developed in some detail in Chapters XIII and XIV. It might seem that logic would require a similar treatment of the practices involved in the processing of raw materials in blast furnaces and steel works. However, the same basic facilities, such as blast furnaces and basic open-hearth furnaces, are used in making pig iron and steel in all the districts. The same is generally true of the equipment for rolling and finishing steel products. These facilities have been described in Chapter IX in the discussions of the properties of the companies engaged in the basic iron and steel industry of the Southeast. Also, the practices are fundamentally the same in all districts. Consequently, it was decided that an extended discussion of blast furnace and steel mill practices in the Southeast would not be attempted.[1] However, there are a number of questions concerning furnace practice which arise from conditions peculiar to the Southeast. Also, throughout the report, mention has been made of situations which give rise to special technical problems. This is especially true of the chapters on the characteristics of ore and coal deposits and on the mining and preparation of ore, coal, and coke. The purpose of this chapter, therefore, is to summarize, and perhaps amplify, the points that have already been made and to add a discussion of the special problems involved in making pig iron and steel in the Southeast.[2]

Preparation of Raw Materials

For many years, the coal mined in the southern coal fields has contained a higher ash content than many of the high-grade coals mined in the northern districts. In addition, the increased use of mechanized equipment to decrease mining labor has caused an increase in all coal producing areas in the ash content of the coal mined. Because of the characteristics of the coal seams, it has long been the practice to wash the southern coals that are used for making blast furnace coke, while most northern plants have escaped this operation until recent years. At the present time, nearly 100 per cent of all Alabama coal used for making metallurgical coke is washed, while only about 20 per cent of the Pennsylvania, West Virginia, and Kentucky coals are being washed. As pointed out in Chapter XIV, excellent methods for washing southern coals have been developed, and washed coals as low as 8 per cent in ash and 0.8 per cent in sulphur are delivered to the coke plants. Increasingly, the northern steel plants are being faced with the problem of providing high-grade coal due to the depletion of the higher-grade low-ash coals and to increased mechanized mining. As a result, large installations of coal washers are now being made in the Pittsburgh and West Virginia coal

[1] The illustrated booklet, *Steel Making at Birmingham,* published by the Tennessee Coal, Iron and Railroad Company, describes in some detail the processes used by that company. There are a number of standard treatises on iron and steelmaking. A very detailed one with illustrations drawn from practice is *The Making, Shaping, and Treating of Steel* by J. M. Camp and C. B. Francis.

[2] The following discussion of technical problems has been largely prepared by E. C. Wright, Professor of Metallurgy, University of Alabama.

districts. Moreover, the northern mines are encountering increasing amounts of sulphur (2.00 per cent) in the coal mined, and much of this cannot be removed by known methods of washing coal. Since sulphur in steel causes as much trouble as phosphorus and more difficult to remove in steel refining processes, the sulphur problem will probably become increasingly troublesome in the northern steel centers. The manufacture of good quality blast furnace coke may therefore become more costly in the northern plants compared to the cost of southern blast furnace coke.

The low content of iron in most southern ores has always caused a much higher coke consumption per ton of pig iron than in areas using higher grade iron ores. Thus, most furnaces using Lake Superior ores (51.5 per cent iron) have been able to smelt pig iron with a coke consumption of 1700-1800 pounds of coke per ton as against 2300-2400 pounds in furnaces operating on Red Mountain hematite ores with 35.0 per cent iron. This difference has always been a high cost penalty on southern furnaces and has long made it appear attractive to beneficiate southern ores to the range of 50.0 per cent iron in order to reduce the coke requirements. The study that has been given to the problem of beneficiating the southern iron ores was reviewed in Chapter XIII. As yet no process has been developed which has clearly demonstrated that it can be operated on an economical basis, with the possible exception of the Spaulding plant of the Republic Steel Corporation.

The fact that the Southeast is characterized by adverse mining conditions and relatively low-grade ore makes it especially important that attention be given to attaining maximum efficiency in operations. Emphasis should be placed on the use of the best engineering skills and on the selection and installation of the kinds of equipment best fitted for reducing the costs of the coal and ore delivered to the coke and blast furnace plants. Mining methods should be used which will result in the recovery of the largest per cent of the ore in the beds in one operation, after development passageways are driven. This depends on perfecting an economical method of concentrating the iron ore. Each company in the industry in the Southeast should devote a definite amount of its appropriations to research on this problem since a satisfactory solution will make it possible to reduce mining costs by mining the entire Big Seam and possibly the ferruginous sandstones. Furthermore, the mineable iron ore reserves of the Southeast will be thereby greatly increased. The high-grade concentrates, if obtained, will result in a lower consumption of coke, and, therefore, a reduction in fuel costs, together with an increase in the capacity of the present blast furnaces to produce pig iron.

Metallurgical Practices and Problems in the Southeast

Differences in the character of the raw materials, coal, iron ore, and fluxing stone in the various steel centers often require different manufacturing techniques, although the same principles are employed in the smelting of the ores and in the refining of the steel. In the southeastern district, the two characteristics which have had the greatest influence upon iron and steelmaking practices are the low iron content of the ores and the presence of phosphorus.

Southern ores, because of their low iron content, require slightly different blast furnaces than those used in other steel districts. These lower-grade ores use much larger amounts of coke per ton of iron produced and require more flux with larger slag volumes than furnaces smelting richer ores. This situation makes it necessary to have larger blast furnaces and to blow greatly increased volumes of wind for a given output of pig iron.

Since most southern pig iron contains from 0.70 per cent to 0.90 per cent phosphorus, the pig iron is not satisfactory for many cast-iron foundry operations. The large cast-iron pipe industry in the South has grown on this high phosphorus pig iron, but most of the product is in the form of cast-iron pipe which can tolerate a high phosphorus content of about 0.50 per cent. Even in this industry, it is necessary to make up the cast-iron melting mix with large amounts of low-phosphorus steel scrap to reduce the phosphorus content of the castings. Many of these foundries use as much as 50 per cent steel scrap in the cupola charge on this account. The growth of a more diversified foundry industry in the South has been greatly retarded by this situation.

A review of the development of steelmaking brings out the influence of high-phosphorus ores on the industry in the South. In 1870, steel production in the United States consisted of 68,750 long tons, which included 1,339 long tons of open-hearth steel and 37,500 long tons of acid Bessemer steel. The steel age had just begun, and the dependence of the infant industries on weak metals such as wrought iron and gray cast iron was still paramount. There was practically no reservoir of iron and steel scrap for remelting, as the consumption of iron in the agrarian economy of that time was very small. All iron and steel products were made from the pig iron smelted in blast furnaces—wrought iron by remelting in puddling furnaces, cast iron by remelting in cupolas, and Bessemer steel by blowing air through molten pig iron to burn out the impurities. The only good refractories available for furnace construction were fire clay and silica, both of which are acid in character and yield slags which are high in silica. In this type of furnace lining, the removal of phosphorus is impossible as it will not enter a slag which is high in silica. As a result, the success of the acid Bessemer steel process depends on the use of Bessemer pig iron containing less than 0.8 per cent phosphorus and Bessemer iron ores with less than .05 per cent phosphorus.

The infant steel industry thus grew up on acid Bessemer steel due to the availability of low phosphorus ore, and, for over 30 years, the method predominated in the steel industry. In 1900, steel production totaled 10,188,329 long tons and consisted of 6,684,770 tons of acid Bessemer steel, 3,398,135 tons of open-hearth steel (much of which was also made in acid-lined furnaces), 100,562 tons of crucible steel and 4,962 tons of other kinds of steel.[3] The spectacular Bessemer process was so cheap and

[3] *Mineral Resources, 1900,* p. 88.

so rapid that it produced steel with much superior properties in great volume and at low cost. Its impact on industrial expansion has never been fully evaluated. The output of wrought iron from puddling furnaces never exceeded 150 pounds per hour, while a 10-ton Bessemer converter produced 80,000 pounds per hour.

The southern iron industry could not participate in this acid Bessemer development on account of the high phosphorus content of the southern ores and pig iron. Similar situations existed in England, France, and Germany. Bessemer himself had to erect his own steel plant and use low-phosphorus ores obtained from Sweden to make a low-phosphorus pig iron. His attempts to use high-phosphorus English pig irons resulted in complete failure. Thomas Gilchrist finally overcame this difficulty in England by developing a refractory converter lining of crushed dolomite and tar. In blowing high-phosphorus pig iron in this type of basic lining, he was successful in reducing the phosphorus content of the metal below .04 per cent, providing the original phosphorus content of the iron exceeded 1.50 per cent. This is the basic Bessemer process which is still widely used in Europe today. Unfortunately, the phosphorus content of southern pig iron (about .80 per cent) was too low to supply the heat necessary for the "afterblow," in which stage the phosphorus is almost entirely oxidized and transferred to the high lime slag as calcium phosphate.

For these reasons, the manufacture of steel in the South lagged far behind the other districts. The stationary open-hearth furnace was invented by Siemens, and the successful operation of this furnace depended on three features: (1) the invention of the regenerative principle of preheating the air used for combustion by interchange with the hot chimney gases, (2) the gasification of coal in producers, and (3) a satisfactory basic refractory such as magnesia (MgO) or dolomite. The reservoir of iron and steel scrap which was accumulating in the iron and steel consuming centers also provided a cheap source of iron-bearing raw material for which there was little market, since the Bessemer steel plant consumed little scrap. This factor enabled the open-hearth process to make low-cost steel, as the ability of the basic lined furnace to eliminate phosphorus made the process universally adaptable to any kind of raw material. At the present time, 90 per cent of American steel is now made by the basic open-hearth process.

The introduction of open-hearth furnaces in the eighties had a great effect on the northern steel plants, but was of little immediate importance to the South. There was little iron and steel scrap available as the metal fabricating industries of the South at that time processed only small quantities of iron and steel. The manufacture of steel from pig iron and iron ore in the open-hearth furnace, while technically possible, is not economical unless supplemented with considerable quantities of scrap. The South had to await the introduction of the Duplex process, which combines the advantages of both the acid Bessemer and basic open-hearth process, before a satisfactory method of making good steel from southern raw material appeared. This practice consists of burning out the silicon, manganese, and carbon from the molten pig iron by blowing air through the bath in an acid lined Bessemer converter. The blown metal, still containing all the phosphorus, is then poured into a basic lined tilting open-hearth furnace, where it is treated with iron ore and burned lime to oxidize the phosphorus and to form calcium phosphate, which enters the slag. This Duplex process makes steel at a cost very similar to stationary open-hearth plants using large amounts of iron and steel scrap. The introduction of the Duplex process at Ensley, Alabama, in 1899 was immediately successful and finally overcame the technical and economic problems which had for so long blocked successful steel manufacture in the South.[4] For forty years

[4] Alabama Geological Survey, *Iron Making in Alabama*. In Chapter XI, "Steel Making in Alabama," Frank Crockard states, "The first attempts in America [to use the duplex process] was that of the Tennessee Coal, Iron and Railroad Company at its Ensley plant in November 1899."

thereafter, the cost of steel in Birmingham was probably the lowest of any United States district. Since 1940, the greatly increased cost of underground coal and iron ore mining in the Birmingham district probably has eliminated much, if not all, of this advantage. The introduction from Venezuela of cheap, high-grade ores with low phosphorus content should have a stimulating effect on the production of iron and steel in the South.

As steel scrap became available in the South, it was possible to install stationary open-hearth furnaces. It is estimated that about 65 per cent of southern steel is now made in stationary furnaces and 35 per cent by the Duplex process.

Possible Changes in Steelmaking Techniques in the South

There has always been the possibility that the basic Bessemer process could be applied to the Birmingham pig irons by raising the phosphorus level of the pig iron to the required amount by the addition of a small amount of phosphate rock to the blast furnace charge. Many of the common types of steel, such as structural shapes, wire rods, pipe, plates, and rails, are successfully made in Europe by this basic Bessemer process, and a more thorough study of the method in the southeastern district seems justified. The English and Alsace-Lorraine ores are high in phosphorus and the process has worked economically there for over 50 years. The high phosphorus slag produced in this process has long been used as fertilizer as it has a similar composition to the high phosphorus slag now made so successfully in the Birmingham district.

The basic Bessemer process has a present appeal as the investment cost for new steel capacity is much lower than for corresponding open-hearth capacity and much less space is needed for a given output of steel. The labor costs (per ton of steel) are also much lower than for the open-hearth, and in this period of rising labor rates, this feature is particularly important. Improved knowledge of the physical chemical principles of steelmaking also indicates that steels for many applications can be made by the Bessemer process that are equal in quality to those made in the open hearth.[5] The chief drawback to increased Bessemer installations is that large blast furnace capacity is required, since little or no scrap is used in making steel in this manner. It would, therefore, not be economical to consider a plant for making Bessemer steel only, but a steel mill wherein about 50 per cent of the output is Bessemer and 50 per cent open-hearth is an attractive combination. The scrap from the Bessemer ingots can be used in the open-hearth, making the plant self-contained in scrap and eliminating dependency on purchased scrap.

One of the chief objections to either acid or basic Bessemer steel made in bottom-blown converters arises from the higher nitrogen content of such steels compared to open-hearth steels. Pig iron usually contains about .003 per cent nitrogen, and basic open-hearth steels have about the same content as the pig iron charged. In either of the Bessemer processes, the nitrogen content is much higher because of the effect of blowing air (77 per cent nitrogen by weight) through the molten steel. Acid Bessemer steel contains .012 per cent to .017 per cent nitrogen, while some basic heats contain as much as .016 to .021, depending on the length of time given to the phosphorus-removing afterblow. Even these small amounts of nitrogen profoundly affect the physical properties of the steel—especially the ductility. Consequently, open-hearth steels are preferred for very soft steels used for severe cold forming work. This is particularly evident in the sheet and strip field, but steels with .015 per cent nitrogen have long been used without difficulty for pipe, wire, structural, and many other steel commodities.

At the present time, there is a definite interest in the use of side-blown converters[6] in the steel industry, and some research work is already underway in this field. The method of blowing the air in the converter on the surface of the molten metal instead of through the metal from the bottom gives two advantages

over the older bottom-blowing procedure. There is little or no absorption of nitrogen and the bath temperature is much higher, due to the fact that it is not chilled by the passage of cold air through the molten steel and that most of the carbon burns to carbon dioxide in side blowing instead of to carbon monoxide as in bottom blowing. The formation of carbon dioxide instead of carbon monoxide generates so much more heat that it becomes difficult to keep the bath from becoming overheated severely, and its temperature must be controlled by additions of cold scrap, by reducing the rate of blowing, or by the size of the converter. It will be necessary to surmount these problems before side-blowing practices, either for acid or basic lined, can be adapted to steel-making on a large tonnage basis. From a chemical standpoint however, it is known that either killed or rimmed steels, low in nitrogen content, are possible by the side-blowing method. If steels could be made in production quantities in properly operated side-blown vessels, it would be difficult to differentiate the resulting products from the standard basic open-hearth steels. Many small side-blown converters, up to five-ton capacity, are used successfully for making steel castings, and there are definite prospects that larger vessels suitable for rolled steel manufacture may be developed in the future.

The use of the side-blown converter with a basic lining may therefore have interesting possibilities for the manufacture of a low nitrogen steel from the high-phosphorus pig irons of the southeastern district. The study of this process should receive serious consideration, as it might well be possible to produce steels in this manner that are equal to the steel now made by the basic open-hearth process. Proper manipulation of the side-blown basic converter operation should also enable the production of a basic slag high enough in phosphorus to be useful as a fertilizer.

Another plausible suggestion which is now being investigated is that of the Duplex Bessemer process. This practice gives steel of low nitrogen content and offers better control of

[5] E. C. Wright, "The Manufacture and Properties of Killed Bessemer Steel," p. 107.

[6] E. C. Sims and F. Toy, "The Turbo-Hearth," p. 694.

the temperature of the bath (the latter being a troublesome problem in the direct side-blowing process discussed above). The method consists of bottom-blowing the molten pig iron in an acid-lined converter to the point where the silicon and manganese are oxidized. This takes from two to three minutes, depending on the amount of silicon in the pig iron, and is easily observed because the long flame of the carbon combustion does not appear until most of the silicon is oxidized. There is no nitrogen increase in this brief bottom-blowing stage, as the carbon content of the bath exceeds 3 per cent. The acid converter is then turned down, the acid slag skimmed off, and the metal is transferred to a basic-lined converter where it is side-blown to the carbon end point. If the metal is too hot, it may be brought to the correct temperature by proper additions of cold scrap (up to 30 per cent) and then side-blown without too much damage to the converter refractories. Steel made by this practice is low in nitrogen and phosphorus and has the same characteristics as open-hearth steel. The process consumes large amounts of scrap and produces a high-phosphorus slag suitable for fertilizer in the basic converter.

General Conclusions Concerning the Basic Industries

The iron industry in the Southeast was established early on a local small unit basis, but the transition to the type of industry that characterizes the present—large integrated plants in a small number of places—was greatly delayed by the character of the ore and coal resources of the region, the lack of a technology to meet the special problems of the industry in the South, and the limited markets arising from the kind of an economy that prevailed in the region.

By the early part of the twentieth century, a modern iron and steel industry was firmly established in the Birmingham area. While the technical and economic problems that confront the industry were not fully solved during the first half of the century, the statistical record of employment, production, and capacity showed

sustained progress. The region showed particularly strong and healthy growth in the production of steel ingots and hot rolled iron and steel products. Still, the basic iron and steel industry in the South in 1950 occupied a relatively low position in the economy, whether measured in terms of its position in the iron and steel industry of the nation or in terms of its position in the total manufacturing activities of the region. It was weak both in total volume and in the production of many kinds of steel mill products that find wide use in a modern industrial economy.

The basic iron and steel industry in the South is operated by some fourteen companies. Six of these have plants in Alabama, one in Georgia, two in Tennessee, and five in Texas or Oklahoma. Three companies have fully integrated iron and steel plants, five do not carry operations beyond the blast furnace, two have open-hearth furnaces and rolling mills but no blast furnaces, and four limit their activities to operating rolling mills and producing small quantities of steel in electric furnaces. In size, the Tennessee Coal, Iron and Railroad Company is by far the largest and is the most influential. The other larger companies include the Republic Steel Corporation, the Sheffield Steel Corporation, the Woodward Iron Company, and the Sloss-Sheffield Steel and Iron Company.

By far the largest proportion of the capacity is in the plants in Birmingham and Gadsden. A district which includes these two cities may be considered as dominating the basic iron and steel industry in the South, but the developments in Texas, particularly those of the Sheffield Steel Corporation and the Lone Star Steel Company, are significant. A review of the properties and activities of the larger companies of the South shows that active post-war programs for the expansion of plant capacity and for the building of facilities for the production of new products are under way.

In the mining and preparation of both ore and coal, the Southeast has had to face difficult problems that have arisen both from the physical conditions under which the deposits occur and from the composition of the ore and the coal as they come from the mines. Underground mining under adverse conditions has made for low production per man employed. The low iron content and the presence of phosphorus have created serious problems with the ore, and the mixture of rock and dirt in the coal has made washing or other methods of cleaning necessary. Much has been done to overcome these difficulties but continued efforts should be directed toward developing improved methods that will strengthen the competitive position of the industry. Important areas for investigation and experimentation are: improvements in methods of mining; beneficiation of the southern ores; increased output from established plants by using blends of foreign and native ores; the production of a wider range of iron and steel products, particularly a low phosphorus pig iron, steel products such as cold rolled sheets, pipe, and tubes, and a wider variety of shapes and forms; and the study of new and improved steelmaking prac-

tices. The fact that the companies with plants in the region are actively engaged both in experimentation and research and in building new and improved plants is encouraging.

While it seems safe to assume that the South, in recent years, has lost much of its advantage of being a low cost producer of iron and steel, the estimates of costs of assembling raw materials at blast furnaces and of producing steel show that costs at Birmingham compare favorably with those in other steel centers.

It must be realized that the production of iron and steel under modern conditions involves many, and very complicated, factors. In the South, there are both favorable and unfavorable conditions. Enough has certainly been said to indicate that the basic industry has had to face serious technical and operating problems, but it seems reasonable to conclude that there are no obstacles inherent in the nature of the basic industries of the South that an aggressive and able leadership in the industry cannot overcome.

PART IV
THE MARKET FOR IRON AND STEEL IN THE SOUTH

INTRODUCTION

The preceding main divisions of this study have dealt with the raw materials available for the production of iron and steel in the South, the history and general characteristics of blast furnaces and steel works in the Southeast, and the technical and operating problems of the basic iron and steel industries of the region. The objective of the present main division of the report is to consider the South as a market for iron and steel products. In the previous parts, attention has been centered primarily on the Southeast. The products of the basic industries located in the Southeast find markets in the Southwest also. Consequently, in Part IV the total Southern market area, as defined in Chapter I, will be the area on which the statistics and the discussion will be based. To a very great extent the chapters will be factual in character and will attempt to develop the information needed for an appraisal of the region's present and potential demand for the products of blast furnaces and steel mills.

The first three chapters will be used to present the background material which is needed as a foundation for the more direct study of the use of iron and steel in the South. The characteristics of an area exercise a powerful influence on its market demands and so Chapter XVII attempts to describe the characteristics of the South that affect the use of iron and steel within its boundaries. The use of iron and steel in the South must be similar in many respects to the pattern of use in the nation as a whole. Also a knowledge of the relative importance of the various market demands of the country provides both a guide to the study of the region and criteria to judge the strengths and weaknesses of conditions found to exist within the region. Chapter XVIII, *The Use Pattern of Iron and Steel*, is designed to meet this need. Study of the use pattern of iron and steel directs attention to the important place occupied by the manufacturing concerns that buy and use iron and steel as raw materials for their finished products. The third background chapter, therefore, discusses the important characteristics of the iron and steel processing and fabricating industries of the United States.

The remaining chapters of Part IV deal with topics that are directly concerned with the consumption of iron and steel in the South. The titles of the chapters should be sufficient to suggest their contents and connections with the general theme of this division: *The Iron and Steel Processing and Fabricating Industries of the South; Trends in the Iron and Steel Processing and Fabricating Industries of the South; Movements of Iron and Steel in the South; the Consumption of Steel Mill Products in the South; and Trends in the South that Affect the Demand for Iron and Steel.*

CHAPTER XVII

CHARACTERISTICS OF THE SOUTH THAT AFFECT THE USE OF IRON AND STEEL

In recent years the South has been the subject of numerous articles, reports and books. These are quite generally available, and this chapter will not attempt to present information for the general enlightenment of the reader. However, the present conditions and future prospects of an industry, or group of industries, can be understood and evaluated only in light of the setting in which they exist and must operate. Consequently, the present chapter attempts to point out some of the important economic characteristics of the South which influence the development of the iron and steel industries of the region.

While measures of general conditions are not items of primary concern, it is necessary to use certain general facts as bench marks in the analysis of the data that are more specifically related to the problems of the industries involved. Such data for 1940 are presented in Table 64. The relative position of the southern regions with respect to population, land area, and income should be particularly helpful in appraising the position occupied by the South. Roughly, the South as a whole had one-fourth of the total land area and population of the nation, but slightly less than 15 per cent of the urban population and 14 per cent of the total income payments to individuals.

Since agriculture holds such a predominant place in the economy of the South, it seems natural to begin the more detailed examination of the South's characteristics by raising the question as to what are the features of the South's agriculture that are of greatest importance to the demand for iron and steel and hence to the development of iron and steel industries. The industrial structure and characteristics of the South form a second topic for

inquiry. These two represent basic fields of activity which engage a large portion of the efforts of the population. From these and other lines of endeavor flow the goods and services and likewise the incomes which sustain the economic life of an area. One of the most comprehensive measures of economic ability, and hence of demand, is provided by income estimates. The third main section, therefore, will be devoted to an analysis of the size and sources of income in the South. Finally, a number of the other underlying factors which exercise an influence on the southern market will be mentioned and discussed briefly. Throughout the chapter the effort will be to present only outstanding facts which are considered as necessary for background purposes and not to attempt the final analyses of particular problems or to arrive at conclusions concerning prospects for the future.

Agriculture

The South has long been looked upon as predominantly rural and agricultural. The 1940 census of population supports this view, since the urban population of the Southern market area was only 35.2 per cent of the total population of the area compared with 56.5 per cent for the nation as a whole. Also 35.2 per cent of all employed persons reported agriculture as their chief source of employment compared with 18.5 per cent for the United States. The war and postwar years have seen sizable shifts away from agriculture in the South, but even so, the position of farming in the economic life of the area has not yet been greatly affected. From the point of view of the development of markets for iron and steel and their products, this emphasis upon agriculture is a fact of the greatest importance. In the first place, an analysis of uses of iron and steel shows that agriculture as a direct source of demand occupies a position well down in the list of various classes of uses. It follows therefore that a region devoted largely to farming has a quite limited market for iron and steel as compared with one that is more industrial and urban. In the second place, the fact that agriculture has held such an important place in the southern economy has meant that the characteristics of agriculture have exercised a greater influ-

Table 64

General Characteristics of the South, 1940

	Southeast	Southwest	South
Population	22,738,429	8,751,258	31,489,687
Land area	430,877	332,927	763,804
Population per square mile	52.8	26.3	41.2
Urban population—number	7,288,263	3,791,052	11,079,315
per cent of total	32.1	43.3	35.2
Number of employed persons—total	7,578,611	2,797,094	10,375,705
in agriculture	2,793,217	854,546	3,647,763
in industry	1,694,101	496,002	2,190,103
in other activities	3,091,293	1,446,546	4,537,839
Per cent of employed persons			
in agriculture	36.9	30.6	35.2
in industry	22.4	17.7	21.1
in other activities	40.8	51.7	43.7
Racial composition			
white	15,412,360	7,591,773	23,004,133
native born	15,252,393	7,337,026	22,589,419
foreign born	159,967	254,747	414,714
negro	7,293,072	1,093,240	8,386,312
other	32,997	66,245	99,242
per cent of total			
native white	67.1	83.8	71.8
foreign born white	.7	2.9	1.3
negro	32.1	12.5	26.6
other	.1	.8	.3
Income payments—total (million dollars)	7,035.7	3,481.9	10,517.6
per capita (dollars)	308	398	333
Per cent of United States			
total population	17.37	6.65	23.92
land area	14.47	11.18	25.66
urban population	9.79	5.09	14.89
employed persons	16.78	6.19	22.97
income payments	9.28	4.59	13.87

Note: A. For purposes of comparison the following figures for the United States are given.

Population per square mile	44.2
Per cent urban of total population	56.5
Per cent of total employed persons	
in agriculture	18.5
in industry	30.0
Per cent of total population	
native born white	81.1
foreign born white	8.7
negro	9.8
Per capita income	$575

B. National Income Unit, U. S. Department of Commerce, furnished special breakdowns to the Bureau of Business Research, University of Alabama. The state totals agree with those published in "Income Payments by State, *Survey of Current Business* (August 1948)

Source: *Census of Population, 1940.*

CHART 19

POSITION OF THE SOUTH IN THE NATION, 1939 AND 1945

AS INDICATED BY SELECTED MEASURES OF ECONOMIC STRENGTH

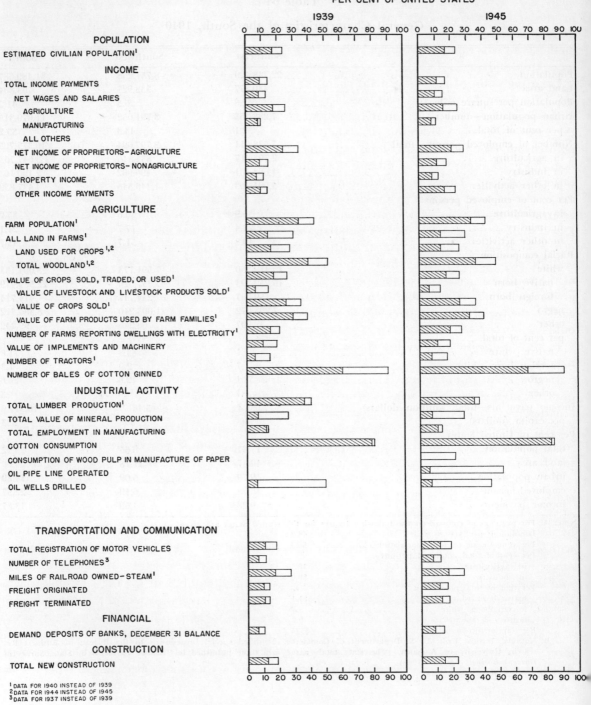

ence upon the total market for iron and steel in the South than has been the case in the North and East. That the importance of this factor has been recognized is evidenced by the fact that the Tennessee Coal, Iron and Railroad Company has maintained a staff of agricultural specialists to work with the agricultural experiment stations and other agricultural agencies in the states of its market area toward the development of implements, equipment, and methods which would encourage the use of more iron and steel.

From the point of view of general characteristics, the Southeast and the Southwest have so many differences that it is desirable to discuss the two separately. However, it should be pointed out that the division along state lines does not give an entirely true picture since the eastern parts of Texas and Oklahoma have many of the same features as those that characterize the Southeast. Also, central and south Florida constitute a quite distinct subdivision of the Southeast. A brief statement of the general characteristics of these three subdivisions of the Southern market area, therefore, will be given, and some of the implications with regard to the use of iron and steel will be pointed out.

In the Southeast, outstanding characteristics may be listed as those below.

1. *The small size of farms.* The average size of farms in 1945 was 84.9 acres compared with a national average of 194.8 acres. Farms under 50 acres constituted 55.9 per cent of all farms in the Southeast compared with 38.4 per cent for the United States.

2. *The emphasis upon field crops.* Field crops sold in 1945 accounted for 53 per cent of the value of all farm products sold or used by farm families in the Southeast compared with 31 per cent for the United States. On the other hand, livestock and livestock products sold accounted for 17.1 per cent of the value of farm products compared with 47.7 per cent for the nation as a whole.

3. *The low investment in equipment per farm.* The average value of implements and machinery per farm in the Southeast in 1945

was $328 compared with $878 for the United States. In the Southeast, 8.5 per cent of the farms reported tractors in contrast to 34.2 per per cent for the country as a whole.

4. *The greater prevalence of tenancy and of non-white operators.* In the Southeast, 46.8 per cent of the farms were tenant-operated compared with the national percentages of 31.7 per cent. Non-whites (almost entirely Negroes) operated 31.7 per cent of the farms in the Southeast compared with 11.8 per cent in the United States. In the Southeast, 76.6 per cent of the non-white operators were tenants compared with 33.0 per cent of the white farm operators.

5. *The relatively low value of the product per farm or per farm person.* In 1945, the value per farm of products sold or used by farm families in the Southeast was $1694 compared with the national figure of $3091. Of the nine southeastern states, only Florida had a value of farm products per farm person in excess of the national figure of $769. Of the others, North Carolina (with $452) had the highest figure and while six of the states had less than $385, or one-half the national average.

These five items do not constitute a full catalogue of the general characteristics of farming in the Southeast but their implications with regard to the market for iron and steel are highly significant, and their influence on past and present developments is great. In general, farming in the Southeast has been carried on with relatively little supplement of man power with mechanical power or the more complicated kinds of tools and equipment. The demand has been largely for hand tools and for horse (or mule) drawn implements and those, for the most part, of the smaller and simpler types. The low productivity in terms of values produced per farm or per farm person has limited the ability of the farm operators to buy additional equipment for their farming operation or appliances for use in their homes. The pressure of the population on the land, as evidenced by the small farms, has cheapened human labor and has tended to slow down the transition to a more mechanized type of agriculture, which involves a change in the ratios between man, land, and capital equipment. The farms operated by the tenant class have been characterized by short-term tenure and frequent moves from farm to farm, and this condition constitutes another obstacle to the change from a simple nonmechanized agriculture, largely operated along traditional lines, to a mechanized and scientifically operated system.

In contrast to the Southeast, Central and Western Texas and Oklahoma are characterized by large farms, a higher degree of mechanization, and values of product per farm and per farm person which compare favorably with the national averages. Also, field crops for sale occupy a less important place in the agricultural economy, and the raising of livestock on a commercial basis is an important activity. These characteristics have made this area an attractive market for mechanized equipment and for such products as wire fence.

The subtropical climate and other favorable conditions have made central and southern Florida one of the major fruit and vegetable producing areas of the United States. This is particularly true of the citrus fruits, especially oranges and grapefruit. The lower Rio Grande Valley in the extreme southern tip of Texas has similar characteristics and a similar agriculture. The development of canning industries, particularly for citrus juices and frozen concentrates, created a specialized market for steel products. Also, the manufacture of cattle feeds from processed citrus pulp has been an important factor in encouraging cattle raising, and this has created markets for steel.

Different kinds of products and different systems, or modes, of farming call for equipment to meet the specialized needs. Hence the particular kinds of crops or livestock in a market area exercise a strong influence on what will be demanded and thus become major factors in determining what metal fabricating industries, if any, are present. This is particularly important in the case of those products in which the region under study occupies a predominant position. It should also be pointed out that the kind of product not only influences the equipment needed on the farm for growing and harvesting, but also the facilities required for transporting, storing, marketing, and possible processing. For these reasons, an examination of the sources from which the South derives its agricultural income is important in this study.

The Bureau of Agricultural Economics, U. S. Department of Agriculture, has published estimates of the cash receipts from the major classes of farm products on a state basis for 1945 and 1946.[1] An analysis of these estimates shows that the South accounted for more than 50 per cent of the cash receipts of the nation's farms from the products listed.

	1945 (per cent of U.S.)	1946 (per cent of U.S.)
Tung nuts	100.0%	100.0%
Cotton		
Lint	91.7%	87.6%
Seed	89.4%	84.5%
Peanuts	91.3%	89.3%
Rice	84.6%	78.5%
Grapefruit	81.7%	85.2%
Sweet potatoes	74.3%	70.6%
Sorghum for grain	59.8%	80.3%
Tobacco	59.5%	66.7%

The South's percentages of the national totals were 25% or more in these additional products.

	1945	1946
Peaches	38.3%	32.0%
Oranges	38.0%	44.4%
Strawberries	37.6%	33.8%
Sugar crops	35.8%	37.3%
Tree nuts	34.5%	27.7%
Broilers (chickens)	26.4%	28.6%
Wool	26.0%	27.3%
Truck crops	24.7%	25.1%

These lists are not sufficiently detailed to bring out all of the special items in which the South occupies a high relative position but they do serve to call attention to important items. Some of those listed have total values that are comparatively small and their effect on the total market is not great, they may

[1] U. S. Department of Agriculture, *The Farm Income Situation.*

have very important places in the economy of particular localities and may be the basis for one or more processing plants. On the other hand, the influence of such crops as cotton, peanuts, and tobacco on the equipment required on the farms and on the marketing and industrial structure of the South needs at the present only to be mentioned.

The location in the South of production of the various farm products is a final topic for discussion. The agricultural economy of the South has been dominated by cotton to such an extent that cotton and the South have become almost synonymous. The attention and publicity given to cotton has probably kept many from realizing that the South has many other crops and that there are many areas of specialized crop production within its limits. It probably is a surprise to many to know that in the South the acreage planted to corn exceeds that of cotton. However, corn has a relatively low yield and is primarily a feed rather than a commercial crop. Also, it should be pointed out that despite the relatively low position held by livestock and livestock products as sources of cash income in the Southeast, the percentages of farms that have hogs, chickens, and cows are relatively high. The average number per farm is small and the animals are kept primarily for home use rather than for commercial purposes. Somewhat the same observation can be made for such feed crops as oats, hay, field peas, and a number of the legumes. This situation means that there is a market, though a quite limited one, for the kinds of equipment commonly associated with the raising of livestock and the production of the feed grains and forage crops.

Cotton is produced in most of the southern market area, but there are a number of notable exceptions. These include central and eastern Tennessee, the mountains of western North Carolina, the Atlantic tidewater area, the state of Florida, the Gulf tidewater area, western Texas, the Texas panhandle, and northern Oklahoma.

Tobacco is grown to some extent in northern and eastern Tennessee, but the largest crops grown in the area covered by this study are in the eastern half of North Carolina and in northeastern South Carolina. Another important belt extends across southern Georgia into northern Florida.

Rice is an important crop in three rather limited areas: one in the coastal section of southwest Louisiana, a second in eastern Texas, and a third in eastern Arkansas.

Peanut culture has its most important locations in southeastern Alabama and southwestern Georgia and in the eastern part of the Carolinas. Another area is in eastern Texas.

Winter wheat is not usually associated with the South and is raised only to a limited extent in the Southeast, in Tennessee and North Carolina, but western Oklahoma and northern and western Texas, particularly the Texas panhandle, constitute a very important part of the wheat growing area of the United States.

Other general field crops of importance are sweet potatoes and the sugar crops. Sweet potatoes are raised very commonly throughout the South with particularly heavy concentrations in south central Louisiana and northeastern Texas. In recent years, extensive experiments have been made to use them as raw material for the production of starch and stock feed. The sugar crops include three separate items: sorghum for syrup, cane for syrup, and sugar cane for sugar. Sorghum for syrup or cane for syrup is raised almost everywhere in the South, the former roughly in the northern half and the latter in the southern half. There are two areas of sugar cane for sugar: one in southern Louisiana and the other in the Lake Okeechobee area in southern Florida.

In the introduction to the chapter on types of farms, the *Census of Agriculture, 1945,* gives a summary of the occurrence of special kinds of farms from which the following references to locations in the southern market areas are abstracted and presented to round out the picture of localization of agricultural products in the South.

Dairy farms—The census mentions only central Tennessee. This does not mean that there are no dairy farms elsewhere in the South but that they do not occur with sufficient frequency to be of especial note.

Poultry farms—Locations mentioned are central North Carolina, northern Georgia, northwestern Arkansas, and, somewhat less important, central Oklahoma and eastern Texas. Chickens are most common, but the census makes especial mention of turkeys in Oklahoma and Texas, broilers in Georgia, and hatchery operations in Texas.

Livestock farms—Mention is made of Tennessee, northern Arkansas, eastern Oklahoma, and eastern Texas as areas with feed and forage. Central Texas and central Oklahoma are mentioned as range cattle areas. Sheep and goats are also important in central Texas.

Fruit and nut farms—Special fruit and nut producing areas are as follows:

South central North Carolina—peaches
Northwestern South Carolina—peaches
Western Tennessee—strawberries
Central Georgia—peaches
Florida—citrus fruits, mainly oranges and grapefruit
Southern Mississippi—pecans and tung nuts
Eastern Louisiana—strawberries
Southern Texas (lower Rio Grande Valley)—citrus fruits, mainly oranges and grapefruit
Northwestern Arkansas (Ozark region)—apples, peaches, and strawberries
East central Arkansas—strawberries
Southwestern Arkansas—peaches

Vegetable farms—Mention is made of occurrences in South Carolina, southwestern Georgia, Florida, Alabama, southern Mississippi, southern Louisiana, lower Rio Grande Valley of Texas, northeastern Texas, and northwestern Arkansas.

Horticultural specialty farms—Florida and eastern Texas are mentioned.

Forest product farms—Western North Carolina, western South Carolina, Georgia, northern Florida, Alabama, Mississippi, northern Louisiana, Arkansas, and eastern Texas.

While cotton is the most important single crop, the demand of southern agriculture for implements, equipment, and other facilities is not entirely conditioned by that one crop, and the existence of a wide variety of other products of sufficient importance to attract national attention suggests that their influence on the market is of considerable significance and also suggests that there may be in process changes which, in time, will assume proportions sufficient to greatly change the agricultural economy of the region. However, the relatively small places which these diverse products have had in the past and their wide scatter over a region which is geographically as large as is the South are factors which help account for the relatively limited demand for many of the types of farm equipment that might be expected in modern agriculture.

INDUSTRIAL STRUCTURE OF THE SOUTH

The industrial classification, as used here, consists of three main divisions: the minerals industries, or mines and quarries; construction; and manufacturing. The data which are first presented are for 1939 and 1940 and are drawn from the labor force statistics of the 1940 *Census of Population* and the 1939 *Census of Manufacturing, Census of Minerals Industries,* and *Census of Construction*. While more recent figures are desirable for many purposes, the 1939 and 1940 census data provide the most comprehensive and reliable means now available for relating the particular lines of activity under examination to the total economy. Also the immediate prewar years provide a good basis for a preliminary analysis. After these data have been discussed, more recent statistics on particular fields will be presented.

Two sets of figures on the number of persons employed are presented in Table 65, and the differences in the quantities are quite considerable. These differences arise from several causes. For one thing, the first set of figures are those for the labor force and represent the condition as of the week of March 24 to 30, 1940. The second set of figures are abstracted from the reports of the censuses of the separate industries and represent the averages for the year 1939. Also, the first represent what individuals told the census enumerators that they were doing or considered their regular kind of employment, while the second are the result of tabulating the number of employees reported by the employing establishments. Then, too, there are certain to be differences in coverage arising from the differences in the manner in which the data were collected. The figures derived from the population census have the advantage of being far more comprehensive and complete, and this makes possible many comparisons, particularly with other lines of endeavor, which cannot be made from the separate industry censuses. On the other hand, the census of a particular industry provides valuable data on many subjects in addition to number of persons employed, such as

wages paid and value of product. As a matter of fact, the relative positions of the Southeast, the Southwest, and the South, as represented by the regional percentages of the United States totals, are very much the same, no matter which set of figures may be chosen.

The 1940 labor force tabulation assigned 2,190,103 of the employed persons in the South to the industrial classification. This constituted 21.1 per cent of the total of employed persons in the region and compares with the corresponding percentage for the nation as a whole of 30.0. The proportion was somewhat lower in the Southwest and slightly higher in the Southeast than in the South as a whole. These

Table 65

Number of Employed Persons and Values Added, or Produced,
in the Minerals Industries, Construction, and Manufacturing, 1939 or 1940

	United States	Southeast	Southwest	South
Number of employed persons, 1940:*				
Minerals industries	913,000	78,142	96,061	174,203
Construction	2,056,274	302,694	137,592	440,286
Manufacturing	10,572,842	1,313,265	262,349	1,575,614
Per cent of U. S. total				
Minerals industries	100.0	8.6	10.5	19.1
Construction	100.0	14.7	6.7	21.4
Manufacturing	100.0	12.4	2.5	14.9
Per cent of total employed persons in:				
Minerals industries	2.0	1.0	3.4	1.7
Construction	4.6	4.0	4.9	4.2
Manufacturing	23.4	17.3	9.4	15.2
Employees in 1939**				
Number				
Minerals industries	813,169	68,484	80,357	148,841
Construction	1,073,655	141,952	66,010	207,962
Manufacturing	8,795,824	1,075,231	176,644	1,251,875
Per cent of United States				
Minerals industries	100.0	8.4	9.9	18.3
Construction	100.0	13.2	6.2	19.4
Manufacturing	100.0	12.2	2.0	14.2
Value added in 1939**				
Amount in thousands of dollars				
Minerals industries	2,579,558	169,793	597,076	766,869
Construction	2,473,181	222,068	121,461	343,529
Manufacturing	24,682,918	2,025,795	556,224	2,582,019
Per cent of United States				
Minerals industries	100.0	6.6	23.1	29.7
Construction	100.0	9.0	4.9	13.9
Manufacturing	100.0	8.2	2.3	10.5

*Source: *Census of Population, 1940*, Labor Force.
**Source: *Census of Minerals Industries, 1939; Census of Business, 1939, IV; Census of Manufactures, 1939.*

data indicate that industrialization in the southern area at that time was well below the national average and far beneath the levels attained by the northeastern quarter of the United States.

In terms of the number of persons employed, the minerals industries constituted the smallest of the three groups for the South as a whole, and construction was much smaller than manufacturing. The labor force statistics indicate that minerals and construction together employed only about 40 per cent as many persons as manufacturing did. If the South's share in the nation's population, 23.9 per cent, is taken as a bench mark, construction in the South approaches closer to having this share of the national total than either of the other two groups: 21.4 per cent of the United States total for construction as compared with 19.1 per cent for the minerals industries and 14.9 per cent for manufacturing. However, this is not true for the Southwest, since in that area the share of the number of persons employed in the minerals industries, 10.5 per cent, is much

larger than the share of total population, 6.7 per cent. The very large development of the petroleum industry accounts for this situation. Mining is relatively weak in the Southeast. In general, the South's position is weaker when measured in terms of values—that is, wages or value added—than in the percentages of persons employed. This indicates a tendency toward low value production per person employed.

THE MINERALS INDUSTRIES OF THE SOUTH

The statistics on the labor force in 1940 provide a further breakdown of the persons employed in the minerals industries and these data are presented in Table 66.

By far the most outstanding fact brought out by the statistics of Table 66 is the very important place held by the South, particularly the Southwest, in the production of crude petroleum and natural gas. Additional facts emphasize this position. In 1939, the South accounted for the following percentages of national totals: production of natural gas, 62.6 per cent, pro-

Table 66

Employment in the Minerals Industries in the Southeast,
the Southwest, the South, and the United States, 1940

	United States	Southeast	Southwest	South
Number of persons employed				
All minerals industries	913,000	78,142	96,061	174,203
Coal mining	527,025	34,546	2,161	36,707
Crude petroleum and natural gas	183,619	17,115	85,681	102,796
Metal mining	117,237	9,155	3,458	12,613
Other mining and quarrying	85,119	17,326	4,761	22,087
Sand and gravel	20,634	3,385	1,888	5,273
Stone quarrying	40,341	6,408	1,104	7,512
Miscellaneous nonmetallic	19,926	6,739	1,667	8,406
Not specified	4,218	794	102	896
Percentage of the United States				
All minerals industries	100.0	8.6	10.5	19.1
Coal mining	100.0	6.6	.4	7.0
Crude petroleum and natural gas	100.0	9.3	46.7	56.0
Metal mining	100.0	7.8	3.0	10.8
Other mining and quarrying	100.0	20.4	5.6	26.0
Sand and gravel	100.0	16.4	9.2	25.6
Stone quarrying	100.0	15.9	2.7	18.6
Miscellaneous nonmetallic	100.0	33.8	8.4	42.2
Not specified	100.0	18.8	2.4	21.2

Source: *Census of Population, 1940*, Labor Force.

duction of natural gasoline, 61.1 per cent, and crude petroleum, 60.0 per cent. In 1948, these percentages were still higher, being 73.4 per cent for natural gas, 64.8 per cent for natural gasoline, 71.9 per cent for liquified petroleum gases, and 65.2 per cent for crude petroleum. Texas and Oklahoma hold the leading positions, but important fields are located in Louisiana and Mississippi. Some development is taking place in southeastern Alabama.

Coal and metal mining are directly connected with the basic iron and steel industries and have been discussed in detail in previous chapters. Consequently, further treatment is not needed at present other than to remind the reader that coal and ore mining in some localities, particularly in the Birmingham district, is conducted on a large scale basis and does create a quite large demand for equipment.

Table 66 also indicates that the South occupies a relatively strong position in the group designated as "miscellaneous nonmetallic." This arises from the fact that the South is an important, and sometimes the chief, domestic source of a number of minerals. The more important of these and their chief locations in the South are listed[2] below.

Asbestos ....Georgia, North Carolina
Barite, crude ....Georgia, Tennessee
Bauxite ....Arkansas, Alabama, Georgia
Clay, raw ....Georgia
Feldspar, crude ....North Carolina
Fuller's earth ....Georgia, Texas, Florida
Garnet, abrasive ......North Carolina
Graphite ....Georgia, Alabama
Gypsum, crude ....Texas
Helium ....Texas
Kyanite ....Georgia, North Carolina
Lead ....Oklahoma
Lime ....Alabama
Manganese ore ....Tennessee, Arkansas, Georgia
Mica ....North Carolina, Georgia
Phosphate rock ....Florida, Tennessee
Pyrites ....Tennessee
Salt ....Louisiana
Sulfur ....Texas, Louisiana
Talc ....North Carolina
Titanium ore: rutile...Arkansas
Zinc ....Tennessee, Oklahoma

[2] Based on lists given in National Resources Planning Board, *Industrial Location and National Resources*, p. 18.

Many of the above items do not provide employment to any considerable number of persons, and the value of their annual product is small. On the other hand, several are of importance either because of important industrial uses or because they are strategic materials and may exercise a strong influence upon the industrial economy of the region.

CONSTRUCTION IN THE SOUTH

The data is Table 67 indicate that the South occupied a position in the nation with regard to the number employed in construction which approximated its share in the total population of the United States. Its percentage of the value added by construction, however, was much lower, being 13.9 per cent as compared with 23.9 per cent of the total population. The indication, therefore, is that building occupied the attention of about the same proportion of the working population in the South as in other parts of the country, but the projects were smaller and value involved lower.

Estimates of the United States Department of Commerce give further indications of the position of the South. These estimates indicate that the position of the South in the several types of construction is quite well balanced and reasonably close to its proportion of the nation's population. It would seem, therefore, that the southern market for building materials should be a quite favorable one in so far as totals are concerned. Also, the 1946 figures indicate a moderate improvement in the South's relative position in the nation.

MANUFACTURING IN THE SOUTH

Because of the great interest in the subject, the variety of the data available, and the possible methods of approach, it would be exceedingly easy to drift into a very detailed description of manufacturing in the South. The discussion, however, will be confined to the relative position of the South with respect to different kinds of manufacturing industries and to the location of manufacturing enterprises in the South. The 1947 *Census of Manufactures* provides the data for the analysis of the kinds of manufacturing, but first the changes in total manufacturing from 1939 to 1947 will be summarized.

GENERAL CHANGES 1939 TO 1947

The data presented by Table 68 record the very substantial increases that occurred during the eight year period from 1939 to 1947. As may be expected, the percentage increases of wages and value added by manufacture were much larger than those of number of establishments and number of production workers because of the effect of increases of prices and wages on series expressed in terms of money units. The number of establishments in the South increased considerably more on a percentage basis than did the number in the United States, 50.83 per cent compared to 38.60 per cent. On the other hand, the per cent of

increase of production workers was smaller in the South (49.15 per cent) than in the nation (52.61 per cent). The Southeast and the Southwest behaved in rather different fashions with regard to the increases of these two measures. The Southwest increased to a greater degree than the nation in number of establishments and the Southeast to a lesser degree. In the case of the number of production workers the reverse was true. The percentage increases in wages and value added by manufacture were larger than those of the nation for both the Southeast and the Southwest.

As a result of the changes between the two dates, the South remained in approximately the same relative position in the nation's total manufacturing as measured in number of production workers. Its share in the total was

Table 67

Value of Construction in the Southeast, Southwest and South, 1939 and 1946

	Value of construction (million dollars)			Per cent of U. S.		
	Southeast	Southwest	South	Southeast	Southwest	South
1939						
Total new construction	787.8	389.1	1,176.9	12.5	6.2	18.7
Total new private construction	414.6	243.8	658.4	10.9	6.4	17.3
Residential	229.7	118.8	348.5	10.9	5.6	16.5
Non-residential	82.8	45.9	128.7	10.6	5.8	16.4
Public utility	67.3	60.7	128.0	9.9	8.9	18.7
Total new public construction	373.2	145.3	518.5	14.9	5.8	20.7
Residential	16.0	2.0	18.0	24.6	3.1	27.7
Non-residential	113.3	47.8	161.1	13.2	5.6	18.8
Military and naval	20.7	9.5	30.2	16.6	7.6	24.2
Highways	136.9	57.3	194.2	15.8	6.6	22.4
Conservation and development	65.0	14.8	79.8	21.0	4.8	25.8
All other	21.3	13.9	35.2	7.8	5.1	12.9
1946						
Total new construction	1,398.6	871.2	2,269.8	13.4	8.3	21.7
Total new private construction	1,040.6	696.5	1,737.1	12.6	8.4	21.0
Residential	403.3	296.3	699.6	12.7	9.3	22.0
Non-residential	410.4	232.5	642.9	12.3	6.9	19.2
Public utility	175.7	141.2	316.9	12.8	10.3	23.1
Total new public construction	358.0	174.7	532.7	16.2	7.9	24.2
Residential	43.1	23.8	66.9	11.7	6.4	18.1
Non-residential	57.4	25.7	83.1	17.7	7.9	25.6
Military and naval	32.9	16.2	49.1	17.5	8.6	26.1
Highway	124.7	61.4	186.1	16.2	8.0	24.1
Conservation and development	64.7	16.0	80.7	27.0	6.7	33.6
All other	35.2	31.6	66.8	11.3	10.2	21.5

Source: U. S. Department of Commerce, "State Distribution of Construction Activity, 1939-1947."

14.78 per cent in 1939 and 14.45 per cent in 1947. It did make substantial gains in relative position in wages and value added, since the former increased from 9.89 per cent of the national total to 11.09 and the latter from 10.46 to 12.05 per cent. This change suggests that the character of manufacturing in the South was changing so that low wages and low valued products were not as characteristic of the region in 1947 as in 1939. While the large absolute changes between the two census years are important, the increase in relative position in wages and value added by manufacture seem to reflect the most significant changes.

KINDS OF MANUFACTURING INDUSTRIES, 1947

The general position of the South in 1947 with respect to the different kinds of manufacturing industries is shown by the statistics for the main industry groups which are given in Table 69.

From the point of view of numbers of production workers, the textile mills products group was far larger than any other group in the South. The second largest was lumber and allied products. Food and kindred products, apparel and related products were third and fourth respectively. These four industry groups

Table 68

Manufacturing in the Southeast, Southwest, South, and United States, 1939 and 1947

	1939	1947	Per cent increase
Number of establishments			
Southeast	17,825	27,996	57.06
Southwest	6,615	8,868	34.06
South	24,440	36,864	50.83
United States	173,802	240,881	38.60
Number of production workers			
Southeast	1,001,405	1,435,161	43.31
Southwest	152,757	286,316	87.43
South	1,154,162	1,721,477	49.15
United States	7,808,205	11,916,188	52.61
Wages (in thousand dollars)			
Southeast	733,564	2,689,336	266.61
Southwest	156,321	663,697	324.57
South	889,885	3,353,033	276.79
United States	8,997,515	30,242,343	236.12
Value added by manufacture (in thousand dollars)			
Southeast	2,010,979	6,900,834	243.16
Southwest	550,305	2,068,491	275.88
South	2,561,284	8,969,325	250.19
United States	24,487,304	74,425,825	203.94
Per cent of United States			
Number of production workers			
Southeast	12.83	12.04	
Southwest	1.96	2.40	
South	14.78	14.45	
Wages			
Southeast	8.15	8.89	
Southwest	1.74	2.19	
South	9.89	11.09	
Value added by manufacture			
Southeast	8.21	9.27	
Southwest	2.25	2.78	
South	10.46	12.05	

Source: *Census of Manufactures, 1947.*

accounted for approximately 62 per cent of all production workers in manufacturing in the South. If the criterion is the relative position in the nation, the South ranks highest in textiles mills products with 45.26 per cent of the total of the nation. The groups that occupy the six next highest ranks are lumber and products (44.59 per cent), tobacco manufacture (42.30 per cent), petroleum and coal products (29.28 per cent), furniture and fixtures (19.60 per cent), chemicals and allied products (19.01 per cent), and food and kindred products (15.13 per cent). The concentration on a relatively small number of industry groups is accompanied by decided weakness in such groups as electrical machinery, instruments and related products, miscellaneous manufactures, machinery, and leather and leather products.

INDUSTRY SPECIALIZATION IN THE SOUTH

One method of measuring the importance of a particular industry in the manufacturing economy of a region is to compare the region's percentage of the national total of the selected industry with the region's percentage of all manufacturing activity. If the special industry participation is equal to that of the region in all manufacturing, it can be concluded that the industry occupies the same relative place in the manufacturing economy of the region that it does in the nation. A greater share indicates a tendency for the region to specialize or place greater emphasis on that particular industry. The reverse naturally would hold for the industries which have a smaller share. This approach was applied to the industry classification in the 1947 *Census of Manufactures,* inter-

Table 69

Number of Production Workers in Manufacturing in the South and the United States
by Main Industry Groups, 1947

Main industry group	Number of production workers		Per cent South of U. S.	Ratio between per cent of U. S. and all mfg. per cent of U. S.
	South	U. S.		
20 Food and kindred products	166,298	1,099,478	15.13	1.05
21 Tobacco manufactures	43,687	103,289	42.30	2.93
22 Textile mills products	519,165	1,147,194	45.26	3.13
23 Apparel and related products	115,856	972,897	11.91	0.82
24 Lumber and products (except furniture)	265,804	596,118	44.59	3.09
25 Furniture and fixtures	55,435	282,780	19.60	1.36
26 Paper and allied products	55,676	388,901	14.32	0.99
27 Printing and publishing industries	38,336	438,135	8.75	0.61
28 Chemicals and allied products	88,664	466,458	19.01	1.32
29 Petroleum and coal products	49,654	169,610	29.28	2.03
30 Rubber products	13,278	214,533	6.19	0.43
31 Leather and leather products	17,064	348,529	4.90	0.34
32 Stone, clay and glass products	50,242	405,755	12.38	0.86
33 Primary metal industries	70,443	1,010,055	6.97	0.48
34 Fabricated metal products	44,477	822,514	5.41	0.37
35 Machinery (except electrical)	47,565	1,244,135	3.82	0.26
36 Electrical machinery	8,611	639,147	1.35	0.09
37 Transportation equipment	54,807	987,142	5.55	0.38
38 Instruments and related products	3,756	181,939	2.06	0.14
39 Miscellaneous manufactures	12,659	397,579	3.18	0.22
Total all manufactures	1,721,477	11,916,188	14.45	1.00

Source: United States figures—*Census of Manufacturers, 1947.*
       Figured for South—special tabulation prepared by U. S. Bureau of the Census for the Bureau of Business Research, University of Alabama.

mediate between the main industry groups given in Table 69 and the most detailed industry breakdown. This is the so-called three digit classification. The following criteria for classifying industries were then set up.

1. Industries whose regional percentage of the U. S. total was three or more times the region's percentage of all manufacturing (very high specialization).
2. Industries whose regional percentage of the U. S. total was from 2 to 2.9 times the region's percentage of all manufacturing (high specialization).
3. Industries whose regional percentage of the U. S. total was from 1 to 1.9 times the region's percentage of all manufacturing (moderate specialization).
4. Industries whose regional percentage of the U. S. total was from one-half to equal to the region's percentage of all manufacturing (low specialization).
5. Industries whose regional percentage of the U. S. total was less than one-half the region's percentage of all manufacturing (very low specialization).

These criteria were applied and the industries were classified accordingly, but, to conserve space, only classes 1, 2, 3, and 5 are shown below.

1. Industries of very high specialization:
   Gum and wood chemicals
   Yarn and thread mills, except wool
   Cotton and rayon broad-woven fabrics
   Tobacco steaming and redrying
   Lumber and timber basic products
   Fertilizers
   Cigarettes
   Chewing and smoking tobacco
2. Industries of high specialization:
   Vegetable and animal oils
   Knitting mills
   Wooden containers
   Petroleum refining
   Paper bags
   Sugar
3. Industries of moderate specialization:
   Cut-stone and stone products
   Cigars
   Miscellaneous wood products
   Men's and boy's furnishings
   Primary nonferrous metals
   Finishing textiles, except wool

   Household furniture
   Miscellaneous food preparations
   Miscellaneous fabricated textiles
   Millwork and related products
   Ships and boats
   Grain-mill products
   Concrete and plaster products
   Pulp, paper, and paperboard
   Industrial organic chemicals
   Cement, hydraulic
   Industrial inorganic chemicals
   Construction and mining machinery
   Structural clay products
   Newspapers
   Transportation equipment, n. e. c.
   Miscellaneous leather goods
   Secondary nonferrous metal
   Miscellaneous textile goods
   Bakery products
5. Industries of very low regional specialization:
   Tin cans and other tinware
   Carpet and rugs
   Woolen and worsted manufactures
   Industrial leather belting
   Office furniture
   Public and professional furniture
   Footwear, except rubber
   Miscellaneous electrical products
   Periodicals
   Pottery and related products
   Children's outerwear
   Blast furnaces and steel works
   Women's and children's undergarments
   Bookbinding and related industries
   Printing trades service industries
   Pressed and blown glassware
   Special-industry machinery, n. e. c.
   Miscellaneous manufactures
   Hats (except cloth and millinery)
   Men's and boy's suits and coats
   Products of purchased glass
   Lithographing
   Paints and allied products
   Soap and related products
   Millinery
   General industrial machinery
   Drugs and medicines
   Tractors and farm machinery
   Leather tanning and finishing
   Miscellaneous machinery parts
   Mechanical measuring instruments
   Women's and Misses' outerwear
   Toys and sporting goods
   Pulp goods and miscellaneous paper products
   Books
   Optical instruments and lenses, and watches and clocks

Envelopes
Miscellaneous fabricated metal products
Nonferrous foundries
Fabricated wire products
Scientific instruments
Medical instruments and supplies
Motor vehicles and equipment
Metal stamping and coating
Service and household machines
Railroad equipment, motorcycles and bicycles
Rubber footwear, and rubber industries, n. e. c.
Leather gloves and mittens
Paper coating and glazing
Communication equipment
Luggage
Insulated wire and cable, and electric lamps
Footwear cut stock
Handbags and small leather goods
Electrical industrial apparatus
Opthalmic goods
Plastics products, n. e. c.
Cutlery, hand tools, and hardware
Jewelry and silverware
Musical instruments and parts, and costume
    jewelry and notions
Miscellaneous publishing and greeting cards
Miscellaneous primary metal industries
Electrical appliances
Photographic equipment
Lighting fixtures
Metalworking machinery
Engine electrical equipment
Office and store machines
Engines and turbines
Fur goods
Reclaimed rubber

Having indicated the industries that are relatively strong and also those that are relatively underdeveloped, certain of the outstanding characteristics of the manufacturing industries of the Southeast and the Southwest may be summarized. For the most part, the outstanding developments have taken place in the processing of materials that are produced in the South—cotton, lumber, tobacco, and petroleum. Furthermore, the developments have been largely in the early stages of the processing. The production of fabricated finished products has not been carried far in most cases, although there are important exceptions and there is at least some production in most categories. Furniture in North Carolina, cigarettes in North Carolina, oil field machinery and equipment in Texas, dyeing and finishing of textiles, and apparel provide examples of finished products that are being produced in quantity.

From the point of view of a market for iron and steel, the outstanding features of the South's manufacturing are (1) the relatively small place held by the metal working industries: iron and steel other than blast furnaces and steel works, nonferrous metals, machinery, and transportation equipment; (2) the fact that the South's industries, by and large, make relatively little use of iron and steel as expendable materials in their manufacturing processes; (3) the demand for iron and steel products in the manufacturing industries is largely for equipment and facilities. From the point of view of expendable materials, petroleum is perhaps the outstanding exception, since this industry creates a great demand for metal containers. To a much smaller degree this is also true of the vegetable oil industry. Canning of foods is a relatively small industry in the South compared with the Pacific Coast and some other parts of the nation, although there is a substantial development, particularly in Florida. Still, the raw materials base of manufacturing in the South consists largely of vegetable products or nonmetallic minerals—cotton, tobacco, wood, and petroleum—and the metals are relatively unimportant. In many of the South's industries, the chief demand is for machinery and other equipment, items which have long lives. This reduces the annual quantities required and places a great part of the emphasis upon repair parts, rebuilding, and alterations. Again the petroleum industry is the great exception because of the extensive developmental activities and the tremendous use of iron and steel in pipe, storage tanks, refinery equipment, and other facilities. The development of pulp and paper and other types of chemical industries also tends to create demands for iron and steel.

Industrial Areas of the South

To provide a representation of the geographic distribution of industrial activities in the South, a detailed analysis was made of the population and labor force statistics of the sixteenth census on a county basis for all of the eleven states in the Southern market area. Based on 1940 statistics, five criteria of industrialization were set up as follows:

1. Number of urban population—15,000 or more
2. Per cent of total population that was urban—40 per cent or more
3. Number of industrial workers (including mining, construction, and manufacturing) —5,000 or more
4. Per cent of all employed persons classed as industrial workers—30 per cent or more
5. Industrial workers per square mile—5 per square mile or more.

Any county which met any one of these minimum criteria was considered an industrial county. This means that the industrial areas include all counties with substantial urban population, whether measured on a percentage or a mass basis and all that have a substantial group of industrial workers, whether the concentration is measured on the basis of total number, percentage of total employed persons, or density with respect to land area. Compared with criteria used by the U. S. Department of Commerce or other agencies, these are admittedly low. It was felt, however, in a study of a region in which industrialization is relatively low that it was better to use measures that would bring out substantial beginnings of industrialization. The maps and tables on the industrial areas of the South represent the results of this analysis.

In general, the industrial areas of the South are quite scattered. Many consist of small areas around a city and have the appearance of islands in the midst of large non-industrialized areas, but there are examples of larger areas. At least four cover relatively large contiguous land areas, have large populations, and include several important industrial centers. These are (a) an area that includes northeastern Tennessee, western North Carolina, and northern South Carolina (designated on Map 19 as Area No. 7) with a land area of 31,165 square miles, a population of 3,198,642, and Johnson City, Tennessee; Raleigh, Durham, Greensboro, Charlotte, Winston-Salem, and Asheville, North Carolina; Greenville, Spartanburg, and Columbia, South Carolina; and Augusta, Georgia, as principal cities; (b) an area that includes eastern Tennessee, northwestern Georgia and two counties of eastern Alabama (Area No. 11), with a land area of 18,370 square miles, a population of 1,872,929, and Knoxville and Chattanooga, Tennessee, and Atlanta, Rome and LaGrange, Georgia, as principal cities; (c) an area in north central Alabama (Area No. 37) with a land area of 7,248 square miles, a population of 864,351, and Birmingham, Gadsden, Anniston and Tuscaloosa as principal cities; and (d) an area in southwestern Louisiana and southeastern Texas (Area No. 53) with a land area of 13,170 square miles, a population of 1,048,211, and Lake Charles and Alexandria, Louisiana, and Beaumont, Port Arthur, Galveston and Houston, Texas, as principal cities. In addition, important but less extensive areas center around New Orleans, Mobile, Tulsa, Jacksonville, Tampa, Shreveport, Columbus (Georgia), Little Rock, Fort Worth, and Dallas. Finally, there are important concentrations in single counties with a large city. Outstanding examples of this type are the counties in which are located Nashville and Memphis, Tennessee; Charleston, South Carolina; Macon and Savannah, Georgia; Pensacola, Florida; Montgomery, Alabama; Jackson, Mississippi; Fort Smith, Arkansas; Oklahoma City, Oklahoma; and Austin, San Antonio, and Corpus Christi, Texas.

The scattered character of the industrial areas is a factor of considerable importance to the iron and steel industry in that it indicates that the region has few concentrated markets with demands for large tonnages of particular kinds of steel products. These data suggest a widely diffused market geographically and one which demands a wide variety of products.

The geographic distribution of the different industries remains to be described. The locations of the mineral industries have already been indicated. Construction tends to be associated with the centers of urban population. The more important of the manufacturing industries are summarized below.

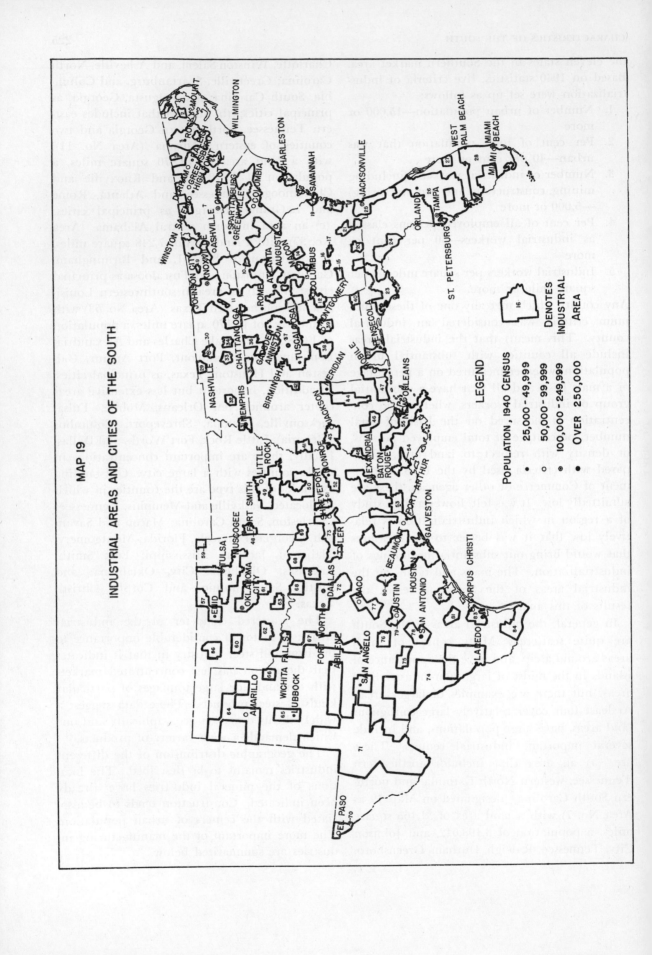

MAP 19

INDUSTRIAL AREAS AND CITIES OF THE SOUTH

LEGEND

POPULATION, 1940 CENSUS

• 25,000 - 49,999
○ 50,000 - 99,999
◉ 100,000 - 249,999
● OVER 250,000

☐ DENOTES INDUSTRIAL AREA

Table 10

Industrial Areas in the South, 1940
Areas with Industrial Concentration

Area number	Location	Principal cities	Area (sq. mi.)	Population	Industrial classes (per cent of industrial workers)								Occupational classification (per cent of all employed persons)			
					Minerals	Construction	Food products	Textiles	Forest products	Iron and steel	Other metals	Other industries	Professional	Skilled and semi-skilled	Farm	Unskilled
2	N.E. North Carolina Washington County	Plymouth, N.C.	336	12,323	...	13.40	.99	.09	65.20	.54	5.57	14.21	10.38	12.95	37.18	39.49
3	N.E. North Carolina; 7 counties—Halifax south to Lenoir	Rocky Mount, N.C. Wilson, N.C. Goldsboro, N.C.	3,760	372,284	.34	19.71	6.17	35.15	15.60	.57	11.83	10.63	9.35	13.02	49.91	27.72
4	S.E. North Carolina; on the coast New Hanover	Wilmington, N.C.	194	47,935	.05	20.36	6.51	12.92	14.43	.76	25.79	19.18	15.55	29.52	6.20	48.73
7	N.E. Tennessee, Western N.C. and Northern S.C.; 60 counties	Johnson City, Tenn. Raleigh, N.C. Durham, N.C. Greensboro, N.C. Charlotte, N.C. Winston-Salem, N.C. Asheville, N.C. Columbia, S.C. Augusta, Ga.	31,165	3,198,642	.65	9.84	3.15	59.14	10.32	.58	4.95	11.37	10.63	18.68	22.36	48.33
8	S.E. South Carolina on coast—Charleston County	Charleston, S.C.	945	121,105	.18	19.45	7.39	.35	9.75	.24	31.93	30.71	13.84	23.67	11.60	50.89
10	N.E. Georgia, Stephens County	Toccoa, Ga.*	180	12,972	.28	9.85	.63	38.29	22.44	11.56	15.86	1.09	11.28	19.41	29.88	39.43
11	Eastern Tennessee and Western Georgia—48 counties from north border of Tenn. to central Georgia	Knoxville, Tenn. Chattanooga, Tenn. Atlanta, Ga. Rome, Ga.	18,370	1,872,929	4.63	12.82	4.57	43.93	7.67	5.13	11.84	9.41	12.32	23.63	16.97	47.08
12	So. Ala.-Ga. on state line —2 counties	LaGrange, Ga. Columbus, Ga.	859	111,269	.32	11.83	9.99	58.80	4.55	2.04	7.36	5.11	9.56	19.17	13.80	57.47
13	Central Georgia; 2 counties	Macon, Ga.	402	94,161	1.54	13.81	8.15	29.58	12.99	1.83	18.44	13.66	13.73	23.55	9.69	53.03
14	Central Georgia Wilkenson County	Gordon, Ga.*	458	11,025	33.70	4.84	.39	.31	21.61	...	2.26	36.89	7.06	9.55	45.58	37.81
18	Midway on Georgia's Atlantic coastline—2 counties	Brunswick, Ga.	854	27,212	...	18.90	11.56	.23	38.88	.36	6.43	23.64	14.49	19.95	4.47	61.09
19	E. coast bordering S.C. Chatham County	Savannah, Ga.	441	117,970	.12	18.18	11.88	1.20	20.97	3.12	25.95	18.58	15.67	27.78	1.83	54.72

No.	Location	Description													
22	Pensacola, Fla.	Extreme Western part of Fla. Escambia County	663	74,667	.38	34.98	8.02	.67	16.37	.52	15.75	23.31	15.19	27.10	3.84	53.87
23	Thomasville, Ga. Tallahassee, Fla.	N.W. Fla. and Thomas Co., Ga., 6 counties	3,917	100,315	.48	24.35	7.40	.90	51.45	.34	8.08	7.00	14.88	19.38	19.06	46.68
24	Perry, Fla.*	Top part west coast of Fla. 2 counties	1,720	18,583	1.05	5.38	1.02	...	86.08	...	4.63	1.84	10.75	16.11	9.89	63.25
25	Jacksonville, Fla.	N.E. corner of Fla.—2 counties	2,036	240,981	.13	25.68	10.46	1.02	11.31	1.49	27.10	22.81	16.65	30.71	3.10	49.54
26	Lakeland, Fla. Tampa, Fla.	Central part of Fla. ranging west coast to east coast—11 counties	9,818	574,114	3.35	24.85	18.38	.77	10.74	.97	15.19	25.75	17.21	24.26	13.75	44.78
28	Miami, Fla.	Southern tip of Fla.—6 counties	8,217	424,325	.68	54.97	9.91	1.75	6.75	1.59	10.61	13.74	18.66	27.37	10.79	43.18
30	Nashville, Tenn.	North central Tennessee Davidson County	532	257,267	.53	18.56	9.68	12.24	4.89	5.67	14.61	33.82	16.09	33.70	4.21	46.00
31	Memphis, Tenn.	S.W. corner of Tenn. Shelby County	751	358,250	.28	21.89	10.62	4.94	15.29	2.73	22.12	22.13	14.52	30.04	8.05	47.39
34	Shelbyville, Tenn.*	South central Tenn. Bedford County	482	23,151	.55	15.74	4.90	48.64	4.07	.63	3.60	21.87	9.04	13.55	40.47	36.94
37	Tuscaloosa, Birmingham, Gadsden, & Anniston, Ala.	North central Ala.—9 counties	7,248	864,351	23.63	8.44	3.73	11.48	6.31	28.22	8.99	9.20	12.48	24.97	12.81	49.74
39	Montgomery, Ala.	So. central part of Ala. Montgomery County	790	114,420	1.16	24.11	12.26	13.19	11.43	.78	20.96	16.11	13.55	25.01	16.21	45.23
43	Jackson, Miss. Vicksburg, Miss.	S.W. Miss. on La. border 2 counties	1,443	146,868	3.25	34.18	9.93	5.44	18.58	1.11	12.32	15.19	14.07	22.86	25.19	37.88
44	Meridian, Laurel, & Hattiesburg, Miss.	S.E. Miss.—4 counties	2,579	161,859	1.05	14.04	5.48	18.48	23.15	.87	14.01	22.92	12.50	18.00	27.34	42.16
47	Mobile, Ala. Biloxi, Miss.	S.E. corner of Miss. and S.W. corner of Ala.—3 counties	2,577	213,374	.33	19.58	17.08	8.72	22.69	.99	22.08	8.53	15.18	25.22	5.19	54.41
49	Little Rock, Hot Springs, & Pine Bluff, Ark.	Central Ark.—4 counties	3,118	282,013	4.32	20.37	8.32	4.30	24.35	1.45	25.90	10.99	16.60	26.61	19.56	37.23
48	Ft. Smith, Ark.	Midway on Ark.-Okla. state line in Ark., Sebastian Co.	529	62,809	8.87	12.56	15.40	2.89	25.04	2.43	12.91	19.90	17.60	29.44	13.52	39.44
50	El Dorado, Ark.	So. central Ark. partially on La. border—4 counties	3,111	114,180	13.97	7.97	2.72	.12	56.22	.78	7.30	10.90	12.06	17.62	27.95	42.37
51	Minden, La.*	N.W. La. on Ark. border	626	33,676	17.84	9.33	.97	.06	54.35	.06	12.03	5.36	10.12	15.04	36.08	38.76
52	Monroe, La.	No. central La., 2 counties	1,225	76,975	4.77	17.52	6.28	.24	51.51	.34	10.25	9.09	13.16	21.03	19.57	46.24
53	Lake Charles, La. Alexandria, La. Galveston, Tex. Port Arthur, Tex. Houston, Tex. Beaumont, Tex. Baton Rouge, La.	S.W. La. and S.E. Texas 15 counties	13,170	1,048,211	9.30	19.58	6.92	1.82	11.08	3.46	19.93	27.91	16.72	30.61	7.68	44.99
55		S.E. La.—7 counties	3,248	690,574	1.82	22.60	16.49	9.30	6.82	2.79	14.25	25.93	16.34	31.48	4.26	47.92

Table 70 (cont'd)

Industrial Areas in the South, 1940
Areas with Industrial Concentration

Area number	Location	Principal cities	Area (sq. mi.)	Population	Industrial classes (per cent of industrial workers)								Occupational classification (per cent of all employed persons)			
					Minerals	Construction	Food products	Textiles	Forest products	Iron and steel	Other metals	Other industries	Professional	Skilled and semi-skilled	Farm	Unskilled
57	Northern Okla. midway on Kan. border—2 counties	Enid, Okla.	1,998	92,568	13.04	18.79	11.92	.32	.82	1.19	15.99	37.93	16.55	28.58	20.29	31.58
58	N.E. Okla.—6 counties	Okmulgee, Muscogee & Tulsa, Okla.	4,188	431,497	31.81	16.20	6.14	2.42	1.38	4.22	15.07	22.76	20.36	32.04	14.42	33.18
59	N.W. corner of Okla., Ottowa County	Picher, & Miami, Okla.	483	35,849	68.30	12.50	3.62	3.86	1.28	.14	6.90	3.40	15.23	21.28	17.39	46.10
61	Central Okla.—5 counties	Oklahoma City, Shawnee, Okla.	3,403	427,257	30.92	20.25	16.18	.93	3.19	2.70	9.91	15.92	20.31	32.82	12.16	34.71
64	Texas Panhandle—7 counties	Amarillo, Tex.	7,551	121,441	27.39	18.15	5.85	.19	.89	1.04	19.95	26.54	20.11	31.63	8.88	39.38
67	No. central Texas—7 counties	Wichita Falls, Tex.	6,153	189,462	44.21	19.11	7.83	1.37	.92	1.69	12.16	12.71	19.57	26.52	20.05	33.86
68	N.E. Texas—3 counties	Sherman & Denison, Tex.	2,800	168,717	.93	28.76	17.39	10.76	7.86	.58	23.62	10.10	15.18	19.07	38.74	27.01
70	Extreme western corner of Texas—El Paso County	El Paso, Tex.	1,054	131,067	2.27	24.42	11.91	5.67	1.45	1.04	39.53	13.71	18.14	28.66	7.91	45.29
71	West central Texas—19 counties	Seminole, Tex.* Crane, Tex.	30,015	223,569	44.81	23.49	6.80	.79	1.03	.53	9.97	12.58	20.43	25.95	17.79	35.83
72	North central Texas—4 counties	Ft. Worth, Tex. Dallas, Tex.	3,807	723,126	3.21	24.38	16.04	11.11	4.96	2.69	18.79	18.82	19.39	34.40	9.15	37.06
73	Northeastern Texas and northwestern Louisiana—4 counties	Shreveport, La. Longview, Tex. Marshall, Tex. Tyler, Tex.	3,015	328,220	26.01	21.96	6.61	1.26	9.36	2.05	16.25	16.50	15.00	23.56	21.61	39.83
77	Central Texas—2 counties	Waco, Tex.	2,114	146,761	1.61	26.54	12.24	14.33	8.29	1.05	21.89	14.05	17.54	23.87	27.12	31.47
78	So. central Tex.—2 counties	San Antonio, Tex.	1,814	350,497	4.25	30.02	17.44	7.96	4.08	2.74	16.79	16.72	17.74	29.37	6.25	46.64
79	South central Texas—Travis County	Austin, Tex.	1,015	111,053	3.13	62.98	8.93	.27	3.17	.69	6.72	14.11	20.86	30.00	10.97	38.17
83	S.E. Texas on the Gulf of Mexico—2 counties	Corpus Christi, Tex.	1,689	106,005	25.99	32.77	7.52	.27	1.99	1.85	14.55	15.06	17.88	27.01	15.32	39.79

*Towns of less than 10,000 population.

Source: Based on *Census of Population, 1940.*

Cotton manufactures: Western North Carolina, central and northwestern South Carolina, southeastern Tennessee, northwestern and western Georgia, eastern Alabama

Knit goods: North Carolina, northwestern Georgia, eastern Tennessee

Rayon textiles: North Carolina, eastern Tennessee, northwest Georgia

Tobacco: Cigarettes, snuff, and chewing tobacco, northern North Carolina; cigars, Florida

Lumber: generally throughout the Southeast, in eastern Texas, and eastern Oklahoma

Furniture: North Carolina, centering in High Point

Rayon: Eastern Tennessee and northern Georgia

Pulp and Paper: Kraft pulp—Gulf Coast areas of Florida, Alabama, Mississippi, and Louisiana; hardwood pulp products—Tennessee and North Carolina

Coke and by-products: Birmingham area

Petroleum products: Texas, Oklahoma, and Louisiana

Aluminum: Alcoa, Tennessee; Baden, North Carolina; Muscle Shoals, Alabama; Mobile, Alabama and Baton Rouge, Louisiana (alumina)

Apparel: Tennessee, Georgia, Texas, Mississippi, North Carolina

Meat products: Texas

Canning and preserving: Florida and Texas

Vegetable oil: generally throughout areas producing cotton and peanuts

Chemicals: Widely scattered throughout the South

Basic iron and steel: Birmingham area, Atlanta, Georgia, Houston, Texas

Iron and steel processing and fabricating: Birmingham area, Chattanooga, northwestern Georgia, Texas (oil field machinery) and structural steel in the large cities.

The above listing does not attempt to include all of the different kinds of manufacturing industries. Also there are plants of the industries named that are located at places other than those indicated. The purpose is to bring out the most important features of the geographic distribution of industries in the South rather than to attempt a complete analysis.

RAILROADS AND PUBLIC UTILITY INDUSTRIES OF THE SOUTH

The services performed by railroads and other transportation agencies and by such utilities as electric power, telegraph, telephone, and pipelines are important factors in the industrialization of a region. These activities also have a direct significance to the iron and steel industry since the operating companies are very important users of the products of the industry. The relative position of the region in these several fields is indicated by the statistics presented in Table 71 and some of the outstanding features will be summarized.

So far as total miles of road can be taken as a measure of railroad facilities, the South occupies a relative position that approximates its share of the nation's population, since it has slightly more than twenty-seven per cent of the total mileage of the railroads of the United States. The data on revenue freight originated and terminated, however, show the South in a much weaker position. In 1939, the region accounted for 13.5 per cent of the revenue freight originated and 13.9 per cent of the revenue freight terminated. By 1946, these proportions had increased to 16.7 per cent and 17.0 per cent respectively. These data indicate a much lower traffic density and suggest that the demand of the soulthern railroads for materials for replacements and maintenance probably represent a smaller percentage of the total demand of the nation's railroads than the region's percentage of total miles of road would suggest. However, this is a field in which the South does occupy an important place.

In the electric utility field, the data on electric energy production and generating capacity indicate a strong position for the region. In 1945, the South's share in the former was 19.0 per cent and in the latter, 18.0 per cent. In view of the importance of agriculture in the area, it is somewhat surprising that the relative position is as strong as these figures indicate.

The importance of the Southwest in the pipeline industry arises from the fact that a very large percentage of these lines originated in oil fields of Texas and Oklahoma. The data on pipeline mileage emphasizes again the important place that petroleum has in the economy of the Southwest and also the fact that the demands originating therefrom constitute one of the most important factors in the background of the iron and steel industry.

The differences in the South's percentage of the miles of telephone companies' wire and cable and the miles of aerial wire apparently reflect the region's low percentage of urban population and the relatively small number of large cities. Furthermore, the relatively small share of the nation's telephones accounted for by the South is a reflection of both its rural

character and the low income of many of its people. The data would seem to indicate that the region has at least these two points of weakness: in the first place, it occupies a relatively low position in those situations (for example, the presence of large cities) where service demands may be expected to be heavy and the demand for facilities likewise to be great; and in the second place, it has as subscribers to the service a relatively low percentage of its people. It is very probable that the statistics of telephone companies are typical of other service concerns that deal directly with individual consumers.

Income in the South

That the southern states occupy low positions in the nation with respect to the incomes of their people is a phenomenon which has received wide publicity, and it is doubtful that

Table 71

Selected Statistics of Railroads, Electric Utilities, Telephones and Oil Pipe Lines in the Southeast, Southwest, and South, 1939 and 1946

	Southeast	Southwest	South
Miles of railroad owned, December 31, 1946			
By Class I steam railways	29,778	18,713	48,491
By Class II steam railways	2,782	986	3,768
By Class III steam railways	1,046	212	1,258
By nonoperating companies	5,619	1,674	7,293
By companies not filing an annual report	420	87	507
All classes			
Official	39,435	21,628	61,063
Unofficial	210	44	254
Total	39,645	21,672	61,317
Per cent of United States			
By Class I steam railways	16.8	10.5	27.3
By Class II steam railways	35.8	12.7	48.4
By Class III steam railways	42.6	8.6	51.3
By nonoperating companies	15.0	4.5	19.5
By companies not filing an annual report	36.9	7.6	44.6
All classes			
Official	17.5	9.6	27.0
Unofficial	39.8	8.3	48.1
Total	17.5	9.6	27.1
Tons of Revenue Freight originated, by Class I railways (thousands of tons)			
1939	98,563	35,795	134,358
1946	158,017	65,504	223,521
Per cent of United States			
1939	9.9	3.6	13.5
1946	11.8	4.9	16.7

Table 71 (cont'd)

Selected Statistics of Railroads, Electric Utilities, Telephones and Oil Pipe Lines in the Southeast, Southwest, and South, 1939 and 1946

	Southeast	Southwest	South
Tons of Revenue Freight terminated by Class I railroads (thousands of tons)			
1939	102,660	32,237	134,897
1946	163,951	60,258	224,209
Per cent of United States			
1939	10.6	3.3	13.9
1946	13.1	4.8	17.9
Electric energy production for public use 1945			
Millions of kilowatt hours	38,602	12,980	51,582
Per cent of United States	14.2	4.8	19.0
Installed capacity of electric generating plants for public use 1945			
Thousands of kilowatts	8,706	2,622	1,328
Per cent of United States	13.8	4.2	18.0
Miles of wire in cables, Class A and Class B telephone carriers			
1939	5,096,900	3,975,838	9,072,738
1945	7,138,977	4,868,251	12,007,228
Miles of wire in cables, Class A and Class B telephone carriers (con'd)			
Per cent of United States			
1939	6.0	4.6	10.6
1945	7.1	4.9	12.0
Miles of aerial wire, Class A and Class B telephone carriers			
1939	732,518	392,288	1,124,806
1945	859,233	441,043	1,300,276
Per cent of United States			
1939	17.1	9.1	26.2
1945	18.8	9.7	28.5
Total telephones, Class A and Class B telephone carriers			
1939	1,241,777	843,532	2,085,309
1945	1,870,426	1,183,744	3,054,170
Per cent of United States			
1939	6.9	4.7	11.6
1945	7.7	4.9	12.6
Business telephones, Class A and Class B telephone carriers			
1939	507,393	326,529	833,922
1945	727,206	443,560	1,170,766
Per cent of United States			
1939	7.4	4.8	12.2
1945	8.3	5.1	13.4
Oil pipe lines operated			
1941	3,879	50,674	54,553
1945	6,652	52,934	59,586
Per cent of United States			
1941	3.7	48.1	51.7
1945	5.9	46.7	52.6

Source:

U. S. Interstate Commerce Commission, *Statistics of Railways in the United States for the Year Ended December 31, 1946; 1940; Statistical Abstract of the United States, 1947*, p. 484;

U. S. Interstate Commerce Commission, *Tons of Revenue Freight Originated and Tons Terminated, 1940; 1946;*

U. S. Interstate Commerce Commission, *Statistics of Oil Pipe Line Companies, Reporting to the ICC for the Year Ended December 31, 1941*, p. 6, Table 5; *December 31, 1945*, p. 7, Table 5; U. S. Federal Communications Commission, *Statistics of the Communications Industry in the United States, 1939*, p. 14; *1945*, p. 7.

Table 72

Estimated Total and Per Capita Income Payments in the United States, the Southeast, the Southwest, and the South, 1939-1947, and Chief Sources of Income Payments in 1946

	United States	Southeast	Southwest	South
Total income payments				
Million dollars				
1939	70,601.0	6,578.4	3,350.3	9,928.7
1940	75,852.0	7,035.7	3,481.9	10,517.6
1941	92,268.0	9,053.4	4,224.2	13,277.6
1942	117,196.0	12,124.9	5,859.1	17,984.0
1943	141,381.0	15,570.9	7,760.3	23,331.2
1944	153,306.0	17,422.2	8,497.8	25,920.0
1945	157,190.0	18,014.9	8,515.3	26,530.2
1946	171,548.0	18,922.9	8,988.6	27,911.5
1947	189,212.0	20,799.2	10,463.3	31,262.5
Per cent of United States				
1939	100.0	9.3	4.7	14.0
1946	100.0	11.5	5.4	16.9
Per capita income payments (dollars)				
1939	539	292	385	318
1940	575	308	398	333
1941	693	388	488	415
1942	876	517	669	558
1943	1,059	657	840	709
1944	1,161	756	957	812
1945	1,192	800	957	844
1946	1,215	806	957	849
1947	1,319	882	1,115	948
Chief sources of income payments, 1946				
Million dollars				
Gross wages and salaries				
Agriculture	2,467.0	383.7	204.5	588.2
Mining	2,445.0	202.1	345.0	547.1
Manufacturing	36,149.0	2,975.6	827.7	3,803.3
Construction	4,259.0	435.7	231.4	667.1
Transportation	8,614.0	960.2	514.5	1,474.7
Power and gas	1,075.0	96.7	64.5	161.2
Communication	1,498.0	131.5	73.0	204.5
Trade	18,989.0	1,828.9	1,027.8	2,856.7
Finance	4,034.0	316.8	166.3	483.1
Government	14,831.0	1,940.9	906.9	2,847.8
Service	9,687.0	1,016.0	423.0	1,439.0
Miscellaneous	2,812.0	285.4	220.5	505.9
Total gross	106,860.0	10,573.5	5,005.1	15,578.6
Deduction for Social Security	1,365.0	127.8	59.6	187.4
Net wages and salaries	105,495.0	10,445.7	4,945.5	15,391.2
Net income of proprietors				
Agricultural	13,788.0	2,634.2	1,036.0	3,670.2
Nonagricultural	22,145.0	2,457.5	1,292.3	3,749.8
Total proprietors	35,933.0	5,091.7	2,328.3	7,420.0
Property income	17,401.0	1,598.9	880.1	2,479.0
Other income payments	12,719.0	1,786.6	834.7	2,621.3
Total income payments	171,548.0	18,922.9	8,988.6	27,911.5

Table 72 (cont'd)

Estimated Total and Per Capita Income Payments in the United States,
the Southeast, the Southwest, and the South, 1939-1947,
and Chief Sources of Income Payments in 1946

	United States	Southeast	Southwest	South
Chief sources of income payments, 1946				
Per cent of United States				
Gross wages and salaries				
Agriculture	100.0	15.6	8.3	23.9
Mining	100.0	8.3	14.1	22.4
Manufacturing	100.0	8.2	2.3	10.5
Construction	100.0	10.2	5.4	15.6
Transportation	100.0	11.1	6.0	17.1
Power and gas	100.0	9.0	6.0	15.0
Communication	100.0	8.8	4.9	13.7
Trade	100.0	9.6	5.4	15.0
Finance	100.0	7.9	4.1	12.0
Government	100.0	13.1	6.1	19.2
Service	100.0	10.5	4.4	14.9
Miscellaneous	100.0	10.1	7.9	18.0
Total gross salaries and wages	100.0	9.9	4.7	14.6
Deduction for Social Security	100.0	9.4	4.4	13.8
Net wages and salaries	100.0	9.9	4.7	14.6
Net income of proprietors				
Agriculture	100.0	19.1	7.5	26.6
Nonagricultural	100.0	11.1	5.8	16.9
Total proprietors	100.0	14.2	6.5	20.7
Property income	100.0	9.2	5.1	14.3
Other income payments	100.0	14.0	6.6	20.6
Total income payments	100.0	11.0	5.2	16.2
Per cent of total income payments				
Gross salaries and wages				
Agriculture		2.0	2.3	2.1
Mining		1.1	3.8	2.0
Manufacturing		15.7	9.2	13.6
Construction		2.3	2.6	2.4
Transportation		5.1	5.7	5.3
Power and gas		0.5	0.7	0.6
Communication		0.7	0.8	0.7
Trade		9.7	11.4	10.2
Finance		1.7	1.9	1.7
Government		10.3	10.1	10.2
Service		5.4	4.7	5.2
Miscellaneous		1.5	2.5	1.8
Total gross salaries and wages		55.9	55.7	55.8
Deduction for Social Security		0.7	0.7	0.7
Net wages and salaries		55.2	55.0	55.1
Net income of proprietors				
Agricultural		13.9	11.5	13.1
Nonagricultural		13.0	14.4	13.4
Total proprietors		26.9	25.9	26.6
Property income		8.4	9.8	8.9
Other income payments		9.4	9.3	9.4
Total income payments		100.0	100.0	100.0

Source: National Income Unit, United States Department of Commerce. See Table 64, Note B.

much needs to be said in the present chapter beyond the presentation of a summary in the form of Table 72 of the estimates of income payments to persons living in the Southeast, the Southwest, and the South.

A few particular points may be emphasized. The first is that the data on total income and on per capita income indicate a considerable improvement in the South with respect to its relationship to the nation as a whole. The second is that the nature of an agricultural economy is such that a state or a region which has a large proportion of its population engaged in farming will make a poor showing with respect to income payments when compared with an area that has a small percentage in agriculture. The data presented in this chapter certainly indicate that the incomes of the southern farmers are low compared with other farmers, but the South's low position with respect to income payments generally is due to this situation only in part. A part arises simply from the fact that it has such a large proportion in agriculture. A third important feature of the situation in the South is that the estimates of wages and salaries indicate relatively low positions not only in manufacturing, but in such important fields of economic activity as trade, communication, finance, and service. This reflects again the fact that the South as a whole has not developed an urban economy to anything like the same degree as the nation as a whole.

Trade and Geographic Factors

The South has long been a producer of bulk raw materials that have been marketed largely outside the region, and a purchaser of finished products. While the colonial economy argument may well be overemphasized, this condition has tended to establish freight rates, transportation facilities, commodity movements, trade practices, and customs which are consistent with the type of economy that has prevailed. The industrialization of the South, particularly the development of finished goods industries, has had a difficult task to break into these established patterns.

Furthermore, there are certain geographic factors that give the great centers of the North and East easy access to important areas of the South. The Atlantic Coast makes a large part of the eastern part of the South accessible by water to the Middle Atlantic ports. In fact, this is also a factor in the Texas Gulf Coast area. The Ohio and Mississippi Rivers provide a waterway which makes possible shipments from such centers as Pittsburgh, Youngstown, Ashland (Kentucky), Cincinnati, Louisville, and St. Louis to Memphis, Baton Rouge, and New Orleans to the important Texas Coast cities. Much of the Southeast is mountainous with the ridges extending generally in a northeasterly and southwesterly direction. The long valleys which lie between these ridges provide natural routes for railroads and highways so that it often has been more convenient and cheaper to transport goods for longer distances from a Northern point than it is to cross ridges to get to a nearer Southern city.

It is convenient to speak of the *southern market,* but the use of such a term should not lead to the assumption that it is one large homogeneous area which radiates from a natural center or a heartland. Actually, the geographic characteristics of the South make the delineation of market areas a difficult and complex job, and this is probably particularly true for iron and steel products.

Summary

The outstanding characteristics of the South that affect the market for iron and steel may be summarized in the following manner.

1. The agricultural characteristics of the South have exercised a very great influence on the market for iron and steel. In part, this arises from the predominant place that agriculture has held in the economy of the region. Other important factors have had to do with the relatively backward state of farming methods in much of the area, high degree of tenancy, low income of farmers, and low degree of mechanization. However, there is a much wider diversity in products and types of farming than is generally realized and there are

many areas that offer promise of expanding markets.

2. Except for the influence of natural gas and petroleum in the Southwest, the industrial development is relatively low compared with the nation as a whole in each of the three main subdivisions: construction, mineral industries, and manufacturing. On the whole, construction is the most highly developed of the three and has offered relatively strong markets for iron and steel structural products. Petroleum in the Southwest has provided the region's greatest concentrated market for iron and steel. Coal and ore mining are carried on in some localities on a scale large enough to create sizable demands for equipment. Manufacturing in the South is relatively weak in the industries that use iron and steel as raw materials or as expendable materials, such as containers. For most of the South's industries, the demand for iron and steel is mainly in the form of structures and equipment.

3. From the point of view of geographic location, industrial areas are widely scattered

and concentrations in areas of any considerable extent are few. Consequently, the South offers few markets for large quantities of iron and steel products of any particular kind.

4. In the development of railroads and public utilities, the South makes a relatively good showing, and these should provide good markets for iron and steel products. However, the relatively poor showing in such an item as telephones suggests weakness for consumer products.

5. Low income in the South, arising in part from the predominance of agriculture, is an unfavorable factor of the greatest importance in limiting the market for iron and steel in the region. Consequently, tendencies toward greater urbanization and higher incomes should do much to strengthen the market.

6. Trade patterns and geographic characteristics of the South are such that the southern producer faces strong competition in much of the region from plants located outside the South.

CHAPTER XVIII

THE USE PATTERN OF IRON AND STEEL

To provide a background for an analysis of the South as a market for iron and steel and their products, the last chapter discussed the characteristics of the region which exercise strong influences on its demands for the products of blast furnaces and steel mills. The present chapter is designed to provide further background material by presenting a description of the use pattern of iron and steel in the United States.

The Use of Pig Iron

The quantity of pig iron entering into the making of steel far surpasses all the other uses. In 1939,[1] the total production of pig iron was reported as 34,808,682 tons,[2] of which only 4,355,609 tons were for sale and the remaining 30,453,073 tons were for the makers' use in manufacturing more refined products. In 1947,[3] the total production of 58,328,912 tons was divided between the two subclasses, 7,683,276 tons and 50,328,912 tons respectively. These two subclasses do not indicate precisely the use that is made of the pig iron, but it is well known that the great bulk of the pig iron for makers' use moves to the steelmaking furnaces as one of the chief raw materials of steel. Some pig iron probably is used in the iron and steel companies' own foundry departments in making ingot molds and other items needed in their operations, but the quantities are relatively small. The Bureau of Mines in 1947

reported that the charge to the various types of steelmaking furnaces included 50,177,381 tons of pig iron. This compares with a total pig iron production of 58,327,231 and is in close agreement with the American Iron and Steel Institute's figure for pig iron produced for makers' use.

The end use of the pig iron made for sale is indicated by the following statistics on grade.[4]

Grade of pig iron for sale	1939 net tons	1947 net tons
Basic	932,505	1,413,019
Bessemer and low phosphorus	367,890	754,590
Foundry	1,767,445	2,796,303
Malleable	1,223,552	2,614,698
Forge	3,800	
All other	60,417	104,666
Total	4,355,609	7,683,276

Since the grades designated as foundry and malleable can be presumed to be primarily for use in foundries, it can be concluded that the pig iron for sale finds its chief market in that industry. This conclusion is confirmed by the reports of the Bureau of Mines which places the consumption of pig iron by cupolas in 1947 at 5,438,727 net tons.

The data cited above indicate that approximately 85 per cent of the pig iron finds its use in the production of steel, 10 per cent as a raw material for foundries and 5 per cent in other uses.

The Use of Foundry Products

In addition to pig iron, foundries use large quantities of iron and steel scrap in their charges. Consequently, the weight of the products which result do not correspond directly to

[1] American Iron and Steel Institute, *Annual Statistical Report,* 1939 and 1947. While data for later years is now (1951) available for many items, use will be made largely of statistics for 1947 because of the larger possibilities of comparisons based on different sources.

[2] Tons, as used in this chapter, can be understood to be net tons unless otherwise stated.

[3] American Iron and Steel Institute, *Annual Statistical Report,* 1939 and 1947.

[4] American Iron and Steel Institute, *Annual Statistical Report,* 1939 and 1947.

the tonnage input of pig iron.[5] The data made available by the Census of Manufactures[6] gives a fairly close index of the more important classes of use of foundry products in 1947.

Classes	Short tons
Gray-iron castings	
Miscellaneous gray-iron castings	8,614,301
Ingot molds and stools for heavy steel ingots	1,873,376
Chilled iron railroad car wheels	
made on conversion basis	529,761
made from manufacturer-owned metal	222,851
Cast iron pipe (including fittings)	
pressure pipe	1,044,278
soil pipe	577,189
Total gray iron castings	12,860,756
Malleable iron castings	902,127

According to these data the largest class of use is for miscellaneous gray iron castings which are largely for parts for appliances, vehicles, machinery, and equipment. The steel industry itself (for ingot molds, etc.) and cast iron pipe share in the use of foundry products on an almost equal basis, while railroad car wheels provide the other large outlet.

The Uses of Steel

In 1947, steel ingot production in the United States totaled almost 85 million tons compared

[5] In 1947, the Bureau of Mines reports the following consumption by cupola furnaces:

Iron and steel scrap (net tons)	
Home	5,240,692
Purchased	5,316,947
Total	10,557,639
Pig iron (net tons)	5,438,727

[6] *Census of Manufactures, 1947*, II, p. 546, Table 6M.

with a little less than 53 million tons in 1939. From this production of steel, the tonnage of finished steel mill products reported by the American Iron and Steel Institute was 66.2 million tons in 1947 and 39 million tons in 1939. It will be noted that there are large differences between the steel ingot and the finished steel product figures. A major portion of this variance is accounted for by the mill scrap that results from the finishing processes. This scrap material is recycled back to the steelmaking furnaces and forms an important part of the charge as is shown by the Bureau of Mines' figures on the use of pig iron and scrap iron and steel.

As already said, the uses for steel are extremely varied and so a complete cataloguing of the products derived from this metal is beyond the scope of this report. The tables and discussions that follow are designed to show the importance of the more outstanding finished products and consuming industries and to point out some of the characteristics of the demand.

According to Table 74, 39 per cent of steel product shipments in 1947 were in the form of plates (sheared and universal) and sheets. Bars accounted for an additional 17.6 per cent. These are forms which find their use largely in the production of manufactured metal products. Heavy structural shapes, wire products, pipes and tubes, and black, tin, and terne plate each accounted for around 7 or 8 per cent of total shipments. The other listed forms occupied much less important places in the total from the point of view of tonnage, although

Table 73

Use of Iron and Steel Scrap and Pig Iron in Steelmaking, 1947
(in short tons)

Kind of furnace	Iron and steel scrap			Pig iron
	Home	Purchased	Total	
Open hearth	21,727,939	17,560,105	39,288,044	45,338,462
Bessemer	212,702	60,261	272,963	4,711,581
Electric	2,053,278	3,171,083	5,224,361	127,338
Crucible	864	1,401	2,265	1,312
Total	23,994,783	20,792,850	44,787,633	50,178,693

Source: *Minerals Yearbook, 1947*, p. 649.

it must be remembered that some of the lower quantity items have high unit values.

Steel products are further divided (according to the kind of steel used) into several classes: carbon steel (the ordinary kind), stainless steel, chromium steel, and other alloy steel products. The great bulk of the steel products belong in the carbon steel class—in 1947, 58,593,552 tons of a total of 63,057,150 or approximately 93 per cent. The tonnage of chromium steel products was small (12,000 tons) and stainless was only slightly more than a quarter of a million tons. These are steels with highly specialized uses. The other alloy steel products have a considerably higher tonnage—in 1947, 4,156,088 tons —but constituted only 6.6 per cent of the total. The stainless products largely took the form of sheets and cold rolled strip. The other alloy products predominantly were shaped into bars or sheets. In these shapes, the specialty steels are in convenient form for the fabricating industries. An item of interest, though small, is the alloy steel in the from of tool steel bars.

Since 1940, the American Iron and Steel Institute has been publishing an analysis of the shipments of the steel mills. From 1940 to 1944, an industry classification was used. In 1945, a revision was made in the reporting, and since that year a breakdown by what is termed a "market classification" is used. The two classifications are not comparable, and neither corresponds to the industry classification used

in the Census of Manufactures. For these reasons, analyses cannot be carried to the detail that may be desired, but a reasonably accurate picture can be gotten of the relative importance of the various users of steel products from the data for 1947 which are presented in Table 76.

Of the total shipments in 1947 of 63,057,150 tons, 4,206,692 tons or 6.7 per cent were exported. The use to which the remainder was put is indicated by the main groups given in Table 76. These classes represent for the most part purchases of steel products intermediate between the steel mill and the ultimate consumer of the finished products.

The largest single class (as given in Table 76) is the one for the jobbers, dealers, and distributors, with a total of 10,484,144 tons. The products shipped to this group include sizable quantities of each kind of steel product and it can be assumed that these products find their way to every type of consumer, domestic, commercial, and industrial. A specialized subclass which is of considerable interest is the jobbers for the oil and gas industry, for which a figure of 938,490 tons is reported.

Another main group which cannot be identified closely with an ultimate end use is the one termed "steel for converting and processing" which accounted for 5,632,824 tons. This steel finds its way into wire and wire products; sheets, pipe and tubes; bolts, nuts and screws;

Table 74

Shipments in 1947 and Production for Sales in 1939 of Steel Products,
All Kinds of Steel, United States

	1939		1947	
	Production for sale (net tons)	Per cent of total	Shipments (net tons)	Per cent of total
Ingots, blooms, billets, tube rounds, etc.	1,305,866	3.7	2,966,748	4.7
Structural shapes (heavy)	2,544,515	7.3	4,436,129	7.0
Steel piling	171,428	0.5	324,224	0.5
Plates (sheared and universal)	2,793,798	8.0	6,345,216	10.1
Skelp	226,508	0.6	160,989	0.3
Rails				
Standard (over 60 pounds)	1,161,988	3.3	2,207,146	3.5
All other	125,109	0.4	211,900	0.3
Joint bars and tie plates	466,247	1.3	678,702	1.1

Table 74 (cont'd)

Shipments in 1947 and Production for Sales in 1939 of Steel Products, All Kinds of Steel, United States

	1939		1947	
	Production for sale (net tons)	Per cent of total	Shipments (net tons)	Per cent of total
Track spikes	119,719	0.3	163,746	0.3
Hot rolled bars				
Carbon	3,292,876	9.4	6,242,416	9.9
Reinforcing				
New billet	1,038,949	3.0	1,277,075	2.0
Rerolled	175,253	0.5	175,833	0.3
Alloy	702,322	2.0	1,741,432	2.8
Total	5,209,400	14.9	9,436,756	15.0
Cold finished bars				
Carbon	592,514	1.7	1,426,701	2.3
Alloy	66,384	0.2	218,802	0.3
Total	658,898	1.9	1,645,503	2.6
Tool steel bars	45,117	0.1	87,279	0.1
Pipes and tubes				
Buttweld	952,974	2.7	1,706,415	2.7
Lapweld	358,919	1.0	389,762	0.6
Electricweld	267,312	0.8	1,122,350	1.8
Seamless	1,686,665	4.8	2,082,686	3.3
Conduit	78,850	0.2	155,335	0.2
Mechanical and pressure tubing	160,862	0.5	661,336	1.1
Wire rods	550,040	1.6	667,282	1.1
Wire				
Drawn	1,354,992	3.9	2,590,963	4.1
Nails and staples	678,786	1.9	799,436	1.3
Barbed and twisted	231,021	0.7	256,991	0.4
Woven wire fence	273,596	0.8	407,295	0.6
Bale ties	59,547	0.1	119,917	0.2
All other wire products	5,766	0.0	......	...
Fence posts	60,439	0.1	......	...
Black plate				
Ordinary	⎰269,341	⎰0.8	801,745	1.3
Chemically treated	⎱	⎱	19,252	0.0
Tin and terne plate				
Hot dipped	⎰2,561,451	⎰7.3	2,093,149	3.3
Electrolytic	⎱	⎱	1,617,659	2.6
Sheets				
Hot rolled	5,087,886	14.6	7,891,798	12.5
Cold rolled	2,021,859	6.1	5,504,578	8.7
Galvanized	1,394,922	4.0	1,609,881	2.5
Strip				
Hot rolled	1,160,513	3.3	1,740,085	2.7
Cold rolled	676,397	1.9	1,613,005	2.6
Wheels (car, rolled steel)	150,750	0.4	356,873	0.6
Axles	73,970	0.2	185,019	0.3
All other	9,724	0.0	......	...
Total steel products	34,955,175	100.0	63,057,150	100.0

Source: American Iron and Steel Institute, *Annual Statistical Report, 1947*, p. 58.

forgings, maintenance and repair parts and supplies for steel plants; and a wide variety of other products. A large portion of these items are sold to fabricators of finished products. The only end use that can be distinguished is the figure of 426,944 tons for forgings for automobiles.

The remaining main classifications (except unclassified) are rather closely related to spe-

cific end uses and, for convenience, may be summarized under the following headings: construction, transportation, extractive industries, agriculture, industrial and electrical machinery, domestic and commercial appliances and equipment, containers, and export.

A total of some 8.5 million tons may be assigned to construction; this includes the two classes—construction and contractor's products.

Table 75

Shipments of Stainless and Alloy Steel Products in the United States, 1947

Products	Shipments (net tons)	Per cent of total of class
Stainless steel products		
Ingots, blooms, billets, slabs, sheet bars, etc.	15,619	5.3
Plates	11,273	3.8
Sheets, hot rolled and cold rolled	99,838	33.8
Strip, hot rolled	1,034	0.4
Strip, cold rolled	101,288	34.3
Bars, hot rolled	25,176	8.5
Bars, cold finished	22,762	7.7
Tube rounds	101	0.0
Pipe and tubes	8,296	2.8
Wire rods	708	0.2
Wire, drawn	8,891	3.0
All other (including structural shapes)	560	0.2
Total stainless steel products	295,546	100.0
All products, 4 per cent and 6 per cent chromium		
Types 501 and 502	12,044	...
All other alloy steel products		
Ingots, blooms, billets, slabs, tube rounds, sheet bars, etc.	379,551	9.1
Structural shapes (heavy)	67,578	1.6
Plates (sheared and universal)	166,106	4.0
Rails, standard (over 60 pounds)	157	0.0
Rails, all other	75	0.0
Bars, hot rolled	1,716,187	41.3
Bars, cold finished	196,200	4.7
Bars, tool steel	62,780	1.5
Pipe and tubes	362,420	8.7
Wire rods	1,311	0.0
Wire, drawn	28,436	0.7
Sheets, hot rolled	745,370	17.9
Sheets, cold rolled	251,474	6.1
Strip, hot rolled	67,972	1.7
Strip, cold rolled	103,719	2.5
Wheels (car, rolled steel)	53	0.0
Axles	558	0.0
All other	6,061	0.2
Total alloy steel products	4,156,008	100.0

Source: American Iron and Steel Institute, *Annual Statistical Report, 1947*, p. 60.

The first of these classes includes shapes, plates, and other products for direct use on construction projects. Two subclasses of interest are the construction materials for oil and gas (1,320,140 tons) and for rail transportation (134,005 tons). The contractor's products include fabricated items such as air conditioning and ventilating equipment, builders hardware, culverts, and plumbing and heating equipment.

Transportation includes the following subclasses.

Automotive, excluding tractors.....	8,846,419 tons
Rail transportation	4,879,879 tons
Shipbuilding	337,961 tons
Aircraft	39,231 tons
Total	14,103,490 tons

To the quantities shown above there may be added the automobile forgings of 426,944 tons and the construction materials for rail transportation of 134,005 tons. On this basis, transportation accounts for approximately 14.7 million tons of the 1947 shipments, or about 23 per cent of the total. Of the various types, automotive vehicles account for the largest tonnages. Shipbuilding and aircraft were quite naturally much below their war-time levels. Automobile consumption includes practically every form of steel mill product, but the concentration is largely on bars (almost 2 million tons), sheets (5 million tons), and strip (800 thousand tons). Rail transportation includes more than one-half of the total shipments of rails, rail accessories, wheels and axles, and large quantities of structural shapes, plates, bars, and sheets for the manufacture of locomotives and cars.

The oil and gas industry is a very large consumer of iron and steel products. The total

Table 76

Net Shipments of Steel Mill Products in the United States by Market Classifications, 1947

Market classifications	All grades		Alloy other than stainless		Stainless	
	Quantity (net tons)	Per cent of total	Quantity (net tons)	Per cent of total	Quantity (net tons)	Per cent of total
Steel for converting and processing...........	5,632,824	8.9	535,552	12.9	22,955	7.8
Jobbers, dealers, and distributors..............	10,484,144	16.6	222,279	5.3	53,364	18.1
Construction, including maintenance.........	6,257,559	9.9	60,667	1.5	1,864	0.6
Contractors' products........................	2,243,399	3.6	30,629	0.7	4,865	1.6
Automotive, except tractors...................	8,846,419	14.0	1,087,135	26.1	35,591	12.0
Rail transportation..........................	4,879,879	7.7	227,072	5.5	4,298	1.5
Shipbuilding	337,961	0.5	11,792	0.3	827	0.3
Aircraft	39,231	0.1	11,062	0.3	4,081	1.4
Oil and gas drilling..........................	930,731	1.5	156,049	3.7	674	0.2
Mining, quarrying, and lumbering.............	287,670	0.5	19,449	0.5	388	0.1
Agricultural	1,244,548	2.0	44,246	1.1	224	0.1
Machinery, industrial equipment, and tools....	3,031,719	4.8	445,808	10.7	23,901	8.1
Electrical machinery and equipment...........	1,595,520	2.5	448,262	10.8	5,635	1.9
Appliances, utensils, and cutlery..............	1,564,722	2.5	23,789	0.6	30,658	10.4
Other domestic and commercial equipment....	1,680,259	2.7	38,594	0.9	7,730	2.6
Containers	5,076,170	8.0	19,741	0.5	13,159	4.5
Ordnance and other military..................	56,908	0.1	8,811	0.2	84	0.03
Unclassified	4,660,795	7.4	589,593	14.2	62,775	21.2
Export	4,206,692	6.7	175,475	4.2	22,473	7.6
Total	63,057,150	100.0	4,156,008	100.0	295,546	100.0
1. fl Forgings, automobile....................	426,944	0.7	186,919	4.5	209	0.1
2. a Jobbers, oil and gas....................	938,490	1.5	57,316	1.4	103	0.03
3. g Rail transportation.....................	134,005	0.2	347	0.008	6	0.002
4. h Oil and gas...........................	1,320,140	2.1	5,104	0.1	570	0.2

Source: American Iron and Steel Institute, *Annual Statistical Report, 1947*, p. 95.

consumption is probably not disclosed by the available data because considerable quantities are probably purchased from dealers for a variety of purposes and are never identified with oil and gas in the statistics. A combination of three items that are available from the American Iron and Steel Institute reports gives an indication of the quantities involved.

Oil and gas drilling	930,731 tons
Construction—oil and gas	1,320,140 tons
Jobbers and distributors—oil and gas	938,490 tons
Total	3,189,361 tons

To the oil and gas might be added the quantity shipped to mining and quarrying (287,670 tons) and the total might be spoken of as representing the extractive industries. The figure so obtained is some 3.5 million tons. In each of the several subdivisions, the largest item in demand was pipes and tubes. In construction for gas and oil, plates are also important.

Industrial and electrical machinery in 1947 had a combined demand of 4,596,431 tons. The kinds of steel products required by the industries in this classification are quite varied and quite large tonnages of structural shapes, plates, bars, pipe and tubes, wire, and sheets are used.

Shipments for use in domestic and commercial appliances and equipment accounted for a total tonnage of 3,244,981 tons in 1947. This classification includes products for consumer use either in homes or in places of business. Some representative items are cooking stoves and ranges, refrigerators, washing machines, general household appliances, metal furniture, office machines, professional and scientific instruments and equipment, toys, and hardware. The steel products used tend to be of the lighter kinds with emphasis on pipes and tubes, wire, and sheets.

Containers constitute a class of great importance from the standpoint both of the quantity of steel consumed and of the service performed. A total of 5,076,170 tons was reported, consisting largely of tin and terne plate, but including also large quantities of hot and cold rolled sheets, strip, and plates. As a matter of fact, by far the largest part of the tin and terne plate

(3,012,298 of a total of 3,710,808 tons) was used in containers.

The final end use which will be mentioned is agriculture. It is probable that the Institute's classification fails to include all the steel that ultimately finds its use in some phase of agriculture, because at least some of the products assigned to jobbers and distributors undoubtedly are sold to farmers for use on farms. Also tractors are classified under the general heading of industrial machinery. The subclasses under agriculture are agricultural machinery, farm service structures, and other agriculture. The total assigned to this class was 1,244,548 tons, or 2 per cent of the total. The pattern of use according to kinds of steel products is quite similar to that of industrial and electrical machinery and equipment.

While the distribution in one year cannot be taken as an accurate measure of the market, the 1947 figures do give an indication of the relative importance of the main classes of users under the postwar conditions that existed at that time. As measured by the tonnages of shipments, the relative importance of the several classifications may be summarized in the following manner.

Main groupings	Per cent of total
Exports	6.7
Steel for converting (of which 0.7 per cent may be applied to transportation)	8.9
Jobbers and distributors (of which 1.5 per cent may be applied to extractive industries)	16.6
Construction (of which 0.2 per cent may be applied to transportation and 2.1 per cent to extractive industries)	13.5
Transportation	22.3
Extractive industries	2.0
Agriculture	2.0
Industrial and electrical machinery	7.3
Domestic and commercial appliances and equipment	5.2
Containers	8.0
Ordnance	0.1
Unclassified	7.4
Total	100.0

From the point of view of the market for steel mill products, a very important fact brought out by the data is that a manufacturer or a series of manufacturers stands between the steel mill and the ultimate consumer for a very large part of the total output. This directs attention to a study of the location and other characteristics of the processing and fabricating industries. For a regional study, the analysis of shipments by market classifications raises questions as to how the area measures up with regard to each of the classes of steel users.

CHAPTER XIX

THE IRON AND STEEL PROCESSING AND FABRICATING INDUSTRIES

The analysis of the use pattern of iron and steel products directs attention to those establishments which buy pig iron or steel mill products to use as raw materials in their manufacturing operations. The industries involved are too numerous and the operations too diverse for a detailed analysis in this general introductory chapter, but a summary statement of outstanding characteristics of the processing and fabricating industries should be helpful, especially to the reader who is not familiar with the structure of the industry.

Operating Characteristics of Processing and Fabricating Industries

The operations of the metal fabricating plants which are most readily seen and perhaps most easily understood are those that have to do with physical manipulations or shaping of the iron or steel into the desired pieces. This is accomplished in a variety of ways, of which the following will be mentioned.

Casting—by which the shaping is accomplished by pouring the molten iron or steel into a previously prepared mold

Rolling—by which the metal is forced into the shape desired by passing it through a succession of revolving rollers

Forging—by which the metal is forced into shape by a hammering process

Drawing—by which the metal is pulled or drawn through a die and thus shaped

Machining—by which the metal is shaped by subjecting it to the actions of such machine tools as lathes, planers, or boring machines in which specially hardened and designed tools cut the grooves, bore the holes, make the threads, or produce the surfaces desired

Bending and twisting—by which the iron or steel bars, shapes, rods, wire, or tubes are bent or twisted into the desired form

Stamping and pressing—by which iron or steel sheets or plates are shaped by the pressure exerted by machanical presses

Grinding and polishing—by which the desired shapes are produced or the kind of surface is attained by the use of abrasives.

A common type of operation is that which provides a means of jointing two or more pieces of metal. Common devices are by threading, by welding or soldering, by riveting, by use of bolts and nuts, and by use of screws or studs. Also, it is often desirable to apply a special coating to an exposed surface, and this gives rise to such processes as tin plating, galvanizing, enameling, and japanning.

Securing the desired shapes and sizes of the various pieces or parts that go to make a finished product is only one of the operating problems of the metal fabricator. Iron and steel products are used under a very wide variety of conditions. Some of these place particular importance on strength, ability to support a load or to withstand a stress; others on resistance to impact, shock or vibration; and still others on the ability to resist the corrosive effect of moisture or of some particular chemical. In some cases toughness is desired; in others, extreme hardness. As a matter of fact, the various quality characteristics might be multiplied almost infinitely. In other words, metallurgical problems and technical methods are involved in securing the desired qualities in the products of the processing and fabricating industries.

Another characteristic of the fabricating industries is that they are largely concerned with making articles that have specific end uses as contrasted with industries whose products are for general purpose use. This statement must not be taken too literally, but it does serve to point to the importance of design as a factor in the fabricating industries. In the making of pig iron or steel, the several quality properties have a close relationship to the ultimate use, and the blast furnace or steel mill must make products that are suitable to the needs of their customers. In the case of the fabricator, however, the problem of designing a product to meet a specific use assumes an even greater importance. In some industries, it becomes perhaps the most critical of all factors. A loom for a cotton textile mill, a power shovel for construction work, or a mechanical loader for a coal mine are examples which show how necessary it is for the manufacturer to fit his product to the specific use to which it is to be put. Furthermore, in many lines, particularly in consumers durable goods (for example, automobiles) appearance is an important consideration. In other words, style may have much to do with manufacturing a product which is successful commercially.

Finally, the production of a finished product usually involves the putting together of the several component parts to form the product. In the case of construction, this is usually termed erection; in the case of most manufactured products, the term "assembly" or "assembling" is used. It is this characteristic which accounts for the word "fabricator."

The common types of operations in metal working industries is reflected in the standard classification used by the Bureau of the Census in the reports sought for the *Census of Manufactures* in 1947. The classification is as follows:

Foundry, except die casting
Die casting
Forging—presses, hammers, or upsetters
Electroplating
Galvanizing and other hot-dip coating
Heat treating or annealing of metals for production purposes
Automatic screw-machine department
Machine shop
Tool and die room
Pattern shop
Plate or structural fabrication
Stamping, blanking, forming, or drawing.

The reports indicate that these operations are carried on in a very large number of the plants of the various processing and fabricating industries.

In concluding this brief discussion of operating characteristics, it should be pointed out that it has not been the purpose here to give a generalized description that could be applied to any or all fabricating plants. In fact, no one plant would be likely to perform all the operations or make use of all the processes mentioned above. Also, no attempt has been made to catalogue all possible operations or processes. As a matter of fact, some plants perform only one or two specialized operations. Others, whose requirements are more varied, will employ a wide variety of combinations to fit their particular needs. The summary of the more basic characteristics is intended to serve as a background for developing the analysis of the factors that control the development of the fabricating industries and hence much of the market for iron and steel products.

What Are the Processing and Fabricating Industries?

In the discussion in Chapter I of what constitutes the iron and steel industries, it was stated that the general definition would be reduced to specific terms by using selected industries, set up in the reports of the 1947 *Census of Manufactures,* as constituting the field for study. These industries included the primary metals group, except the industries specifically designated as nonferrous; the fabricated metal products group, except collapsible tubes and foils; the machinery group; the transportation equipment group; the instruments and related products group; and selected industries from the electrical machinery, furniture and fixtures, and miscellaneous manufactures groups. All of these industries except blast furnaces, steelworks and rolling mills, and electrometallurgical products are considered as belonging in the processing and fabricating classification. The number of industries thus selected is 144. The products of these industries number in the thousands. Consequently, it is not feasible to deal with either the industries or the products individually, and use will be made of groupings and of summary statements.

The discussion in this chapter and in the following chapters will be based primarily on the *Census of Manufacturers* of 1947, but there is need to make use of the information that is available from other sources. Therein are many problems. The industry classifications of the 1947 census follow in the main the Standard Industrial Classification which was adopted in 1946 for use by government agencies. This differs widely from the classifications used in the former censuses of manufactures, and, consequently, direct comparability is obtained only in the limited number of cases where the older census reports have been reclassified and retabulated. Also differences exist in the classifications used by the other agencies that have collected and published data. Mention was made in the last chapter of the differences between the systems used by the Census of Manufactures and the American Iron and Steel Institute. The War Production Board used still a different classification, and, consequently, it is difficult to relate the reports of activities during the war either to the prewar or the postwar statistics. Differences such as these are particularly troublesome in dealing with a group whose constituent industries are as numerous and diverse as the one under study. As a result, many comparisons must be made in terms of approximations.

The general groupings of the industries, together with the number of establishments, the number of production workers, the wages paid, and the value added by manufacture in 1947 and 1939, are given in Table 77.

Relative Position of the Processing and Fabricating Industries in the Manufacturing Structure

The processing and fabricating industries may be looked upon as being built upon the basic iron and steel industries. Table 78 is an attempt to indicate the accumulation of value which occurs. The data presented have the defect of showing only the cost of materials for the blast furnace industry and thus tend to give the impression that the other industries are engaged only in the refinement and fabrication of the products of the blast furnaces. As a matter of fact, raw materials, other than pig iron or steel made directly from pig iron, enter into the manufacturing processes at numerous points. The important part played by iron and steel scrap was discussed in Chapter VII. The various alloying and coating materials are also important. In the fabricating industries, nonferrous materials often form as large, or a larger, part of the finished product than iron and steel does. However, the reported costs of raw materials contain so much duplication that only the data of the industry that forms the first rung of the ladder has any significance for an analysis of this kind, and, for this reason, the figures on costs are confined to those of the blast furnace industry.

An examination of the data indicates that the value added by the basic industries in 1947 was approximately twice the cost of materials, parts, fuel, and purchased electricity of the blast furnace industry. The value added by the processing and fabricating industries was ten times the similar figures of the basic industries. While the data leave much to be desired, they do emphasize strongly the place that the processers and fabricators have in the production of the values finally attached to the products which find their way into use.

The importance of the iron and steel processing and fabricating industries in the industrial structure of the nation is further emphasized by the relative position of these industries in the total of manufacturing in the United States. Table 79 presents a summary of the situation in 1947 and 1939. These data indicate that the group of industries under study accounted for 36 to 41 per cent of the nation's manufacturing activity in 1947, depending upon the measure that may be chosen as an index. Comparisons with 1939 supports the conclusion that the iron and steel processing and fabricating industries increased in relative importance by increasing at a faster rate than total manufacturing.

Table 77

Processing and Fabricating Iron and Steel Industries in the United States, 1947 and 1939

Industry	1947				1939			
	Number of establishments	Number of production workers	Wages paid (in $1,000)	Value added by manufacture (in $1,000)	Number of establishments	Number of production workers	Wages paid (in $1,000)	Value added by manufacture (in $1,000)
Iron and steel foundries	1,936	239,272	672,116	1,121,522	1,501	123,809	152,545	295,012
Miscellaneous primary metal industries	811	107,412	329,706	740,155	439	52,004	73,828	192,218
Fabricated metal products	16,672	815,366	2,172,124	4,883,095	9,479	446,876	541,789	1,385,296
Tin cans and other tinware	217	40,890	105,689	231,953	195	29,277	33,722	116,152
Cutlery, hand tools, and hardware	1,866	131,604	339,163	728,426	1,212	75,175	86,213	208,968
Heating and plumbing equipment	1,276	126,725	339,029	789,524	1,036	78,330	93,763	244,851
Structural metal products	4,507	172,690	486,737	1,143,553	3,099	83,429	109,979	288,601
Metal stamping and coating	4,437	159,926	414,874	861,173	1,920	80,649	96,074	225,317
Lighting fixtures	1,206	39,883	97,351	247,619	568	20,477	23,238	64,731
Fabricated wire products	977	52,543	136,195	282,147	705	32,901	38,269	90,937
Miscellaneous fabricated metal products	2,186	91,105	253,086	598,700	744	46,638	60,531	145,739
Machinery (except electrical)	17,906	1,244,135	3,592,771	7,812,455	8,860	536,082	769,570	2,036,965
Engines and turbines	151	71,826	218,538	408,099	94	18,846	28,097	72,684
Tractors and farm machinery	1,102	139,629	381,574	753,762	421	60,144	85,862	210,958
Construction and mining machinery	747	88,905	255,047	641,397	562	36,750	52,796	159,256
Metal working machinery	4,293	172,982	541,586	1,131,182	1,470	80,954	133,510	326,235
Special-industry machinery	4,106	173,592	512,363	1,095,558	2,239	77,246	107,393	268,233
General industrial machinery	2,191	164,249	472,472	1,189,229	1,380	72,799	103,926	302,024
Office and store machines	357	84,340	247,458	503,854	251	42,989	58,352	146,043
Service and household machines	1,088	180,771	504,203	1,105,798	650	67,906	92,666	273,576
Miscellaneous machinery parts	3,871	167,841	459,530	983,576	1,793	78,448	106,968	277,956
Electrical machinery (selected)	3,421	557,541	1,453,549	3,404,332	1,622	207,903	277,245	788,787
Electrical industrial apparatus	1,523	247,149	666,948	1,576,180	682	91,990	131,687	362,308
Electrical appliances	326	37,271	96,654	236,241	118	13,572	16,286	42,150
Insulated wire and cable	171	18,185	45,375	103,722	79	15,696	18,638	50,265
Engine electrical equipment	110	37,978	102,144	196,351	90	17,043	23,675	66,066
Radios and related products	857	142,478	324,300	773,233	305	45,484	47,568	125,429
Telephone and telegraph equipment	90	53,630	167,488	384,417	43	14,433	26,977	98,715
Communication equipment, n.e.c.	101	7,781	19,826	46,767	62	2,893	4,010	12,905
X-ray and therapeutic apparatus	116	5,621	15,354	38,635	77	1,920	2,708	12,057

Electrical products, n.e.c.	127	7,448	15,460	48,786	166	4,872	5,696	18,892
Transportation equipment	3,711	987,142	2,939,815	5,869,196	2,012	544,553	867,224	1,772,573
Motor vehicles and equipment	1,904	599,301	1,797,805	3,819,076	1,128	393,617	637,497	1,304,395
Aircraft and parts	332	162,596	476,297	954,575	131	48,761	77,720	183,873
Ships and boats	1,110	132,033	394,371	586,558	608	69,241	107,570	179,898
Railroad equipment	122	75,691	224,867	415,607	68	24,709	34,313	82,251
Motorcycles and bicycles	76	13,659	37,732	72,838	36	6,973	8,974	19,011
Transportation equipment, n.e.c.	167	3,862	8,743	20,542	41	1,252	1,150	3,145
Small arms and small arms ammunition	42	15,997	43,173	83,154	36	9,265	11,799	30,746
Professional, scientific, and controlling instruments	2,599	181,939	467,785	1,080,336	1,292	84,867	107,703	333,409
Scientific instruments	216	15,023	41,831	83,010	125	6,529	10,067	30,627
Mechanical measuring instruments	463	40,937	109,196	245,144	227	15,075	19,954	59,463
Optical instruments and lenses	114	5,228	14,025	26,743	31	2,209	3,266	7,159
Medical instruments and supplies	980	29,617	71,281	184,665	552	14,624	15,743	64,626
Ophthalmic goods	184	19,744	46,224	81,530	91	10,252	12,246	30,745
Photographic equipment and supplies	366	36,273	101,765	264,784	160	16,434	23,868	87,816
Watches, clocks, clockwork operated devices	276	35,117	83,463	194,460	106	19,744	22,559	52,973
Furniture and fixture industries selected as metal users	3,880	114,977	289,184	658,163	2,809	68,244	77,587	193,759
Miscellaneous industries selected as metal users	8,400	226,586	514,399	1,179,814	5,187	142,916	145,678	377,470
Total processing and fabricating industries	59,378	4,490,367	12,474,622	26,832,222	33,237	2,216,519	3,024,968	7,406,235

Source: *Census of Manufactures, 1947.*

Table 78

Value Contributed by the Iron and Steel Industries in the United States, 1947 and 1939
(in thousand dollars)

	1947	1939
Cost of materials, fuel, electricity, and contract work in blast furnace industry		
Materials, parts, containers, and supplies..........................	751,673	
Fuels, total..........	629,048	
Bituminous coal........	4,776	
Anthracite	1,207	
Coke	617,472	
Fuel oils	909	
Gas.........	2,104	
Other fuels	2,580	
Purchased electricity........	5,060	
Contract and commission work..........	104	
Total	1,385,885	463,719
Value added by the basic industries		
Blast furnaces.........	328,060	87,083
Steel works and rolling mills.........	2,275,697	1,147,548
Electrometallurgical products	55,493	15,868
Total of basic industries..........	2,659,250	1,250,499
Value added by the processing and fabricating industries		
Iron and steel foundries.........	1,121,522	295,012
Miscellaneous primary metals industries.........	740,155	192,218
Fabricated metals industries.........	4,883,095	1,385,296
Machinery (except electrical).........	7,812,455	2,036,965
Selected electrical machinery industries.........	3,404,332	788,787
Transportation equipment.........	5,869,196	1,772,573
Small arms and small arms ammunition.........	83,154	30,746
Instruments and related products.........	1,080,336	333,409
Selected furniture and fixtures industries.........	658,163	193,759
Selected miscellaneous manufacturing.........	1,179,814	377,470
Total processing and fabricating industries.........	26,832,222	7,406,235

Source: *Census of Manufactures, 1947.*

Table 79

Relative Position of the Iron and Steel Processing and Fabricating Industries
in the Manufacturing Structure of the United States, 1947 and 1939

Year and item	All manufacturing	Iron and steel processing and fabricating	Per cent processing and fabricating of total
1947			
Number of production workers......................	11,916,188	4,490,363	37.7
Wages paid (thousand dollars).........................	30,242,343	12,474,722	41.2
Value added by manufacture (thousand dollars)........	74,425,825	26,832,222	36.1
1939			
Number of production workers......................	7,808,205	2,216,519	28.4
Wages paid (thousand dollars).........................		3,024,968	
Value added by manufacture (thousand dollars)........	24,487,304	7,406,234	30.2

Source: *Census of Manufactures, 1947.*

The Relative Importance of Individual Industries

Having discussed the importance of the iron and steel processing and fabricating industries as a class, some additional details concerning the component industries should be given. The relative importance of the primary subclasses of the entire group is brought out by the following tabulation which expresses each subclass as a percentage of the total of all the processing and fabricating industries in 1947.

Subclass	Number of production workers (per cent)	Value added by manufacture (per cent)
Machinery (except electrical)...	27.8	29.1
Transportation equipment.....	22.0	21.9
Fabricated metal products.....	18.2	18.2
Electrical machinery (selected).	12.4	12.7
Foundries and miscellaneous primary metal products......	7.7	6.9
Selected miscellaneous industries	5.3	4.7
Professional and scientific instruments	4.0	4.0
Selected furniture and fixtures.	2.6	2.5
Total processing and fabricating	100.0	100.0

It can be seen readily that the great bulk of the entire classification is accounted for by the subclasses listed first in the above tabulation. Machinery, transportation equipment, and fabricated metal products comprise almost 70 per cent of the total, whether measured in terms of the number of production workers or the value added by manufacture. If electrical machinery and foundries and miscellaneous primary metal industries are added, the per cent of the total is increased to almost 90. These five subclasses might be said to include the industries that are primarily concerned with metal working, while the others represent operations which add relatively little to the totals.

As already stated, the number of the individual industries makes a detailed discussion almost impossible. To call attention to some of the more important of the industries, measured by the value added by manufacture, the 35 industries, whose value added in 1947 exceed a quarter of a billion dollars, are listed in Table 80. It should be pointed out that the mere listing of a quantitative measure does not give a complete or final indication of an industry's importance. The table serves to call attention to the larger industries and to provide a background for the analysis of the processing and fabricating industries of the South in the chapters that follow.

Table 80

The Thirty-five Largest Iron and Steel Processing and Fabricating Industries as Indicated by Value Added by Manufacture, 1947

	Value added by manufacture (in $1,000)
1. Motor vehicles and parts.............	3,577,404
2. Radios and related products............	773,233
3. Gray-iron foundries...................	732,647
4. Metal stampings......................	642,483
5. Aircraft	605,983
6. Refrigeration machinery	597,486
7. Heating and cooking apparatus, n.e.c....	589,192
8. Motors and generators...............	569,745
9. Shipbuilding and repairing...........	517,504
10. Cutting tools, jigs, fixtures, etc.........	480,375
11. Construction and mining machinery.....	470,132
12. Structural and ornamental products.....	440,701
13. Farm machinery (except tractors)......	421,700
14. Electric control apparatus.............	395,175
15. Valves and fittings, except plumber's....	393,860
16. Telephone and telegraph equipment....	384,417
17. Boiler shop products..................	358,764
18. Special-industry machinery, n.e.c........	348,565
19. Machine tools........................	347,965
20. Hardware, n.e.c......................	346,457
21. Tractors	332,062
22. Internal-combustion engines...........	327,152
23. Wire drawing........................	314,788
24. Metal working machinery, n.e.c........	302,842
25. Bolts, nuts, washers, rivets.............	285,451
26. Power-transmission equipment..........	283,647
27. Pumps and compressors...............	282,476
28. Railroad and street cars...............	273,130
29. Machine shops.......................	271,870
30. Steel foundries......................	267,214
31. Wirework, n.e.c......................	266,426
32. Photographic equipment...............	264,784
33. Ball and roller bearings..............	259,060
34. Textile machinery....................	256,436
35. Aircraft engines......................	251,158

Source: *Census of Manufactures, 1947*, II.

Location of the Industries

It is not the purpose in this section to attempt a detailed description of the location of the several industries that belong in the processing and fabricating group or to enter into a discussion of the factors that control, or least influence, the location of these industries. An outline, rather sketchy perhaps, of the general situation with regard to geographic location should serve present needs. In approaching the subject several questions might be asked. Are the industries widely dispersed or closely concentrated, geographically? What areas have the greatest concentration? How do the geographic distributions of these particular industries compare with the distribution of manufacturing generally? The present discussion will be confined largely to answers to these questions for the 144 industries selected from the 1947 *Census of Manufactures* as constituting the iron and steel processing industries.

One measure of the extent to which an industry has its constituent units widely or narrowly dispersed is the number of states which have at least one establishment of the industry. An analysis on this basis shows that the individual industries in the group under discussion vary widely as is brought out by the following summary.

1. Number of industries with establishments in 38 or more states 25
2. Number of industries with establishments in 25 to 37 states 44
3. Number of industries with establishments in 13 to 24 states 62
4. Number of industries with establishments in less than 13 states 13
   Total 144

The industries in the first group may be considered as those which are very widely dispersed and those in the last group as being highly concentrated. The titles of those in each of the two groups are listed below.

Widely dispersed industries—Gray-iron foundries; fabricated structural steel and ornamental metal ware; boiler shop products; sheet metal works; machine shops; agricultural machinery (except tractors); mattresses and bedsprings; partitions, shelves, lockers, and office and store fixtures; screens and weather stripping; venetian blinds; hand tools; auto stamping and pressed metal products; electroplating and polishing; food processing machinery; special industry machinery, n.e.c.; refrigerators; truck and bus bodies; boatbuilding and repairing; surgical and orthopedic appliances and supplies; games and toys; sport and athletic goods; hand stamps, stencils, and brands; brooms and brushes; morticians goods; signs and advertising display.

Highly concentrated (geographically) industries—Safes and vaults; steam engines, turbines, and water wheels; typewriters; sewing machines; vacuum cleaners; aircraft engines and parts; aircraft propellers and parts; locomotives and parts; watch cases; umbrellas, parasols and canes; furniture and fixtures, n.e.c.; small arms; and small arms ammunition.

The list of widely dispersed industries consists largely of those that perform operations of a general nature and in many respects have the character either of service industries to other manufactures or of industries whose products are in very common usage in all parts of the nation. On the other hand, the highly concentrated industries seem to be those that have a highly specialized product or group of products.

A comparison of the total number of establishments in an industry and the number of states that have at least one establishment in that industry shows that there is a close relationship between these two characteristics. This is not a surprising situation because an industry must necessarily have a number of establishments before it can be widely dispersed. On the other hand, it could have a large number of establishments closely clustered in only a few areas. The tendency to cluster undoubtedly does occur in the iron and steel industries, but these data would seem to indicate that, as plants multiply, there is a tendency for the industry to spread geographically.

Another factor which influences these data should be mentioned, at least as a caution against going too far in generalizing; this is that the manner in which industries are defined can have a very great effect on the statistics. Some of the industry definitions are such that a wide scope is included, and establishments are classed as belonging together, although the products and operations are quite diverse. On the other hand, some industry classes include only establishments that produce highly specialized products with relatively few varieties. This situation arises from the fact that there are no generally accepted criteria to determine what constitutes an industry. As a result, every classification is largely influenced by what seems most convenient and feasible. Whether there are many or few establishments in a class or whether the class is widely dispersed or highly concentrated in a few areas may be determined largely by the decisions that were made in setting the limits of the class.

To provide a means of describing the location of the processing and fabricating industries, the number of establishments of each of the 144 industries was used as the measure. The United States was divided into eight regions in the following manner.

New England—Maine, New Hampshire, Vermont, Massachusetts, Connecticut, and Rhode Island

Middle Atlantic — New York, New Jersey, Pennsylvania, Delaware, Maryland, District of Columbia, Virginia, and West Virginia

Lake and Ohio River—Ohio, Indiana, Illinois, Kentucky, Michigan, and Wisconsin

West North Central—Minnesota, North Dakota, South Dakota, Iowa, Missouri, Nebraska, and Kansas

Rocky Mountain—Montana, Idaho, Wyoming, Colorado, Utah, Nevada, New Mexico, and Arizona

Pacific Coast — Washington, Oregon, and California

South — North Carolina, South Carolina, Georgia, Florida, Tennessee, Alabama, Mississippi, Arkansas, Louisiana, Oklahoma, and Texas

The problem of describing location was approached from two angles— (a) that of absolute dispersion or concentration and (b) that of relative dispersion or concentration as measured in terms of total manufacturing. In the first, the criterion was the percentage of the total number of establishments of an industry that occurred in each region. The second involved a comparison of the percentage of the establishments of a particular industry with the region's percentage share of all manufacturing establishments. In other words, the question was raised as to whether a region had a larger or smaller share of the establishments of the industry under examination than it had of all manufacturing plants. It must be admitted immediately that the number of establishments is not a precise measure, but it has the advantage of being the only regularly published measure that is available for all industries and all states. For the purpose of indicating occurrence, it is adequate.

The data show a heavy concentration of the iron and steel processing and fabricating industries in the Middle Atlantic and the Lake and Ohio River regions. These states are, of course, generally known to be highly industrialized and are often referred to as constituting the manufacturing heart of the nation. However, the evidence provided by the analysis of number of establishments indicate that the concentration of the iron and steel industries in these two regions is much greater than that of all manufacturing. In support of these conclusions a summary of the analyses is offered.

The Middle Atlantic and Lake and Ohio River regions in 1947 together had

75 per cent or more of the establishments in 23 of the iron and steel processing and fabricating industries

From 70 per cent to 74.9 per cent of the establishments in 28 industries

From 60 per cent to 69.9 per cent of the establishments in 48 industries

From 50 per cent to 59.9 per cent of the establishments in 30 industries

Less than 50 per cent of the establishments in 15 industries.

The two regions accounted for 56.9 per cent of all manufacturing establishments in the United States. Of the 144 iron and steel processing and fabricating industries, the share of the two regions equaled, or exceeded, their all-manu-

CHART 20

GEOGRAPHIC DISTRIBUTION OF ESTABLISHMENTS IN IRON AND STEEL INDUSTRIES IN THE UNITED STATES, 1939

TOTAL NUMBER OF ESTABLISHMENTS IN EACH INDUSTRY EQUALS 100 PER CENT

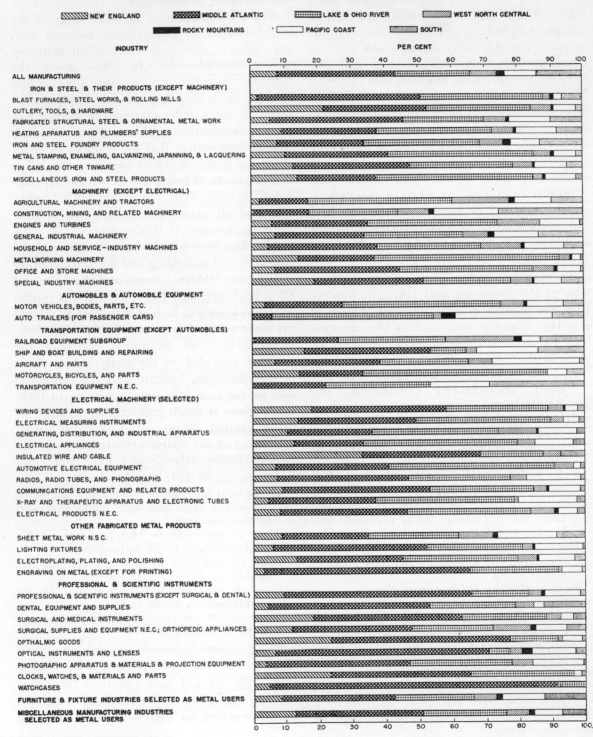

SOURCE: CENSUS OF MANUFACTURES, 1939

CHART 21

GEOGRAPHIC DISTRIBUTION OF ESTABLISHMENTS IN IRON AND STEEL INDUSTRIES IN THE UNITED STATES, 1947

TOTAL NUMBER OF ESTABLISHMENTS IN EACH INDUSTRY EQUALS 100 PER CENT

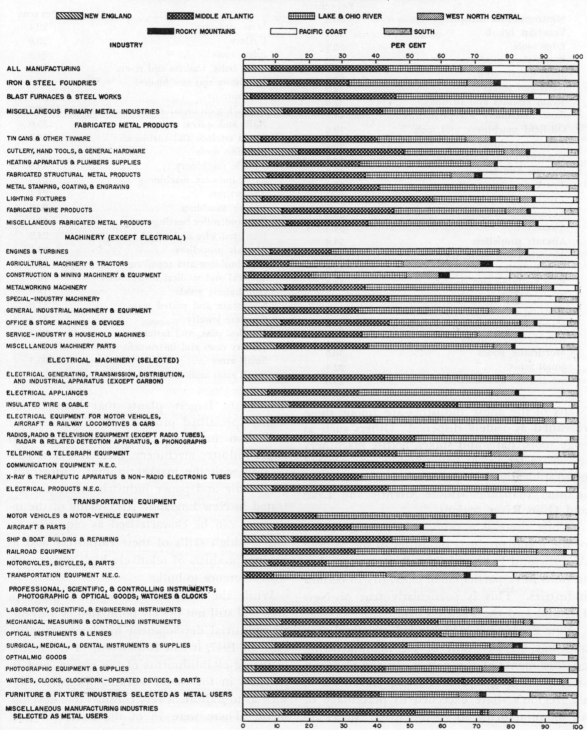

SOURCE: CENSUS OF MANUFACTURES, 1947

facturing percentage in 117 of the industries and was less in 27. The industries in this latter category along with the percentage shares are listed below.

	Per cent
Mattresses and bedsprings	50.6
Venetian blinds	43.1
Edge tools	52.1
Boiler shop products	53.0
Sheet-metal work	52.5
Nails and spikes	52.9
Steam engines and turbines	47.0
Farm machinery, except tractors	44.1
Oil-field machinery and tools	19.6
Textile machinery	40.1
Woodworking machinery	44.5
Blowers and fans	49.0
Truck and bus bodies	52.6
Truck trailers	37.0
Automobile trailers	53.5
Aircraft	34.5
Aircraft propellers	53.8
Aircraft equipment, n.e.c.	33.3
Ship building and repairing	48.2
Boat building and repairing	38.3
Transportation equipment, n.e.c.	41.3
Sporting and athletic goods	53.8
Hand stamps, stencils, and brands	55.9
Brooms and brushes	52.7
Morticians' goods	50.5
Small arms	32.4
Small arms ammunition	25.0

Many of the above industries are among those classified as widely dispersed. Others such as edge tools, nails and spikes, textile machinery are characterized as being highly concentrated geographically, but the area of concentration is other than the Middle Atlantic and Lake and Ohio River regions.

While there is a pronounced concentration of the metal products industries in the Middle Atlantic and Lake and Ohio River areas, other sections have participated, especially in certain industries. This is particularly true of New England and the Pacific Coast.

New England is a highly industrialized area and has 8.4 per cent of the manufacturing establishments of the nation. In the iron and steel processing and fabricating classification, the region's share exceeded its percentage of all manufacturing in 76 industries. In 34 in-

dustries, its percentage of the total exceeded the all-manufacturing percentage by 1.5 times, or more, and in 26 by two times, or more. The industries in this last group are listed below.

	Per cent
Wire drawing	22.4
Cutlery	20.0
Edge tools	31.5
Nuts, bolts, washers and rivets	17.3
Handsaws and saw blades	16.9
Oil burners	21.9
Engraving on metal	23.7
Nails and spikes	25.0
Steam engines and turbines	35.3
Machine tools	18.7
Textile machinery	40.3
Paper-industry machinery	27.5
Typewriters	21.4
Sewing machines	20.0
Ball and roller bearings	20.2
Insulated wire and cable	24.0
Aircraft propellers	23.1
Boat building and repairing	17.2
Surgical and medical instruments	18.0
Ophthalmic goods	18.0
Silverware and plated ware	33.6
Costume jewelry	33.4
Needles, pins, and fasteners	21.3
Jewelry cases and instrument cases	20.0
Small arms	35.3
Small arms ammunition	25.0

These are largely plants that manufacture highly specialized products. In the case of at least two industries, textile machinery and paper industry machinery, there is a close connection with the market in that, historically, the textile and paper industries were concentrated in New England. Also, many of the industries can be characterized as requiring relatively high skills of their employees and as having products of relatively high unit values with reference to bulk.

While the Pacific Coast region is large in area and still not thickly populated as a whole, its industrial development has been conspicuous. In 1947, it had 10 per cent of the manufacturing establishments of the nation, and its position in the metal working industries was such as to indicate a very considerable development. There were 78 of the iron and steel processing and fabricating industries for which the region's share exceeds its all-manufacturing percentage. In 33 of these industries, the ratio between the region's industry percentage and the all-manufacturing percentage was 1.5, or more, and in 15 the ratio exceeds 2.0. The industries in this last class are noted below.

	Per cent of U. S.
Venetian blinds	20.2
Welded and heavy riveted pipe	24.0
Galvanizing	20.8
Safes and vaults	26.9
Steel springs	21.0
Oil-field machinery and tools	25.7
Woodworking machinery	25.5
Truck trailers	29.4
Aircraft	34.5
Aircraft engines and parts	22.8
Aircraft equipment	51.5
Ship building and repairing	21.6
Boat building and repairing	21.1
Automobile trailers	30.6
X-ray and therapeutic apparatus	26.6

The position of the Pacific Coast with respect to the aircraft industries is particularly outstanding. The oil field machinery and parts industry is directly connected with the petroleum industry of the region. In general, however, there seems to be a tendency for the Pacific Coast to develop plants to supply the market in that area with the more common types of industrial and commercial metal products.

The development of the iron and steel processing and fabricating industries in the South is relatively low. The region had 15.3 per cent of the manufacturing establishments of the nation. Only thirteen of the processing and fabricating industries showed a percentage that exceeded the region's share of all manufacturing. In only three was the ratio between the industry percentage and all manufacturing in excess of 1.5, and in only one was the ratio in excess of 2.0. The industries in which the South had the largest share are listed below.

	Per cent of U. S.
Oil-field machinery and tools	48.7
Venetian blinds	24.2
Metal barrels, drums, and pails	22.9

Mattresses and bedsprings	22.2
Morticians' goods	20.9
Ship building and repairing	20.6
Truck trailers	20.2
Brooms and brushes	19.7
Transportation equipment, n.e.c.	19.2
Boat building and repairing	18.1
Blowers and fans	17.2
Textile machinery	16.6
Boiler shop products	15.9

In addition, there are several industries in which the South's share of establishments was only slightly smaller than its all manufacturing percentage. The industries that came closest were woodworking machinery, truck and bus bodies, gray-iron foundries, and fabricated steel and ornamental metal products.

The oil-field machinery and tools industry occurs principally in Texas, and its location is greatly influenced by the concentration of the petroleum industry in that area. The importance of the lumber and textile industries in the South offers an explanation of its relatively strong showing in woodworking and textile machinery. The South has long been known to have the largest concentration in the nation of manufacturers of cast iron pipe, but the inclusion of cast iron pipe shops in the gray iron foundry industry in the 1947 Census hides this situation so far as the statistics are concerned. While there have been some very important developments, it can scarcely be said that the iron and steel processing and fabricating industries occupy an important place in the industrial economy of the South.

Thus, from the point of view of location, the iron and steel processing and fabricating industries include some that are widely dispersed over the country and many that tend to be limited largely to particular areas. By far the greatest concentrations occur in the Middle Atlantic and Lake and Ohio River states. There are, however, industries which these areas do not dominate. Also some of the industries which are largely claimed by this industrial heart of the nation have significant occurrences elsewhere. These are conditions which no regional study of the iron and steel industries can overlook. Certainly, careful study must be given to factors which brought about the present situations, since they are likely to influence the future.

Use of Iron and Steel by the Processing and Fabricating Industries

In the preceding chapter, the general pattern of use of iron and steel, as reflected in the reports of the United States Bureau of Mines and the American Iron and Steel Institute, was discussed. The data there presented were based on reports from the blast furnaces and steelworks and represent an analysis of sales or shipments to different classes of customers. Often the ultimate destination of the steel could not be known to the reporting company (as in the case of sales to jobbers). For that reason, the above mentioned sources do not provide the means of identifying all the steel that reached the processing and fabricating industries. The reports do have the advantage of giving a complete cross section of the disposition of all the pig iron and steel produced as seen from the point of origin, and the conclusions drawn from the analysis of these data are highly significant. While large quantities of steel mill products find their way to the ultimate consumer in the form in which they leave the rolling mills—for example, wire and wire fence, nails, pipe, and concrete reinforcing bars—an important result of the analysis was to emphasize the importance of the processors and fabricators as users of iron and steel.

In the 1947 Census of Manufactures, the Bureau of the Census asked for a report of materials consumed and, as a result, was able to publish statistics on the consumption of iron castings, steel castings, and steel mill products. At least two general limitations apply to these data. Any attempt to collect information of this kind from a large number of respondents is very likely to be incomplete. It is probably safe to assume that the establishments failing to report were small and that the omissions do not greatly influence the results. The other limitation is that the individual industries in a large group often represent successive stages in fabrication, and, as a result, totals derived

from reports may include the same iron or steel in somewhat altered form. This means that totals of the materials reported by a number of industries may contain duplications. Another difficulty that arises in this particular case is that differences in classification prevent direct comparisons of the statistics provided by the *Census of Manufactures* and the American Iron and Steel Institute. While these limitations must be recognized, the Census data presented in Table 81 provide the basis for comparing the consumption of iron and steel products by the metal fabricating industries with the use of copper and aluminum, and Table 82 gives a picture of the relative importance of the several industry groups as iron and steel users that is sufficiently accurate for present purposes.

From Table 81, one can see that iron and steel products are used by metal fabricating industries in far greater quantities than copper or aluminum. For mill shapes and forms, the total reported for steel is more than 39 million tons compared with 874 thousand tons for copper and copper based alloys and 360 thousand tons for aluminum and aluminum based alloys. Iron castings with a total of 4.2 million tons greatly exceed steel castings at 794 thousand tons. Copper and aluminum castings are much smaller—103 thousand and 108 thousand tons, respectively. Copper and aluminum products have higher values per ton than iron and steel, and this reduces the disparity considerably when value is used as the measure. An examination of the detailed data by industry shows that, with few exceptions, steel shapes and forms occupy the predominant position from the point of view of quantities consumed. There are only two industries in which the reported consumption of copper and copper based alloys exceeds that of iron and steel. These are metal plumbing fixtures and insulated wire and cable. Other important users of copper products are motor vehicles and parts, valves and fittings, metal stampings, motors and generators, engine electrical equipment, transformers, screw machine products, bolts and nuts, electrical control apparatus, and refrigerator machinery. The aircraft industry is the only one of the metal fabricating industries that reports a use of aluminum which is greater than the consumption of steel. Metal stamping and motor vehicles are two other industries which report the use of quite large quantities of aluminum. These data emphasize the predominant position of iron and steel in the metal fabricating industries, but, at the same time, show that other metals have important places as supplementary, or competing materials in many of the industries and occupy first place in a few of the industries selected as constituting the iron and steel processing and fabricating industries.

While group totals must be viewed with some suspicion, the fabricated metal products group with a total of over 18 million tons must be considered as the leader in quantity of steel consumed. Transportation equipment with 9¼ million tons ranks second, machinery with 6.4 million is third, miscellaneous primary metals industries with 5.3 million is fourth,[1] and electrical machinery is fifth. The big users of iron castings and steel castings are the machinery and the transportation equipment groups. If the welded and heavy riveted pipe and primary metals, n.e.c., industries are eliminated from present consideration because of possible duplication with other industries, there were eleven industry subclasses that reported consumption of one million tons or more.

[1] Wire drawing	457,822
Welded and heavy riveted pipe	1,401,299
Primary metals n.e.c.	1,818,279
Iron and steel forgings	1,630,208
Total	5,307,608

Table 81

Consumption of Metal Shapes and Forms, and Castings by Metal
Fabricating Industries in the United States, 1947

Kind of product	Quantity (Short tons)	Value (Thousand dollars)
Steel mill shapes and forms	39,383,069	3,799,438
Carbon steel		
Bars and bar shapes	5,728,608	482,990
Sheets and strip	15,687,915	1,442,573
Structural shapes	3,429,007	244,564
Plates	4,596,336	351,914
Wire	1,756,704	195,510
All other shapes and forms	5,510,703	600,923
Alloy steel (except stainless)		
Bars and bar shapes	1,673,154	202,634
All other mill shapes and forms	802,791	120,884
Stainless steel		
All shapes and forms	197,851	157,446
Iron castings		
Rough and semifinished (received from the foundry)	4,237,868	898,240
Steel castings		
Rough and semifinished (received from the foundry)	793,796	245,185
Copper and copper base alloys		
Brass and wire mill shapes and forms (rolled, drawn and extruded)	873,816	560,173
Castings, rough and semifinished (received from the foundry)	103,144	83,222
Aluminum and aluminum base alloys		
Mill shapes (rolled, drawn, and extruded)	360,183	203,667
Castings, rough and semifinished (received from the foundry)	108,322	105,874

Source: *Census of Manufactures, 1947;* U. S. Bureau of the Census, *Consumption of Metal Mill Shapes—1947.*

Industry subclass	Tons
Structural metal products	7,382,861
Motor vehicles and equipment	6,653,185
Tin cans and other tin ware	3,106,461
Miscellaneous fabricated metal products	2,733,090
Metal stamping and coating	2,504,469
Tractors and farm machinery	1,854,909
Railroad equipment	1,785,531
Electrical industrial apparatus (except carbon)	1,482,982
Service and household machines	1,251,393
Heating and plumbing equipment	1,151,280
Construction and mining machinery	1,034,471

In addition to these, there are, of course, numerous industries that use substantial quantities of iron and steel, but the heavy tonnage consumption by a relatively small number of industry groups makes the location of the industries in these groups a factor of very great importance in the market for the steel produced at any given center.

Distribution of Sales of Iron and Steel Processing and Fabricating Industries

A final topic which will be discussed in this chapter as constituting an important part of the background for the study of the iron and steel industries is the distribution of the sales of the iron and steel processing and fabricating industries by main types of outlets. A summary of the outstanding characteristics of the industries in this respect, when related to the kinds of products produced and the market forces which influence distribution, should help to make data on the structure and trends of the industries more intelligible.

The primary source which provides information of the kind desired is the report of the Bureau of the Census on "Distribution of Manufacturer's Sales, 1939." The classification of industries used in this report differs from

Table 82

Consumption of Steel Mill Shapes and Iron and Steel Castings by Metal Fabricating Industries in the United States, 1947

Industry	Iron castings (short tons)	Steel castings (short tons)	Steel mill shapes and forms (short tons)
Fabricated metal products	232,566	20,543	18,834,946
Tin cans and other tinware			3,106,461
Cutlery, hand tools, and hardware	52,384	3,633	849,063
Heating and plumbing equipment	133,318	3,645	1,151,280
Fabricated structural metal products	27,731	10,868	7,382,861
Metal stamping and coating*	7,710	905	2,504,469
Lighting fixtures	3,656	1,179	127,009
Fabricated wire products	3,564	313	980,713
Miscellaneous fabricated metal products**	4,203		2,733,090
Machinery (except electrical)	2,128,615	470,506	6,420,110
Engines and turbines	240,426	19,741	127,230
Tractors and farm machinery	568,669	58,304	1,854,909
Construction and mining machinery	104,113	201,595	1,034,471
Metal working machinery	259,790	53,107	296,677
Special-industry machinery	304,889	34,226	458,307
General industrial machinery	335,277	60,826	880,133
Office and store machines	16,609	250	118,826
Service and household machines	167,023	9,012	1,251,393
Miscellaneous machinery parts***	131,819	33,445	398,164
Electrical machinery†	240,305	21,023	2,149,150
Electrical industrial apparatus	206,331	20,202	1,482,982
Electrical appliances	10,297	159	218,162
Insulated wire and cable			40,416
Engine: electrical equipment	18,718	662	237,694

Table 82 (cont'd)

Consumption of Steel Mill Shapes and Iron and Steel Castings by Metal Fabricating Industries in the United States, 1947

Industry	Iron castings (short tons)	Steel castings (short tons)	Steel mill shapes and forms (short tons)
Radios and related products	1,030	......	97,382
Telephone and telegraph equipment	2,667	......	59,957
Communication equipment	1,262	......	12,557
Transportation equipment	1,621,591	271,105	9,264,046
Motor vehicles and equipment	1,469,169	90,837	6,653,185
Aircraft and parts	14,614	427	45,523
Ships and boats	2,564	4,393	664,601
Railroad equipment	131,085	174,419	1,785,531
Motorcycles and bicycles	4,159	1,029	114,206
Transportation equipment, n.e.c.††	......	......	......
Furniture and fixtures	......	......	1,006,315
Wood household furniture except upholstered	......	......	33,278
Household furniture, upholstered	......	......	8,053
Metal house furniture, except upholstered	......	......	249,417
Mattresses and bed springs	......	......	136,626
Wood office furniture	......	......	1,003
Metal office furniture	......	......	261,774
Public building furniture	......	......	29,851
Professional furniture	......	......	25,509
Partitions and fixtures	......	......	255,648
Restaurant furniture	......	......	3,817
Furniture and fixtures, n.e.c.	......	......	1,339
Other iron and steel processing and fabricating	13,935	7,060	1,708,402
Iron and steel forgings	......	......	1,630,208
Mechanical measuring instruments	13,307	7,060	41,204
Photographic equipment and supplies	628	......	13,785
Needles, pins, and fasteners	......	......	23,205
Grand total	4,237,868†††	793,796†††	39,383,069

*No data for industries 3464, powder metallurgy; 3465, enameling japanning, and lacquering; 3466, galvanizing and other hot-dip coating; 3467, engraving on metal; and 3468, electroplating, plating, and polishing.

**No data for industry 3492, safes and vaults.

***No data for industries 3592, fabricated pipe and fittings; and 3599, machine shops (jobbing and repair).

†No data for industries 3693, X-ray and therapeutic apparatus and non-radio tubes; and 3699, electrical products, n.e.c.

††No data for industries 3723, aircraft propellers and propeller parts; and 3799, transportation equipment, n.e.c.

†††The grand totals for iron castings and steel castings exceeds the total of the industry figures shown because of omission to avoid disclosure of figures for individual companies.

In several industries which are components of the industry groups shown in this table data was not reported because of the small number of establishments reporting.

The above table does not include several industries included in this study as iron and steel processing and fabricating industries because of possible duplication of materials with other industries. Reported consumption figures for steel mill shapes and forms are available for the following:

     Wire drawing ... 457,822
     Welded and heavy riveted pipe.... 1,401,299
     Primary metals, n.e.c. ... 1,818,279

Source: *Census of Manufactures, 1947*, based primarily on *Bureau of the Census, Consumption of Metal Mill Shapes . . . 1947*, supplemented by the reports on particular industries.

CHART 22

DISTRIBUTION OF MANUFACTURERS SALES OF IRON AND STEEL INDUSTRIES
BY TYPE OF OUTLET, 1939

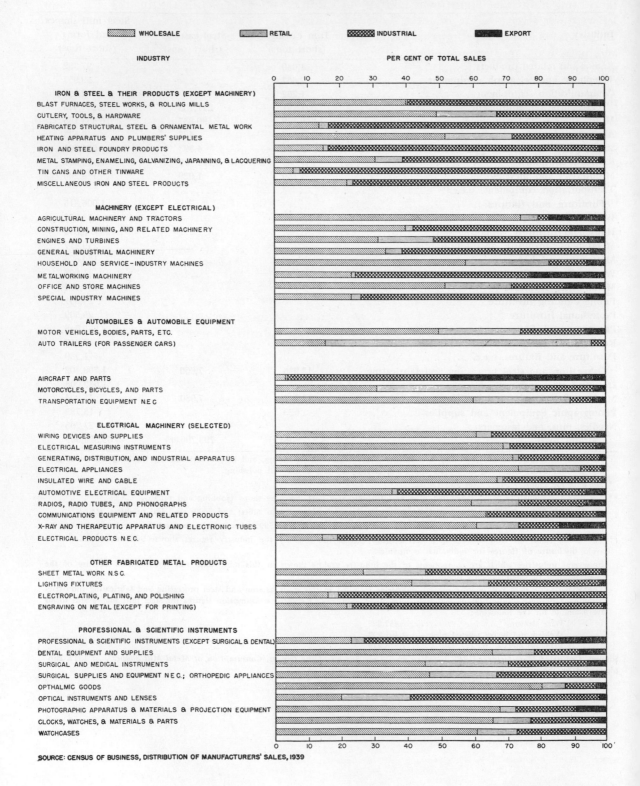

SOURCE: CENSUS OF BUSINESS, DISTRIBUTION OF MANUFACTURERS' SALES, 1939

the one employed in the preceding discussion, but 122 industries were selected as giving essentially the same coverage of the processing and fabricating industries. Statistics by kind of outlet were not given for five of these industries. These are machine shop repairs, locomotives and parts, cars and car equipment (railroads and street railways), shipbuilding and repairing and boat building and repairing. Thus, the analysis is based upon 117 industries. A further qualification must be mentioned because the Bureau of Census' disclosure rules has resulted in certain combinations of classes in particular industries which has probably resulted in introducing some inaccuracies in the figures given in Table 83. The Census report used eight classes of outlets. For present purposes, these have been combined into four.

1. Wholesale distribution, which includes:
   Manufacturers' owned wholesale branches
   Wholesalers and jobbers
2. Retailers or consumers direct, which includes:
   Manufacturers' owned retail stores
   Retailers (including chains)
   Consumers at retail (not including industrial)
3. Industrial users
4. Export, which includes:
   Export intermediaries
   Export direct to buyers in other countries.

Table 83 gives a summary of the results obtained by grouping the several industries according to the percentage of sales made through each of the four general types of outlets.

The data on the distribution of manufacturers' sales emphasize again the important place that industrial users occupy in the market of the products of the iron and steel processing and fabricating industries. Of the 117 industries for which data are available, 46 marketed more than 50 per cent of their product by sales to industrial users and 23 additional industries marketed from 30 per cent to 49.9 per cent to this class of buyers.

The next most common outlet was through one of the various types of wholesale distribution. Of the 117 industries, 37 sold 50 per cent or more of their products through wholesale outlets, and an additional 39 sold from 30 per cent to 49.9 per cent. Thus, the great bulk of the product of these industries moved into use either directly to industrial users or through wholesale distributors. Since such a large proportion of the processing and fabricating industries are dependent on connections with either industrial buyers or wholesale outlets, or both, attention is directed to the need of studying the industrial structure and the factors influencing wholesale distribution of the region which is being examined.

While the two classes of outlets discussed in the preceding paragraphs were in the leading positions, nearly all of the industries disposed

Table 83

Types of Sales Outlets Used by Iron and Steel Processing and Fabricating Industries, 1939

Per cent of total sales made through designated outlet	Kind of outlet			
	Wholesale distribution (number of industries)	Retailers or consumers direct (number of industries)	Industrial users (number of industries)	Export (number of industries)
75 per cent and over	6	1	16	..
50 per cent to 74.9 per cent	31	6	30	..
40 per cent to 49.9 per cent	19	6	11	1
30 per cent to 39.9 per cent	20	3	12	1
20 per cent to 29.9 per cent	22	12	12	2
10 per cent to 19.9 per cent	10	23	20	10
0.1 per cent to 9.9 per cent	9	57	15	97
None shown	..	9	1	6
Total number of industries	117	117	117	117

Source: *Census of Business, 1939*, V, "Distribution of Manufacturers' Sales."

of some of their products in ways that could be directly identified with exports, and all but nine made some use of direct sales to retailers or to consumers on a retail level. However, there were relatively few that made extensive use of these outlets. There were fourteen that sold for export 10 per cent or more of their product. These were files, fire arms, tractors, agricultural machinery, construction and similar machinery, oilfield machinery and tools, machine tools, metal working machinery and equipment, office and store machines, sewing machines, aircraft and parts, X-ray and therapeutic apparatus, electrical products, n.e.c., and professional and scientific instruments. Also, there were 28 industries which sold 20 per cent, or more, of their product to retailers or to consumers at retail. These industries were cutlery and edge tools; oil burners, domestic and industrial; stoves, ranges, etc.; vitreous enameled products; office and store machinery; laundry equipment, domestic; sewing machines, domestic and industrial; motor vehicles, bodies, parts, and accessories; automobile trailers (for passenger cars); motorcycles, bicycles, and parts; transportation equipment, n.e.c.; lighting fixtures; mattresses and bedsprings; office furniture; morticians' goods; venetian blinds; window and door screens; window shades; silverware and plated ware; pens and mechanical pencils; costume jewelry; jewelry cases and instrument cases; optical instruments, surgical and medical instruments; surgical supplies; children's vehicles; games and toys; and sporting and athletic goods. The industries in each of these lists produce specialized finished products predominantly in the machinery and appliance class. It would seem that the industries of this type have found it advantageous in many cases to deal more directly with the consumers than would be the case if distribution were handled through the regular wholesaling or jobber channels.

The report of the Temporary National Economic Committee on "The Structure of American Industry"[2] presents information supple-

menting that which has been presented. The report makes available data on 1,807 manufactured products. Of these, 532 can be classed as products of the iron and steel processing and fabricating industries. While these items cannot be presented as scientifically selected samples, they do indicate some of the outstanding characteristics of the output of the iron and steel industries. Of the 532, 439 are classed as having other producers as their immediate purchasers. With reference to their ultimate use, 121 are classed as consumer goods, 115 as construction materials, 7 as producers' supplies, and 289 as producers' goods, including over 200 machinery and equipment items.

Some additional observations concerning the connection between types of distributive outlets and the geographic distribution of the markets for the products of the iron and steel processing industries may be offered. The industries which sell primarily to industrial users may be divided into two classes. One includes those industries whose output moves either to other manufacturers for further processing or to erectors. The other consists of the producers of equipment or supplies required in the operations of an industry. In either case, the location of the market for the product is immediately determined by the locations of the consuming industries. Some of these products are used by many different industries: for example, power boilers; mechanical power transmission equipment; elevators, escalators, and conveyers; and steam engines and turbines. In such cases, a widely dispersed market may be expected, but it will be one that tends to be distributed in proportion to the degree of industrialization. On the other hand, many industries produce equipment or supplies that are intended for a single industry or, at most, only a small number of industries. Examples are manufacturers of construction equipment, mining machinery and equipment, textile machinery, and printing trades machinery and equipment. Some of these industries are widely distributed over the entire nation: for example, the printing and publishing industry. Others are very definitely localized—the production of petroleum, the

2 U.S. Temporary National Economic Committee, *The Structure of Industry,* monograph No. 27, pp. 513-533.

textile industry, and the paper and pulp industry.

Agricultural machinery presents an interesting problem. For one thing, the industry is a quite broad classification which includes hundreds of different products whose only common characteristic is that they are used primarily on farms. Nearly all of these items are designed for some particular end use. With very little modification, some find markets on the farms of all sections of the nation. On the other hand, many of the more complicated kinds of farm machinery are designed for special crops or for special soil, or surface, conditions, and the markets for such products tend to be localized or regionalized by the geographic distributions of the crop or by other special characteristics. In the South, the influence of such crops as cotton, tobacco, and peanuts on equipment needs is obvious.

Another group of processors and fabricators includes manufacturers of products which are used primarily in construction, such as cast iron pipe; fabricated structural steel; doors, window sash, etc. (metal); and enameled-iron

sanitary ware and other plumbers' supplies. The markets of such products tend to be associated with the distribution of population, particularly urbanization, and with income or buying power. Much the same comment can be made concerning consumer durable items, including refrigerators, domestic laundry equipment, lighting fixtures, and electrical appliances.

In conclusion, it can be said that the data on the distribution of the products of the iron and steel processing and fabricating industries should serve as a strong reminder of two important considerations in any attempt to appraise the prospects of these industries. The first is that the industries are producers of specialized products which must have well established contacts with markets in order to exist. The second is that the patterns of use are intricate and closely interwoven into the entire economic structure of the nation. Consequently, considerable caution needs to be used in making assertions that industry will follow steel, if that is understood to imply immediate changes.

CHAPTER XX

THE IRON AND STEEL PROCESSING AND FABRICATING INDUSTRIES OF THE SOUTH

The importance and general characteristics of the iron and steel processing and fabricating industries of the nation have been discussed in the preceding chapter, and the next step is to examine the development in the South. The purpose of the present chapter is to describe the situation in the postwar period as indicated by the Census of Manufactures of 1947. For this purpose, the general situation in the South with regard to the processing and fabricating industries will be summarized briefly and then more detailed analyses will follow. The discussion will center around the following questions: What are the iron and steel processing and fabricating industries of the South? How important are they? What are their most important characteristics? Where are they located within the South? The next chapter will deal with the important trends in the iron and steel processing and fabricating industries of the South.

The Place of the Iron and Steel Processing and Fabricating Industries in the South

If the iron and steel processing and fabricating industries of the South are considered as a group, the general situation can be summarized by a three-fold statement. These industries as a whole have a relatively small share of the total of the same group of industries in the United States. Their relative position in the region's manufacturing structure is far weaker than is that of iron and steel processing and fabricating in the nation's manufacturing. The processing and fabricating industries of the South are not as highly developed with respect to the basic iron and steel industries of

the region as is the case in the nation as a whole. The statistical support for these conclusions is given in Tables 84, 85, and 86.

The percentages of the national totals given by Table 84 for the iron and steel processing and fabricating industries in the South may well be compared with the South's share of total manufacturing in 1947 as indicated by the following measures: by number of establishments, 15.30 per cent; by number of production workers, 14.45 per cent; by wages paid, 11.09 per cent; by value added by manufacture, 12.05 per cent. The relatively low position of the processing and fabricating industries is brought out in sharp relief by this comparison.

In Table 85, the position occupied by the iron and steel processing and fabricating industries in the total manufacturing structure of the South and the nation is shown. The relatively low development in the South is shown by the fact that only 11.64 per cent of the production workers employed in manufacturing in the South are in the processing and fabricating group compared with 37.68 per cent for the nation. Similar conditions are indicated by the other measures of activity.

While the iron and steel processing and fabricating industries as a group bulk up into much larger totals than the basic industries in both the South and the United States do, the ratios for the region are much smaller than those for the nation. For the South, the totals of the processing and fabricating industries are from 7.2 to 8.4 times as large as those of the basic industries, depending on whether wages paid or value added by manufacture are used as measures. For the United States, the corresponding ratios are 8.6:1 and 10.1:1.

The Constituent Iron and Steel
Processing Industries
of the South

RELATIVE POSITION OF CONSTITUENT
INDUSTRY GROUPS

To provide a more convenient approach to the description of the iron and steel processing industries of the South, the 144 individual industries selected as belonging in the general category have been summarized into 32 groups.[1] Tables 87 and 88 provide a breakdown of the

[1] As far as possible the 32 groups have been set up to represent the secondary industry or three digit classification of the Census of Manufactures, but, in the case of selected electrical machinery and selected miscellaneous industries, the primary group only was used and the problem of avoiding disclosure made it necessary to use a general catch-all class which crossed the lines of the Census primary group classifications.

Table 84

Iron and Steel Processing and Fabricating Industries of the South and the United States, 1947

Item	The South	United States	Per cent South of the U.S.
Number of establishments	4,230	59,378	7.12
Number of production workers	200,322	4,490,367	4.46
Wages paid (thousand dollars)	467,791	12,474,622	3.75
Value added by manufacture (thousand dollars)	1,038,234	26,832,222	3.87

Source: *Census of Manufactures, 1947.* Figures for South from a special tabulation prepared by Bureau of the Census.

Table 85

Importance of the Iron and Steel Processing and Fabricating Industries in the Total Manufacturing Structure, South and United States, 1947

Item	Per cent of total manufacturing	
	The South	United States
	(Total manufacturing in South = 100 per cent)	(Total manufacturing in United States = 100 per cent)
Number of establishments	11.47	24.65
Number of production workers	11.64	37.68
Wages paid	13.95	41.25
Value added by manufacture	11.58	36.05

Source: *Census of Manufactures, 1947.*

Table 86

Relationship Between the Processing and Fabricating Industries and the Basic Iron and Steel Industries; the South and the United States, 1947

Items	The South			United States		
	Basic industries	Processing and fabricating	Ratio P & F to basic	Basic industries	Processing and fabricating	Ratio P & F to basic
Number of establishments	29	4,230	145.9:1	320	59,378	185.6:1
Number of production workers	25,203	200,322	7.9:1	478,960	4,490,367	9.4:1
Wages paid ($1,000)	65,078	467,797	7.2:1	1,454,985	12,474,622	8.6:1
Value added by manufacture ($1,000)	123,582	1,038,234	8.4:1	2,659,250	26,832,222	10.1:1

Source: *Census of Manufactures, 1947.*

Table 87

Iron and Steel Processing and Fabricating Industries by Industry Groups, South Compared with the United States, 1947

Industry group	Number of establishments			Number of production workers			Value added by manufacture		
	United States	South	Per cent South of U.S.	United States	South	Per cent South of U.S.	United States ($1,000)	South ($1,000)	Per cent South of U.S.
Iron and steel foundries	1,936	260	13.43	239,272	22,661	9.47	1,121,522	96,022	8.56
Miscellaneous primary metal industries	811	15	1.85	107,412	601	0.56	740,155	4,196	0.57
Tin cans and other tinware	217	20	9.22	40,890	2,891	7.07	231,953	17,712	7.64
Cutlery, hand tools, and hardware	1,866	55	2.95	131,604	1,063	0.81	728,426	5,177	0.71
Heating and plumbing equipment	1,276	96	7.52	126,725	10,928	8.62	789,524	46,653	5.91
Structural metal products	4,507	615	13.65	172,690	22,843	13.23	1,143,553	132,189	11.56
Metal stamping and coating	4,437	126	2.84	159,926	2,754	1.72	861,173	12,154	1.41
Lighting fixtures	1,206	17	1.41	39,883	127	0.32	247,619	495	0.20
Fabricated wire products	977	38	3.89	52,543	1,308	2.49	282,147	6,558	2.32
Miscellaneous fabricated metal products (except collapsible tubes and metal foil)	2,186	60	2.74	91,105	2,401	2.64	598,700	16,738	2.80
Tractors and farm machinery	1,102	126	11.43	139,629	5,634	4.03	753,762	21,858	2.90
Construction and mining machinery	747	150	20.08	88,905	16,338	18.38	641,397	117,518	18.32
Metalworking machinery	4,293	45	1.05	172,982	450	0.26	1,131,182	2,381	0.21
Special-industry machinery, n.e.c.	4,106	265	6.45	173,592	8,734	5.03	1,095,558	49,093	4.48
General industrial machinery	2,191	172	7.85	164,249	7,001	4.26	1,189,229	42,264	3.55
Scales and balances	75	6	8.00	4,874	32	0.66	34,766	128	0.37
Service and household machines	1,088	69	6.34	180,771	3,198	1.77	1,105,798	18,593	1.68
Miscellaneous machinery parts	3,871	184	4.75	167,841	6,130	3.65	983,576	34,395	3.50
Typewriters	28	....	....	23,838	....	....	121,385	....	....
Selected electrical machinery	3,421	94	2.75	557,541	5,993	1.07	3,404,332	38,405	1.13
Motor vehicles and equipment	1,904	165	8.67	599,301	11,635	1.94	3,819,076	79,831	2.09
Ships and boats	1,110	208	18.74	132,033	29,186	22.11	586,558	128,898	21.98
Transportation equipment, n.e.c.	167	32	19.16	3,862	589	15.25	20,542	2,540	12.36
Aircraft, railroad equipment, motorcycles, and bicycles	530	17	3.21	251,946	13,397	5.32	1,448,020	59,083	4.09
Scientific instruments	216	21	9.72	15,023	313	2.08	83,010	1,992	2.40
Mechanical measuring instruments	463	19	4.10	40,937	1,407	3.44	245,144	8,196	3.34
Medical instruments and supplies	980	61	6.22	29,617	590	1.99	184,665	2,517	1.36
Ophthalmic goods	184	5	2.72	19,744	193	0.98	81,530	557	0.68
All other instrument and related products industries	756	14	1.85	76,618	1,253	1.64	485,987	3,622	0.75
Selected miscellaneous manufactures	8,442	713	8.45	242,583	9,796	4.04	1,262,968	37,000	2.93
Selected furniture and fixture industries	3,468	524	15.11	86,236	9,938	11.52	482,780	46,955	9.73
Other selected industries	817	38	4.65	156,195	938	0.60	931,185	4,514	0.48
Total processing and fabricating industries	59,378	4,230	7.12	4,490,367	200,322	4.46	26,832,222	1,038,234	3.87
Total all manufacturing	240,881	36,864	15.30	11,916,188	1,721,477	14.45	74,425,825	8,969,325	12.05

Iron and Steel Processing and Fabricating Industries by Industry Groups
Per Cent of Processing and Fabricating Industries and Per Cent of All Manufacturing South and United States Compared, 1947

	Per cent of processing and fabricating industries				Per cent of all manufacturing			
	Number production workers		Value added		Number production workers		Value added	
	South	U.S.	South	U.S.	South	U.S.	South	U.S.
Iron and steel foundries	11.31	5.33	9.25	4.18	1.32	2.01	1.07	1.51
Miscellaneous primary metal industries	0.30	2.39	0.40	2.76	0.03	0.90	0.05	0.99
Tin cans and other tinware	1.44	0.91	1.71	0.86	0.17	0.34	0.20	0.31
Cutlery, hand tools, and hardware	0.53	2.93	0.50	2.71	0.06	1.10	0.06	0.98
Heating and plumbing equipment	5.46	2.82	4.49	2.94	0.63	1.06	0.52	1.06
Structural metal products	11.40	3.85	12.74	4.26	1.33	1.45	1.47	1.54
Metal stamping and coating	1.37	3.56	1.17	3.21	0.16	1.34	0.14	1.16
Lighting fixtures	0.06	0.89	0.05	0.92	0.01	0.33	0.01	0.33
Fabricated wire products	0.65	1.17	0.63	1.05	0.08	0.44	0.07	0.38
Miscellaneous fabricated metal products (except collapsible tubes and metal foil)	1.20	2.03	1.61	2.23	0.14	0.76	0.19	0.80
Tractors and farm machinery	2.81	3.11	2.11	2.81	0.33	1.17	0.24	1.01
Construction and mining machinery	8.16	1.98	11.32	2.39	0.95	0.75	1.31	0.86
Metalworking machinery	0.22	3.85	0.23	4.22	0.03	1.45	0.03	1.52
Special-industry machinery, n.e.c.	4.36	3.87	4.73	4.08	0.51	1.46	0.55	1.47
General industrial machinery	3.49	3.66	4.07	4.43	0.41	1.38	0.47	1.60
Scales and balances	0.02	0.11	0.01	0.13	0.002	0.04	0.001	0.05
Service and household machines	1.60	4.03	1.79	4.12	0.19	1.52	0.21	1.49
Miscellaneous machinery parts	3.06	3.74	3.31	3.67	0.36	1.41	0.38	1.32
Typewriters	....	0.53	....	0.45	....	0.20	....	0.16
Selected electrical machinery	2.99	12.41	3.70	12.69	0.35	4.68	0.43	4.57
Motor vehicles and equipment	5.81	13.34	7.69	14.24	0.68	5.03	0.89	5.13
Ships and boats	14.58	2.94	12.43	2.19	1.70	1.11	1.44	0.79
Transportation equipment, n.e.c.	0.29	0.09	0.24	0.08	0.03	0.03	0.03	0.03
Aircraft, railroad equipment, motorcycles, and bicycles	6.69	5.61	5.69	5.38	0.78	2.11	0.66	1.94
Scientific instruments	0.16	0.33	0.19	0.31	0.02	0.13	0.02	0.11
Mechanical measuring instruments	0.70	0.91	0.79	0.91	0.08	0.34	0.09	0.33
Medical instruments and supplies	0.29	0.66	0.24	0.69	0.03	0.25	0.03	0.25
Ophthalmic goods	0.10	0.44	0.05	0.30	0.01	0.17	0.01	0.11
All other instrument and related products industries	0.63	1.71	0.35	1.81	0.07	0.64	0.04	0.65
Selected furniture and fixture industries	4.96	1.92	4.52	1.80	0.58	0.72	0.52	0.65
Other selected industries	0.47	3.48	0.43	3.47	0.05	1.31	0.05	1.25
Selected miscellaneous manufactures	4.89	5.40	3.56	4.71	0.57	2.04	0.41	1.70
Total processing and fabricating industries	100.00	100.00	100.00	100.00	11.64	37.68	11.58	36.05
Total all manufacturing					100.00	100.00	100.00	100.00

Source: *Census of Manufactures, 1947.*

totals previously presented. These data provide the basis for a discussion of some of the outstanding characteristics of the Southern industries. Later, the analysis will be carried to greater detail by examining the statistics of the individual 144 industries.

The data by industry groups show that the relatively low position of the South in the iron and steel processing and fabricating industries holds not only for the totals of the entire classification, but very generally for the several groups as well. If, as has been done a number of times previously, the South's per cent of total manufacturing in the United States is taken as a basis of comparison, the data in Table 87 show that there were only three industry groups in which the South's share of the number of production workers exceeded its share of the production workers in all manufacturing. These groups and the region's per cent of the nation's production workers in each group were construction and mining machinery, 18.38 per cent; ships and boats, 22.11 per cent; and transportation equipment, n.e.c., 15.25 per cent. The South's per cent of all production workers in manufacturing was 14.45. In one other group, structural metal products, the South's share was only slightly smaller, 13.23 per cent.

In only six other industry groups were the region's percentages of the nation's totals of production workers in excess of five per cent. These were selected furniture and fixture industries, 11.52 per cent; iron and steel foundries, 9.47 per cent; heating and plumbing equipment, 8.62 per cent; tin cans and tinware, 7.07 per cent; aircraft, railroad equipment, motorcycles, and bicycles, 5.32 per cent; and special industry machinery, n.e.c., 5.03 per cent. The remaining twenty-two groups were below five per cent. In one group, typewriters, the South had no representation, and in seven others the region's share was less than one per cent. These were miscellaneous primary metals; cutlery, hand tools, and hardware; lighting fixtures; metal working machinery; scales and balances; ophthalmic goods; and other selected industries.

Another approach is to compare the relative position occupied by each industry group, in the total of the iron and steel processing and fabricating industries of the South, with the corresponding figures for the nation. To provide the statistical means of making such a comparison, each industry group in the South was expressed as a percentage of the total of processing and fabricating industries in the South. Similar percentages were computed for the United States. These figures are given in Table 88. An examination of the data shows that there were nine of the industry groups which occupied a higher relative position among the processing and fabricating industries of the South than they did in the nation as a whole. These groups and the percentages, based on the number of production workers, for the South and the United States are noted below.

Industry group	Per cent of production workers in all processing and fabricating industries	
	South	United States
Iron and steel foundries	11.31	5.33
Heating and plumbing equipment	5.46	2.82
Tin cans and tinware	1.44	0.91
Structural metal products	11.40	3.85
Construction and mining machinery	8.16	1.98
Special-industry machinery, n.e.c.	4.36	3.87
Ships and boats	14.58	2.94
Aircraft, railroad equipment, motorcycles and bicycles	6.69	5.61
Selected furniture and fixture industries	4.96	1.92

This approach confirms the conclusion that a relatively small number of the industry groups have developed in the South to a degree comparable to that of the nation. Also, the data suggests a very considerable lack of balance.

RELATIVE POSITIONS OF INDIVIDUAL INDUSTRIES

The industry groups used in the above discussion serve to bring out the situation with respect to the different types of iron and steel processing and fabricating industries in the South, but may hide the position of particular industries, and, for that reason, an examination of the information on the individual industries is desirable. The number of separate items makes it necessary to adopt some method of analyzing and summarizing the data. The special statistical device that will be used is known as the location quotient. It is designed to present a view of a particular industry related to the general industrial development of an area. It is computed by dividing the region's share of the industry in question (for example, the South's per cent of the United States total of structural metal products) by the region's share of all manufacturing—that is, the South's per cent of all manufacturing. Because the information is more complete on the number of production workers than any other measure of activity, the location quotients were calculated on that basis. A quotient of one indicates that an industry's relative position in the region's industrial structure is the same as that which it occupies in the nation as a whole. A quotient of more than one indicates that the industry in question occupies a more important place in the manufacturing structure of an area than it does in the nation. In other words, there is evidence that the area tends to place emphasis on or to specialize in that industry. The reverse, of course, is true in cases where the quotient is less than one. For the South, with the location quotients calculated on the basis of the number of production workers, the equivalents between the quotients and the South's per cent of the United States are as follows:

Location quotient	Equivalent per cent South of United States
1.00	14.45
0.75	10.84
0.50	7.23
0.30	4.34

A summary of the location quotients of the iron and steel processing industries in the South is given by Table 89. Because lack of information made it necessary to combine eleven of the individual industries with some other industry, it was possible to determine location quotients for only 133 industries, or combinations of industries, of a possible number of 144.

Table 89

Iron and Steel Processing and Fabricating Industries of the South, Classified According to Their Location Quotients, 1947

Location quotient of industry	Number of industries
1.0 and higher	10
0.75 to 0.99	5
0.50 to 0.74	10
0.30 to 0.49	21
0.10 to 0.29	24
0.0001 to 0.09	51
No establishments and no quotient	12
	133
Industries combined with one of above	11
Total number of industries	144

Source: Computed from special tabulation by the U. S. Bureau of the Census and estimates by the Bureau of Business Research, University of Alabama.

Perhaps the most conspicuous fact set forth by Table 89 is the very low degree of occurrence in the South of many of the processing and fabricating industries. Sixty-three of the individual industries either had no representation in the region or had location quotients of less than 0.1 (or in terms of the South's per cent of the United States, less than 1.45 per cent). The twenty-five industries having the highest ratings in 1947 with respect to location quotients are listed below.

	Industry	South's per cent of production workers	Location quotient
1	Oil-field machinery and tools	58.81	4.07
2	Boat building and repairing	26.82	1.86
3	Ship building and repairing	21.39	1.48
4	Venetian blinds	21.21	1.47
5	Mattresses and bed springs	17.63	1.22
6	Boiler shop products	16.04	1.11
7	Structural and ornamental products	15.80	1.09
8	Truck trailers	15.72	1.09
9	Morticians' goods	15.41	1.07
10	Transportation equipment, n.e.c.	15.25	1.06
11	Gray iron foundries	13.08	0.91
12	Metal barrels, drums, and pails	13.07	0.90
13	Optical instruments and lenses	13.05*	0.90*
14	Woodworking machinery	12.22	0.85
15	Restaurant furniture, and furni-		

	ture and fixtures, n.e.c......	10.97	0.76
16	Automobile trailers...........	10.63	0.74
17	Aircraft	10.51	0.73
18	Heating and cooking apparatus, n.e.c.............	9.74	0.67
19	Truck and bus bodies........	9.47	0.66
20	Window and door screens......	9.34	0.65
21	Sheet-metal work	8.86	0.61
22	Signs and advertising displays..	8.39	0.58
23	Blowers and fans..............	7.77	0.54
24	Brooms and brushes...........	7.67	0.53
25	Partitions and fixtures........	7.64	0.53

*Actual figures not available. This percentage and location quotion based upon an estimate.

As indicated by Table 89, there were twelve industries in which the South had no representation. These are, in the main, relatively small industries in the nation and are all producers of finished products, many of which are highly specialized in character. The titles of the twelve industries are as follows:

Files
Safes and vaults
Paper-industries machinery
Mechanical stokers
Typewriters
Sewing machines
Transformers
Aircraft engines
Watch cases
Children's vehicles
Beauty and barber shop equipment
Locomotives and parts.

It should be pointed out that these are industry titles and that an establishment must be engaged in the manufacture of a particular product as its principal line to be classified as belonging in the industry which carries the title of the product. In other words, the fact that the South had no establishment classified as belonging in any one of the twelve industries is not conclusive proof that none of the products suggested by the title was manufactured in the South. It is, however, doubtful that any such items would have a significant place in the region's industrial economy.

SIZE OF CONSTITUENT INDUSTRIES IN THE SOUTH

The location quotients provide one means of analyzing the relative importance of the several industries. Another characteristic of importance is that of size. How important are the various industries as employers of labor or as producers of values in the form of finished products? To indicate size, the total number of production workers reported for an industry in the South will be used. The distribution given in Table 90 shows that there were twenty iron and steel processing and fabricating industries in the South that employed more than 2,500 production workers each. Of these, only five employed more than 10,000. At the other end of the scale were the sixty-three industries which employed less than 500 production workers each. In other words, there were some of the industries that were rather large employers of labor, but the large proportions were small.

Table 90

Iron and Steel Processing and Fabricating Industries Classified According to Number of Production Workers, 1947

Number of production workers reported as employed in an industry	Number of industries
10,000 or more.............................	5
5,000 to 9,999.............................	3
2,500 to 4,999.............................	12
1,000 to 2,499.............................	20
500 to 999.................................	18
100 to 499.................................	35
1 to 99....................................	28
No establishment—no production workers.....	12
	133
Industries combined with one of above........	11
Total number of industries.................	144

Source: Compiled from special tabulation by the U. S. Bureau of the Census.

The industries that occupy the most important places in the South from the point of view of size are shown by the following listing of the twenty iron and steel processing and fabricating industries of the South that employed the largest number of production workers in 1947.

Industry	Number of production workers
Ship building and repairing	24,542
Gray-iron foundries (includes cast-iron pipe)	20,576
Oil-field machinery and tools	13,356
Aircraft	11,599
Structural and ornamental products	10,155
Boiler shop products	8,971
Heating and cooking apparatus, n.e.c.	8,955
Motor vehicles and parts	7,105
Farm machinery (except tractors)	4,898
Boatbuilding and repairing	4,644
Mattresses and bed springs	4,489
Valves and fittings	3,648
Special industry machinery, n.e.c.	3,552
Sheet-metal work	3,111
Construction and mining machinery	2,982
Tin cans and other tinware	2,891
Morticians' goods	2,811
Radios and related products	2,773
Textile machinery	2,696
Refrigeration machinery	2,686

Eleven of these industries are included in the list of those that rank highest with respect to their location quotients. The fact that the other nine have low location quotients indicates that the South does have some industries that provide employment to quite significant numbers, even though the regions' share of the national totals may be small.

SOUTH'S PARTICIPATION IN IMPORTANT INDUSTRIES

In the preceding paragraphs, an attempt has been made to classify the iron and steel processing and fabricating industries of the South according to relative position and size. The question may now be raised as to the extent to which the South participates in the industries that occupy the leading positions in the United States. In Chapter XIX, two lists were given which will be used as the bases for answering this question. One was a list of the 35 highest ranking processing and fabricating industries of the nation as measured in terms of value added by manufacture. The other was a list of the industry groups that rank highest as consumers of steel shapes and forms. In general, an examination of the industries included on these lists shows that the South's

participation in many of the larger industries is very small.

Table 91

The South's Participation in the Thirty-five Largest Iron and Steel Processing and Fabricating Industries of the United States, 1947

Rank in U.S.	Industries (selected according to value added by manufacture in U.S.)	South's per cent of United States number of production workers
1	Motor vehicles and parts	1.27
2	Radios and related products	1.95
3	Gray-iron foundries	13.08
4	Metal stampings	1.21
5	Aircraft	10.51
6	Refrigeration machinery	2.48
7	Heating and cooking apparatus, n.e.c.	9.74
8	Motors and generators (electrical)	0.53
9	Ship building and repairing	21.39
10	Cutting tools, jigs, fixtures, etc.	0.43
11	Construction and mining machinery	4.50
12	Structural and ornamental products	15.80
13	Farm machinery (except tractors)	6.39
14	Electrical control apparatus	1.87
15	Valves and fittings (except plumbers)	5.54
16	Telephone and telegraph equipment	0.50
17	Boiler shop products	16.04
18	Special industry machinery, n.e.c.	6.61
19	Machine tools	0.16
20	Hardware, n.e.c.	0.47
21	Tractors	1.17
22	Engines and turbines	0.02
23	Wire drawing, welded and heavy-riveted pipe	0.54
24	Metalworking machinery, n.e.c.	0.09
25	Bolts, nuts, washers, and rivets	1.87
26	Power-transmission equipment	1.54
27	Pumps and compressors	4.47
28	Railroad and street cars	2.90*
29	Machine shops	3.80
30	Steel and malleable-iron foundries	2.55
31	Fabricated wire products	2.49
32	Photographic equipment	0.42
33	Ball and roller bearings	0.34
34	Textile machinery	5.94
35	Aircraft engines and parts	...

*Actual figures not available; based on an estimate.

Source: *Census of Manufactures, 1947.* Figures for South derived from special tabulation by the Bureau of the Census.

Table 91 is summarized below.

South's per cent of United States (in terms of production workers) in the 34 largest fabricating industries of the nation	Number of industries
Over 14.45 per cent	3
10.84 to 14.44	1
7.23 to 10.83	2
4.34 to 7.22	6
1.45 to 4.33	9
0.01 to 1.44	13
0	1
Total	35

Since the South's share of all the production workers in manufacturing in the United States is 14.45 per cent, the summary of the region's participation in the 35 most important processing and fabricating industries shows not only low percentages but also a low degree of development compared with manufacturing generally. Of the 35 industries, the South's share is 7.22 per cent of the United States (equivalent of a location quotient of 0.49), or less, in 29 industries. Of the top 10 ranking industries, there were 6 in which the South had less than 2.5 per cent of the production workers.

The relationship between the South's participation in the iron and steel processing and fabricating industries and its position as a market for steel mill products is high-lighted by the statistics presented in Table 92. In only three of the leading steel-using industries did the South have as much as ten per cent. These were fabricated structural metal products, construction and mining machinery, and ship and boatbuilding and repairing. Fair percentages were shown for tin cans and other tinware (7.07 per cent) and heating apparatus and plumbers' supplies (8.62 per cent). However, the region's share was less than three per cent in such important steel-using industry groups as motor vehicles; miscellaneous fabricated metal products; metal stampings, coatings, and enameling; railroad equipment; electrical generating, transmission, and industrial equipment; service industry and household machines; fabricated wire products; cutlery, hand tools, and general hardware; and miscellaneous primary metals. Such a situation constitutes one of the very serious limitations of the southern market.

SIZE OF ESTABLISHMENTS IN THE SOUTH

Two other general characteristics of the iron and steel processing and fabricating industries of the South will be considered. These have

Table 92

Position of South in Industries That Are Large Users of Steel

Industry groups	Tons of steel shapes and forms, United States, 1947	Per cent South of United States number of production workers
Structural metal products	7,382,861	13.23
Motor vehicles and equipment	6,653,185	1.94
Miscellaneous primary metal products	5,307,608	0.56
Tin cans and other tinware	3,106,461	7.07
Miscellaneous fabricated metal products	2,733,090	2.64
Metal stamping and coating	2,504,469	1.72
Tractors and farm machinery	1,854,909	4.03
Railroad equipment	1,785,531	1.93
Electrical industrial apparatus, except carbon	1,482,982	1.00
Service and household machines	1,251,393	1.77
Heating and plumbing equipment	1,151,280	8.62
Construction and mining machinery	1,034,471	18.38
Fabricated wire products	980,713	2.49
General industrial machinery	880,133	4.26
Cutlery, hand tools, and hardware	849,063	0.81
Ships and boats	664,601	22.11

Note: The above industry groups correspond to the three digit Census classification.

Source: *Census of Manufactures, 1947.*

Average Size of Establishments in Processing and Fabricating Industries in the South and United States in Terms of Production Workers Per Establishment, 1947

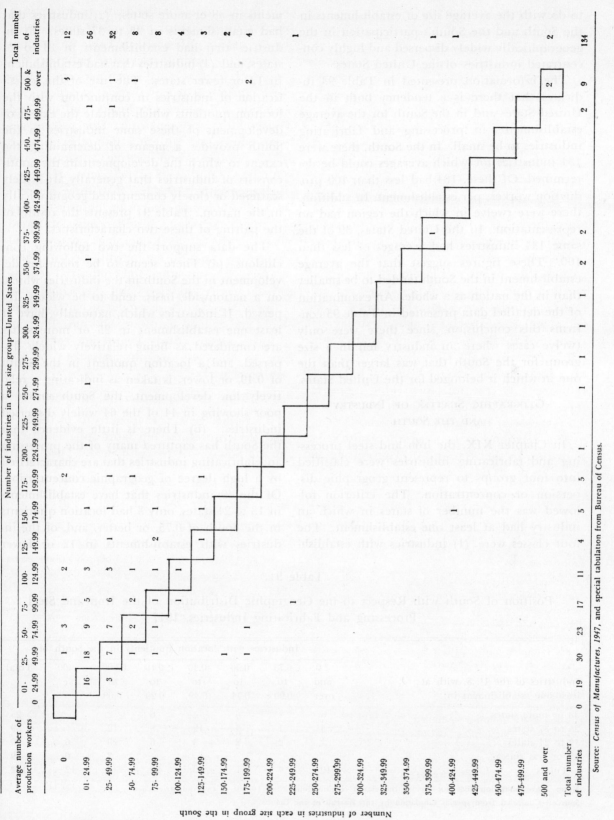

Source: *Census of Manufactures, 1947*, and special tabulation from Bureau of Census.

to do with the average size of establishments in the South and the South's participation in the geographically widely dispersed and highly concentrated industries of the United States.

The information presented in Table 93 indicates that there is a tendency both in the United States and in the South for the average establishments in processing and fabricating industries to be small. In the South, there were 134 industries for which averages could be determined. Of these, 104 had less than 100 production workers per establishment. In addition, there were twelve in which the region had no representation. In the United States, 89 of the same 134 industries had averages of less than 100. These figures suggest that the average establishment in the South tended to be smaller than in the nation as a whole. An examination of the detailed data presented in Table 93 confirms this conclusion, since there were only twelve cases where an industry fell in a size group for the South that was larger than the one in which it belonged for the United States.

GEOGRAPHIC SCATTER OF INDUSTRY AND THE SOUTH

In Chapter XIX, the iron and steel processing and fabricating industries were classified into four groups to represent geographic dispersion or concentration. The criterion followed was the number of states in which an industry had at least one establishment. The four classes were (1) industries with establishments in 38 or more states; (2) industries that had establishments in 25 to 37 states; (3) industries that had establishments in 13 to 24 states; and (4) industries that had establishment in 12 or fewer states. The use of this classification of industries in conjunction with the location quotients which indicate the extent of development of these same industries in the South provides a means of determining the extent to which the development in the South consists of industries that generally are widely scattered or closely concentrated geographically in the nation. Table 94 presents the results of the pairing of these two characteristics.

The data support the two following conclusions. (a) There seems to be room for development in the South in the industries which, on a nationwide basis, tend to be widely dispersed. If industries which, nationally, have at least one establishment in 25 or more states are considered as being relatively widely dispersed, and a location quotient in the South of 0.49, or lower, is taken as indicating a relatively low development, the South makes a poor showing in 44 of the 64 widely dispersed industries. (b) There is little evidence that the South has captured many of the processing and fabricating industries that are characterized by a high degree of geographic concentration. Of the 49 industries that have establishments in 13 to 24 states, only 3 had location quotients in the South of 0.75, or better, and, of the industries with establishments in 12 or fewer

Table 94

Position of South with Respect to the Geographic Distribution of the Iron and Steel Processing and Fabricating Industries, 1947

Industries of the U. S. with at least one establishment in:	Industries with location quotients in the South of							Total
	1.0 and over	0.75 to 0.99	0.50 to 0.74	0.30 to 0.49	0.10 to 0.29	0.0001 to 0.09	.00	
38 or more states	6	1	6	4	6	2		25
25 to 37 states	3	1	3	12	8	12		39
13 to 24 states	1	2	2	3	6	29	6	49
12 or less states						3	6	9
Totals	10	4	11	19	20	46	12	122

Note: This tabulation does not include the eleven combinations which consist of two industries each.

Source: Compiled from special tabulation by the Bureau of the Census.

states, none had high location quotients to represent their development in the South. In fact, only 3 of the industries in this latter class had any southern representatives at all.

Location of the Iron and Steel Processing and Fabricating Industries Within the South

The data on a state and local basis is not nearly so complete as that on the South as a whole, since the disclosure rules of the Bureau of the Census applies to a greater extent on smaller areas than on larger ones. Still a sufficiently clear picture of the more important locations can be obtained for present purposes. The first approach will be to examine the statistics for the several states and later to attempt to determine locations more definitely by the use of county data.

The distributions on a state basis indicate that the iron and steel processing and fabricating industries are quite widely scattered over the entire South and that each of the states has quite a variety of industries. As indicated by Table 95, Texas has by far the largest number of establishments and the greatest variety in terms of different kinds of industries. No doubt the very large size of the state was an important factor in bringing about this situation. In the Southeast, the northern and eastern states, with the exception of South Carolina, tended to have the greater number of establishments and the greater variety of industries. In other words, North Carolina,

Table 95

Location of the Iron and Steel Processing and Fabricating Industries in the South; Number of Establishments by States and Industry Groups and Number of Different Kinds of Industries by States, 1947

	Number of establishments by industry groups										
	Iron and steel foundries	Other primary metals (except non-ferrous)	Fabricated metals industries	Machinery (except electrical)	Selected electrical machinery	Transportation equipment	Instruments and related products	Selected furniture industries	Selected miscellaneous industries	Totals	Number of different kinds of industries
Southeast											
North Carolina	35		62	116	9	29	8	56	48	363	64
South Carolina	15		22	23	1	8	3	24	21	117	35
Georgia	23		86	96	11	35	5	59	59	374	75
Florida	12		117	56	13	90	10	75	109	482	74
Tennessee	31	3	115	87	12	20	9	32	63	372	70
Alabama	60		86	59	9	23	6	34	37	314	60
Mississippi	8		20	24	1	21	3	10	23	110	43
Arkansas	6		25	21		13	3	18	35	121	48
Louisiana	14		78	47	1	53	5	28	49	275	51
Total Southeast	204	3	611	529	57	292	52	336	444	2,528	
Southwest											
Oklahoma	13	1	89	126	3	31	19	30	38	350	71
Texas	43	11	327	370	34	99	49	188	231	1,352	113
Total Southwest	56	12	416	496	37	130	68	218	269	1,702	
Total South	260	15	1,027	1,025	94	422	120	554	713	4,230	
Total United States	1,936	811	16,672	17,906	3,421	3,711	2,599	3,880	8,442	59,378	
Per cent of United States											
Southeast	10.54	0.37	3.66	2.95	1.67	7.87	2.00	8.66	5.26	4.26	
Southwest	2.89	1.48	2.50	2.77	1.08	3.50	2.62	5.62	3.19	2.87	
Total South	13.43	1.85	6.16	5.72	2.75	11.37	4.62	14.28	8.45	7.12	

Source: *Census of Manufactures, 1947.*

Georgia, Florida, Tennessee, and Alabama out-ranked Mississippi, Arkansas, and Louisiana. Florida in particular made a strong showing on the basis of number of establishments and different kinds of industry.

Rather surprisingly, Florida had the largest number of establishments among the south-eastern states in five of the eight main groups of the processing and fabricating industries. Texas had the largest number in the South in all groups except iron and steel foundries. In general, the establishments in the several industry groups were widely distributed to the several states. The other primary metals group is the main exception, since establishments occurred only in Tennessee, Oklahoma, and Texas. Electrical machinery also is not as evenly distributed as are the groups.

It would be highly desirable to parallel the information on the distribution of establishments among states with similar statistics of numbers of production workers or for some other measure of activity, but lack of data makes this impossible. It is possible, however,

to secure a very good indication of the situation from statistics on the main industry groups by states. The distribution of the number of production workers in the iron and steel processing and fabricating industries within the South presents quite a different picture from that indicated by the number of establishments. For the six industry groups represented in Table 96, the three most important states are Texas, Alabama, and Tennessee. Together these three states account for 153,271 or 66.7 per cent of the 229,659 production workers in the six groups in the entire South. A wide gap exists between the third state, Tennessee, with 37,979 production workers, and the fourth state, Georgia, with 15,189. The smallest numbers of production workers occur in South Carolina (3,042) and Arkansas (4,959). It should be pointed out that the statistics for the primary metals group include blast furnaces and steel works and nonferrous metals. The blast furnace and steel works industries are considered in this study as being basic iron and steel industries rather than belonging in

Table 96

Distribution of Production Workers in the South by Primary Industry Groups
of the Iron and Steel Processing and Fabricating Industries and by States, 1947

State	Group 33 primary metals*	Group 34 fabricated metals	Group 35 machinery	Group 36 electrical machinery	Group 37 transportation equipment	Group 38 instruments	Total
North Carolina	1,731	2,282	3,320	3,358	1,068	35	11,794
South Carolina	717	334	1,113	....	878	....	3,042
Georgia	2,458	3,034	5,327	1,226	3,078	66	15,189
Florida	300	1,817	1,095	183	4,832	....	8,227
Tennessee	13,409	12,953	4,640	1,044	4,556	1,377	37,979
Alabama	34,520	6,219	6,035	349	7,524	35	54,682
Mississippi	234	393	825	....	4,886	11	6,349
Arkansas	2,672	667	382	....	276	962	4,959
Louisiana	714	3,092	1,595	70	8,390	68	13,929
Oklahoma	3,103	2,722	4,905	....	1,034	341	12,106
Texas	10,585	10,964	18,327	1,714	18,285	735	60,610
Southern states, but not available by states	....			667		126	793
Total	70,443	44,477	47,565	8,611	54,807	3,756	229,659

*Includes blast furnaces and steel works, in Alabama 19,592, in the South 24,338, considered in this study as basic iron and steel industries.

Source: *Census of Manufactures, 1947.*

processing and fabricating. The total number of production workers in these two industries in the South in 1947 was 24,338. Of these, 19,552 were in Alabama and the remainder primarily in Texas, Tennessee, and Georgia. However, the elimination of these industries from the total cannot materially change the conclusions. If the four states of Texas, Alabama, Tennessee, and Georgia were considered to have had all of the blast furnaces and steel works, they would still have 70 per cent of all remaining production workers in the six groups. It seems evident from these data that the relatively wide distribution indicated by the number of establishments results from many small establishments and that this is off-set by a quite pronounced concentration of the larger establishments in a few states.

Thus far the study of location of the iron and steel processing and fabricating industries within the South has been on the basis of totals or industry groups. Such data tend to give an appearance of geographic dispersion to a greater extent than does a study of the occurrence of establishments of individual industries. To present this aspect of the situation, the following summary of the occurrence of establishments of the 144 industries included in the whole classification is given.

Industries having one or more establishments in:	Number of industries
11 states	16
10 states	7
9 states	10
8 states	6
7 states	9
6 states	10
5 states	8
4 states	13
3 states	16
2 states	20
1 state	17
Industries with no establishments in South	12
Total	144

There are 39 of the 144 industries which have establishments in eight or more of the southern states. On the other hand, there are 65 industries, including those with no establishments, that have all their establishments in three or fewer states. Thus, the South has a considerable number of industries that occur in most of its states, but many more that are located in only a few states, or are absent entirely.

A comparison of the geographic dispersion of industries in the South with the national dispersion shows that, in general, the industries that are widely scattered in the South have the same characteristic nationally. A similar correspondence seems to apply to those that occur in only a few states. The data seem to indicate, however, that the occurrence in the South of the geographically concentrated industries is not as high as a random distribution throughout the nation would indicate.

The question may be raised as to the relationship between the over-all size or importance of the several processing and fabricating industries and their degree of geographic scatter. To represent size, the number of production workers has been used, and this characteristic has been associated with the number of states in which an industry occurs. The results of this tabulation are given in Table 97.

The outstanding facts brought out by the data in Table 97 are summarized below.

1. The widely dispersed industries, those occurring in eight or more southern states, account for 27 of the 40 industries with 1,000 or more production workers in the South. On the other hand, the industries with establishments in four or fewer states account for only two of these larger industries. These are aircraft and railroad and street cars.

2. Quite a large number of the widely dispersed industries—with establishments in eight or more states—have relatively small numbers of production workers. Thirteen have less than 1,000 production workers each.

3. The industries that occur in only a few states are heavily weighted with those that have very small numbers of production workers. Of the 54 industries that have establishments in four or fewer states (not counting those that have no establishments in the South) 26 or

practically one-half have less than 100 production workers each.

In general, establishments of the iron and steel processing and fabricating industries are widely scattered among the eleven southern states. Also, each of the several states has quite a variety of different kinds of industries. However, when occurrence is measured in terms of numbers of production workers, it becomes evident that a few of the states have the large proportion of the total. Leaders are Texas, Alabama, Tennessee, and Georgia. On an individual industry basis, it appears that a large proportion of the industries occur in only a very few of the southern states. Furthermore, a considerable proportion of the widely dispersed industries are also small in size. These are conditions which suggest a widespread underdevelopment of the metal-using industries in most states of the South.

IMPORTANT CENTERS OF PROCESSING AND FABRICATING IN THE SOUTH

In the study of the location of important centers of the processing and fabricating industries in the South the first approach was the examination of the census data on the number of establishments in each county. The number of establishments with 100 or more

employees in the six main industry groups most directly connected with iron and steel processing and fabricating was used as a criterion of the importance of a county. The number of counties in each of the southern states which had at least one such establishment is shown in the following listing.

State	Number of counties
North Carolina	13
South Carolina	4
Georgia	17
Florida	5
Tennessee	18
Alabama	14
Mississippi	5
Arkansas	7
Louisiana	10
Oklahoma	8
Texas	25
Total	126

Of these 126 counties, however, only eleven had ten or more establishments with as many as 100 employees and fourteen more had from five to nine such establishments. The larger establishments, therefore, were concentrated in a small number of counties.

The names of the counties that, in 1947, had five or more establishments with 100 or more employees are listed below.

Table 97

Relationship Between Total Number of Production Workers in the Several Iron and Steel Processing and Fabricating Industries in the South and the Number of Southern States in Which the Industries Occur, 1947

Production workers in an industry	Number of southern states in which establishments occur											Total number of industries
	11	10	9	8	7	6	5	4	3	2	1	
10,000 or more	2		1			1		1				5
5,000 to 9,999		1	1	1								3
2,500 to 4,999	5	1	2		1	2	1					12
1,000 to 2,499	5	4	3	1		3	3			1		20
500 to 999	1	1	1		4	3	2	1	3			18
100 to 499	3		2	3	2	2	1	8	7	6	1	35
1 to 99					1		1	3	7	7	9	28
Total industries	16	7	10	7	8	10	9	12	18	14	10	121

Source: *Census of Manufactures, 1947,* and special tabulation on the South from Bureau of the Census.

Note: The total number of industries, 121, excludes 12 industries with no establishments in the South but includes 11 two-industry combinations (counted only as one each).

County	Principal city	State	Number of establishments with 100 or more employees
Jefferson	Birmingham	Alabama	43
Harris	Houston	Texas	34
Dallas	Dallas	Texas	26
Hamilton	Chattanooga	Tennessee	26
Fulton	Atlanta	Georgia	21
Tulsa	Tulsa	Oklahoma	21
Orleans	New Orleans	Louisiana	19
Calhoun	Anniston	Alabama	13
Davidson	Nashville	Tennessee	12
Shelby	Memphis	Tennessee	11
Etowah	Gadsden	Alabama	11
Oklahoma	Oklahoma City	Oklahoma	8
Jefferson	Beaumont	Texas	7
Taurrant	Ft. Worth	Texas	7
Knox	Knoxville	Tennessee	7
Guilford	Greensboro and High Point	North Carolina	6
Duval	Jacksonville	Florida	6
Mobile	Mobile	Alabama	6
Galveston	Galveston	Texas	6
Forsyth	Winston-Salem	North Carolina	5
Mecklenburg	Charlotte	North Carolina	5
Muscogee	Columbus	Georgia	5
Hillsborough	Tampa	Florida	5
Colbert	Sheffield	Alabama	5
El Paso	El Paso	Texas	5

These counties are widely scattered, particularly those with ten or more of the larger establishments. In fact, the only suggestion of a concentration of several counties that might be considered as comprising a processing and fabricating district consists of Jefferson, Calhoun, and Etowah counties in Alabama, and Hamilton County, Tennessee.

A second source of information on important industrial locations is provided by the tables of the *Census of Manufactures, 1947,* on metropolitan areas and principal industrial counties. Full data are not published, but the available statistics for the six industry groups that have been used on previous occasions are presented in Table 98. While the data are incomplete, the concentration of a large part of the metal working industries of the South in a relatively small number of local areas is further emphasized. Also, the wide scatter of these areas over the South is again shown.

Conclusions Concerning Processing and Fabricating Industries in the South

There are comparatively few of the iron and steel processing and fabricating industries in which the South has attained a strong position. This is true whether viewed from the standpoint of the region's share in national totals or of the development in the processing and fabricating industries compared with manufacturing generally in the South. The data indicate a high development in ship and boat-building and repairing. This, no doubt, has been influenced by the existence of many miles of waterways and extensive coastlines. The industry, however, is a highly variable one. The structural steel fabricated products industry also has a relatively strong position. This industry is closely related to population, particularly urban, and to industrial and commercial development. Another industry of importance is gray iron foundries. Related rather closely to this industry is the manufacturing of heating and plumbing equipment. However, the high phosphorous pig iron and limitations of markets has tended to restrict development and to make these industries less well-rounded than is desirable. In the whole field of machinery, equipment, and appliances, despite some very significant developments, the South occupies a relatively low position. The influence of distinctly southern products or conditions may be seen most conspicuously in the oil-field machinery and equipment industry and to a lesser degree in textile machinery.

The representation of the South in the industries that rank high in the nation, whether measured in terms of value of products or consumption of steel, is generally low, and this constitutes one of the great weaknesses of the South as a market for steel.

Generally, the establishments of the processing and fabricating industries in the South seem to have a smaller average size than in the United States. Also there are few of the industries that are characterized by high geographic concentration that have attained any great development in the South, and many of those that generally are widely dispersed have relatively weak representation in the region.

It is scarcely necessary in concluding this chapter to emphasize further the points of weakness of the South with regard to the iron and steel processing and fabricating industries. Enough has been said to show that the markets for steel products are influenced greatly by the existing lack of development in many of the iron and steel-using industries. The picture is not entirely dark. There are a number of the metal-working industries in which the South has made a quite creditable showing. Establishments in nearly all of the industries under study, though often small and widely scattered, are operating in the region. Furthermore, there are dozens of individual firms that have a successful experience behind them to demonstrate that metal-working industries have a place in the expanding economy of the area.

Table 98

Number of Production Workers in the Metals Industries Groups, Metropolitan Areas and Industrial Counties of the South, 1947

	Group 33 primary metals	Group 34 fabri-cated metals	Group 35 machin-ery	Group 36 elec-trical machin-ery	Group 37 transpor-tation equip-ment	Group 38 instru-ments	Total 33-38
Cabarrus Co., N.C.	†	*	*	†	†	†	†
Forsyth Co., N.C.	151	716	99	1,683	*	*	2,649
Gaston Co., N.C.	65	*	412	†	*	†	477
Guilford Co., N.C.	103	478	490	†	*	*	1,071
Greenville Co., S.C.	†	*	833	†	†	†	833
Spartanburg Co., S.C.	347	28	150	†	†	†	525
Atlanta Metro. Area, Ga.	2,056	1,533	2,162	720	1,801	66	8,338
Davidson Co., Tenn.	187	1,892	315	151	2,702	236	5,483
Hamilton Co., Tenn.	3,211	6,295	2,094	*	434	*	12,034
Shelby Co., Tenn.	273	1,177	1,063	324	1,216	*	4,053
Birmingham Metro. Area, Ala.	20,321	4,372	3,534	335	1,565	*	30,127
New Orleans Metro. Area, La.	439	1,917	135	*	7,483	60	10,034
Houston Metro. Area, Texas	3,614	4,156	9,044	431	1,023	355	18,623
Dallas Co., Texas	353	2,940	2,425	740	2,604	104	9,166
Jefferson Co., Texas	241	1,015	213	*	948	†	2,417
Tarrant Co., Texas	694	331	1,046	34	10,740	82	12,527
Total of above	32,052	26,850	24,015	4,418	30,516	903	118,757
Total in South	70,443	44,477	47,565	8,611	54,807	3,756	229,659
Per cent of South in above areas	45.50	60.37	50.49	51.31	55.68	24.04	51.71

*Data not available.

†No establishments.

Source: *Census of Manufactures, 1947.*

CHAPTER XXI

TRENDS IN THE IRON AND STEEL PROCESSING AND FABRICATING INDUSTRIES OF THE SOUTH

Having discussed in some detail the situation with regard to the iron and steel processing and fabricating industries of the South in 1947, it is pertinent to raise a question as to the direction and degree of the changes that have been taking place in this group of industries. A special retabulation of the 1939 Census of Manufactures makes available statistics for that year that are comparable with the 1947 data and provides the basis for a thoroughgoing study of the changes in the status of the industries as of the two census years. Also, considerable information for the intervening war and postwar years is available so that the record for the inter-census years can be traced with a reasonable degree of accuracy. Unfortunately, information for the years preceding 1939 is very spotty. A census of manufactures was taken biennially from 1919 to 1939, but industry classifications and the rules for reporting were changed several times. These changes and the application of disclosure rules have made the published reports for the states of the South so incomplete and difficult to interpret that they are of little value in an attempt to trace the changes in the processing and fabricating industries. The task of piecing together the story of change from miscellaneous bits of information for as many industries as are involved was too great to be attempted. Consequently, this chapter will be confined to a study of changes during the eight-year period from 1939 to 1947.

As indicated in the preceding paragraph, the comparison of conditions in 1947 with those in 1939, as reported by the Census of Manufactures, constitutes the chief foundation for the discussion. A series of tables present the essential statistics. Table 99 gives a summary for 1939 which is similar to that presented in

the preceding chapter for 1947. Table 100 presents the percentages of increase from 1939 to 1947 for each of the industry groups in the South and in the United States, and Table 101 compares the relative positions of the South in the several groups in 1939 and 1947, stated in terms of the per cents of the totals for the nation which are represented by the industry in the South.

Over-All Changes, 1939 to 1947

To serve as a starting point for the discussion of the changes shown by the data, attention is directed first to the totals for the iron and steel and processing and fabricating industries and for all manufacturing. To provide for convenient reference, the percentages of change from 1939 to 1947 are summarized below.

	Per cent increases	
	South	United States
Iron and steel processing and fabricating		
Number of establishments	78.7	78.7
Number of production workers	148.1	102.6
Value added by manufacture	352.7	262.3
All manufacturing		
Number of establishments	50.8	38.6
Number of production workers	49.2	52.6
Value added by manufacture	250.2	203.9

Each measure of activity given above shows a very substantial increase. The change in the value added by manfacture has, of course, been magnified by the general increase in prices during the period, but the number of establishments and the number of production workers have not been inflated by this condition. In fact, increased mechanization, larger plants, and larger output per worker probably mean that the increases in physical output were more

Table 99

The Iron and Steel Processing and Fabricating Industries of the South and the United States, 1939

Industry	South				United States			Per cent South of U. S.		
	Number establishments	Production workers	Wages	Value added	Number establishments	Production workers	Value added	Number establishments	Production workers	Value added
Iron and steel foundries	194	14,476	13,433	29,162	1,501	123,809	295,012	12.9	11.7	9.9
Miscellaneous primary metals industries	5	162	186	438	439	52,004	192,218	1.1	0.3	0.2
Tin cans and other tinware	19	1,965	1,981	8,460	195	29,277	116,152	9.7	6.7	7.3
Cutlery, hand tools, and hardware	22	726	591	1,506	1,212	75,175	208,968	1.8	1.0	0.7
Heating and plumbing equipment	62	7,772	6,365	14,509	1,036	78,330	244,851	6.0	9.9	5.9
Structural metal products	313	8,953	9,268	27,644	3,099	83,429	288,601	10.1	10.7	9.6
Metal stamping and coating	54	1,604	1,357	3,345	1,920	80,649	225,317	2.8	2.0	1.5
Lighting fixtures	4	60	46	120	568	20,477	64,731	0.7	0.3	0.2
Fabricated wire products	24	533	370	1,135	705	32,901	90,937	3.4	1.6	1.2
Miscellaneous fabricated metal products	21	1,149	1,123	2,940	744	46,638	145,739	2.7	2.5	2.0
Tractors and farm machinery	43	1,145	925	2,780	421	60,144	210,958	10.2	1.9	1.3
Construction and mining machinery	128	7,921	11,806	34,860	562	36,750	159,256	22.8	21.6	21.9
Metalworking machinery	8	25	24	92	1,470	80,954	326,235	0.5	0.03	0.03
Special-industry machinery, n.e.c.	138	3,807	3,666	10,190	2,239	77,246	268,233	6.2	4.9	3.8
General industrial machinery	86	1,688	1,939	7,336	1,380	72,799	302,024	6.2	2.3	2.4
Service and household machinery	40	1,264	1,246	3,359	650	67,906	273,576	6.2	1.9	1.6
Miscellaneous machinery parts	175	2,743	2,960	7,842	1,793	78,448	277,956	9.8	3.5	2.8
Selected electrical machinery	33	573	569	1,703	1,622	207,903	788,787	2.0	0.3	0.2
Ships and boats	84	6,414	6,807	13,075	608	69,241	179,898	13.8	9.3	7.3
Transportation equipment, n.e.c.	12	264	171	477	41	1,252	3,145	29.3	21.1	15.2
Motor vehicles, aircraft, railroads, motorcycles, and bicycles	87	5,515	7,336	29,687	1,363	474,060	1,589,530	6.4	1.2	1.9
Scientific instruments	5	50	83	145	125	6,529	30,627	4.0	0.8	0.5
All other instruments and related products	30	696	808	1,650	1,167	78,338	302,782	2.6	0.9	0.5
Selected miscellaneous manufactures	430	5,318	4,135	11,112	5,223	152,181	408,216	8.2	3.5	2.7
Selected furniture and fixture industries	343	5,668	4,780	14,152	2,608	53,459	151,096	13.2	10.6	9.4
Other selected industries	7	257	191	601	546	76,620	261,390	1.3	0.3	0.2
Total processing and fabricating	2,367	80,747	82,160	229,319	33,237	2,216,519	7,406,235	7.1	3.6	3.1
Total all manufacturing	24,440	1,154,184	889,897	2,561,278	173,802	7,808,205	24,487,304	14.1	14.8	10.5
Per cent processing and fabricating industry of all manufacturing	9.7	7.0	9.2	9.0	19.2	28.4	30.2			

Source: Census of Manufactures, 1939, and special tabulation, Bureau of the Census.

Table 100

Per Cent Increases in the Iron and Steel Processing and Fabricating Industries of the South and the United States, 1939-1947

Industry	South				United States		
	Number establishments	Production workers	Wages	Value added	Number establishments	Production workers	Value added
Iron and steel foundries	+ 34.0	+ 56.5	+ 284.9	+ 229.3	+ 29.0	+ 93.3	+280.2
Miscellaneous primary metals industries	+200.0	+ 271.0	+ 944.1	+ 858.0	+ 84.7	+106.5	+285.1
Tin cans and other tinware	+ 5.3	+ 47.1	+ 239.6	+ 109.4	+ 11.3	+ 39.7	+ 99.7
Cutlery, hand tools, and hardware	+150.0	+ 46.4	+ 256.2	+ 243.8	+ 54.0	+ 75.1	+248.6
Heating and plumbing equipment	+ 54.8	+ 40.6	+ 256.7	+ 221.5	+ 23.2	+ 61.8	+222.5
Structural metal products	+ 96.5	+ 155.1	+ 486.3	+ 378.2	+ 45.4	+107.0	+296.2
Metal stamping and coating	+133.3	+ 71.7	+ 280.0	+ 263.3	+131.1	+ 98.3	+282.2
Lighting fixtures	+325.0	+ 111.7	+ 306.5	+ 312.5	+112.3	+ 94.8	+282.5
Fabricated wire products	+ 58.3	+ 145.4	+ 582.7	+ 477.8	+ 38.6	+ 59.7	+210.3
Miscellaneous fabricated metal products	+185.7	+ 109.0	+ 497.4	+ 469.3	+193.8	+ 95.3	+310.8
Tractors and farm machinery	+193.0	+ 392.1	+1177.3	+ 686.3	+161.8	+132.2	+257.3
Construction and mining machinery	+ 17.2	+ 106.3	+ 287.3	+ 237.1	+ 32.9	+141.9	+302.7
Metalworking machinery	+462.5	+1700.0	+4354.2	+2488.0	+192.0	+113.7	+246.7
Special-industry machinery, n.e.c.	+ 92.0	+ 129.4	+ 452.5	+ 381.8	+ 83.4	+124.7	+308.4
General industrial machinery	+100.0	+ 314.8	+ 730.0	+ 476.1	+ 58.8	+125.6	+293.8
Service and household machinery	+ 72.5	+ 153.0	+ 427.3	+ 326.5	+ 67.4	+166.2	+304.2
Miscellaneous machinery parts	+ 5.1	+ 123.5	+ 388.1	+ 338.6	+115.9	+114.0	+253.9
Selected electrical machinery	+184.8	+ 945.9	+1978.0	+2155.1	+110.9	+168.2	+331.6
Ships and boats	+147.6	+ 355.0	+1084.9	+ 885.8	+ 82.6	+ 90.7	+226.1
Transportation equipment, n.e.c.	+166.7	+ 123.1	+ 493.0	+ 432.5	+307.3	+208.5	+553.2
Motor vehicles, aircraft, railroads, motorcycles, and bicycles	+109.2	+ 353.9	+ 739.9	+ 367.9	+ 78.6	+ 79.6	+231.0
Scientific instruments	+320.0	+ 526.0	+ 968.7	+1273.8	+ 72.8	+130.1	+171.0
All other instruments and related products	+230.0	+ 394.7	+ 709.5	+ 802.5	+104.2	+113.1	+229.4
Selected miscellaneous manufactures	+ 65.8	+ 84.2	+ 311.1	+ 233.0	+ 61.6	+ 59.4	+209.4
Selected furniture and fixture industries	+ 52.8	+ 75.3	+ 286.9	+ 231.8	+ 33.0	+ 61.3	+219.5
Other selected industries	+528.6	+ 277.4	+ 393.2	+ 672.4	+ 63.4	+110.2	+269.5
Total processing and fabricating	+ 78.7	+ 148.1	+ 469.4	+ 352.7	+ 78.7	+102.6	+262.3
Total all manufacturing	+ 50.8	+ 49.2	+ 276.8	+ 250.2	+ 38.6	+ 52.6	+203.9

Source: *Census of Manufactures, 1939; 1947;* special tabulation by the Bureau of the Census.

than those indicated by changes in number of establishments and workers.

Comparisons of the percentages of increase give a clue to the changes that took place in relative positions. In cases where the increases for the South were greater than the corresponding increases for the nation, a strengthening of the South's position is indicated. This situation is shown for the number of production workers and the value added by manufacture for the iron and steel processing and fabricating industries and for the number of establishments and value added by manufacture for all manufacturing industries. On the other

hand, the percentage of increase in the number of establishments for the South is slightly smaller than that of the United States, indicating that the region's share of establishments in the iron and steel processing and fabricating industries remained practically unchanged. Also, the per cent increase in the number of production workers in all manufacturing industries in the South was much smaller,[1] and hence the South failed to improve its relative position in that respect.

[1] The situation leading to this result is discussed in some detail in Chapter XXIV.

Table 101

Relative Position of the Iron and Steel Processing and Fabricating Industries of the South Expressed as Per Cents of the United States, 1939 and 1947

| Industry | Per cent South of United States | | | | | |
| | Number establishments | | Production workers | | Value added | |
	1939	1947	1939	1947	1939	1947
Iron and steel foundries	12.9	13.4	11.7	9.5	9.9	8.6
Miscellaneous primary metals industries	1.1	1.9	0.3	0.6	0.2	0.6
Tin cans and other tinware	9.7	9.2	6.7	7.1	7.3	7.6
Cutlery, hand tools, and hardware	1.8	3.0	1.0	0.8	0.7	0.7
Heating and plumbing equipment	6.0	7.5	9.9	8.6	5.9	5.9
Structural metal products	10.1	13.7	10.7	13.2	9.6	11.6
Metal stamping and coating	2.8	2.8	2.0	1.7	1.5	1.4
Lighting fixtures	0.7	1.4	0.3	0.3	0.2	0.2
Fabricated wire products	3.4	3.9	1.6	2.5	1.2	2.3
Miscellaneous fabricated metal products	2.7	2.7	2.5	2.6	2.0	2.8
Tractors and farm machinery	10.2	11.4	1.9	4.0	1.3	2.9
Construction and mining machinery	22.8	20.1	21.6	18.4	21.9	18.3
Metalworking machinery	0.5	1.1	0.03	0.3	0.03	0.2
Special-industry machinery, n.e.c.	6.2	6.5	4.9	5.0	3.8	4.5
General industrial machinery	6.2	7.9	2.3	4.3	2.4	3.6
Service and household machinery	6.2	6.3	1.9	1.8	1.6	1.7
Miscellaneous machinery parts	9.8	4.8	3.5	3.7	2.8	3.5
Selected electrical machinery	2.0	2.8	0.3	1.1	0.2	1.1
Ships and boats	13.8	18.7	9.3	22.1	7.3	22.0
Transportation equipment, n.e.c.	29.3	19.2	21.1	15.3	15.2	12.4
Motor vehicles, aircraft, railroads, motorcycles, and bicycles	6.4	7.5	1.2	2.9	1.9	2.6
Scientific instruments	4.0	9.7	0.8	2.1	0.5	2.4
All other instruments and related products	2.6	4.2	0.9	2.1	0.5	1.5
Selected miscellaneous manufactures	8.2	8.5	3.5	4.0	2.7	2.9
Selected furniture and fixtures industries	13.2	15.1	10.6	11.5	9.4	9.7
Other selected industries	1.3	4.7	0.3	0.6	0.2	0.5
All processing and fabricating	7.1	7.1	3.6	4.5	3.1	3.9
All manufacturing	14.1	15.3	14.8	14.5	10.5	12.1

Source: *Census of Manufactures, 1939; 1947;* special tabulation by the Bureau of the Census.

Table 102

Percentage of Total Manufacturing Accounted for by the Iron and Steel Processing and Fabricating Industries in the South and the United States, 1939 and 1947

	South		U. S.	
	1939	1947	1939	1947
Number of establishments.......	9.7	11.5	19.2	24.7
Number of production workers..	7.0	11.6	28.4	37.7
Wages paid...................	9.2	14.0	...	...
Value added by manufacturing.	9.0	11.6	30.2	36.1

Source: *Census of Manufactures, 1939; 1947;* special tabulation by the Bureau of the Census.

Another significant change is indicated by the fact that both in the South and in the United States the percentages of increase of each of the three measures of activity are larger for the processing and fabricating industries than for all manufacturing. This situation indicates that the metal-using industries occupied more important relative positions in the total manufacturing structure of the South and the nation in 1947 than in 1939.

The effect of the comparative percentages of increase on the position of the iron and steel processing and fabricating industries of the South can readily be seen by examining the data which follows.

	South as per cent of United States	
	1939	1947
Iron and steel processing and fabricating		
Number of establishments..........	7.1	7.1
Number of production workers......	3.6	4.5
Value added by manufacturing......	3.1	3.9
All manufacturing industries		
Number of establishments..........	14.1	15.3
Number of production workers......	14.8	14.5
Value added by manufacturing......	10.5	12.1

Stating the percentages in terms of the shares of total manufacturing accounted for by the iron and steel processing and fabricating in-

dustry provides a view of the changes from a somewhat different angle.

	Per cent processing and fabricating industries of all manufactures			
	South		U. S.	
	1939	1947	1939	1947
Number of establishments....	9.7	11.5	19.2	24.7
Number of production workers	7.0	11.6	28.4	37.7
Value added by manufacture.	9.0	11.6	30.2	36.1

The relatively low position that the processing and fabricating industries occupy in the manufacturing economy of the South has been discussed in detail in the preceding chapter. The totals for 1939 and 1947 indicated that the developments in the South tended to strengthen the position of this group of industries both with respect to the nation and to other industries in the region. However, the increases in the South occurred at a time when large increases were taking place in other parts of the United States, with the result that the region did not strengthen its relative position in the nation in every case.

Changes, 1939 to 1947, in Industry Groups

The next step is to see whether the changes indicated by the totals are representative of the behavior of the constituent industries. To provide information on this question, the tables classify the individual industries into 26 groups.[2] In examining the per cent changes that are shown for the individual industry groups, the reader should remember that some of the industries in the South had very small figures in 1939. For example, the lighting fixtures industry reported 60 production workers; steel springs, 10; and scientific instruments, 50. In such cases, the establishment of an additional small plant or two results in a large per cent of increase and one large plant gives a very large per cent of increase, but still may

[2] Twenty-six groups were used to get as high a degree of comparability between the data for 1947 and 1939. The application of the disclosure rules do not permit using the thirty-four group classification as presented in Chapter XX.

Table 103

Per Cent Increases in the Iron and Steel Processing and Fabricating Industries of the South Compared with the United States, 1939-1947

	Number of industry groups
South per cent of increase greater than United States	
Number of establishments	21
Number of production workers	19
Value added by manufacture	20
United States per cent of increase greater than the South	
Number of establishments	5
Number of production workers	7
Value added by manufacture	6

Source: Prepared from special tabulations for the South by Bureau of the Census; *Census of Manufactures, 1939; 1947.*

leave the total of the industry small compared with other industries and may have little effect on the region's relative position.

The chief interest at present is to get a general view of what happened between the two census years rather than to discuss individual industries. To accomplish this objective, the percentages calculated for the 26 industry groups were analyzed in several different ways. The results are presented in Tables 103, 104, and 105.

While there were industry groups which did not increase in the South as much as either the corresponding group in the nation or as total manufacturing, the general showing indicates a widespread strength in the development of the processing and fabricating industries in the

Table 104

Per Cent Increases in the Iron and Steel Processing and Fabricating Industries as Compared with the Per Cent Increases in All Manufacturing, South and United States, 1939-1947

	Per cent increase in all manufacturing	Processing and fabricating, number of industry groups which had		
		Larger per cent of increase than all manufacturing	Smaller per cent of increase than all manufacturing	Same per cent of increase as all manufacturing
South				
Number of establishments	50.8	22	4	
Number of production workers	49.2	23	3	
Wages paid	276.8	23	3	
Value added by manufacture	250.2	19	7	
United States				
Number of establishments	38.6	20	5	1
Number of production workers	52.6	25	1	
Value added by manufacture	203.9	24	2	

Source: Prepared from special tabulations for the South by Bureau of the Census; *Census of Manufactures, 1939; 1947.*

Table 105

Changes in the Per Cent Share of the Totals of the Iron and Steel Processing and Fabricating Industries of the United States Accounted for by the South, 1939-1947

	Number of industry groups in which the South's relative position in the nation		
	Increased	Decreased	Remained unchanged
Number of establishments	20	4	2
Number of production workers	18	7	1
Value added by manufacture	19	4	3

Source: Prepared from special tabulations for the South by Bureau of the Census; *Census of Manufactures, 1939; 1947.*

South and an improvement in the relative position of the region in a large proportion of the industry groups.

To see whether there were differences in the increases recorded for the industry groups which had attained considerable size in the South and in the small industries, the 26 industry groups were arranged in order of size as indicated by the number of production workers. Eight of the industry groups reported 5,000, or more, production workers in 1939, iron and steel foundries with 14,476 being the largest; eight more reported more than 1,000, but less than 5,000 production workers; seven, more than 100, but less than 1,000 production workers; and three had less than 100 production workers. The changes that took place in the industries in these classes is of interest. Measured in terms of the number of production workers, the first size class had four of its eight industry groups increase more than 100 per cent, the second had six of eight, the third had six of seven, and, in the fourth, all three industry groups increased more than 100 per cent. As would be expected, these data indicate that large percentage increases were not as frequent among the large industry groups as among the smaller ones. Still, large increases occurred in the larger groups and were not confined to the small industries. A check on the changes in relative positions indicates a rather similar condition. In the first size class, three of the eight industry groups experienced decreases in their percentages of the national total. In the second size class, two of the eight industry groups and, in the third size class, two of the seven industry groups also had decreases in their percentages of the national totals. On the other hand, all of the three industry groups in the smallest size class strengthened their relative position, but, as may be expected, were still very small in 1947. The general conclusion is that the tendency to make decided increases appeared in all sizes of the processing and fabricating industries of the South. On the other hand, the smaller increases percentage-wise occurred more frequently among the large and well-established industries, such as

iron and steel foundries and heating and plumbing equipment. This is to be expected.

In Chapter XX, a rather detailed analysis was made of the characteristics of the iron and steel processing and fabricating industries of the South. Data are not available to provide material for a study of the changes that may have occurred between 1939 and 1947 with respect to many of the criteria that were used in the previous chapter, and it is questionable that much would be gained by making elaborate comparisons, even though it were possible to do so. However, the changes in the industry groups which rank high as consumers of steel have an important bearing on market prospects and will be reviewed. Table 106 presents the pertinent information.

The South's weakness in many of the sixteen industry groups that are shown in Table 92 as the ranking consumers of steel in the nation has already been discussed. In five of these the increases from 1939 to 1947, as measured in production workers, were not sufficient to improve the South's relative position in the nation. This is further evidence that the improvement of the market for steel in the South by building up the metal-using industries is not an easy task. The five groups that lost in relative position are metal stamping and coating, service and household equipment, heating and plumbing equipment, construction and mining equipment, and cutlery, hand tools, and hardware. On the other hand, there were nine industry groups of the large consumers in which the South did strengthen its position and in addition it seems safe to assume that its share in the motor vehicle industry, though small, increased during the eight-year period.

Changes in Individual Industries, 1939 to 1947

The analysis of the data on the twenty-six industry groups indicates that a decided and widespread, though not unanimous, improvement in the status of the iron and steel processing and fabricating industries of the South had taken place between 1939 and 1947. This conclusion is further confirmed by an examination of the data on the individual industries. Comparisons on this level are hampered by differences in the extent to which detailed statistics can be made available in the two census years. These differences make it necessary in a number of cases to use combinations of two to four individual industries to get comparable figures. The following analysis, however, attempts to use the most detailed industry breakdowns that can be developed.

Because of the situation pointed out in the preceding paragraph, the total number of industries, or industry groups, is 120 instead of the 144 industry classification used in Chapter XX. For further study these industries were separated into six classes.

1. Industries for which the number of production workers are available in both 1939 and 1947.
   (a) In which the South's per cent of the United States increased...............,...... 53
   (b) In which the South's per cent of the United States decreased............. 19

(c) In which the South's per cent of the United States was unchanged........ 1
   —
   Total 73
2. Industries which had no establishments in the South in 1939 but some in 1947, and number of production workers reported in 1947.............................. 5
3. Industries which had no establishments in the South in 1939 and some in 1947, but number of production workers not reported 6
4. Industries that had no establishments in the South either in 1939 or in 1947...... 9
5. Industries that reported establishments in the South in 1939 but none in 1947...... 2
6. Industries with establishments in the South both in 1939 and in 1947 but no data available on number of production workers (other than in main group totals)
   (a) Number of establishments increased.. 19
   (b) Number of establishments decreased.. 1
   (c) Number of establishments unchanged 5
   —
   Total 25
   —
   Total number of industries.............. 120

Table 106

Changes in Position of the South in the Sixteen Iron and Steel Processing and Fabricating Industry Groups That Rank Highest as Steel Consumers, 1939-1947

Rank in 1947 as steel users in United States	Industry	Per cent increase in South	Per cent South of United States 1939	1947
1	Structural metal products..................	155.1	10.7	13.2
2	Motor vehicles*...........................			1.9
3	Miscellaneous primary metal products.......	271.0	0.3	0.6
4	Tin cans and other tinware................	47.1	6.7	7.1
5	Miscellaneous fabricated metal products.....	109.0	2.5	2.6
6	Metal stamping and coating...............	71.7	2.0	1.7
7	Tractors and farm machinery..............	392.1	1.9	4.0
8	Railroad equipment*......................			1.9
9	Electrical machinery (selected).............	945.5	0.3	1.1
10	Service and household equipment...........	153.0	1.9	1.8
11	Heating and plumbing equipment...........	40.6	9.9	8.6
12	Construction and mining machinery........	106.3	21.6	18.4
13	Fabricated wire products..................	145.4	1.6	2.5
14	General industrial machinery..............	314.8	2.3	4.3
15	Cutlery, hand tools and hardware..........	46.4	1.0	0.8
16	Ship and boatbuilding and repairing........	355.0	9.3	22.1

*In 1939 motor vehicles, railroad and street railway cars, and motorcycles and bicycles were combined to get significant figures. For the combined industries the percent increase was 353.9 and the South's percent of the United States was 1.2 in 1939 and 2.9 in 1947.

Source: Derived from Table 92 (Chapter XX) and Tables 100 and 101 (Chapter XXI).

Since data on the number of production workers is available for the 73 industries in the first group, the relationship between the relative position of the South in these industries and the changes that have taken place can be analyzed in the manner indicated by Tables 107 and 108.

Evidence of improvement in the position held by the iron and steel processing and fabricating industries of the South predominates in the data just presented. Of the 73 industries for which data on employment in the South was available, 53 had increases that were great enough compared with the increases in the nation as a whole to bring about a strengthening of the South's relative position. In addi-

tion, 11 industries that were not represented in the South in 1939 had establishments in the region in 1947. These include screw machine products, tractors, electrical welding apparatus, electrical industrial apparatus, insulated wire and cable, watches and clocks, dental equipment and supplies, silverware, needles and pins, jewelry and instrument cases, and small arms. Furthermore, 19 of the 25 industries, for which the number of establishments in 1939 and 1947 was the only information available, had more establishments in 1947 than in 1939.

On the unfavorable side, there were 19 industries in which the South lost in relative position as measured in terms of percentages of the total number of wage earners in the

Table 107

Change in Relative Position of the South in 73 Iron and Steel Processing Industries Between 1939 and 1947, as Measured in Terms of Number of Production Workers

		Number of industries		
Relative position of the industry (South's per cent of United States), 1939		South's per cent of United States		
	Total	Increased	Decreased	Unchanged
15 per cent or more	5	1	4	
10 per cent to 14.9 per cent	6	4	2	
5 per cent to 9.9 per cent	16	11	5	
1 per cent to 4.9 per cent	31	23	8	
Less than one per cent but above 0	15	14	..	1
Total	73	53	19	1

Source: *Census of Manufactures, 1947* and special tabulation by the Bureau of the Census.

Table 108

Size of Percentage Changes in Number of Production Workers in the South, 1939-1947, in 73 Iron and Steel Processing Industries

		Number of industries				
Percent change in number of production workers in the South		Industries classified by South's per cent of U. S.				
	Total	Less than 1%	1% — 4.9%	5% — 9.9%	10% — 14.9%	15% and over
200 per cent increase and over	33	13	16	4	..	..
100 per cent to 199 per cent increase	18	2	8	4	3	1
75 per cent to 99 per cent increase	4	..	1	1	1	1
50 per cent to 74 per cent increase	5	..	2	1	1	1
25 per cent to 49 per cent increase	7	..	1	3	1	2
0.1 per cent to 24 per cent increase	2	..	2	..	..	..
Decrease	4	..	1	3	..	..
Total	73	15	31	16	6	5

Source: Calculated from *Census of Manufactures, 1939; 1947.*

industry. In only four cases was the lower relative position due to an absolute decrease. The increases of the number of production workers in the South in the other 15 industries were not large enough to maintain the region's position in the nation. Also, two industries which had plants in the South in 1939 were not represented in 1947, and, of the industries for which there was no information on production workers, there were decreases in the number of establishments in one industry and no gains in five others. On the whole, these unfavorable changes were greatly outweighed by the favorable. Perhaps the most serious aspect of the unfavorable changes was the fact that the South lost in relative position in several of the industries in which it had attained the strongest place. Among these industries were gray iron foundries; transportation equipment, n.e.c.; mattresses and bed springs; and heating and cooking apparatus.

The summary of the percentages of change in production workers given in Table 108 indicates a strong tendency toward very large percentages of increase, since 51 of the 73 industries had increases of more than 100 per cent. Optimism created by these figures should be tempered by the fact that in 15 of these industries the South's share in the national total in 1939 was less than 1.0 per cent, and in 24 more the share was from 1.0 per cent to 5.0 per cent. This means that the numbers of production workers in many of the industries with large percentage increases were small and that the increases in terms of employees or dollars of value were not great. Still quite sizable increases are shown for the more important industries of the region. Among the more important industries with large percentage increases were oil-field machinery; ship and boat building and repairing; truck trailers; automobile trailers; metal barrels, drums and pails; boiler shop products; structural and ornamental products; woodworking machinery; textile machinery; signs and advertising displays; sheet metal works; venetian blinds; partitions and fixtures; and transportation equipment.

The changes during the eight-year period re-

sulted in a decided increase in the number of processing and fabricating industries which provided employment to large numbers of production workers. In 1939, there was only one industry, gray iron foundries, that employed more than 10,000 workers. In 1947, by the addition of structural and ornamental products, oilfield machinery and tools, ship and boat building, and air craft, there were five in this size class. Also, in 1939, there were 17 industries which employed from 1,000 to 9,999 production workers and, in 1947, this number had been increased to 32.

Changes in the Years Between 1939 and 1947

No census of manufactures was taken between 1939 and 1947 and, consequently, detailed figures are not available for any intervening year that are comparable to those which form the basis of the preceding sections. Many reports on particular industries were made during the war years and several have been published, but comprehensive statistics that permit comparison of the industries in the South with the United States totals are scarce, and none are entirely satisfactory. Moreover, space does not permit a detailed analysis of the year-to-year changes, and the estimates of employment prepared by the United States Bureau of Labor Statistics will be sufficient to indicate the more important tendencies. Before further explanation is made, one qualification on the statistics should be pointed out—that the employment figures are for main industry groups and follow the original classification used in the 1939 Census of Manufactures. Consequently, it is not possible to include all the industries that have been considered as comprising the iron and steel processing and fabricating industries. Furthermore, certain industries are included, particularly blast furnaces and steel works and rolling mills, that have not been considered as part of the processing and fabricating group. As a result, the data and the observations offered in Table 109 and the following paragraphs lack much in precision.

The statistics in Table 109 reflect the high level of activity attained during the war years, the reductions that came in 1945 and 1946, and the return to somewhat higher levels in 1947. Compared with 1939, the wartime increases in four of the iron and steel industry classes—iron and steel, electrical machinery, machinery except electrical, and transportation equipment— were much more pronounced than the increases in total manufacturing. By far the most spectacular was the record of transportation equipment. The tremendous expansion in shipbuilding, a large proportion of which was located along the Atlantic and Gulf Coasts of the South, accounts for much of the increased employment. A second big factor was the emphasis on the building and modification of

aircraft. After 1944, a sharp decline in employment in transportation equipment plants is shown which indicates the purely war character of much of the expansion. Still, it is significant that employment remained in 1946 and 1947 at levels far above that of 1939. The two machinery classifications showed more moderate, but still quite substantial increases, during the war and retained the gains well in the postwar years. The iron and steel group includes the basic industries of blast furnaces and steel works. Employment in this group was more than double the 1939 figure in 1943 and 1944 and remained in 1947 almost 50 per cent above 1939. Of the groups shown in Table 109, automobiles received the smallest stimulation from the war effort, but, in 1947, had a percentage

Table 109

Estimated Employment in All Manufacturing and in the Iron and Steel Industries in the South, 1939 and 1947

Industry	July-Sept. (Avg.) 1939	1943 (Avg.)	1944 (Avg.)	1945 (Avg.)	1946 (Avg.)	Jan.-June (Avg.) 1947
Estimated number of employees						
All manufacturing	1,444,645	2,397,701	2,396,747	2,129,610	1,960,175	2,048,010
Iron and steel industries						
Iron and steel group	69,713	139,485	149,767	123,507	92,203	103,813
Electrical machinery	2,393	5,091	9,355	9,244	5,853	10,711
Machinery except electrical	26,853	59,792	68,147	68,096	58,967	61,740
Transportation equipment	6,845	416,497	431,069	256,508	60,656	65,816
Automobiles	7,512	7,149	9,589	9,107	9,332	10,612
Total iron and steel	113,316	628,014	667,927	466,462	227,011	252,692
Per cent South of United States						
All manufacturing	14.24	13.80	14.01	13.92	13.64	13.31
Iron and steel industries						
Iron and steel group	6.06	6.85	7.43	6.74	5.58	5.66
Electrical machinery	0.67	0.56	0.97	1.10	0.87	1.42
Machinery except electrical	3.93	3.77	4.39	4.79	4.34	4.06
Transportation equipment	3.47	14.11	14.87	13.93	9.75	11.06
Automobiles	1.86	0.85	1.09	1.22	1.14	1.11
Total iron and steel	4.06	7.54	8.04	6.99	4.43	4.47
Per cent of 1939						
All manufacturing	100.0	166.0	165.9	147.4	135.7	141.8
Iron and steel industries						
Iron and steel group	100.0	200.1	214.8	177.2	132.3	148.9
Electrical machinery	100.0	212.8	390.9	386.3	244.6	447.6
Machinery except electrical	100.0	222.7	253.8	253.6	219.6	229.9
Transportation equipment	100.0	6,084.7	6,297.6	3,747.4	886.1	961.5
Automobiles	100.0	95.2	127.6	121.2	124.2	141.3
Total iron and steel	100.0	554.2	589.4	411.6	200.3	223.0

Source: U. S. Bureau of Labor Statistics with supplements from the Atlanta Regional Office of the Bureau of Labor Statistics and estimates by Bureau of Business Research.

gain over 1939 that was almost as great as that of the iron and steel group.

While the South had large wartime increases in the industries covered by this chapter, decided increases in the South's share in the national totals occurred only in transportation equipment. A large part of the increases in that classification was transitory. The 1944 figures also show gains over 1939 in the South's relative position in the iron and steel group and in electrical machinery and machinery other than electrical, but show decreases in automobiles and in all manufacturing. In general, it can be concluded that the war effort had relatively little effect on increasing the South's share in the processing and fabricating industries, except in transportation equipment. This statement, however, should not be interpreted as discounting the importance of the large absolute gains that were made.

Effect of the War Facilities Expansion

During the war, over 3.8 billion dollars was expended in the South on the expansion of war facilities in the manufacturing field. Of this, three billion dollars was financed by the Federal government and 821 million dollars came from other sources. A discussion of the changes that occurred between 1939 and 1947 would

not be complete unless consideration was given to the possible effects of this huge expansion program on the iron and steel industries of the region. To provide a background for discussion, the statistics on the value of the projects are given in Table 110.

The report of the National Planning Association on the disposal of southern war plants holds that there was no disposal problem with regard to privately financed war facilities because "they were built with a twofold purpose, (a) to meet a war demand and (b) to be useful in peacetime activity."[3] The inquiries made in connection with the present study confirm this conclusion and indicate that the privately financed facilities have been additions to the peacetime facilities. On the other hand, difficulty was encountered in finding peacetime uses for many of the government financed projects. The kind of financing, therefore, has considerable interest in a study of the lasting effects of the war expansion.

As three of the large programs, aircraft, ship construction, and ordnance, were largely federally financed, large shrinkages in activity in these lines were logical. In iron and steel, machinery, and electrical equipment, a sub-

[3] Frederick L. Deming and Weldon A. Stein, *Disposal of Southern War Plants*, p. 3.

Table 110

Manufacturing Facilities Expansion in the South, Value of Projects Initiated, July 1940-June 1945 (in million dollars)

Industry	Total value of projects			Construction value	Equipment value
	Total	Federally financed	Non-federally financed		
Iron and steel	155.6	87.9	67.8	58.3	97.3
Machinery and electrical equipment	40.3	25.7	14.6	12.9	27.4
Aircraft	355.1	333.9	21.2	230.9	124.4
Ship construction	297.7	267.3	30.4	179.5	118.2
Total iron and steel	848.7	714.8	134.0	481.4	367.3
Ordnance	1,192.0	1,158.3	33.7	734.5	457.5
Nonferrous metals	391.2	294.8	96.4	154.4	236.8
Chemicals	1,148.2	791.7	356.5	223.4	924.8
Food processing	59.8	14.0	45.8	31.3	28.5
Other manufacturing	231.4	77.2	154.2	63.6	167.8
Total all manufacturing	3,871.3	3,050.8	820.5	1,688.6	2,182.7

Source: Frederick L. Deming and Weldon A. Stein, *Disposal of Southern War Plants.*

stantial proportion of the financing was classi-fied as nonfederal. It is reasonable to expect that most of these installations have had a con-tinuing use. The industries that are not di-rectly concerned with iron and steel—nonfer-rous metals, chemicals, food processing, and other manufacturing—received strong support from private capital, and the wartime expan-sion in these industries probably had much greater effect in building up the permanent manufacturing equipment of the region than did the spectacular expenditures for aircraft, shipbuilding, and ordnance.

While substantial sums were invested in plants that represented permanent additions to the iron and steel processing and fabricating facilities of the South, it would seem that the expenditures on projects in these lines were so much greater in other sections of the United States that the war facilities expansion program did little to improve the relative position of the South. A big expansion did take place in ship-building and aircraft and some of the increased capacity continued in use, but the shrinkage in these lines and in ordnance was great. The war program, no doubt, had the effect of giving a large number of workers and enterprises ex-perience in metalworking operations, and in

this way may have created conditions favorable to the growth of processing and fabricating plants.

Changes in Location Within the South

An elaborate analysis of changes in location within the South will not be attempted. While a great mass of detailed information is avail-able on plants located in the South, differences in classifications and difficulties of identifica-tion of establishments at different points of time make a complete analysis a major task. The data from the 1947 *Census of Manufac-tures* served as the basis for the discussion in Chapter XX, but the detailed state and county industry statistics for 1939 have not been re-tabulated according to the new code and so are not directly comparable to the 1947 figures. In the present section, the discussion will be based primarily on two sets of data. The first consists of the state estimates of employment of the Bureau of Labor Statistics which were used in previous discussions of changes in em-ployment in the South. The second group of statistics was derived from the county tables giving the number of enterprises by industry group as published in the reports of both the

Table 111

Employment in the Iron and Steel Fabricating Industries in the Southern States,
1939, 1944, and 1947

State	Estimated number of employees			Rank in South		
	1939 (Average July-Sept.)	1944	1947 (Average Jan.-June)	1939	1944	1947
North Carolina	4,132	42,472	14,683	6	8	6
South Carolina	1,230	4,247	2,733	9	10	11
Georgia	10,186	79,480	15,835	4	3	5
Florida	3,636	62,195	10,797	8	4	7
Tennessee	19,775	55,695	31,329	3	6	3
Alabama	38,756	98,546	60,871	1	2	2
Mississippi	1,143	17,252	9,701	10	9	9
Arkansas	583	826	2,837	11	11	10
Louisiana	4,112	56,137	16,736	7	5	4
Oklahoma	5,763*	52,277	10,770	5	7	8
Texas	24,000	198,800	76,400	2	1	1

*Estimated by the Bureau of Business Research, University of Alabama.

Source: U. S. Department of Labor, *Estimates of Employment in Manufacturing Industries, by State, 1943-1946,* supplemented by special reports from the Atlanta Regional Office, Bureau of Labor Statistics, and cooperating state agencies.

1939 and the 1947 *Census of Manufactures.* Because of differences in the systems of classification, the data for the two years cannot be made strictly comparable, but it was felt that approximate comparability could be obtained by a careful selection and combination of industry groups in the two years.

The emphasis during the war on such operations as shipbuilding, airplane manufacture and modification, and ordnance manufacture quite clearly changed the location pattern in the South. If the five industry groups that include iron and steel and their products, electrical machinery, machinery other than electrical, transportation equipment, and automobiles are taken to represent the iron and steel

fabricating industries, there were six states that had larger percentages of increase in employment during the war years than had the South as a whole. These were Georgia, Florida, Mississippi, Louisiana, Oklahoma, and Texas. As a result, these states gained during the war years in relative position in the region. In 1939, Texas ranked as the second state in employment in the iron and steel industries, but, in 1944, having replaced Alabama, it was first. Georgia advanced from fourth place among the southern states to third; Florida from eighth to fourth place; Louisiana from seventh to fifth place; and Mississippi from tenth to ninth place. On the other hand, Alabama, Tennessee, and North Carolina dropped into lower ranks

Table 112

Number of Counties in the Southern States
Classified by the Number of Establishments in the Iron and Steel Industries, 1939 and 1947

State	Number of counties with							Total
	1 or 2 estab.	3 to 7 estab.	8 to 15 estab.	16 to 25 estab.	26 to 35 estab.	36 to 49 estab.	50 and more estab.	
1939*								
North Carolina	20	12	1	1	2	0	0	36
South Carolina	5	4	3	0	0	0	0	12
Georgia	19	7	3	0	0	0	1	30
Florida	17	7	1	2	1	0	0	28
Tennessee	21	6	0	1	2	0	1	31
Alabama	17	5	2	1	0	0	1	26
Mississippi	15	8	0	0	0	0	0	23
Arkansas	18	4	0	0	0	0	0	22
Louisiana	18	8	0	1	0	0	1	28
Oklahoma	11	13	0	0	0	1	1	26
Texas	54	19	6	1	2	1	2	85
Total South	215	93	16	7	7	2	7	347
1947**								
North Carolina	30	15	2	3	0	1	1	52
South Carolina	14	3	4	0	0	0	0	21
Georgia	29	10	3	3	0	0	1	46
Florida	18	6	5	1	1	2	1	34
Tennessee	22	6	1	0	1	0	3	33
Alabama	14	6	2	3	0	0	1	26
Mississippi	20	6	2	1	0	0	0	29
Arkansas	18	3	0	2	0	0	0	23
Louisiana	10	11	1	2	0	0	1	25
Oklahoma	22	6	2	0	0	0	2	32
Texas	56	14	8	3	1	0	4	86
Total South	253	86	30	18	3	3	14	407

*In 1939, the census industry groups, 14, 16, 17, 18, and 19 were considered as constituting the iron and steel industries.

**In 1947, the census industry groups, 33, 34, 35, 36, 37, and 38 were considered as constituting the iron and steel industries.

Source: *Census of Manufactures, 1939; 1947.*

among the eleven states in 1944 than they occupied in 1939.

The employment estimates for 1947, however, indicate that with the closing or reduction of operations of the plants most directly connected with the war, there was a considerable tendency to return to the prewar pattern. Tennessee, which had held third place in the South in 1939 but dropped to sixth in 1947, ranked again as the third state in employment in the iron and steel processing and fabricating industries in 1947. North Carolina, which had lost position, also returned to its prewar rank—sixth—and Georgia dropped back from its wartime position as third state in the region to fifth. Still, there was not a complete return to the prewar status quo. For one thing, the number of employees in the several states was much larger in 1947 than in 1939. Then, too, Texas retained its position as the top-ranking state, and Alabama remained in second place. Louisiana moved from a wartime rank of fifth to fourth in 1947, and Florida and Mississippi ranked higher in 1947 than in 1939. These changes indicate that the changes during the period resulted in strengthening the positions of Florida and the states of Texas, Louisiana, and Mississippi. This suggests a development of the industry to the South and West.

In an attempt to throw some light on the nature of changes in areas smaller than states, the statistics presented in Table 112 were compiled. Care was taken to get combinations of groups in each year that give approximations to the total of all iron and steel fabricating industries, but as indicated previously, the figures for 1939 and 1947 are not strictly comparable and caution must be used in drawing conclusions. These data were also used in the preparation of Maps 20 and 21 which show the location of establishments of the iron and steel industries in 1939 and 1947.

There apparently was some increase between 1939 and 1947 in the number of counties in the South which had at least one establishment of the iron and steel industries, but the increase is quite modest. A more detailed examination indicates a considerable shifting in the coun-

ties which had few establishments—more specifically in the class with one or two establishments and in the class with three to seven establishments. There were 73 counties in the South in which establishments were reported in 1939 but none in 1947. On the other hand, there were 136 counties that are included in 1947 but not in 1939. These were in counties with seven establishments or fewer. On the other hand, no county that was reported as having eight or more establishments in 1939 was excluded in 1947 as having no establishments, and all of the counties that were reported as having eight or more establishments in 1947 are included in 1939 list as having at least one establishmen. Thus, there was a considerable stability in the counties which had several establishments in the industry.

There seems to have been a considerable tendency for counties to increase the number of establishments. In all, there were 156 counties that were in the same class in 1939 and 1947 with regard to the number of establishments; 25 counties that dropped to a lower class in 1947 than in 1939; and 90 counties that increased the number of establishments sufficiently to move into a higher class in 1947. In 1947, there were 38 counties which reported 16 or more establishments in the iron and steel industries. These, with the number of establishments in 1939 and 1947, are listed below.

| | | Number of establishments | |
County	State	1939	1947
Harris	Texas	132	275
Dallas	Texas	89	242
Jefferson	Alabama	91	148
Tulsa	Oklahoma	77	144
Fulton	Georgia	65	120
Tarrant	Texas	44	89
Orleans	Louisiana	51	86
Dade	Florida	34	84
Hamilton	Tennessee	52	76
Oklahoma	Oklahoma	49	75
Shelby	Tennessee	33	73
Bexar	Texas	32	68
Davidson	Tennessee	31	52
Mecklenburg	North Carolina	27	52
Duval	Florida	22	49
Hillsborough	Florida	21	39

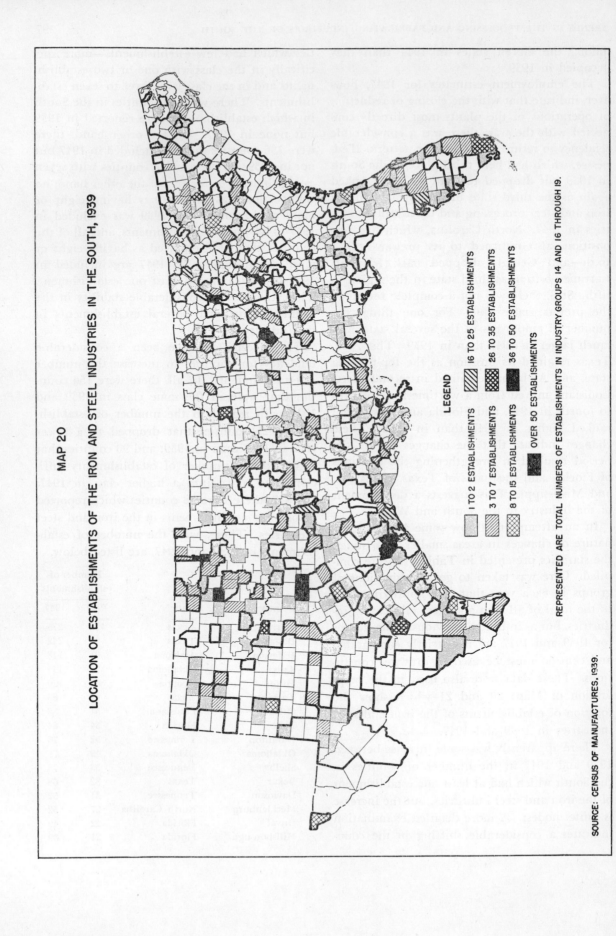

MAP 20

LOCATION OF ESTABLISHMENTS OF THE IRON AND STEEL INDUSTRIES IN THE SOUTH, 1939

LEGEND

	1 TO 2 ESTABLISHMENTS	16 TO 25 ESTABLISHMENTS
	3 TO 7 ESTABLISHMENTS	26 TO 35 ESTABLISHMENTS
	8 TO 15 ESTABLISHMENTS	36 TO 50 ESTABLISHMENTS
		OVER 50 ESTABLISHMENTS

REPRESENTED ARE TOTAL NUMBERS OF ESTABLISHMENTS IN INDUSTRY GROUPS 14 AND 16 THROUGH 19.

SOURCE: CENSUS OF MANUFACTURES, 1939.

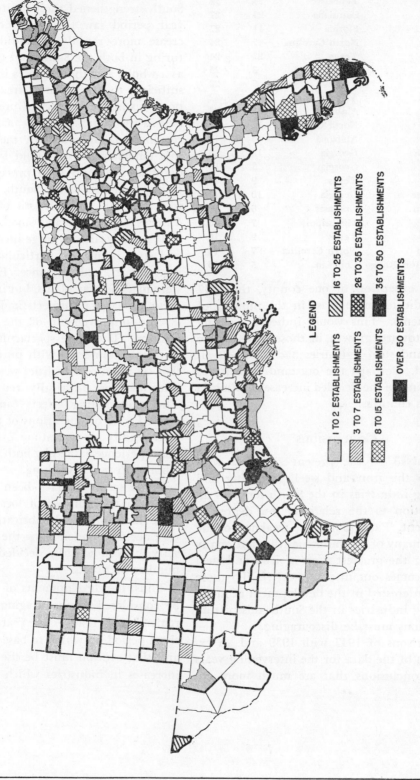

MAP 21

LOCATION OF ESTABLISHMENTS OF THE IRON AND STEEL INDUSTRIES IN THE SOUTH, 1947

LEGEND

1 TO 2 ESTABLISHMENTS

3 TO 7 ESTABLISHMENTS

8 TO 15 ESTABLISHMENTS

16 TO 25 ESTABLISHMENTS

26 TO 35 ESTABLISHMENTS

36 TO 50 ESTABLISHMENTS

OVER 50 ESTABLISHMENTS

REPRESENTED ARE TOTAL NUMBERS OF ESTABLISHMENTS IN INDUSTRY GROUPS 33 THROUGH 38.

SOURCE: CENSUS OF MANUFACTURES, 1947.

Guilford	North Carolina	31	39
Jefferson	Texas	24	33
Knox	Tennessee	25	32
Caddo	Louisiana	23	27
Pinellas	Florida	11	27
Gaston	North Carolina	17	24
Wichita	Texas	27	24
Orange	Florida	3	23
Pulaski	Arkansas	6	23
Calhoun	Alabama	13	22
Mobile	Alabama	17	22
Forsyth	North Carolina	12	22
Etowah	Alabama	14	19
Chatham	Georgia	12	19
DeKalb	Georgia	3	19
El Paso	Texas	9	18
Muscogee	Georgia	10	17
Sebastian	Arkansas	6	16
Hinds	Mississippi	7	16
Nueces	Texas	9	16
Catawba	North Carolina	7	16
East Baton Rouge	Louisiana	5	16

With the exception of one county, the 1947 figures indicate an increase in the number of establishments. This would indicate a strong tendency toward growth in those areas where the iron and steel industries had become well established. Perhaps the outstanding features brought out are the decided increases in Florida and Texas counties.

Conclusions

An analysis of the present situation with respect to the iron and steel processing and fabricating industries in the South tends to direct attention to the relatively low degree of development. Particularly, the weakness of the region in many of the industries that nationally are among the greatest users of iron and steel products comes out in strong relief. To those who are interested in the development of metal fabricating industries in the South, this picture of conditions must be discouraging.

Comparisons of 1947 with 1939 and an examination of the data for the intervening years support conclusions that are much more en-

couraging. On the whole, the iron and steel processing and fabricating industries in the South strengthened their positions. The eight-year period saw this group of industries increase more rapidly than did total manufacturing in both the South and the United States as a whole, and the increases in the South were sufficient to bring about strengthened relative positions in the number of production workers and in the value added by manufacture in the region as compared with the nation. While this tendency did not hold for all of the individual iron and steel processing and fabricating industries of the South, large percentage increases were characteristic of most of the industries both large and small.

The war years saw large increases in the iron and steel industries, particularly in shipbuilding, aircraft, and ordnance. Huge investments were made in war plants, but it is doubtful that these special war projects had much influence on the improvement of the South's relative position. The more spectacular increases were so closely connected with purely war demands that cessation of hostilities was followed by discontinued or drastically reduced operations. The most lasting effects came from the increased scale of operations of plants that could turn readily to peace-time products and from the experience gained by both management and labor with metal working.

There seems to have been a significant increase in the number of locations which had some kind of metal fabricating plant and a very decided tendency for the larger centers of activity to show quite decided increases in the number of plants.

Thus, the developments of recent years may be considered as encouraging, but it must be remembered that eight years is a relatively short period on which to base a study of trends and that caution must be used in interpreting increases in industries which still are small.

CHAPTER XXII

MOVEMENTS OF IRON AND STEEL IN THE SOUTH

One of the approaches to a study of the market for a commodity or group of commodities in a given area is to examine the information on the quantities of the products under study that move into and away from the area and to attempt to learn as much as possible about the movements that take place within the boundaries of the area. This is the task to which this chapter addresses itself rather than to an analysis of freight rates and transportation facilities as factors in determining the limits of market areas or the location of fabricating plants. It is planned as a step in the process of describing the market for iron and steel in the South and of providing a basis for a quantity evaluation of the size of the market. It should, of course, provide a basis for a future discussion of the relationship of transportation to industrial development.

Background of Movements in the South

To provide a background for the discussion of the quantitative data on iron and steel movements, some of the more important facts concerning the following topics will be presented.

1. The iron and steel centers competing for the southern market
2. The transportation facilities used in iron and steel movements in the South
3. Factors influencing ability of the several producing centers to reach southern markets
4. Distribution points in the South for iron and steel.

Following the discussion of these four preliminary topics, the statistics of the movements of the several types of iron and steel products will be examined.

THE IRON AND STEEL CENTERS COMPETING FOR THE SOUTHERN MARKET

Interest in this study quite naturally centers on southern iron and steel plants, and this directs attention immediately to Birmingham and Gadsden, Alabama. The Atlantic Steel Company at Atlanta, Georgia, and the Sheffield Steel Company's plant at Houston, Texas, are other points of origin of steel and steel products within the South. The Atlanta plant is small and produces a limited range of shapes and forms. While the Houston plant is much larger and has a larger number of products, it too represents only a relatively small percentage of the total capacity of the South.

Birmingham is located near the geographic center of the southern market area as set up in this study. In an arc around the area are a number of the most important iron and steel producing centers of the nation. Most important of these are Sparrow's Point, Maryland; Bethlehem, Pennsylvania; Pittsburgh, Pennsylvania; Chicago, Illinois; and Pueblo, Colorado. In addition, consideration must be given to the Ohio River Valley plants such as those at Wheeling and Wierton, West Virginia; Stuebenville and Middletown, Ohio; Ashland, Kentucky; and the plants of the Leclede Steel Company and the Granite City Steel Company near St. Louis. That producers of iron and steel companies have an interest in the southern market is evidenced by the fact that sales offices or sales representatives in one or more of 31 southern cities are maintained by some 58 of the companies that are listed in the 1948 *Directory of Iron and Steel Works of the United States and Canada* and that do not have plants in the South.

A number of factors[1] account for the ability of plants located outside the region to enter the market. In some portions of the area, trans-

---

[1] For a discussion of factors controlling the length of haul of steel, see Board of Investigation and Research, *The Economics of Iron and Steel Transportation,* p. 69.

portation costs are lower from an outside point than from a southern plant. In Chapter X, the discussion of the capacity of the southern basic iron and steel industry to produce the various kinds of iron and steel mill products showed that many important products are not produced in the South. Until recently, all the steel pipe and tubes and the cold rolled sheets and bars, many of the various kinds or sizes of plates and structural shapes, and all the alloy and stainless steel products had to come from outside the region, and even today the South's capacity to produce these products is either non-existent or very limited. Naturally, the outside plants have cultivated the market. Another important factor which has influenced greatly the movements of steel has been the price policies followed by the steel industry. The discussion of this subject, however, is postponed to a later chapter.

TRANSPORTATION FACILITIES USED IN IRON AND STEEL MOVEMENTS

It is safe to assume that most of the bulk shipments of iron and steel, from basic iron and steel plants to their customers, are by rail. The Interstate Commerce Commission publishes statistics on the tons of revenue freight originated and terminated by classes of commodities and by states. These data provide the basis for determining the size of the net movements to, or from, the South for the various classes of iron and steel products. These tabulations, however, do not permit the tracing of shipments from the point of origin to destination. In other words, they do not show where steel terminated in a southern state had its origin or where the steel originated in a particular state was destined to be terminated. In 1939, the Board of Investigation and Research conducted a *Carload Traffic Survey* and later published an analysis of its findings with respect to iron and steel in its report, *The Economics of Iron and Steel Transportation*. In the case of cast iron pipe, useful estimates of the volume and character of movements are provided by *Transportation Factors in the Location of the Cast Iron Pipe Industry*, a pub-

lication of the United States Department of Commerce.

While the rail movements tend to dominate, water movements of iron and steel and their products into, and away from, the South are important. These movements may be divided into four classes: (1) by barge down the Ohio River and the Mississippi River and by the Intracoastal Canal to Texas points; (2) by barge down the Warrior-Tombigbee River waterway and by the Intracoastal Canal to New Orleans and Texas points; (3) coastwise shipments to, and from, the South Atlantic and Gulf ports of the South; and (4) foreign exports from southern ports. The annual reports of the Chief of Engineers, United States Army, are the source of information on these movements.

Movements by truck form the third, and final, general type of transportation. There is no source of quantitative data, and knowledge of what occurs in this area is very general in character. It is frequently asserted that the iron and steel companies discriminate against trucks and in favor of railroads. Steel plants probably are not equipped to handle the loading of large quantities of iron or steel products by trucks, but there is at least one case where the establishment of a very low freight rate on large quantity shipments presumably was due to truck competition. The Board of Investigation and Research[2] concludes that "except in localities where absence of railroads requires heavy products to move by highways, such as oil fields of the Southwest, trucks are used for lighter types of iron and steel" and "the primary importance of truck deliveries to the ordinary steel buyer is convenience rather than cost." In an appendix[3] to its report, the Board summarizes the replies of members of the American Steel Warehouse Association concerning movements of steel by truck in the first quarter of 1943. None of the replies is from a southern point. With one exception, the replies have to do with shipments from the ware-

[2] *Economics of Iron and Steel Transportation*, p. 48.
[3] *Economics of Iron and Steel Transportation*, pp. 173-174.

houses (or deliveries to customers) rather than receipts from steel plants. For deliveries, however, trucks account for large percentages of the totals, particularly in the larger cities. If this can be assumed to apply to the South, deliveries from warehouses in the South to customers in the South would not change the net balance of movements into, or out of, the region. However, there probably are deliveries that cross the region's borders from warehouses in the North and East to customers in the South, or vice versa. Since the South is a deficit area for steel and steel products, a considerable quantity probably entered the region in the form of truck deliveries from warehouses outside the area. No basis for making an estimate of the quantities involved has been found.

FACTORS INFLUENCING ABILITY OF THE SEVERAL CENTERS TO REACH SOUTHERN MARKETS

While a study of comparative freight rates alone cannot delineate the market areas that naturally fall to each of the several producing centers, such a study provides a convenient approach to an analysis of the comparative positions of the competitors for the market. With the aid of the Birmingham Traffic Association, the railroad freight rates on iron and steel articles were determined from various shipping points to selected destinations. The shipping points used were Birmingham, Sparrow's Point, Bethlehem, Pittsburgh, Chicago, and Minnequa (Pueblo) Colorado. Most of the destination points were selected because they were near the place where the rates from Birmingham and a competing location were equal. Map 22 presents these data and indicates the area[4] in which Birmingham has a rail rate advantage over the five important centers mentioned. It also indicates, at the various destinations, which of the five is the southern city's closest competitor.

While sharp boundaries should not be drawn, limits of the area in which Birmingham has an advantage over the other five extend from

[4] The situation shown by Map 22 corresponds closely to that presented in *Economics of Iron and Steel Transportation,* p. 149.

Charleston, South Carolina, northward into North Carolina around Wadesboro or Rockingham; then range to the northwest across North Carolina into northeastern Tennessee, between Elizabethtown and Bristol, and across the southwest tip of Virginia and eastern Kentucky to points just south of Lexington and Louisville. From there, the breaking points in rates occur just south of the Ohio River in Kentucky and along the northern boundary of Arkansas. The comparative rates indicate that Birmingham has a comparative advantage in Oklahoma only in the southeastern corner, but in Texas its advantage extends to points west of Dallas and Fort Worth, Waco and San Antonio. In the eastern part of the area to a point near Bristol, Tennessee, Birmingham's nearest competitor is Sparrow's Point. Pittsburgh occupies that position in only a small segment in eastern Kentucky. From Lexington, Kentucky, to Oklahoma, Chicago is in the competitive position and Minnequa, in Texas.

Having described the situation with respect to the comparative freight rates from Birmingham and five of the other important steel centers, it is important immediately to point out the factors which modify and, in fact, often cancel the effects of a comparative advantage in rail rates. In the first place, there are a number of other originating points for steel shipments. From the point of view of the Birmingham and Gadsden plants, the Atlantic Steel Company offers competition on some kinds of products to the East and the Sheffield Steel Company's plant at Houston competes for markets in Texas and Louisiana. The Ohio River Valley plants should be in position to reach farther to the South in Kentucky than Pittsburgh or Chicago reach, and the plants near St. Louis must be able to market their products to an advantage in Western Tennessee and in much of Arkansas.

Transportation by water constitutes another modifying factor. The Pittsburgh and Ohio River plants can barge their products to Memphis, New Orleans, and Houston and can distribute from warehouses located at these cities. By coastwise shipments, Sparrow's Point can

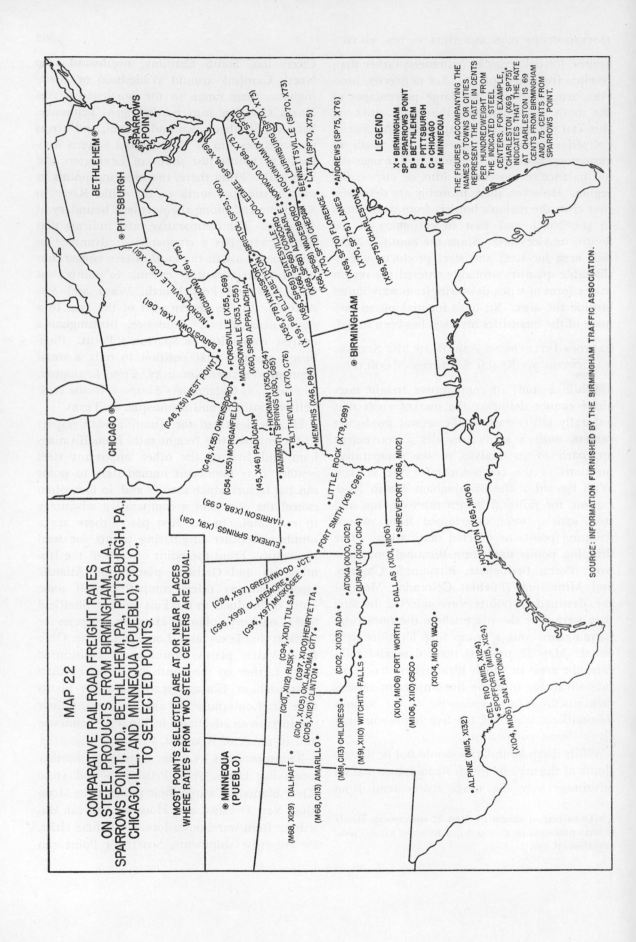

MAP 22

COMPARATIVE RAILROAD FREIGHT RATES
ON STEEL PRODUCTS FROM BIRMINGHAM, ALA.,
SPARROWS POINT, MD., BETHLEHEM, PA., PITTSBURGH, PA.,
CHICAGO, ILL., AND MINNEQUA (PUEBLO), COLO.,
TO SELECTED POINTS.

MOST POINTS SELECTED ARE AT OR NEAR PLACES
WHERE RATES FROM TWO STEEL CENTERS ARE EQUAL.

LEGEND

X = BIRMINGHAM
SP = SPARROWS POINT
B = BETHLEHEM
P = PITTSBURGH
C = CHICAGO
M = MINNEQUA

THE FIGURES ACCOMPANYING THE
NAMES OF TOWNS OR CITIES
REPRESENT THE RATE IN CENTS
PER HUNDREDWEIGHT FROM
THE INDICATED STEEL
CENTERS. FOR EXAMPLE,
"CHARLESTON (X69, SP75)"
INDICATES THAT THE RATE
AT CHARLESTON IS 69
CENTS FROM BIRMINGHAM
AND 75 CENTS FROM
SPARROWS POINT.

SOURCE: INFORMATION FURNISHED BY THE BIRMINGHAM TRAFFIC ASSOCIATION.

reach such Atlantic coast points as Wilmington, North Carolina; Charleston, South Carolina; Savannah, Georgia; Jacksonville and Miami, Florida as well as Houston, Texas. The Board of Investigation and Research points out[5] that barge shipments are largely for stock because river movements are not fast enough to meet small-lot buying for early delivery. The average consumer of steel is not in position to handle the large quantities that steel producers claim must be hauled to make operations of their barges economical. This situation offsets the lower cost of water transportation and limits the use of barge shipments unless the steel mill company owns and operates its own barges and warehouses at the points of destination. This is the case with some of the larger producers.

The privileges extended to shippers by the railroad companies may enable steel from a producer to reach points that would not seem possible under the standard rates. One example is the granting of a special rate on large quantity shipments. Another is the fabrication-in-transit privileges[6] by which fabricators of structural steel may buy steel at a mill and move it to the point of final use under a through rate but can stop it at an intermediate point for fabrication without losing the privilege of the through rate—a rate lower than the sum of the separate rates for the two hauls. Railways require only equivalents if the way bills are not older than one year. The way bills may be accumulated and applied as the fabricator chooses. The result is, that under certain circumstances, fabricators can practically nullify the limiting effects that freight rates ordinarily would have on the distances steel can be moved.

The policies of the selling company constitute still another modifying element. A large corporation with several plants may build each of the plants to produce certain specialized products. At the same time, the corporation may wish to offer its customers a full line of

[5] *Economics of Iron and Steel Transportation*, p. 48.

[6] For a fuller explanation of the practice and examples of the possible effects, see *Economics of Iron and Steel Transportation*, pp. 139-142.

products and is willing, under a delivered price system, to absorb freight in order to do so.

The limited range of the steel products of the southern mills constitute the final modifying factor that will be mentioned. If Birmingham cannot offer the desired product, then the fact that it may have a lower freight rate has no effect. Whether such a product will be bought in the South depends on the ability of the user to get it from some other point at a price, including transportation cost, which he can afford to pay. It should be pointed out that, with the higher quality specialty items, the differentiation of products becomes sharper and more directly identified with a particular producer, the value per pound or per ton becomes higher, and the percentage of the total cost that is represented by the freight charge becomes smaller. As a result, in such items as tool steel and stainless steel products, freight rates have little influence in determining where purchases will be made.

DISTRIBUTION POINTS FOR IRON AND STEEL IN THE SOUTH

Iron and steel products tend to move in large quantities from the producing plants. While large customers may handle direct shipments in large quantity lots, to a very great degree, shipments are made to producer-owned warehouses or to jobbers and wholesalers located at important central distribution points. Consequently, the immediate concern of the producer of basic iron and steel products has to do with reaching the distribution centers.

Many of the demands for iron and steel and their products are closely associated either with concentrations of population in cities or with the kind or degree of the industrialization of an area. As pointed out previously, cities and industrial areas are quite widely scattered in the South. Agriculture plays an extremely important part in the region, and this too makes for scattered demand which can best be met by distribution through wholesaling centers. From the point of view of iron and steel, the most important large markets are those caused by the petroleum and natural gas fields of

Table 113

Wholesaling Centers of the South with Indicators of Importance in Steel Warehousing and Metal Working Industries

Wholesaling center	Wholesale sales (in $1,000)		Membership in American Steel Warehouse Association, Inc. (A)		Warehouses listed in W. P. B. Directory (B) Number with inventories			Number of establishments, 1947 in Metal Working Industries with 100 or more employees in county (C)	Number of sales offices of iron and steel companies listed in Iron and Steel Works Directory, 1948 (B)
	1939	1948	Members	Associates	Total number	Over 500 tons	100 to 500 tons		
Group I									
Atlanta, Ga.	465,115	2,137,396	3	13	12	1	6	21	31
Dallas, Texas	475,454	2,195,991	3	8	9	1	7	26	22
Houston, Texas	457,911	1,683,286	11	16	21	4	11	34	38
Memphis, Tenn.	433,254	1,965,255	2	4	9	3	3	11	6
New Orleans, La.	437,639	1,328,364****	3	8	10	3	4	19	16
Group II									
Birmingham, Ala.	182,932	817,744	7	5	13	5	1	43	13
Charlotte, N. C.	207,901	969,576	..	1	5	0	1	5	4
Fort Worth, Texas	148,386	647,795	3	3	4	0	3	7	9
Jacksonville, Fla.	151,633	616,983	3	1	8	1	2	6	3
Oklahoma City, Okla.	193,322	532,928	4	3	5	2	0	8	2
Group III									
Chattanooga, Tenn.	69,374	260,152	..	6	3	1	0	26	9
Greensboro, N. C.	57,395	273,840	..	..	2	0	1	6	2
Knoxville, Tenn.	67,308	265,660	..	..	2	0	0	7	3
Miami, Fla.	88,065	375,604	..	..	6	2	2	2	..
Nashville, Tenn.	127,347	441,380	1	..	10	2	2	12	1
San Antonio, Texas	123,108	447,796	3	..	5	0	0	4	3
Tampa, Fla.	87,997	298,143	1	..	7	2	3	5	..
Tulsa, Okla.	75,410	345,402	2	10	5	1	0	21	16
Group IV									
Amarillo, Texas	35,072	236,028**	..	..	5	0	1	2	2
Columbia, S. C.	46,576	191,715	..	..	3	0	2	..	..
Corpus Christi, Texas	46,181	128,851	..	..	2	2	0	1	..
El Paso, Texas	48,766	211,775	2	..	6	1	1	5	1
Greenville, S. C.	49,875	169,906	..	..	3	0	2	4	..
Jackson, Miss.	37,098	152,751	..	..	2	0	0	1	..
Little Rock, Ark.	73,500	241,154	1	..	5	3	3	2	..
Lubbock, Texas	32,742	173,693	2	..	5	1	1	..	1

City								
Mobile, Ala.	43,976	160,084	2	1	4	1	2	6
Montgomery, Ala.	52,851	189,242**	..	..	1	0	1	1
Raleigh, N. C.	27,102	197,871	..	2	2	0	2	1
Savannah, Ga.	67,581	193,084	..	3	3	0	0	3
Shreveport, La.	66,868	232,225	1	5	5	0	2	3
Spartanburg, S. C.	23,373	123,310	..	2	2	0	1	1
Waco, Texas	33,051	132,340	1	3	3	0	1	..
Winston-Salem, N. C.	41,752	135,845	..	1	1	0	1	5

*Montgomery County.

**Part in Potter County, part of city in Randall County reported one establishment but entire County (Randall) has sales of only $3,569,000.

***Does not include 15 administrative auxiliary units.

Notes: A. Cities other than those above that have members or associate members of the American Steel Warehouse Association: Georgia—LaGrange; Louisiana—Baton Rouge, Harvey, Houma, Lake Charles, New Iberia, Natchez; North Carolina—Ashville, Wilmington; Oklahoma—Picher; South Carolina—Charleston; Texas—Abilene, Austin, Beaumont, Brownville, Galveston, Harlingen, Odessa, Orange, San Angelo, and Temple.

B. Cities other than those above that are listed in the War Production Board Directory as having two or more warehouses. (Number in parenthesis). Alabama—Anniston (2), Tuscaloosa (2); Arkansas—Fort Smith (3), Pine Bluff (2); Georgia—Albany (2), Athens (2), Augusta (2), Columbus (2), Macon (4); Louisiana—Monroe (2); Mississippi—Vicksburg (2); North Carolina—Ashville (2); South Carolina—Anderson (2), Charleston (3); Tennessee—Kingsport (2), Morristown (2); Texas—Austin (2), Pampa (2), San Angelo (2), Witchita Falls (4).

C. Cities other than those above that are located in counties with five or more establishments in metal working industries (Groups 33-39) that employ 100 or more persons. (Number such establishments in parenthesis.) Alabama—Anniston (13), Gadsden (11), Sheffield (5); Georgia—Columbus (5); Texas—Beaumont (7), Galveston (6).

D. Cities listed in Iron and Steel Works Directory as having sales offices of iron and steel companies including those with plants in the South. (Number of such offices in parenthesis.) Alabama—Gadsden (1), Sheffield (1); Louisiana—Harvey (1); Oklahoma—Ardmore (1); Bartlesville (1), Muskogee (1), Sand Springs (1), Wewoka (1); Texas—Abilene (1), Beaumont (3), Daingerfield (1), Longview (1), Midland (2), Odessa (3), Rusk (1), Wichita Falls (1).

Source: *Census of Business, 1948,* V, "Wholesale Trade," *1939;* II, "Wholesale Trade"; *Directory of Iron and Steel Works, 1948;* American Steel Warehouse Association, *Roster,* August 1947; U. S. War Production Board, *Directory of Warehouse Distributors of General Steel Products.*

Texas, Oklahoma, and Louisiana together with their related refineries and pipe lines and by the relatively small number of areas in which sizable concentrations in iron and steel processing and fabricating industries occur.

For much of the South, it seems reasonable to assume that the factors influencing the location of distribution of iron and steel products will be the same as those for other commodities. As a result, Table 113 is based upon the statistics for general wholesaling, but gives additional data that indicate the position held by the various cities in the distribution of iron and steel products. The table lists 34 of the more important wholesaling centers of the South and gives the figures for the total wholesale sales in 1939 and 1948. The cities are arranged in four groups according to the size of their wholesale sales. The first five will be readily recognized as the great trade centers of the South; Atlanta, Dallas, Houston, Memphis, and New Orleans. The data on the number of steel warehouses, sales offices of iron and steel companies, and numbers of the larger establishments in the iron and steel processing and fabricating industries indicate that the five cities are leading points of interest in the iron and steel trade. Birmingham, by virtue of its position in both the basic iron and steel industry and in the processing and fabricating industry, quite naturally occupies a prominent place. Chattanooga's place in the metal-working industries makes it a center that attracts the attention of the iron and steel trade. One of the most conspicuous features brought out by the data is the position of such points in the

Southwest as Fort Worth, Tulsa, Oklahoma City, San Antonio, El Paso, and Shreveport. It is also significant that steel warehouses and sales offices of iron and steel companies are located in many of the relatively small cities of Texas and Oklahoma. In the Southeast, the more important centers, other than those already mentioned, appear to be Jacksonville, Charlotte, and Nashville.

It seems fair to say that the distribution of iron and steel products in the South is largely a problem of meeting demands for relatively small quantities, widely scattered over the wide expanse of the region, with the demands associated with oil and natural gas in Texas, Oklahoma, and Louisiana, and with the metalworking industries of Birmingham, northern Alabama, and Chattanooga as the most important concentrations.

Movements of Pig Iron in the South

The reports for 1947 and 1948 of traffic on the inland waterways and the Gulf Intercoastal Canal show only small movements of pig iron on the Mississippi River and none on the Warrior-Tombigbee. The movements on the intercoastal canal likewise were small. Coastwise receipts and shipments at southern ports were almost nonexistent and the only foreign exports of pig iron of any consequence were 29,000 tons in 1947 and 6,000 tons in 1948 from Mobile. Consequently, the data on rail movements tell the story.

The statistics of the originations and terminations presented in Table 114 indicate a net outward movement from the South and can be

Table 114

Tons of Pig Iron Originated and Terminated in Carload Lots as Revenue Freight
in the South, 1940 and 1946-1948

Year	Net tons originated	Net tons terminated	Net outward movements (excess of originations over terminations)
1940	1,243,715	841,281	402,434
1946	1,105,540	767,560	337,980
1947	1,228,181	902,056	326,125
1948	1,410,827	918,009	492,818

Source: U. S. Interstate Commerce Commission, *Tons of Revenue Freight Originated and Tons Terminated . . . 1940; 1946-48.*

interpreted to mean that the South produces more than it consumes and must seek a market outside the region. The state figures show that Alabama was the leading southern state, both in originations and terminations. Of the total originations in the South in 1947 of 1,228,181 tons, 1,146,310 came from Alabama. In 1948, the corresponding figures were 1,410,827 tons and 1,110,314. Texas, in 1948, was the only other southern state that reported a sizable quantity—263,255 tons. The differences between Alabama and the other states were not as great for terminations as for originations, the Alabama quantities being 620,146 tons in 1947 and 632,257 tons in 1948. Still, Tennessee with 138,636 tons in 1947 and 147,838 tons in 1948 was the only other state with terminations of more than 75,000 tons. Alabama's position in originations is, of course, a reflection of its predominance in the South in blast furnaces.

The concentration of cast-iron pipe in Alabama and gray iron foundries and other iron foundry industries in Alabama and Tennessee accounts for the situation in terminations.

Information from the waybill studies of the Board of Investigation and Research throws some additional light upon the movements of pig iron. Table 115 presents statistics abstracted from the tabulations of that study. The figures represent the shipments made on selected days in 1939. Consequently, it must be remembered that the data are subject to the variations inherent in a sample so chosen and also that they represent prewar conditions. Furthermore, the figures are stated in terms of the territories used in rate-making. The southern and southwestern territories do not correspond exactly to the areas set up in this study. The most important differences are that the southern territory includes southern Virginia and Kentucky

Table 115

Freight Movements of Pig Iron, Within the South, to the South and from the South as Shown by the 1939 Carload Traffic Survey

	Number of cars	Weight by pounds in thousands	Average miles per car	Average rate per 100 pounds	Average weight per car
Within the South					
Within Southern Territory	456	53,475.5	154	6.1	117,270
Southern to Southwestern Territory	2	122.4	767	27.0	61,200
Within Southwestern Territory	...	....	...	...	....
Southwestern to Southern	...	....	...	...	....
Total within South	458	53,597.9			
To the South					
Official to Southern Territory	...	....	...	...	....
Western to Southern Territory	...	....	...	...	....
Mountain-Pacific to Southern Territory	...	....	...	...	....
Official to Southwestern Territory	3	215.4	844	45.5	71,787
Western to Southwestern Territory	...	....	...	...	....
Mountain-Pacific to Southwestern Territory	...	....	...	...	....
Total to South	3	215.4	...	...	
From the South					
Southern to Official Territory	176	19,292.7	797	26.8	109,617
Southern to Western Territory	7	694.7	888	34.0	90,243
Southern to Mountain-Pacific Territory	...	....	...	...	....
Southwestern to Official Territory	...	....	...	...	....
Southwestern to Western Territory	...	....	...	...	....
Southwestern to Mountain-Pacific Territory	...	....	...	...	....
Total from the South	183	19,987.4			
Total United States	2,786	322,130.1			

Source: 1939 Carload Traffic Survey, Board of Investigation and Research (photostat copies of selected work sheets).

and the southwestern territory includes southern Missouri. Roughly, the official territory includes the area east of the Mississippi River and north of the southern territory. The western territory corresponds approximately to the west north central division as set up by the Bureau of the Census. The mountain-Pacific includes the Rocky Mountain and Pacific states.

The figures indicate that little of the pig iron used in the South came from outside and that a very large proportion which originated in the southern territory was delivered within the same territory, moved, on the average, rather short distances, and paid a low average rate. In fact, an additional tabulation not summarized in Table 115 shows that 240 of the 456 carloads moved less than 100 miles. The next most important movement of pig iron originating in the southern territory was to official territory, which, in weight, was slightly more than one-third the size of the movement within the southern territory. The shipment from the southern territory to the western territory exceeded that to the southwestern.

A flow chart of rail shipments of pig iron for one day in October, 1939, published in the *Economics of Iron and Steel Transportation*[7] shows shipments from Birmingham into Virginia, southwest Pennsylvania, southern Ohio, northern Illinois, the St. Louis area, Iowa, and western Missouri. Most of the shipments, however, are to northern Alabama, southeast Tennessee, and northwest Georgia. It would seem,

[7] *Economics of Iron and Steel Transportation*, p. 64.

therefore, that the statistical evidence indicates that the total market for southern pig iron was first of all in places relatively close to Birmingham and then in the East and North. In former years, Birmingham pig iron sold in large quantities on the Atlantic seaboard and north of the Ohio River. However, interviews with Birmingham producers of merchant pig iron indicated that increased costs and higher freight rates have decidedly shortened the distance that their product can move.

Movements of Cast Iron Pipe in the South

There were only small movements of cast-iron pipe on the Mississippi River, and the Gulf Intracoastal Canal in 1947 and 1948. In 1948, 39,085 tons were reported as shipped down the Warrior River, but none was reported in 1947. In these two years, no export from southern ports appears in the statistics, but coastwise shipments, largely from Mobile, of 41,611 tons in 1947 and 45,109 tons in 1948 were reported. In 1948, Houston had coastwise receipts of a little less than 10,000 tons. Since Alabama is the source of some 60 per cent of the cast-iron pipe produced in the United States, it seems reasonable to infer that the Houston receipts were for pipe shipped from Mobile.

As in the case for pig iron, the only data that reflect substantial movements are those for rail traffic. The summary figures for revenue freight originations and terminations of cast-iron pipe are given in Table 116.

Table 116

Tons of Cast-Iron Pipe Originated and Terminated in Carload Lots as Revenue Freight in the South, 1940 and 1946-1948

Year	Net tons originated	Net tons terminated	Net outward movements (excess of originations over terminations)
1940	725,620	336,478	389,142
1946	646,322	289,088	357,234
1947	908,379	418,633	489,746
1948	1,003,511	440,905	562,606

Source: U. S. Interstate Commerce Commission, *Tons of Revenue Freight Originated and Tons Terminated . . . 1940; 1946-48.*

In each year for which data are given in Table 116, the net outward movement from the South exceeded the terminations in the South. While the possibility of duplications in the figures due to reshipment prevents drawing conclusions as to the ratios between pipe used in the South and pipe shipped out of the South, it is quite evident that the South is a surplus producer and that a large portion of the product must find a market elsewhere. The predominant position of Alabama as a source of cast-iron pipe is reflected in the originations. In 1947, 835,768 tons of the South's total of 908,379 tons and, in 1948, 932,305 tons of 1,003,511 tons originated in Alabama.

The United States Department of Commerce used the detailed data assembled by the Board of Investigation and Research in the carload traffic survey of 1939 to prepare estimates for 1939 of state-to-state movements of cast-iron pipe.[8] While the figures directly represent the condition some eleven years ago, the continued movement away from the South would indicate that the general pattern has not changed greatly. Table 117 shows the estimated terminations in the several states and compares those that originated in the South with the total of all terminations in each state.

Table 117

Estimated Carload Rail Traffic Terminations of Cast-Iron Pipe and Fittings by States, Showing Terminations That Originated in the South, 1939

Terminating states	Terminations originating in the South (pounds)	Total terminations (pounds)
New England	619,254	3,419,715
Maine	42,500	421,790
New Hampshire	218,500	280,783
Vermont	....	....
Massachusetts	234,654	1,358,405
Rhode Island	73,000	554,561
Connecticut	50,600	804,176

[8] U.S. Department of Commerce, *Transportation Factors in the Location of the Cast Iron Pipe Industry*, pp. 14-16.

Middle Atlantic	3,629,145	9,842,258
New York	1,293,599	3,238,520
New Jersey	604,611	1,110,893
Pennsylvania	992,978	2,675,330
District of Columbia	198,640	395,558
Delaware	....	468,654
Maryland	211,815	950,765
Virginia	104,013	476,439
West Virginia	223,489	526,099
Lake and Ohio River	9,350,818	11,707,134
Ohio	1,054,332	1,410,630
Indiana	1,026,372	1,341,454
Illinois	2,450,334	3,237,899
Michigan	3,163,438	3,683,472
Wisconsin	917,522	1,218,184
Kentucky	738,820	815,495
West North Central	2,985,115	4,353,152
Missouri	1,081,636	1,284,530
Minnesota	500,364	853,432
Iowa	770,205	1,185,853
North Dakota	41,600	41,600
South Dakota	74,876	122,926
Nebraska	106,457	272,234
Kansas	409,977	592,577
Rocky Mountain	423,369	2,119,657
Montana	....	240,464
Idaho	....	69,227
Wyoming	....	....
Colorado	312,305	1,422,616
Arizona	....	140,174
New Mexico	111,064	111,064
Utah	....	73,357
Nevada	....	62,758
Pacific Coast	429,839	2,153,150
Washington	62,184	402,885
Oregon	....	113,800
California	367,655	1,636,465
South	20,201,330	22,078,649
North Carolina	94,740	853,198
South Carolina	420,760	1,027,713
Georgia	1,372,211	1,470,706
Florida	2,934,569	2,934,569
Tennessee	494,350	572,590
Alabama	6,853,301	6,991,931
Mississippi	456,314	456,314
Arkansas	39,672	39,672
Louisiana	2,900,192	2,980,575
Oklahoma	325,166	325,166
Texas	4,310,055	4,426,215

Source: U. S. Department of Commerce, *Transportation Factors in Location of Cast Iron Pipe Industry.*

The very large figure shown for Alabama can scarcely be considered as an indicator of ultimate consumption in the State, but probably is associated with the State's position as the largest producer of cast-iron pipe. Some prob-ably went to fabricators and some to be dis-tributed by truck or other means of transporta-tion. In the South, the terminations largely originated within the region, actually in Ala-bama. The only important exceptions were North Carolina and South Carolina, which re-ceived most of their shipments from Virginia. Shipments were also received in the southern states from Rhode Island, Pennsylvania, Mary-land, Ohio, Indiana, Illinois, and Kentucky, but the quantities were comparatively small.

Perhaps the most significant fact that is brought out by the data of Table 117 is the evidence of the widespread distribution of southern cast-iron pipe and fittings. Shipments that originated in the South are represented as reaching destinations in all but nine of the states. The only states that did not show ter-minations were Vermont, Delaware, Montana, Idaho, Wyoming, Arizona, Utah, Nevada, and

Oregon. In sixteen of the 38 states[9] that are outside the South, more than half the termina-tions were estimated as originating in the South.

It can be concluded that cast-iron pipe, like pig iron, is a product for which the South is a surplus producer. However, the market area outside the South is geographically much more widely extended than that of pig iron.

Movements of Steel Mill Products

RAIL MOVEMENTS

The situation in the South with respect to steel mill products differs considerably from that which exists for pig iron and cast-iron pipe in at least these two respects: first, the area is a deficit producer and shipments into the area exceed the out movements; and second, water movements are of considerable impor-

[9] Counting the District of Columbia as a state.

Table 118

Tons of Iron and Steel Mill Shapes and Forms Originated and Terminated in Carload Lots as Revenue Rail Freight in the South, 1940, 1946, 1947, and 1948

Iron and steel mill product	1940			1946		
	Originated	Terminated	Excess terminated	Originated	Terminated	Excess terminated
Iron and steel rated 6th class........	8,747	240,068	231,321	328,401	113,177	215,224*
Rails, fastenings, etc.................	65,073	93,785	28,712	102,387	149,119	46,732
Iron and steel pipe and fittings......	338,059	766,999	428,940	219,985	1,441,511	1,221,526
Iron and steel nails and wire not woven.	113,228	235,220	121,992	125,049	287,011	161,962
Iron and steel rated 5th class........	696,396	1,984,764	1,288,368	1,162,068	2,990,809	1,828,741
Railway car wheels, axles and trucks..	26,473	26,786	313	46,957	48,681	1,724
Totals	1,247,976	3,347,622	2,099,646	1,984,847	5,030,308	3,045,461

Iron and steel mill product	1947			1948		
	Originated	Terminated	Excess terminated	Originated	Terminated	Excess terminated
Iron and steel blooms, billets, ingots..	22,496	57,110	34,614	16,968	57,154	40,186
Iron and steel bars, rods, and slabs..	15,001	32,911	17,910	33,032	19,670	13,362*
Iron and steel, n.o.s................	124,738	88,167	36,571*	54,377	78,738	24,361
Iron and steel nails and wire (woven and not woven)..................	267,324	655,949	388,625	313,377	695,489	382,112
Iron and steel pipe and fittings, n.o.s..	297,570	2,025,392	1,727,822	335,518	2,440,991	2,105,473
Rails and railway track material.....	90,676	157,503	66,827	83,135	109,667	26,532
Manufactured iron and steel.........	1,303,699	3,450,315	2,146,616	1,217,703	3,507,108	2,289,405
Totals	2,121,504	6,467,347	4,345,843	2,054,110	6,908,817	4,854,707

*Originations exceeded terminations.

Source: U. S. Interstate Commerce Commission, *Tons of Revenue Freight Originated and Tons Terminated . . . 1940; 1946-48.*

tance. The second characteristic makes it necessary to present statistical data on barge and ship movements as well as rail traffic. The data on rail movements are presented in Tables 118 and 119.

A change in the classification system used by the Interstate Commerce Commission was made in 1947, but the effect on the comparability of the iron and steel mill products data for 1947 and 1948 with that of earlier years is not sufficient to influence greatly the conclusions as to the direction and approximate magnitude of the rail movements. In each of the years, originations in the South were about three per cent of the nation's total and terminations, approximately ten per cent. The net balance of terminations over originations, which might be called the net inward movement by rail, increased from two million tons in 1940 to three million tons in 1946, 4.3 million tons in 1947, and 4.9 million tons in 1948. The several product classifications showed an excess of terminations over originations in all cases except "iron and steel rated 6th class," in 1946, and iron and steel bars, rods, and slabs, in 1948. The classes

that showed very large inward movements were iron and steel pipe and fittings and iron and steel rated fifth class, in 1940 and 1946, as well as iron and steel pipe and fittings and manufactured iron and steel, in 1947 and 1948.

From the point of view of the individual states, several facts stand out. Alabama was the only state in 1947 and 1948 for which originations exceeded terminations. Texas, with a net inward rail movement of 1.8 million tons in 1947 and slightly more than two million tons in 1948, is the state with the largest tonnages, by far. Louisiana, Oklahoma, and Texas together accounted for a little more than two-thirds of the net inward rail movement in 1947 and almost 80 per cent in 1948. Florida and Tennessee rank next in the size of the net movements, while South Carolina, Arkansas, and Mississippi seem to attract the smallest shipments.

Although 1939 has come to seem rather remote, the data summarized in Table 120 from the tabulations of the traffic survey for iron and steel, 6th class, iron and steel pipe and fittings, and iron and steel rated 5th class give

Table 119

Tons of Steel Mill Forms and Shapes Originated and Terminated in Carload Lots as Revenue Freight in the Several States of the South, 1947 and 1948

State	1947			1948		
	Originated	Terminated	Excess terminated	Originated	Terminated	Excess terminated
Southeast	1,400,678	3,538,498	2,137,820	1,299,222	3,484,044	2,184,822
North Carolina	21,792	237,442	215,650	23,385	234,394	211,009
South Carolina	14,147	113,311	99,164	8,322	108,944	100,622
Georgia	145,309	368,611	223,302	140,274	357,422	217,148
Florida	42,419	407,464	365,045	44,236	427,912	383,676
Tennessee	244,686	573,506	328,820	218,312	644,625	426,313
Alabama	784,971	658,683	126,288*	744,330	598,800	145,530*
Mississippi	30,658	212,200	181,542	13,579	194,955	181,376
Arkansas	12,776	148,283	135,507	10,989	143,335	132,346
Louisiana	103,920	818,998	715,078	95,795	773,657	677,862
Southwest	720,826	2,928,849	2,208,023	754,888	3,424,773	2,669,885
Oklahoma	108,159	488,197	380,038	105,040	708,975	603,935
Texas	612,667	2,440,652	1,827,985	649,848	2,715,798	2,065,950
Total South	2,121,504	6,467,347	4,345,843	2,054,110	6,908,817	4,854,707
Total United States	67,531,891	66,795,953		67,753,840	66,127,921	
Per cent South of United States	3.1	9.7		3.0	10.5	

*Originated exceeded terminated.

Source: U. S. Interstate Commerce Commission, *Tons of Freight Originated and Tons Terminated . . . 1947; 1948.*

Table 120

Freight Movements in Carload Lots of Iron and Steel Rated Sixth Class, Iron and Steel Pipe and Fittings and Iron and Steel Rated Fifth Class Within the South, to the South and from the South as Shown by the 1939 Carload Traffic Survey

	Iron and steel rated 6th class				Iron and steel pipe and fittings				Iron and steel rated 5th class			
	Number of cars	Weight by pounds (in thousands)	Average miles per car	Average rate per 100 pounds	Number of cars	Weight by pounds (in thousands)	Average miles per car	Average rate per 100 pounds	Number of cars	Weight by pounds (in thousands)	Average miles per car	Average rate per 100 pounds
Within the South												
Within Southern Territory	35	3,281.3	297	13.9	37	1,825.9	429	40.1	812	51,815.4	374	24.9
Southern to Southwestern Territory	....	....	....	....	72	4,616.3	687	55.0	102	6,103.7	819	55.1
Within Southwestern Territory	4	401.4	388	29.2	247	17,395.5	444	39.2	138	8,185.8	420	41.8
Southwestern to Southern Territory	....	....	....	....	1	20.7	1,049	167.6	2	78.3	472	60.0
Total within the South	39	3,682.7	....	....	357	23,858.4	....	....	1,054	66,183.2	....	....
To the South												
Official to Southern Territory	1	47.4	1,415	100.0	149	7,738.0	884	60.4	452	23,017.8	797	54.9
Western to Southern Territory	....	....	....	....	....	....	....	....	2	110.6	968	58.1
Mountain-Pacific to Southern Territory	....	....	....	....	....	....	....	....	....	....	....	....
Official to Southwestern Territory	3	241.1	1,150	70.9	240	15,077.8	1,407	85.8	220	11,915.8	1,167	80.4
Western to Southwestern Territory	....	....	....	....	3	193.9	1,192	57.2	84	6,889.4	958	67.6
Mountain-Pacific to Southwestern Territory	....	....	....	....	1	86.4	30	3.3	4	252.5	1,774	82.8
Total to the South	4	288.5	....	....	393	23,096.1	....	....	762	42,186.1	....	....
From the South												
Southern to Official Territory	3	249.0	452	22.2	47	2,435.1	825	46.8	62	4,120.3	697	39.8
Southern to Western Territory	....	....	....	....	16	874.8	1,152	60.9	5	370.3	1,080	78.4
Southern to Mountain-Pacific Territory	....	....	....	....	2	136.4	2,477	110.0	72	6,144.3	2,697	81.4
Southwestern to Official Territory	....	....	....	....	2	154.6	750	75.4	8	711.6	941	35.8
Southwestern to Western Territory	1	97.0	298	19.0	2	131.1	773	69.7	4	177.4	604	42.0
Southwestern to Mountain-Pacific Territory	....	....	....	....	1	66.9	1,804	99.0	1	61.8	1,959	30.3
Total from South	4	346.0	....	....	70	3,798.9	....	....	152	11,585.7	....	....
Total United States	3,762	384,243.4	....	....	4,465	279,219.8	....	....	24,937	1,726,251.4	....	....

Source: 1939 Carload Traffic Survey, Interstate Commerce Commission (photostat copies of selected work sheets).

an indication of the origins and destinations of shipments. It is very probable that the shipments within a territory include many from warehouses and jobbers located inside the boundaries of the territory. Such movements are really reshipments of steel previously received from a steel mill. As a result, such figures do not necessarily represent shipments from steel mills. Attention, therefore, will be directed principally to the movements across territorial lines. The shipments to the southern territory in terms of thousands of pounds weight is summarized below.

	Iron & steel 6th class	Iron & steel pipe	Iron & steel 5th class
From Southwestern Territory	....	20.7	78.3
From Official Territory	47.4	7,738.0	23,017.8
From Western Territory	....	......	110.6
Total	47.4	7,758.7	23,206.7

A similar summary for movements to the southwestern territory follows.

	Iron & steel 6th class	Iron & steel pipe	Iron & steel 5th class
From Southern Territory	....	4,616.3	6,103.7
From Official Territory	241.1	15,077.8	11,915.8
From Western Territory	....	193.9	6,889.4
From Mountain-Pacific Territory	....	86.4	252.5
Total	241.1	19,974.4	25,161.4

The data indicate that movements into the southern territory come almost entirely from the official or eastern territory and those from the southwestern and western are small. The southern territory and the western territory have a substantial participation in the shipments of iron and steel pipe and fittings and iron and steel rated fifth class into the southwestern territory, but the total shipments from the official territory are larger than those from any other territory for iron and steel fifth class and predominate in iron and steel pipe.

While frequent shipments from the southern territory to the official, western, and mountain-Pacific territories are indicated, and, in the case of iron and steel fifth class, in quite large quantities, the shipments to the South are larger than those from the South except in iron and steel sixth class where the quantities are small. This harmonizes with the originations and terminations data presented by Table 118 and indicates a net inward movement into the region.

Compared with movements to the South from other territories, the carload shipments within the South moved, on the average, shorter distances, and the freight charge was less. If movements from official territory to the South are compared with movements from the southern territory to official territory, the latter movements usually were for shorter distances and at lower rates. This probably indicates that the southern shipments did not penetrate far into the official territory. Of interest also are the rather large shipments from the southern territory to the mountain-Pacific territory.

The flow maps presented in *Economics of Iron and Steel Transportation*[10] give more specific indications of origins and destinations of shipments. Although the lines on the maps are sometimes hard to follow, the movements indicated may be summarized as indicated below.

Rail shipments of steel bars for one day in April, 1939
  Shipments originating in Birmingham or Gadsden to:
    Nashville; Chattanooga; Western Mississippi; Jacksonville, Florida; West coast of Florida; Pensacola; Mobile; and New Orleans.
  Shipments originating in Atlanta to:
    New Orleans and Pensacola.
  A shipment indicated from Sheffield, Alabama, to Chattanooga.
  Much evidence of shipping into the South is shown:
    From Pittsburgh to South Carolina and North Carolina.
    From Sparrow's Point to South Carolina.
    From Pittsburgh to points in Arkansas.
    From St. Louis to points in Louisiana and Texas.
    From Kansas City into northern Texas.

Rail shipments of steel sheets for one day in November, 1939
  From Birmingham to Atlanta and east Florida.
  From Gadsden to the west coast.
  From Memphis to the Texas Panhandle.
  From Houston to northeast Texas.

10 *Economics of Iron and Steel Transportation*, opposite pp. 64-66.

Numerous shipments into the South are indicated:
 From eastern Ohio or Pittsburgh to Atlanta and
  a point near Columbus, Georgia.
 From Ohio to central South Carolina.
 From Chicago to Oklahoma.
 From Ohio or Pittsburgh to Texas Panhandle.
 From Chicago to northeast Texas.

*Rail shipments of tin plate for one day in April,
August, and November, 1939*
 From Birmingham to Tampa, Mobile, New Orleans,
 Houston, central Kansas, and west coast points both
 in the Los Angeles and San Francisco areas.

Shipments to the South:
 From Chicago to New Orleans.
 From east Ohio to Knoxville, Tennessee.

*Rail shipments of steel plates for one day in April,
August, and November, 1939*
 From Chattanooga to a point in Virginia.
 From Birmingham and Gadsden:
  To Chattanooga, Nashville, Memphis, east Texas,
  Houston, New Orleans, Mobile, southeast Georgia
  (Savannah), Atlanta, and eastern Pennsylvania or
  New Jersey.
 From Houston to northeast Texas.

Table 121

Water Movements of Steel Mill Products in the South by the Mississippi River and the Warrior-Tombigbee River, 1939, 1947, and 1948

(in net tons)

	Mississippi River			Black Warrior,
Year and kind of movement	Mouth of Ohio to but not including Baton Rouge	Baton Rouge to but not including New Orleans	New Orleans to mouth of passes	Warrior and Tombigbee Rivers
1939				
Total	896,891	544,525	949,182	277,562
Upbound	1,954	.....	.....	1,303
Outbound (Upbound)	3,284	36	385,649	.....
Inbound (Upbound)	3,927	2,099	31,129	.....
Through (Upbound)	5,572	14,796	2,650	.....
Downbound	39,183	.....	.....	203,798
Outbound (Downbound)	49,636	1,225	.....	72,433
Inbound (Downbound)	304,545	.....	268,438	28
Through (Downbound)	488,790	526,369	261,316	.....
1947				
Total	659,211	548,743	698,926	124,469
Upbound	3,347	.....	1,035	.....
Outbound (Upbound)	11,409	354	42,591	.....
Inbound (Upbound)	3,645	1,108	3,156	1,037
Through (Upbound)	12,056	15,380	128,435	.....
Downbound	6,995	.....	350	.....
Outbound (Downbound)	2,684	1,417	851	123,432
Inbound (Downbound)	91,574	6,625	81,950	.....
Through (Downbound)	527,501	523,859	440,558	.....
1948				
Total	679,624	563,582	668,081	123,980
Upbound	3,770	.....	.....	.....
Outbound (Upbound)	1,519	800	6,262	.....
Inbound (Upbound)	3,083	1,345	6,963	501
Through (Upbound)	60,147	63,230	153,124	.....
Downbound	3,547	.....	224	.....
Outbound (Downbound)	512	2,707	70	123,479
Inbound (Downbound)	113,258	7,060	110,796	.....
Through (Downbound)	493,788	488,440	390,642	.....

Source: U. S. Engineer Department, *Annual Report,* Part 2, 1939, 1947, and 1948.

Shipments into the South:
  From eastern Pennsylvania to Atlanta and Bir-
    mingham.
  From western New York to New Orleans.
  From Pittsburgh to Memphis.
  From Sparrow's Point or eastern Pennsylvania to
    Chattanooga.
  From Pittsburgh and Chicago to Oklahoma.
  From Chicago to New Orleans and Houston.

While the sample may seem quite limited, the evidence points to a very intricate pattern of movements that apparently involves much cross hauling. It is clear that many steel centers were shipping into the area, particularly in the Carolinas and Oklahoma and Texas.

WATER MOVEMENTS

Water movements both on inland waterways and at ports are important in the South, and the data are presented in Tables 121, 122, and 123.

Table 122

Water Movements of Steel Mill Products by Gulf Intracoastal Canal, 1939, 1947, and 1948
(in net tons)

	Pensacola Bay, Florida to Mobile Bay, Alabama	Mobile Bay, Alabama to New Orleans, Louisiana	Mississippi River, Louisiana to Sabine River, Texas*	Sabine River, Texas to Galveston, Texas†	Galveston to Corpus Christi, Texas
1939					
Total	869	49,221	391,562	314,341	......
Inbound	......	......	2,832	2,060	......
Outbound	......	......	9,711	......	......
Through					
Eastbound	401	4,929	7,750	1,330	......
Westbound	468	44,292	371,269	310,951	......
Internal					
Eastbound	......	......	......	......	......
Westbound	......	......	......	......	......
1947					
Total	2,618	99,774	492,328	352,203	31,078
Inbound	......	......	72,842	29,924	29,854
Outbound	......	......	40,736	345	5
Through					
Eastbound	837	3,637	19,462	14,403	......
Westbound	1,781	96,137	354,555	307,531	1,219
Internal					
Eastbound	......	......	1,454	......	......
Westbound	......	......	3,279	......	......
1948					
Total	2,924	104,217	497,043	384,754	19,821
Inbound	......	......	49,997	38,082	14,369
Outbound	......	......	42,943	1,020	15
Through					
Eastbound	......	2,895	65,943	59,650	67
Westbound	2,924	101,322	330,779	286,002	5,370
Internal					
Eastbound	......	......	4,681	......	......
Westbound	......	......	2,700	......	......

*The figures for 1939 are for Mississippi River to Calcasieu River, Louisiana.

†The figures for 1939 are for Port Arthur, Texas, to Galveston, Texas.

The figures for 1939 for Calcasieu River, Louisiana to Port Arthur, Texas, are: Total—357,128; Through, eastbound—2,335; Through, westbound—354,793.

Source: U. S. Engineer Department, *Annual Report*, Part 2, 1939, 1947, and 1948.

Table 123

Foreign and Coastwise Trade in Steel Mill Products at Southern Ports, 1939, 1947, and 1948
(in net tons)

Year and port	Foreign		Coastwise	
	Imports	Exports	Receipts	Shipments
1939				
Charleston	3,206	......	11,348	1,271
Savannah	2,817	56,887	19,027	5,859
Jacksonville	1,718	479	23,368	3,627
Tampa	1,072	8	25,019	1,777
Pensacola	263	7,730	489	......
Mobile	1,089	61,630	11,014	383,458
New Orleans	16,369	136,167	61,765	100,996
Beaumont	....	......	15,881	421
Orange		......	......	......
Port Arthur		......	4,385	......
Sabine Pass Harbor	....	......	......	......
Galveston Channel	702	4,353	79,200	1,631
Houston Channel	16,347	9,334	304,585	8,082
Total	43,583	276,588	556,078	507,122
1947				
Charleston	....	774	84	2,574
Savannah		5,319	472	3,270
Jacksonville	....	84	3,281	7
Tampa		3,968	12,119	69
Pensacola	4	19,336	......	......
Mobile	....	29,613	1,867	75,234
New Orleans	121	345,343	36,377	50,792
Beaumont	....	975	......	......
Orange	....	......	......	......
Port Arthur	1	178	......	......
Sabine Pass Harbor	....	......	......	......
Galveston Channel	....	17,144	254	396
Houston Channel	....	41,831	91,041	3,348
Total	126	464,565	145,495	135,690
1948				
Charleston	782	3,934	14	587
Savannah	400	3,415	17	......
Jacksonville	146	3,731	......	......
Tampa	658	4,055	11,913	855
Pensacola	....	11,822	......	......
Mobile	2,806	52,295	3,424	109,420
New Orleans	4,456	336,234	25,736	47,287
Beaumont	....	3,646	......	......
Orange	....	2	......	......
Port Arthur	....	568	......	......
Sabine Pass Harbor	....	......	......	......
Galveston Channel	211	5,759	......	1,094
Houston Channel	26,995	47,365	94,983	2,888
Total	36,454	472,826	136,087	162,131

Source: U. S. Engineer Department, *Annual Report,* Part 2, 1939, 1947, and 1948.

On the Mississippi River, the heavy downstream movement is an item of importance. On the section of the river where products enter or leave the South, the mouth of the Ohio to, but not including, Baton Rouge, the inbound movement of steel mill products which moved down the river was 304,545 tons in 1939, 91,574 tons in 1947, and 132,558 tons in 1948. These shipments are terminated within the section with Memphis as the largest river port. The through down river movement was 488,790 tons in 1939, 527,501 tons in 1947, and 493,788 tons in 1948. In contrast, the total traffic moving up the river was 14,737 tons in 1939, 30,507 tons in 1947, and 68,519 tons in 1948. A check on the statistics for the Ohio River indicates that the down shipments on the Mississippi originated largely at Pittsburgh and to a lesser extent at Ohio River port cities. The through shipments on the upper section of the Mississippi River can be traced to New Orleans and, to a large extent, by way of the Intracoastal Canal to the Texas coast.

A rather large movement of steel mill products is shown on the Warrior-Tombigbee River. This tonnage originates in Birmingham. In 1939, a downbound movement (that is, a movement which terminates within the limits of the waterway) of 203,798 tons was recorded. This tonnage probably was closely connected with the heavy exports (63,820 tons) and coastwise shipments (213,772 tons) made that year from Mobile. The outbound movements on the Warrior-Tombigbee of 72,433 tons in 1939, 123,432 tons in 1947, and 123,479 tons in 1948 appear largely to move westward from Mobile on the Intracoastal waterway to New Orleans and thence to the Texas coast.

The Mississippi River thus serves as a means of transportation for iron and steel products to such distribution points as Memphis, Baton Rouge, and New Orleans, and provides the first stages of the water route to Texas. The Warrior-Tombigbee serves a similar purpose for traffic from Birmingham to Mobile, New Orleans, and the Texas coast.

The statistics presented by Table 123 indicate that exports of steel mill products from southern ports are of considerable significance. New Orleans was the port from which by far the greatest tonnages were exported, 136,167 tons in 1939, 345,343 tons in 1947, and 336,234 in 1948. Houston with 9,334 tons in 1939, 41,831 tons in 1947, and 47,365 tons in 1948 and Mobile with 61,630 tons in 1939, 29,613 tons in 1947 and 52,295 in 1948 were the next most important exporters. Imports were almost nonexistent in 1947, but, in 1948, some 27,000 tons were reported for Houston and smaller quantities for New Orleans and Mobile.

In the coastwise shipments of iron and steel products, Mobile held the leading position in each of the three years shown with 383,458 tons, 75,234 tons, and 109,420 tons, in 1939, 1947 and 1948, respectively. Rather large shipments were made from New Orleans, too. Houston was the most important destination of coastwise movements as indicated by receipts of 304,585 tons in 1939, 91,041 tons in 1947, and 94,983 in 1948. New Orleans was second in the size of receipts, but the coastwise shipments were larger and so the net movement was away from, rather than toward, New Orleans. Substantial coastwise receipts are shown also for Tampa. The origins of the coastwise receipts and the destinations of the coastwise shipments are not shown, but it is generally understood that large shipments are made from Mobile to the Pacific coast. Shipments probably are made also to Houston, although barge shipments by way of the Warrior-Tombigbee River and the Intercoastal Waterway would seem to be preferable. Baltimore and Philadelphia with steel from Sparrow's Point and other eastern plants are logical points of origin for coastwise receipts at southern ports.

TOTAL NET MOVEMENTS OF STEEL MILL PRODUCTS

The information available on movements of iron and steel works products provides the basis for getting reasonably close approximations of the net movements by rail and water. The data also indicate that steel is shipped into the South by most of the important steel-producing centers and that each state of the region receives some of its steel from outside. The areas of greatest competition, however, are the Atlantic tidewater and the central and western portions of Oklahoma and Texas.

While it is difficult to match the product classifications used by the Interstate Commerce Commission in reporting rail traffic and the United States Army Corps of Engineers in reporting water-borne commerce, the totals are sufficiently comparable to make the following summary for 1947 useful.

	Tons
Total terminations of steel mill products in the South in 1947	6,467,347
Less total originations	2,121,504
Net rail movements to the South	4,345,843
Add—movements to South on Mississippi River (mouth of Ohio to but not including Baton Rouge)	

	Tons
Through downstream movement	527,501
Inbound downstream movement	91,574
Add imports	126
Coastwise receipts	145,495
	5,110,539
Less movements from South on Mississippi River (mouth of Ohio to but not including Baton Rouge)	
Through upstream movement	12,056
Outbound upstream movement	11,409
Less exports	464,565
Coastwise shipments	135,690
Net rail and water movements to South	4,486,819

Movements of Finished Iron and Steel Products in the South

Products of the iron and steel processing and fabricating industries other than cast-iron pipe are often difficult to identify in the various

Table 124

Tons of Finished Iron and Steel Products Originated and Terminated as Revenue Freight in the South, 1947 and 1948

Product	1947			1948		
	Originated	Terminated	Difference (term. minus orig.)	Originated	Terminated	Difference (term. minus orig.)
Tanks, n.o.s.	122,191	142,644	20,453	87,377	134,788	47,411
Agricultural implements, n.o.s.	73,509	253,945	180,436	105,927	322,838	216,911
Agricultural imp. parts, n.o.s.	13,120	39,771	26,651	19,848	40,352	20,504
Machinery and machines, n.o.s.	258,961	723,676	464,715	208,834	710,433	501,599
Machinery parts	61,736	168,811	107,075	48,042	159,953	111,911
Business office machines	1,181	1,293	112	765	1,151	386
Railway equip. moved on wheels	71,593	102,748	31,155	53,196	54,886	1,690
Railway equip. S. U. not moved on own wheels	6,407	11,026	4,619	5,382	5,449	67
Railway equipment parts	78,480	210,734	132,254	78,687	113,372	34,685
Vehicles other than motor	28,571	68,811	40,240	25,332	63,186	37,854
Automobiles, passenger	75,634	492,469	416,835	80,328	489,220	408,892
Automobiles, freight	66,670	158,707	92,037	63,612	167,341	103,729
Vehicles, motor	33,433	195,793	162,360	46,247	267,231	220,984
Auto. and auto. trucks, K. D.	2,817	12,274	9,457	3,007	7,016	4,009
Vehicle parts	116,499	525,275	408,776	98,494	563,933	465,439
Airplanes, aircraft, and parts	13,326	24,469	11,143	12,095	22,544	10,449
Hardware, n.o.s.	21,906	40,475	18,569	13,017	30,032	17,015
Household utensils	6,826	22,773	15,947	5,051	19,679	14,628
Refrigerators, freezing apparatus	24,470	180,440	155,970	16,116	254,042	237,926
Laundry equipment	5,585	72,753	67,168	3,444	103,232	99,788
Stoves, ranges, and parts	102,495	164,093	61,598	88,805	187,505	98,700
Tools and parts	6,024	11,881	5,857	3,500	8,809	5,309
Containers, metal	335,649	468,908	133,259	380,459	502,835	122,376
Totals	1,527,083	4,093,769	2,566,686	1,447,565	4,229,827	2,782,262

Source: U. S. Interstate Commerce Commission, *Tons of Revenue Freight Originated and Tons Terminated . . . 1947; 1948.*

commodity classifications used by the Interstate Commerce Commission and the United States Corps of Engineers, and so it is entirely possible that some items may have been either included or excluded improperly in the tables that have been constructed to represent the movements in this class. In general, the data confirm the widely held opinion that the South receives a large part of the finished products that it uses from manufacturers who are located outside the region. Data similar to those used for steel mill products are presented by Tables 124 to 128.

Only a brief summary of the data on movements of finished iron and steel products will be attempted. Relatively small quantities move on the inland waterways and in coastwise trade compared with steel mill products. Exports from New Orleans and several of the other ports were important, but the outstanding features are those that are brought out by the freight traffic statistics. In each of the products listed in Table 124 and in each of the eleven states of the South, terminations exceeded originations. It is quite evident that the South buys finished iron and steel products in quantity from other regions. This fits directly into the situation with respect to the limited extent to which the processing and fabricating industries have been developed and to the problems related to future developments. While there is much more to the problem of location than discovering products that are being bought from the outside, the presence of sizable markets for products that might be manufactured from raw materials which are near at hand at least presents a challenge.

The rail and water movements of the finished iron and steel products can be summarized in a manner similar to that used for the steel mill products.

Table 125

Tons of Finished Iron and Steel Products Originated and Terminated as Revenue Freight in the Several Southern States, 1947 and 1948

	1947			1948		
	Originated	Terminated	Difference (term. over orig.)	Originated	Terminated	Difference (term. over orig.)
Southeast						
North Carolina	34,138	201,371	167,233	21,516	203,504	181,988
South Carolina	18,943	100,750	81,807	10,906	108,667	97,761
Georgia	226,152	518,990	292,838	228,463	585,861	357,398
Florida	153,739	411,390	257,651	149,362	393,877	244,515
Tennessee	275,723	406,608	130,885	298,215	419,098	120,883
Alabama	159,040	269,362	110,322	137,459	293,234	155,775
Mississippi	48,795	113,069	64,274	32,266	109,761	77,495
Arkansas	49,016	124,768	75,752	39,296	144,636	105,340
Louisiana	137,301	463,933	326,632	128,360	464,118	335,758
Total Southeast	1,102,847	2,610,241	1,507,394	1,045,843	2,722,756	1,676,913
Southwest						
Oklahoma	62,483	230,231	167,748	52,624	268,567	215,943
Texas	361,753	1,253,297	891,544	349,098	1,238,504	889,406
Total Southwest	424,236	1,483,528	1,059,292	401,722	1,507,071	1,105,349
Total South	1,527,083	4,093,769	2,566,686	1,447,565	4,299,827	2,782,262
Total United States	26,343,520	25,781,629	....	26,693,356	25,995,684	....
Per cent of United States						
Southeast	4.2	10.1	....	3.9	10.5	....
Southwest	1.6	5.8	....	1.5	5.8	....
Total South	5.8	15.9	....	5.4	16.3	....

Source: U. S. Interstate Commerce Commission, *Tons of Revenue Freight Originated and Tons Terminated . . . 1947; 1948.*

	Tons
Terminations of finished iron and steel products in the South in 1947	4,093,769
Less total originations	1,527,083
Net rail movements to the South	2,566,686
Add—movements to South on Mississippi River (mouth of Ohio to but not including Baton Rouge)	
Through downstream movement	39,196
Inbound downstream movement	68,204
Add imports	651
Coastwise receipts	12,509
	2,687,246
Less—movements from South on Mississippi River (mouth of Ohio to but not including Baton Rouge)	
Through upstream movement	3,217
Outbound upstream movement	1,188
Less—exports	444,284
Coastwise shipments	15,142
Net rail and water movements to South	2,223,415

These figures cannot be considered to have a high degree of precision, but they do give an approximate measure of the size of the movement to the South.

Conclusions

The analysis of the movements of iron and steel products in 1947 and 1948 shows that there were net movements of pig iron and cast-iron pipe away from the South and indicates that the region was producing surpluses of these products which were finding markets in other parts of the country. On the other hand, the net movements of steel mill products and finished iron and steel products were heavily toward the South, indicating that the basic iron and steel industry was not producing steel mill products in quantities sufficient to meet the demands of southern users and that the processing and fabricating industries were not

Table 126

Water Movements of Finished Iron and Steel Products in the South by Mississippi and Warrior-Tombigbee Rivers in Tons, 1947 and 1948

(in net tons)

Year and kind of movement	Mississippi River			Black Warrior, Warrior and Tom-bigbee Rivers
	Mouth of Ohio to but not including Baton Rouge	Baton Rouge to but not including New Orleans	New Orleans to mouth of passes	
1947				
Total	314,612	65,183	66,679	....
Upbound	94,025	4,750	1,072	....
Outbound (Upbound)	1,188	9,129	5,044	....
Inbound (Upbound)	10,977	1,616	1,957	....
Through (Upbound)	3,217	4,342	7,155	....
Downbound	94,109	....	246	....
Outbound (Downbound)	3,696	2,428	1,956	....
Inbound (Downbound)	68,204	2,646	13,155	....
Through (Downbound)	39,196	40,272	36,094	....
1948				
Total	272,507	46,219	76,711	1,186
Upbound	58,400	25	92	....
Outbound (Upbound)	350	3,189	7,578	....
Inbound (Upbound)	4,173	5,755	6,023	111
Through (Upbound)	5,510	6,141	18,364	....
Downbound	83,301	60	38	....
Outbound (Downbound)	6,484	2,426	2,391	1,075
Inbound (Downbound)	92,135	1,172	14,191	....
Through (Downbound)	22,154	27,451	28,034	....

Source: U. S. Engineer Department, *Annual Report*, Part 2, 1947, 1948.

manufacturing finished products in quantities that were as great as the market was taking. To avoid over-hasty conclusions, it should immediately be said that the mere existence of these differences in the region between production and demand do not in themselves constitute proof that an expansion is warranted. Other factors such as the locations of the markets, optimum size of plant, availability of raw materials and labor, and costs of transportation must be considered in arriving at final conclusions.

Table 127

Water Movements of Finished Iron and Steel Products by Gulf Intracoastal Waterway, in Tons, 1947 and 1948

(in net tons)

	Pensacola Bay, Florida to Mobile Bay, Alabama	Mobile Bay, Alabama to New Orleans, Louisiana	Mississippi River, Louisiana to Sabine River, Texas	Sabine River, Texas to Galveston, Texas	Galveston to Corpus Christi, Texas
1947					
Total	3,285	3,450	40,520	2,703	876
Inbound	....	....	6,883	960	766
Outbound	....	....	18,899	60	110
Through					
Eastbound	870	1,481	6,803	192	....
Westbound	2,415	1,969	4,427	1,489	....
Internal					
Eastbound	....	....	1,811	2	....
Westbound	....	....	1,697	....	....
1948					
Total	2,933	12,559	75,060	18,363	271
Inbound	....	....	16,466	4,309	....
Outbound	....	....	26,538	958	....
Through					
Eastbound	778	3,407	8,807	2,841	20
Westbound	2,155	9,152	19,312	10,215	241
Internal					
Eastbound	....	....	2,028	40	10
Westbound	....	....	1,909	....	....

Source: U. S. Engineer Department, *Annual Report,* Part 2, 1947, 1948.

Table 128

Foreign and Coastwise Trade in Finished Iron and Steel Products at
Southern Ports, in Tons, 1947 and 1948
(in net tons)

	Foreign		Coastwise	
	Imports	Exports	Receipts	Shipments
1947				
Charleston	....	1,142	224	237
Savannah	....	4,953	13	747
Jacksonville	....	1,430	421	615
Tampa	2	1,658	654	250
Pensacola	....	28,831	200	951
Mobile	....	39,054	1,225	3,154
New Orleans	631	243,422	5,534	7,832
Beaumont		822	....	20
Orange	....	....	....	....
Port Arthur	1	268	....	....
Sabine Pass	....	....	....	....
Galveston Channel	1	81,763	45	39
Houston Channel	16	40,941	4,193	1,297
Total	651	444,284	12,509	15,142
1948				
Charleston	248	4,425	50	200
Savannah	108	5,059	....	7
Jacksonville	1,043	840	....	93
Tampa	88	2,235	240	23
Pensacola	....	1,475	....	....
Mobile	78	8,121	1,575	3,896
New Orleans	9,151	201,481	3,379	5,993
Beaumont	....	7	....	....
Orange	....	3	....	....
Port Arthur	....	40	91	....
Sabine Pass	....	....	....	....
Galveston Channel	2	2,910	....	27
Houston Channel	6,352	37,989	7,202	483
Total	17,070	263,585	12,537	10,722

Source: U. S. Engineer Department, *Annual Report*, Part 2, 1947, 1948.

CHAPTER XXIII

THE CONSUMPTION OF STEEL MILL PRODUCTS IN THE SOUTH

The previous chapter examined the data on movements of iron and steel and their products in the South. The task set for the present chapter is to arrive at an approximation of the quantity of steel mill products used in the South. Consumption may be studied on at least two levels. One may be designated as the steel mill shipment level. The other may be called the ultimate consumption level. The first attempts to determine the quantities of steel shapes and other products, in the forms produced by the steel mills, that are used in an area by manufacturers, fabricators, construction contractors, and other users. The second attempts to determine the quantities of steel which find use in an area in the form of finished products such as automobiles, commercial and household equipment and appliances, industrial machinery, farm implements, and building and other structures without regard to the places where the finished products may have been manufactured. While ultimate consumption is a factor of basic importance in evaluating the potential development of an area, it is also a subject on which data are scarce and difficult, if not impossible, to shape into a comprehensive estimate. The attention for the present, therefore, is on consumption at the steel mill shipment level.

Methods of Securing Consumption Figures

Several approaches to the problem of getting consumption figures on an area basis are possible, and the reader's understanding of the data which will be presented later should be increased by a brief summary of the more important types.

1. Consumption statistics on an area basis might be based on reports of steel producers on the quantities of their products shipped to the area.

2. Consumption statistics on an area basis might be based on reports of steel users of the quantities used in their operations.

3. Estimates of the quantities consumed may be prepared that make use of the various available sources of information and of the opinions of those who have been in intimate contact with the problems.

It scarcely needs to be said that each of these alternatives presents its own problems, but some further discussion should be helpful.

The only attempt to get data on steel consumption on areas smaller than the nation on the basis of reports of steel producers was that made by the Temporary National Economic Committee, which requested the major steel corporations to report their shipments by state of destination in 1937. The tabulations of these returns provide the only statistics on a state basis which cover all kinds of uses. As mentioned previously, the American Iron and Steel Institute, since 1940, has been securing reports from member companies of total shipments (on Form AIS 16) broken down according to the industry or market classification of the user. There has been considerable sentiment in the industry to have the reporting done on a state-of-destination basis, but this has not yet been done. While reporting by producers has many advantages in securing complete coverage, there are difficulties also. The shipper often does not have accurate information of the uses to which materials are to be put and may not know the final destinations of the steel that is being shipped. These conditions apply particularly to shipments to jobbers. Another difficulty arises in shipments to other members of the industry of such steel products as wire rods or ingots or billets which in turn are made into steel mill products in somewhat altered forms. If care is not taken, duplication will result.

Several attempts have been made to get information from reports of the users of steel. The War Production Board required reports of stocks and consumption as a part of the system of war-time controls. The Bureau of the Census has tabulated many of these reports and has published in its *Facts for Industry* series some very valuable data on consumption. Directly applicable to this study are the figures for carbon steel consumption by states in the third quarter, 1942. In 1939, selected manufacturing industries were requested to report materials used on the schedule for the Census of Manufactures. The Bureau of the Census made this request again in the 1947 Census of Manufactures and the published reports indicate that an excellent response was obtained. The main difficulty with data derived from the users of steel is that only one class of user has been covered, namely, the manufacturers of iron and steel products. The number of different kinds of users is so great that it would be a very difficult task to get all of them to report. In addition, it would be almost impossible to eliminate duplications that result from several respondents reporting the use of the same steel at different stages of fabrication.

At least two methods may be used in the preparation of estimates of steel consumption. One method is to proceed from a known fraction of the consumption and expand this fraction (or blow it up) to represent the whole. This is a common method used by market analysts of producing corporations who know the sales of the corporation's own product and estimate the company's per cent of participation in the market. A similar procedure would be to make sampling surveys and expand the results so obtained to secure a figure for the whole.

A second method of estimation is to base the estimate for the desired area upon statistics for the nation as a whole and apportion or allocate a portion to the area. There are several ways by which the allocation may be accomplished. Perhaps the simplest is to compute a series of allocating percentages which represent the area's participation in the total. An alternative is to prepare formulas based upon the relationship between the consumption of steel and one or more factors for which statistics can be obtained. The use of correlation analysis to test relationships and regression equations in making the estimates represents this type of approach.

As suggested by the preceding discussion, considerable data are available and several of the steel corporations have market research divisions actively engaged in the study of steel consumption. Government agencies have also had an interest in the field. One of the leading periodicals of the industry, *Iron Age,* has made several studies of steel consumption and has published estimates for the use by the metal-using industries on a state basis.[1] Still, difficulty was encountered in securing data that represent all kinds of uses in the South and consequently several estimates were prepared for use in this study.

The Estimates of Steel Consumption in the South

The estimate first attempted was for 1939. The statistics obtained by the Temporary National Economic Committee for 1937 provided one important basis for work. A series of correlation analyses was made testing relationships between the available figures on steel consumption and a number of indicators of economic development, such as the number of workers in iron and steel producing and using industries, the percentage of urban population, and the number of tons of freight originated or terminated. From this work, estimates were prepared which were considered to be first approximations. Market research departments of the leading iron and steel companies were contacted and asked for their comments on the figures. Constructive criticisms and additional information on a number of points were ob-

[1] The Iron Age, *Basic Marketing Data,* II.

tained. Revised estimates were then prepared which gave approximations of the total tonnage for each of the 48 states and a breakdown for the South of the total by kinds of steel product.

A second estimate was for the steel used in the metal-using industries of the South during the first quarter of 1945. The *Facts for Industry* series[2] provide detailed information on consumption of steel by metal-using industries in the United States during the war years. Supplementary information on the number of workers and value of shipments of the industries in the South made it possible to work out the region's participation in each of the industries, and these percentages were then applied to the nationwide consumption figure for the industry. In this manner, an estimate for the South was obtained.

The third estimate was for consumption by the metal-using industries in 1947 which was based upon a survey of the Alabama industries. A questionnaire was used and companies contacted either by direct interview or by mail. A high percentage of returns was obtained. The returns were tabulated according to the industry classification used for unemployment compensation reports. The results of the Alabama survey and unemployment compensation reports of the number of workers employed in the states of the South in the industry classifications included in the survey were used to prepare an estimate for the South.

The Census of Manufactures collected and tabulated data on the use of steel by selected industries in 1947. Statistics on the use in the United States has been published for the several industries. Also totals and some detailed information are available on a state basis. As a result, it is possible to get a total based on published figures for steel consumed by manufacturing industries in the South in 1947. In addition, the Bureau of the Census prepared for the Bureau of Business Research a special tabulation which gave a breakdown of the total reported consumption of steel mill products in

the South by industries. As a test of procedures, estimates were calculated by using the South's percentages of national totals of the several industries as the basis for allocating to it a portion of the total steel reported for each of the industries. One estimate was based on the number of production workers as the criterion for allocation and a second, on value added by manufacturing. Both gave totals for the South which were quite close to the total obtained from published state figures. The estimate based on the number of production workers was closer.

The fact that the three last mentioned estimates apply only to manufacturing industries constitutes a limitation that prevents them from being used to represent the total market. The statistics published by the American Iron and Steel Institute on net shipments in 1947 of steel products in the United States by market classifications[3] were used as the basis for an over-all estimate. Information from a variety of sources[4] was used to construct allocating percentages for the several market classes and subclasses which were used to represent the South's share of the total. The total of the quantities allocated to the South provides an over-all estimate for 1947.

All of these attempts have value. Some cover only segments of the total and all are affected to different degrees by characteristics inherent in the primary data. In common with most estimates, relationships are assumed which cannot be proved by any direct test other than that of consistency or reasonableness. Since a multiplicity of figures have been brought together, a serious problem arises as to how to utilize the pertinent data in a manner that will not be confusing. The plan which will be

---

2 U. S. Bureau of the Census, "Fabricated Metal Products"; "Facilities Expansion"; "Quarterly Summary of Materials Consumption . . ."

3 These data are the same as those used in developing the pattern of steel use in Chapter XVIII.

4 Some of the sources used were the special tabulations of the 1947 Census of Manufactures for the South; W. P. B. reports on shipments by steel warehouses; U. S. Department of Commerce estimates of construction; Interstate Commerce Commission statistics of railroads and reports on revenue freight originated and terminated; and U. S. Bureau of Mines reports on mineral production.

followed will be to base the discussion primarily on the over-all estimate for 1947 and to present the other estimates later to supplement the analysis.

Estimated Consumption of Steel Mill Products in the South, 1947

An approximation of the total consumption, or perhaps better called, disappearance, can be derived from the estimate of net rail and water movements of steel mill products into the South and the production of hot rolled iron and steel products in the South. Neither of these two figures can be considered as precise

measurements because questions can be raised as to whether there has been a proper selection of items to constitute the totals. Questions can also be raised as to whether the net movement figure and production of hot rolled products are strictly comparable. In addition, omission of changes in stocks of steel products on hand at the beginning and end of the year and unaccounted for movements (for example, by truck) mean that the net movement and production figures do not account entirely for the steel mill products that were used in the South during the year. Still, the sum of the two quantities should give an approximation of

Table 129

Estimated Shipments of Steel Products to South, by Market Classifications, All Grades of Steel Including Alloy and Stainless, Compared with United States, in Tons, 1947

Market classification	United States	South	Per cent South of U. S.
Steel for converting and processing	5,632,824	76,717	1.36
Jobbers, dealers, and distributors	10,484,144	1,859,835	17.74
Construction, including maintenance	6,257,559	1,861,683	29.75
Contractors' products (two classes)			
Culverts and concrete pipe	219,323	56,585	25.80
Other contractors' products	816,262	53,057	6.50
Automotive	8,846,419	150,389	1.70
Rail transportation	4,879,879	785,007	16.09
Shipbuilding	337,961	72,662	21.50
Aircraft	39,231	1,648	4.20
Oil and gas drilling	930,731	511,902	55.00
Agricultural	1,244,548	109,962	8.84
Machinery, industrial equipment and tools (except construction and related products)	2,676,584	204,268	7.63
Electrical machinery and equipment	1,595,520	13,964	0.88
Appliances, utensils, and cutlery (except cooking stoves and ranges, and refrigerators)	580,061	13,024	2.25
Other domestic and commercial equipment (except manufacturers' hardware)	1,468,042	82,875	5.65
Containers	5,076,170	416,999	8.21
Ordnance and other military	56,908	14,227	25.00
Classifications omitted above and put in different groupings for distribution purposes:			
Air conditioning, ventilating equipment and refrigerators	742,003	22,260	3.00
Builders' and manufacturers' hardware	392,494	1,962	0.50
Plumbing, heating and cooking	1,270,195	123,209	9.70
Mining, quarrying and lumbering, and construction equipment	642,805	32,140	5.00
Total before unclassified	54,189,663	6,464,375	11.93
Unclassified	4,660,795	556,033	11.93
Total, all groups	58,850,458	7,020,408	11.93

Source: United States figures—American Iron and Steel Institute, *Annual Statistical Report, 1947;* estimates for South—Bureau of Business Research, University of Alabama.

total consumption which at least should be useful as a check on the more elaborate estimates. The calculation of the apparent disappearance for 1947 by this method is shown below.

Net rail and water movement of steel mill products into the South—tons	4,486,819
Production of hot rolled iron and steel products in the South	
Alabama (reported production)—tons	2,572,277
Tennessee, Georgia and Texas,[5] estimated production—tons	594,548
	3,166,825
Apparent disappearance in the South—tons	7,653,644

As indicated above, the estimate for 1947, on which the discussion largely will be centered, was based upon the American Iron and Steel Institute report of shipments of steel products by market classification. To represent domestic use, this classification has 18 main groups and 84 subgroups. An attempt was made to allocate to the South its share of each one of the subgroups. Such an apportionment, of course, cannot be highly accurate, particularly in the case of some of the subgroups, but it does bring about a careful weighing of the many factors which influence the distribution of steel. A summary of the results obtained by this procedure is given in Table 129.

The total estimated consumption in the South of 7,020,408 tons is smaller than the apparent disappearance calculated from rail and water movement and production figures of 7,653,644, but the two figures are about as close as can be expected when the diverse methods of calculation and the nature of the primary data are taken into consideration.[6] As compared with the total of the production of hot rolled iron and steel products in the South, estimated at 3,166,825 tons, consumption appears to be more than twice as great. As shown in Table 129, the classes that are estimated to have used over 100,000 tons are: construction (including maintenance), 1,861,683 tons; jobbers, dealers, and distributors, 1,859,835 tons; rail transportation, 785,007 tons; oil and gas drilling, 511,902 tons; containers, 416,999 tons; machinery, industrial equipment, and tools (except construction and related products), 204,268 tons; automotive, 150,389 tons; plumbing, heating, and cooking equipment, 123,209 tons; and agriculture (including implements), 109,962 tons. Several classes that rank among the top consumers nationally were assigned relatively small tonnages in the South on account of the low development in the region in that particular use. These include steel for converting and processing; electrical machinery and equipment; other domestic and commercial equipment (except manufactured hardware); contractors' products other than culverts and concrete pipe; air conditioning, ventilating equipment, and refrigerators; mining, quarrying, and lumbering and construction equipment; and builder's and manufacturer's hardware. The estimates serve to bring to the foreground the effect of the South's weakness in the processing and fabricating industries upon the demand for steel mill products.

The shipment figures for construction in the United States were broken down into ten subclasses. With the exception of oil and gas, the subclasses cover approximately the same construction activities as those included in the

---

[5] The estimate for Tennessee, Georgia, and Texas was made in the following manner: The American Iron and Steel Institute reported a production of 1,077,079 tons of finished hot rolled iron and steel products for Kentucky, Tennessee, Georgia, and Texas. The reported capacity of the four states for hot rolled iron and steel products is 1,263,400 tons. The capacity for Tennessee, Georgia, and Texas is 697,400 tons, or 55.2 per cent of the total of the four. This percentage applied to the production of 1,077,079 tons gives the estimates used above.

[6] An independent estimate made by the Commercial Research Division of the Tennessee Coal, Iron and Railroad Company arrived at a total consumption of 6,505,000 net tons—a total given by permission of the company. Also, the National Industrial Conference Board published an estimate in the *Conference Board Business Record* (August 1950) that average annual shipments to the South (the same eleven states as used in this study) in 1947-48 were 11.8 per cent of a national total of 60,408,000 tons. Shipments made to the South, according to this estimate, would be 7,128,144 tons.

estimates of construction which have been made by the United States Department of Commerce. Consequently, the Department's estimates for the states of the South were used to arrive at an allocation to the South of 23 per cent of the total of the nine subclasses. The use in oil and gas construction was considered to be related primarily to pipe lines, refineries, and other structures connected with the basic petroleum and natural gas industry. The criteria used for the apportionment was derived from the statistics on pipe lines. As of December 31, 1946, the South was reported to have 61,269 miles, or 52.6 per cent, of the total of 116,544 miles of pipe lines in the United States. During the year, a net increase of 2,754 miles was shown and, of this, the South accounted for 1,898 miles, or 68.9 per cent. The proportion of the 1,320,140 tons of steel indicated as used in oil and gas construction in the nation to be allocated to the South was set at 55 per cent. The total estimate for construction in the South, therefore, consists of 1,135,606 tons of steel for general building and maintenance and 726,077 tons for oil and gas.

The data that seemed most applicable to jobbers, dealers, and distributors, other than oil and gas, were those provided by the reports of the War Production Board on shipments from warehouses.[7] The figures were reported for war years, but they were detailed by products and the composition corresponded reasonably well to the product breakdown for 1947 of the American Iron and Steel Institute classifications of jobbers, dealers, and distributors. It was assumed that the relative position of the South in the nation had not changed greatly between 1944 and 1947. The War Production Board reports make a distinction between general steel products and merchant trade products and provide shipment figures which permitted calculating the South's share in each product. The estimates for 1947 were worked out, product by product, and the quantity shown in Table 129 is the sum of the indi-

vidual allocations. In general, the South's share in general steel products was relatively low, averaging about 7.0 per cent. In the merchant trade products, such as standard pipe, coated sheets, nails and staples, bale ties and wire products, the region has a much larger share, the average per cent of participation being around 24.7 per cent. The quantity assigned to the oil and gas trade was treated separately because of the high southern participation which was set at 60 per cent, or slightly less than the percentage of the nation's petroleum that was produced in the South in 1947. The combination of the estimates for general steel products, merchant trade products, and the oil and gas trade accounts for the relatively high percentage for the South of the national total for jobbers, dealers, and distributors shown in Table 129.

The quantities assigned to rail transportation in the United States are given for eight subclasses, as shown below.

	United States	Estimate for South Per cent of U.S.	Estimate for South Tons
Railroad rails, track work, and equipment	2,099,319	...	594,751
Freight cars—railroad shops	630,289	17.0	107,149
Freight cars—independent builders	1,551,404	2.9	44,991
Passenger cars—railroad shop	61,116	17.0	10,390
Passenger cars—independent builders	82,014	2.9	2,378
Locomotives—railroad shops	137,578	17.0	23,388
Locomotives—independent builders	250,568	...	......
Street railway and rapid transit	67,591	2.9	1,960
Total rail transportation	4,879,879		785,007

The quantity assigned to the South for rails, trackwork and equipment was based upon the report to state public service commissions for new rails laid of 331,006 tons.[8] To this was added an allowance for track accessories and other steel that was based upon the ratios be-

[7] U. S. Bureau of the Census, "Steel Warehouses, General Steel Products . . .," "Steel Warehouses, Merchant Trade Products . . ."

[8] Representatives of the Commercial Research Division of the Tennessee Coal, Iron and Railroad Company obtained these data directly from the state reports.

tween these items and rails as derived from the figures for the nation. Data from the *Census of Manufactures* indicated that approximately 2.9 per cent of the production workers on the railroad and street railway car building industry were in the South and this percentage was used as the allocation factor for private car builders. No locomotive builders are located in the South. For railroad shops, recent information was extremely vague. The 1935 *Census of Manufactures* was the last which included railroad repair shops as a manufacturing industry. In that year, 16.8 per cent of the wage earners in the industry were located in the South. According to *Statistics of Railroads*, Interstate Commerce Commission, the southern district accounted for 19.5 per cent of the total expenditure for maintenance of equipment in 1935 and 19.7 per cent in 1947. While the expenditure for maintenance of equipment is not a direct measure of railroad shop operations, the percentages derived from these data indicate that the relative position of the southern railroads in the nation had not changed greatly from 1935 to 1947 and 17 per cent, approximately the 1935 *Census of Manufactures* ratio, was used as the allocating factor.

Two criteria were considered in deciding on an allocation factor of 55 per cent for oil and gas drilling. The 1947 *Census of Manufactures* shows that 58.8 per cent of the production workers in the oilfield machinery and tools industry of the United States were located in the South. The estimates by the United States Department of Commerce of construction expenditures for crude petroleum and natural gas drilling in 1947 indicate 53.2 per cent of the total was made in the South.

The discussion of the four classes that were assigned the largest tonnages in the South indicates in some detail the procedures followed and at the same time brings to the front factors which may be assumed to exercise the strongest influence on demand in the South. Petroleum and natural gas, together, constitute the strongest single factor. Shipments for this use are included in three classes: oil and gas construction, oil and gas jobbers and distributors, and

oil and gas drilling. The total estimated for the South is slightly more than 1.8 million tons or approximately 25 per cent of the total estimated for all uses in the South. The high place held by building construction is also significant, since this class of activity is closely associated with urbanization and industrialization and can be expected to continue to be a strong source of demand in an area that is changing from a predominately rural and agricultural economy to one in which industries and concentrations of population have an increasingly important part. The demand originating from rail transportation is important, but probably is stabilized and, under ordinary circumstances, will not increase greatly. Many of the remaining classifications are reflections of the development, or lack of development, of metal-using industries. The amounts allocated to the South are the results of applying the analyses developed in Chapter XXI of the iron and steel processing and fabricating industries of the South.

The question may well be asked, "Given a consumption of approximately seven million tons of steel mill products in the South, what does this mean in terms of the different kinds of products?" A direct estimate on this basis will not be attempted, but a calculation has been made that is based on the assumption that the use in the South in each market classification followed the pattern for the country as a whole. These figures are not presented as estimates of consumption in the South because the region certainly has its own peculiar characteristics, but rather as a pattern which the existing industries and other market demands would indicate as probable. Table 130 presents the figures.

The calculated quantities indicate that the structure of the market in the South, as represented by the relative importance of the various classes of users, places emphasis, from the quantity point of view, on structural shapes, plates, bars, pipe, and sheets. The products in which the calculated figures for the South constitute more than 15 per cent of the total net shipments to domestic users were structural shapes;

Table 130

Consumption of Steel Mill Products in South by Kind of Product, Assuming Consumption in
the Several Market Classifications Follows the National Pattern
Net Shipments to Domestic Users, 1947

	Net shipments to domestic users		
Kind of product	United States* net tons	South net tons	Per cent South of U. S.
Ingots, blooms, billets, slabs, sheet bars, and tube rounds......	2,628,142	137,594	5.24
Skelp	100,382	5,236	5.22
Wire rods.........................	628,232	30,743	4.89
Structural shapes (heavy)....................	4,073,574	880,655	21.62
Steel piling	270,085	77,400	28.66
Plates (sheared and universal).................	5,889,916	981,191	16.66
Rails—Standard (over 60 lbs.).....................	1,920,927	284,161	14.79
—All other........................	169,892	17,316	10.19
Joint bars	149,450	22,069	14.77
Tie plates	459,111	68,789	14.98
Track spikes.........................	146,623	22,505	15.35
Bars—Hot rolled........................	7,531,838	681,428	9.05
—Cold finished	1,585,519	150,031	9.46
—Concrete reinforcing.....................	1,271,344	289,396	22.76
—Tool steel	85,804	9,916	11.56
Pipe and tubes—Buttweld	1,596,284	257,112	16.11
—Lapweld	372,898	81,437	21.84
—Electricweld	1,062,484	317,517	29.88
—Seamless	1,893,216	495,676	26.18
—Conduit	151,313	21,975	14.52
—Mechanical and pressure....................	629,020	75,132	11.94
Wire—Drawn	2,484,067	151,813	6.11
—Nails and staples.....................	775,782	127,144	16.39
—Barbed and twisted....................	217,453	36,437	16.76
—Woven wire fence....................	401,132	66,577	16.60
—Bale ties	119,298	18,537	15.54
Black plate—Ordinary	713,043	63,074	8.85
—Chemically treated	18,209	1,421	7.80
Tin and terne plate—Hot dipped..........................	1,586,802	133,380	8.41
—Electrolytic	1,558,189	129,168	8.29
Sheets—Hot rolled........................	7,087,761	596,284	8.41
—Cold rolled........................	5,391,218	284,481	5.28
—Coated	1,540,230	176,153	11.44
Electrical sheets and strip........................	459,137	5,888	1.28
Enameling sheets.........................	226,384	15,070	6.66
Strip—Hot rolled........................	1,666,594	117,848	7.07
—Cold rolled........................	1,480,457	111,643	7.54
Wheels	325,297	50,836	15.63
Axles	183,351	27,375	14.93
Total	58,850,458	7,020,408	11.93

*Excludes exports and shipments to members of the industry for further processing.

Source: United States—American Iron and Steel Institute, *Annual Statistical Report, 1947.* South—calculated on the basis of using
the same per cent distribution by products in each market classification for the South as in the United States.

Note: This is not intended as an estimate of the quantities actually consumed in the South, but as an indication of what southern
consumption would be if it followed the national pattern.

steel piling; plates (sheared and universal); track spikes; concrete reinforcing bars; pipe and tubes, buttweld, lapweld, electricweld, and seamless; nails and staples; barbed and twisted wire; woven wire fence; bale ties; and wheels. These are products largely associated with construction and with petroleum and gas. On the other hand, possible demands in quite considerable quantities are indicated for such products as tin and terne plate, cold rolled sheets, cold rolled strip, and cold finished bars. Whether the actual demand exists at present is problematic, but the kinds of industries now in existence indicate that a potential market for the products should develop. The data presented in Table 130 should have value in indicating the kinds of steel which the market in the South should require.

Consumption of Steel Products by the Iron and Steel Processing and Fabricating Industries of the South, 1947

Having presented the estimate of the over-all use of steel in the South, attention can well be directed to consumption by the metal-using industries. As already stated, the Census of Manufactures collected and published data that apply directly to this problem. These figures, however, cannot be reconciled directly with the over-all estimate because the classification of industries used by the Bureau of the Census in its tabulations and the market classification of the American Iron and Steel Institute follow quite different principles. Consequently, it is impossible to select certain classes or subclasses from the over-all estimate which together will cover the same ground as the Census of Manufactures. As a result, the data based on the latter source must be presented as more or less detached but supplementary information.

It was pointed out in the discussion of possible approaches to the study of the quantities of steel mill products consumed that three estimates have been prepared to represent the consumption in the metal-using industries of the South in 1947. A comparison of the totals obtained by these estimates with the total shown in Table 131 throws light on the probable consumption.

1. Total reported consumption of steel mill products in metal-fabricating establishments in the South according to 1947 *Census of Manufactures*.................. 2,524,520

2. Total estimated consumption of steel mill products in metal-fabricating industries of the South based on 1947 *Census of Manufactures* reports for industries in United States allocated to the South according to share of production workers 2,373,039

Table 131

Tons and Value of Steel Mill Shapes Consumed by Iron and Steel Processing and Fabricating Establishments, United States and South, 1947

Industry	Tons of steel mill shapes consumed			Value of steel mill shapes consumed (In thousands of dollars)		
	United States	South	Per cent South of U. S.	United States	South	Per cent South of U. S.
Structural metal products........................	7,382,861	960,605	13.01	597,740	85,524	14.31
Structural and ornamental products............	3,874,821	559,854	14.45	284,341	46,295	16.28
Boiler shop products..........................	2,289,266	378,742	16.54	196,035	36,655	18.70
Other structural metal products*..............	1,218,774	22,009	1.81	117,364	2,574	2.19
Motor vehicles and equipment....................	6,653,185	50,528	0.76	597,204	5,518	0.92
Truck and bus bodies.........................	210,504	12,795	6.08	18,775	1,678	8.94
Truck trailers................................	91,479	20,529	22.44	9,288	2,098	22.59
Automobile trailers...........................	6,802	1,975	29.04	919	233	25.35
Motor vehicles and parts......................	6,344,400	15,229	0.24	568,222	1,509	0.27

Table 131 (cont'd)

Tons and Value of Steel Mill Shapes Consumed by Iron and Steel Processing and Fabricating Establishments, United States and South, 1947

Industry	Tons of steel mill shapes consumed			Value of steel mill shapes consumed (In thousands of dollars)		
	United States	South	Per cent South of U. S.	United States	South	Per cent South of U. S.
Tin cans and other tinware	3,106,461	274,263	8.83	354,994	32,234	9.08
Miscellaneous fabricated metal products	2,733,090	233,898	8.56	238,270	18,239	7.65
Metal stamping and coating	2,504,469	26,926	1.08	247,765	2,747	1.11
Tractors and farm machinery	1,854,909	83,666	4.51	159,924	7,558	4.73
Iron and steel forgings	1,630,208	5,658	0.35	120,936	433	0.36
Electrical industrial apparatus	1,482,982	7,832	0.53	166,083	1,207	0.73
Service and household machines	1,251,393	20,135	1.61	142,406	2,711	1.90
Refrigeration machinery	822,462	16,944	2.06	92,878	2,360	2.54
Other service and household machinery**	428,931	3,191	0.74	49,528	351	0.71
Heating and plumbing equipment	1,151,280	79,519	6.91	117,717	9,878	8.39
Construction and mining machinery	1,034,471	188,268	18.20	94,635	20,217	21.36
Furniture and fixtures	1,006,418	43,508	4.32	90,725	5,236	5.77
Fabricated wire products	980,713	42,801	4.36	124,559	4,208	3.38
General industrial machinery	880,133	32,560	3.70	97,206	3,712	4.13
Pumps and compressors	125,305	6,621	5.28	16,237	1,057	6.51
Elevators and escalators	54,804	5,124	9.35	5,005	354	7.07
Conveyors	238,959	14,337	6.00	21,329	1,158	5.43
Blowers and fans	87,068	2,628	3.02	9,648	370	3.83
General industrial machinery, n.e.c.	115,548	2,553	2.21	16,072	652	4.06
Other general industrial machinery industries***	258,449	1,297	0.5	28,915	121	0.4
Cutlery, hand tools, and hardware	849,063	3,002	0.35	102,681	369	0.36
Ships and boats	664,601	335,808	50.53	49,114	24,080	49.03
Special-industry machinery	458,307	37,771	8.24	63,884	5,814	9.10
Food-products machinery	90,845	2,852	3.14	15,068	354	2.35
Textile machinery	105,893	5,235	4.94	16,914	1,301	7.69
Woodworking machinery	26,562	4,738	17.84	3,986	569	14.27
Special-industry machinery, n.e.c.	199,033	24,946	12.53	21,723	3,590	16.53
Other special-industry machinery industries†	35,974	......	....	6,193	......	....
Miscellaneous machinery and parts	398,164	1,169	0.29	62,152	246	0.40
Engines, electrical equipment	237,694	......	....	23,738	......	....
Electrical appliances	218,162	2,182	1.00	24,916	287	1.15
Engines and turbines	127,230	......	....	18,106	......	....
Lighting fixtures	127,009	395	0.31	15,905	48	0.30
Office and store machinery	118,826	......	....	18,988	......	....
Insulated wire and cable	40,416	......	....	6,528	......	....
Other metal fabricating industries††	2,491,024	94,026	3.77	270,646	6,081	2.25
Total	39,383,069	2,524,520	6.41	3,799,438	236,347	6.22

*Includes: Metal doors, sash and trim, and sheet metal work.

**Includes: Domestic laundry equipment; laundry and dry-cleaning machinery; sewing machines; vacuum cleaners; measuring and dispensing pumps; and service and household machines, n.e.c.

***Includes: Industrial trucks and tractors; power-transmission equipment; industrial furnaces and ovens; and mechanical stockers.

†Includes: Paper-industry machinery; and printing-trades machinery.

††Difference between the total reported usage and the quantities and values accounted for by the specific industries given above.

Source: *Census of Manufactures, 1947;* Bureau of the Census, Special tabulation; "Consumption of Metal Mill Shapes . . . 1947"; "Consumption of Steel Mill Shapes . . . 1947."

3. Total estimated consumption of steel mill products in metal-fabricating industries based upon a special survey of Alabama industries and expanded by unemployment compensation data to cover the South 3,088,578

4. The *Iron Age* estimate (1948)........... 2,091,646

Of these, the *Iron Age* has much the lowest estimate. The fact that the figures represent 1948 makes the difference greater because consumption in 1948 was generally somewhat above that of 1947. The estimate based on the Alabama sample is the highest. In part, this may be explained on the grounds that the estimate covers industries for which the census made no reports. The estimate listed second shows that in this case, the total of an estimate made by allocating a share of national totals to the region comes quite close to the reported figure. This is of interest because it provides one case where an estimate based on the allocation procedure can be checked directly against a reported figure.

The census data can scarcely be considered as an exact measurement of consumption because the accuracy of reporting is not known, and there are industries which the census omits from its consumption reports. Also, it must be admitted that the estimates are based on assumptions that have not been proved. Still it seems reasonable to conclude that the total of the steel mill products used by the metal-fabricating industries of the region ranged somewhere between 2.5 and 3 million tons. If consideration is given to the important place held by steel mill products such as rails, oil country goods, and wire products, that find use in the area without further fabricating by a manufacturer, the over-all estimate of seven million tons compared with a use of 2.5 to 3 million tons by the metal fabricators does not seem unreasonable.

The over-all view of the consumption of steel mill products by metal-fabricating industries in the South needs to be supplemented by more detailed data on the position occupied by the various industries in the total use. A special tabulation of the steel consumption reports for 1947 of the *Census of Manufactures* provides the information which is presented in Table 131. Both the quantity and value of the steel consumed by the various industry groups or industries in the South and the United States are shown. The groups are arranged in order of the number of tons of steel reported consumed in the nation. In the case of several groups, a more detailed breakdown of the constituent industries is given. In general, the data on steel consumption are consistent with the analyses presented in Chapters XX and XXI of the iron and steel processing and fabricating industries. A brief summary of the outstanding facts, however, will be given.

One of the conspicuous features of consumption in the South is the concentration in a relatively small number of industry groups. There are five industry groups in the South that reported 100,000 tons or more. The total for these five groups was 1,992,842 tons, or 78.9 per cent of the region's total. In the United States, these same groups accounted for only 37.9 per cent of the total consumption by metal fabricators. The five are structural metal products, tin cans and other tinware, miscellaneous metal fabricated products, construction and mining machinery, and ships and boats.

A second important characteristic of the situation in the South is the very low position that the South occupied in several of the industry groups that nationally were among the largest users of steel. In the United States, motor vehicles and equipment were reported as using 6,653,185 tons of steel. The South's share of this was only three-fourths of one per cent. The only subdivisions of the group in which the South made a relatively good showing were the two small industries of truck trailers and automobile trailers. Metal stamping and coating used a total of 2,504,469 tons in the United States and only 26,926 tons in the South, or slightly more than one per cent. Other important groups in which the South had very small shares are listed below.

	United States' consumption	South's consumption	Per cent South of U. S.
Iron and steel forgings	1,630,208	5,658	0.35
Electrical industrial apparatus	1,482,982	7,832	0.53
Service and household machines	1,251,393	20,135	1.61
Cutlery, hand tools, and hardware	849,063	3,002	0.35

The total consumption of the six industry groups mentioned in this paragraph was 14,-371,300 tons, or approximately 36.5 per cent of the consumption of all metal fabricating industries in the United States. In these industries, the South accounted for only 0.8 per cent of the total for the nation.

A third characteristic is the weakness of the South in the manufacture of finished metal products and in the industries closely associated with such products. The industries mentioned in the preceding paragraph fall in this class. Other such industries are electrical appliances, electrical equipment for engines, engines and turbines, lighting fixtures, and office and store machinery. In addition, the South's representation can scarcely be called strong in most of the industries manufacturing agricultural and industrial machinery.

While Table 131 brings the weaknesses of consumption by the metal-fabricating industries in the South into sharp focus, the picture is not entirely dark. There are a number of industries in which the region has made at least a substantial beginning and some in which it holds a very important place. The group in which the South had the largest share of the national total was in ship and boat building and repair, in which the South's consumption was slightly more than 50 per cent of the total. The group with the largest tonnage in the South was structural metal products with a total of 960,605 tons. As mentioned above, there were four other groups whose reported consumption exceeded 100,000 tons. In one of these groups, construction and mining machin-

ery, there was one industry, oilwell machinery and equipment, in which the South holds a predominant position in the nation. Other finished product industries in which the South made at least a fairly good showing were truck trailers, automobile trailers, woodworking machinery, special industry machinery, elevators and escalators, miscellaneous fabricated metal products, heating and plumbing equipment, truck and bus bodies, conveyors, pumps and compressors, and textile machinery.

It has previously been pointed out that the *Census of Manufactures* industry classification and the American Iron and Steel Institute's market classification are quite different in principal. Also, it is very probable that many establishments secure much of their supplies of steel products from jobbers and distributors. These conditions prevent anything but rough checks between the statistics presented in Table 131 and the over-all estimates of Table 129. Comparisons of such general groups as construction, industrial machinery and equipment, domestic and commercial appliances, and equipment, electrical machinery, and containers do not suggest serious inconsistencies between the two sources. The quantity figures of corresponding groups differ quite considerably, but the relative positions in the structure are much the same. Perhaps the largest difference is in shipbuilding, where the *Census of Manufactures* shows much larger figures than does the Institute.

Steel Consumption of Metal-Using Industries by States

The *Censue of Manfactures 1947* provides the only source from which steel consumption of metal-fabricating industries in the South can be obtained that is based entirely on reports of the consuming industries. These figures should be of interest. The tons of steel mill shapes and forms reported for metal-fabricating establishments in each of the states of the South are shown in Table 132.

Table 132

Number of Tons of Steel Mill Shapes and Forms Consumed by Metal Fabricating Establishments in States of the South, 1947

State	Tons
North Carolina	79,773
South Carolina	16,620
Georgia	126,030
Florida	144,438
Tennessee	250,630
Alabama	463,284
Mississippi	256,102
Arkansas	16,396
Louisiana	217,115
Total Southeast	1,570,388
Oklahoma	198,648
Texas	755,484
Total Southwest	954,132
Total South	2,524,520
United States	39,383,069
Per cent South of United States	6.41

Source: U. S. Bureau of the Census, "Geographic Distribution of Consumption of Metal Mill Shapes and Forms and Castings: 1947," *Census of Manufactures, 1947,* Series MC 100-10.

The figures shown in Table 132 place Texas and Alabama in the leading positions among the states—the total of the two states being almost one-half the total of the South. Mississippi has a larger figure than the previous analysis would indicate as probable and Tennessee and Georgia have somewhat smaller figures. The metal-using industries of the Carolinas and Arkansas seem to have quite a small demand.

The Bureau of the Census has also published the results of a tabulation which gives the consumption of steel mill shapes and forms by metal-fabricating industries in metropolitan areas and selected counties.[9] Data are available for nine local areas in the South. The total consumption reported in these areas was 1,357,-156 tons, or 53.8 per cent of the total for the South. Thus, the use of steel by manufacturing concerns is largely concentrated in a few centers, but these local areas are widely scattered

[9] U. S. Bureau of the Census, "Consumption of Steel Mill Shapes and Forms . . ."

over the area. The metropolitan areas and selected counties for which data are available are shown below.

	Tons
Atlanta Area	63,352
Chattanooga Area in Tennessee (Hamilton County)	98,501
Memphis Area (Shelby County)	50,381
Birmingham Area (Jefferson County)	367,343
Mobile Area (Mobile County)	26,831
New Orleans Area	163,023
Houston Area (Harris County)	360,060
Dallas County, Texas (Dallas)	118,263
Jefferson County, Texas (Beaumont)	109,402
Total	1,357,156

Consumption of Steel Mill Products in the South Before 1947

It would be highly desirable to compare the consumption of steel in the South in 1947 with that of earlier years. As previously pointed out, several sets of figures are available, but the compilations or estimates have been made under such varied conditions that a high degree of comparability cannot be claimed. However, the total figures do have considerable interest and provide general indicators of the changes that have taken place. Therefore they will be presented and discussed briefly.

The several estimates or compilations may be divided into two groups: first, those that have to do with total consumption of steel in the South; and second, those that have to do only with consumption by the Metal-fabricating industries.

In the first group there are four sets of figures.

1. The compilation made by the T.N.E.C. from reports of steel producers of shipments of steel in 1937 to destinations in the several states
   Total for the South....3,525,200 tons

2. An estimate for 1939 made by the Bureau of Business Research, University of Alabama, based on the T.N.E.C. figures for 1937, correlation analysis of relation of steel consumption with other factors, and supplementary information obtained from others
   Total for the South....3,242,500 tons

3. An estimate for 1939 based on allocating to the South a share of the steel consumed in the

United States for various purposes (The approach is similar to that followed in the over-all estimate for 1947 but the limitations of the data available for 1939 are much more serious than in the later year)
Total for the South by this estimate 3,779,091 tons

4. (a) An estimate of total disappearance of steel mill products in 1940 based upon the statistics of movements on railroads, inland waterways, ocean shipments, and production of rolled iron and steel products in the South (This estimate is similar to one made for 1947)
              Total for the South ....4,507,580 tons
  (b) An estimate for 1939 of 80.29 per cent of the 1940 estimate made in 4a above (Production of rolled iron and steel products in 1939 was 80.29 per cent of 1940)
             Total for the South ... 3,619,136 tons

The totals for 1939 range from 3.2 million to 3.8 million tons. This range is not surprising, and it seems reasonable to conclude that the steel mill products consumed in the South in 1939 were somewhat in excess of 3 million tons compared with the estimate of 7 million tons for 1947. Thus an approximate doubling of annual consumption in the eight year period is indicated.

The totals for steel consumption by metal fabricators in the South from the several sources follow.

1. Carbon steel consumption in the South by metal-fabricating industries as compiled from the reports to the War Production Board[10]
    Third quarter 1942.............. 814,222 tons
    1942, at the third quarter rate—
       four times the third quarter....3,256,888 tons

2. Estimate of steel consumption of metal-fabricating industries based on War Production Board reports of consumption for the United States and reports of number of employees in the United States and the South

    First Quarter 1945
    Carbon steel .... 671,444 tons
    Alloy steel .... 89,192 tons
    Total steel .... 760,636 tons

    1945, at the first quarter rate—
    four times the first quarter
    Carbon steel ... .2,685,776 tons
    Alloy steel .... 356,768 tons
    Total steel ....3,042,544 tons

[10] U. S. Bureau of the Census, "United States Consumption of Carbon Steel . . ."

Comparisons of the quantities indicated for 1942 and 1945 with the *Census of Manufactures'* tabulation of 2,524,520 tons for 1947 indicate a decline from the war-time consumption. In view of the large quantities used in shipbuilding and other munitions, a decrease in the use of steel mill products by fabricating industries in the South is not surprising. The fact that it was not greater is evidence that the adjustment to a peacetime basis was quite successfully carried out by the industries involved.

Conclusion

While precise figures on the consumption of steel mill products in the South cannot be presented, sufficient information is available to permit the preparation of estimates that are indicative of the quantities used. In 1947, the total consumption by all types of users can be placed at approximately seven million tons, or approximately twice the quantity produced in the region. Uses associated with petroleum and natural gas constitute a very important factor in total demand. Other important sources of demand are building construction and jobbers and distributors.

In general, the use of steel mill products by processing and fabricating plants in the South is relatively low. The consumption is concentrated largely in five industry groups: structural metal products, tin cans and other tinware, miscellaneous metal-fabricated products, construction and mining machinery, and ships and boats. The region is conspicuously weak in consumption by such important steel-using industries as motor vehicles, electrical industrial apparatus, and service and household machines. In industrial machinery, manufacturing consumption is also low although there are several types, notably oil-field machinery and equipment, textile machinery, and woodworking machinery, in which substantial progress has been made.

While consumption for non-manufacturing uses is widely scattered in the South, the use of steel mill products by fabricating industries is largely concentrated in Texas, Alabama, Tennessee, and Georgia. The most important centers of consumption are Birmingham, Houston, New Orleans, Dallas, Beaumont, Chattanooga, and Atlanta.

In 1939, the total consumption of steel mill products was probably between 3 and 3.5 million tons. It seems safe to conclude that consumption in 1947 was approximately double what it was eight years earlier. The available data indicate that the use in 1947 was somewhat lower than it was at the peak of the war period, but the continued high level of the postwar years is indicative of a very substantial increase in the market in the South.

CHAPTER XXIV

TRENDS IN THE SOUTH AFFECTING CONSUMPTION OF IRON AND STEEL

In the preceding chapters, the preponderance of the evidence has supported the conclusion that, compared with the size of its population or area, the South has had a relatively low development of the metal-using industries and that its consumption of iron and steel on the mill shipment level has been comparatively small. Factors contributing to the condition are (1) the South is largely rural and agricultural in character and its agriculture has made relatively little use of mechanical equipment; (2) the South's income and consumer purchasing power is low; (3) there are relatively few places where population and industrial activities are concentrated to a degree sufficient to provide big markets for products typically made from iron and steel; (4) the South's industries have been developed around the processing of such raw materials as cotton, forest products, and tobacco and (with the exception of the petroleum industry), have created relatively small direct demands for iron and steel as raw material; (5) geographically, much of the South can be reached by water and rail routes quite easily from the older and more highly developed processing and fabricating centers of the North and East. The chapters on the trends of the processing and fabricating industries and the movement and consumption of iron and steel in the South have indicated that the situation in the region has greatly improved since 1939. It is the purpose of the present chapter to examine the data on changes of a more general economic character to see what light such changes may throw on the potential demand for iron and steel.

Within the limits of one chapter it is not possible to treat all of the numerous elements which have a bearing on the market of a group of products which are as numerous and varied as those derived from iron and steel. Even with those topics that have been chosen for discussion, limitations must be placed on the extent to which detailed information can be presented and resort must frequently be made to summaries of findings.

The topics that have been selected for consideration are as follows:

1. Trends in the number of people living in the South
2. Trends toward urbanization in the South
3. Changes in manner of living
4. Changes in what people do to make a living
5. Trends affecting the ability to produce
6. Trends in income in the South
7. Trends in agriculture in the South
8. Trends in manufacturing in the South.

The primary objective in the study of the trends in each of these fields is to bring to the front the probable effects on the market of iron and steel and their products rather than to make a general economic analysis.

Trends in Number of People in the South

The number of consumers or potential customers is one of the basic factors in appraising the market possibilities of an area. During the first half of the twentieth century, the population of the South increased from 17,911,872 in 1900 to 35,464,786 in 1950, or 98.0 per cent. This is a large increase in number of persons, but was approximately the same per cent of increase as occurred in the United States as a whole. Consequently, the South has remained in approximately the same relative position. Its highest per cent of the nation's total population during the fifty year period was 23.92 in 1940 and its lowest was 23.40 in 1950. The Southwest increased somewhat more rapidly than the nation and hence rose in relative position, while the reverse was true in the Southeast. Florida and Texas, throughout the period, had percentages of increase that were decidedly larger than the United States. North Carolina also made a strong showing except that its per cent of increase from 1940 to 1950 was slightly less than the nation's. Mississippi, Arkansas, and Oklahoma made the weakest showings. In total numbers, then, the South made little change in relative position, but the increase in absolute numbers was large.

With regard to racial composition, the fifty year period has seen the white race increase at a considerably faster rate than the Negro. In the Southeast, the percentage of Negroes dropped from 42 per cent in 1900 to 32.1 per cent in 1940, and, in the Southwest, the decrease was from 17.9 per cent to 12.6 per cent. In 1950, the percentage of non-whites in the population was reported as being 29.0 in the Southeast and 10.9 in the Southwest. The relatively unfavorable social and economic position of the Negro makes it highly probable that the heavy Negro migration from the South will continue and that the future will see still lower percentages.

The high birth rate, migration from the South, and the relatively young age of the region's population has been discussed by almost every writer on the South and needs no elaboration here other than to point out one implication. If the region should retain its high fertility rate and if industrialization or other developments should provide improved opportunities for making a living, a large increase in population can take place by the simple process of the cessation or slowing down of the flow of migration away from the region. Furthermore, the migrants consist largely of persons of working ages and, consequently, a reduction in migration would mean an immediate increase in the labor force.

Shift Toward Urbanization

Of particular significance to the demand for iron and steel and their products is the shift of the South's population away from the farm and the open country to the city, since so many of the large uses are associated with urbanization. The data on the character and degree of the movement to towns and cities is therefore of great interest.

In 1950, the South had 26 cities with populations of 100,000 or more, 24 cities with populations of from 50,000 to 99,999, and 50 cities with populations of 25,000 to 49,999.[1] These 93 cities in 1950 had a total population of 9,383,558 of the South's total of 35,464,786, or 26.5 per cent. In 1900, these same cities had 9.9 per cent of the South's people. Between these two dates, the percentages rose steadily, being 12.9 per cent in 1910, 15.9 per cent in 1920, 20.7 per cent in 1930, and 21.9 per cent in 1940. These same facts may be stated somewhat differently by giving the comparative percentages of increase. The population of the 100 cities increased 429.0 per cent between 1900 and 1950 while the total population of the South outside the 93 cities increased 61.6 per cent. These data give conclusive evidence of a very large growth in the population of the larger cities.

A somewhat more inclusive measure of the increased urbanization of the South is provided by the classification long used by the Bureau of the Census which designates persons living in towns and cities of 2,500 or more as constituting the urban population. The statistics of urban population of the South for 1950 and earlier census years are given in Table 133.

The statistics on urban population serve further to support the conclusion that the South has rapidly been moving toward an urbanized civilization. The data also show that a considerable difference exists between the Southeast and the Southwest in that the move-

[1] These include the unincorporated place of Oak Ridge, Tennessee, but not Bristol, Tennessee-Virginia or Kannapolis (unincorporated), N.C.

ment has been more rapid and complete in the Southwest, particularly Texas; in fact, the per cent of urban population in that area apparently does not differ greatly from the United States as a whole. In the Southeast, the increase likewise has been very rapid, but even then the per cent urban in 1950 (using the old or comparable definition of urban) was slightly less than the national figure for 1900. In the Southeast, the states with the largest urban percentages are Florida and Louisiana, while Mississippi and Arkansas had the lowest percentages.

Changes in the Manner of Living

Much of the increased use of products made from iron and steel can be traced directly to changes in the manner in which people live. Consequently, an important consideration in an attempt to appraise the future of the market for iron and steel in the South has to do with the extent to which the people of the region are sharing in the changes that are taking place. The trend toward urbanization in itself involves decided changes in manner of living on the part of those who move to the city from the country, but it should be remembered that changes are taking place also both within the city and the country. While space does not permit detailed analyses of trends, the reader will be reminded of some of the general movements. Then the trends in the use of electricity will be discussed in a little more detail as

representing a kind of development that is having widespread effects on the use of metal products.

During the early part of the century, large segments of the South's population lived in practical isolation from contact with any but close neighbors. With the prevalent low levels of income, the living conditions of the masses were very primitive. The past twenty or twenty-five years have seen decided improvements, although nearly all measure of social or economic well-being continue to show the South in a low position as compared with the non-South. The automobile and good roads have had a powerful influence in breaking down conditions of isolation. The expanded programs of the public schools; the work of county farm, home demonstration, and public health agents; and the efforts of social, civic, and business organizations have all had a part in changing attitudes and habits. The result is that the South has been moving rapidly to eliminate many of the differences in modes of living that have characterized the past.

Electric energy has come to have such a close connection with trade and industrial activity and with methods of living under modern conditions that statistics on the production and use of electricity are important general indicators of conditions. Consequently, a brief review of these data will be given to supplement the discussion of changes in manner of living.

The increase in generator capacity and pro-

Table 133

Urban Population of the South, 1900-1950

Year	Urban population—number of persons			Urban as per cent of total population			
	Southeast	Southwest	South	Southeast	Southwest	South	U. S.
1900	1,952,868	579,176	2,532,044	13.9	15.1	14.1	39.7
1910	3,019,020	1,257,079	4,276,099	18.4	22.6	19.4	45.7
1920	4,145,055	2,050,706	6,195,761	22.6	30.6	25.0	51.2
1930	6,032,268	3,211,029	9,243,297	29.4	39.1	32.2	56.2
1940	7,288,263	3,791,052	11,079,315	32.1	43.3	35.2	56.5
1950 (old)*	9,871,156	5,719,918	15,591,074	38.7	57.5	44.0	
1950 (new)**	11,022,347	5,977,541	16,999,888	43.2	60.1	47.9	63.7

Source: *Census of Population, 1950.*

*Old definition of urban population.   **New definition of urban population.

duction of electric current in the South and in the nation during the past twenty years has been very large. The total generating capacity of the South increased from 4.8 million kilowatts in 1930 to 10.3 million in 1948, or an increase of 114 per cent. Between the same years, the electric energy generated increased from 11.7 billion kilowatt hours to 52.9 or 353 per cent. These increases in the South were larger percentagewise than in the United States as a whole, and, as a result, the region improved its relative position in the nation. In generating capacity, the South had 15 per cent of the national total in 1930 and 18.2 per cent in 1948 and, in current generated, it increased from 13.2 per cent in 1930 to 18.7 per cent in 1948.

The changes in the number and kind of customers using electrical current are particularly significant to the present discussion, and a comparison of the situation in 1931 (the first year data on rural customers are given) and 1948 is given in Table 134.

The increases in customers in the residential, or domestic, and the rural classifications in the South both in numbers and in the region's

share of national totals are especially impressive and should have particular significance to manufacturers of the wide range of household appliances and equipment that require electricity and also of many types of equipment that find use on farms which have access to power lines. The increases in the number of commercial and industrial customers are smaller percentagewise than those of the first two named classes, but there was a significant increase in the per cents of the totals of the nation that are accounted for by the South. The data on the production and use of electricity supports the conclusion that the South is making rapid progress in the modernization of its homes and its business establishments.

Changes in What People Do to Make a Living

The occupations by which people make a living have direct effects on the kind and quantities of commodities which they will buy. The statistics on occupations of the 1950 census were not available at the time that this analysis was being made and so use had to be made of

Table 134

Number of Customers for Electrical Current in the South by Classes of Service in 1931 and 1948

Item	1931	1948	Per cent increase or decrease
Number of customers			
All agencies	2,680,701	7,665,771	+186.0
Residential or domestic	2,062,659	6,273,518	+204.1
Rural (district rural rates)	70,319	429,425	+510.7
Commercial and industrial			
Small	501,827	893,016	+ 78.0
Large	31,808	40,641	+ 27.8
Street and highway lighting	8,539	5,710	− 33.1
Other public authorities	5,549	23,375	+321.2
South as per cent of United States			
All agencies	10.9	18.8	
Residential or domestic	10.5	18.7	
Rural (district rural rates)	10.1	25.3	
Commercial and industrial			
Small	13.5	17.4	
Large	9.1	19.9	
Street and highway lighting	24.8	18.8	
Other public authorities	21.1	21.1	

Source: Edison Electrical Institute, *Statistical Bulletin*, 1931 and 1948.

less comprehensive data. Four different series representing different fields of activity will be used. These have to do with agriculture, manufacturing, retail trade, and wholesale trade. The statistics are derived from the special censuses that have been taken in these fields.

According to the Census of Agriculture of 1945, the farm population of the South or number of persons living in occupied dwellings on farms remained almost stationary from 1920 to 1940, the total for the region being approximately 13.5 million. During this period, the total population of the South increased rapidly and, consequently, the farm proportion was losing in relative position. Between 1940 and 1945, a sharp decrease in farm population took place, since the totals for the South dropped from 13,327,770 to 9,790,692, or a decrease of 26.5 per cent. The reported number of hired or family workers[2] on farms showed more decided declines, dropping from 5,771,557 in 1935 to 4,100,835 in 1940 and then to 3,223,-

2 These data are subject to considerable question since they are not comparable in the several census years as to dates taken, age of workers covered, and the concept of the worker. See *Census of Agriculture, 1945*, II, 281-282.

962 in 1945. This suggests that many of the members of farm families were finding employment in fields other than agriculture. The decreases in both farm population and the number of hired and family farm workers in the South are greater percentagewise than in the United States as a whole.

The relationship of the decline in farm population and in number of farm workers to the quantity and kinds of goods and services that will be demanded on the farm market can scarcely be determined on the basis of the population statistics alone. Certainly a hasty conclusion that it indicates a decline in the demand for iron and steel products for agricultural use should not be drawn, because such a shift in population may well be a necessary part of changes in the agricultural economy. For example, mechanization may call for increased use of steel rather than the opposite.

Manufacturing provides a second source of employment, and the statistics on the number of production workers published in the reports of the Census of Manufactures may be used as indicators of the changes that have taken place in this field of activity. A word of caution should be given concerning the use of these

Table 135

Number of Production Workers in Manufacturing in the Southeast, Southwest, South, and United States, 1899-1947

Year	Southeast	Southwest	South	United States	Per cent of United States		
					Southeast	Southwest	South
1899	436,030	40,985	477,015	4,501,919	9.7	0.9	10.6
1904	530,003	54,522	584,525	5,181,660	10.2	1.1	11.3
1909	674,099	83,373	757,472	6,261,736	10.8	1.3	12.1
1914	687,723	92,164	779,887	6,602,287	10.4	1.4	11.8
1919	838,089	135,316	973,405	8,464,916	9.9	1.6	11.5
1921	682,654	110,948	793,602	6,475,474	10.5	1.7	12.3
1923	882,752	127,847	1,010,599	8,194,170	10.8	1.6	12.3
1925	901,205	133,125	1,034,330	7,871,409	11.4	1.7	13.1
1927	936,046	144,695	1,080,741	7,848,070	11.9	1.8	13.8
1929	973,840	166,193	1,140,033	8,369,705	11.6	2.0	13.6
1931	724,394	117,443	841,837	6,163,144	11.8	1.9	13.7
1933	764,857	113,878	878,735	5,787,611	13.2	2.0	15.2
1935	860,606	123,473	984,079	7,203,794	12.0	1.7	13.7
1937	1,014,771	159,052	1,173,823	8,569,231	11.8	1.9	13.7
1939	1,001,405	152,757	1,154,162	7,808,205	12.8	2.0	14.8
1947	1,435,161	286,316	1,721,477	11,916,188	12.0	2.4	14.4

Source: *Census of Manufactures, 1947*.

data in comparisons extending over a long period of time because of the changes that have been made from time to time in definitions and in the determination of the kinds of activities and establishments to be included in manufacturing. In general, the earlier census compilations tended to include a wider range of establishments than those made in more recent years. Consequently, direct comparisons tend to understate increases rather than to overstate.

The data presented by Table 135 show a very considerable increase from 1939 to 1947 in the total number of production workers in manufacturing in the South. The statistics for these two census years are comparable, showing an increase from 1,154,162 to 1,721,477, or 49.2 per cent. The number in 1939, however, was not much larger than that reported in 1929; 1927, 1925, and 1923 were not much below the 1929 level. As pointed out above, the census in the twenties had a wider coverage than in 1939 and 1947 and hence the actual increase was probably more favorable than the data indicate. The numbers shown in the earlier years of the century were much smaller, the figure for 1899 being 477,015. In interpreting the figures, the severe setback suffered by manufacturing during the depression of the thirties must not be overlooked. Apparently, there was a decided increase during the first twenty-nine years of the century and the increase between 1939 and 1947 may well be looked upon as a resumption of the earlier trend.

While there has been a decided increase in absolute numbers of production workers, the South has not gained much in relative position in the United States since 1925. In fact it lost slightly between 1939 and 1947 since its per cent of the nation's total was 14.8 in the former year and 14.4 in the latter. Even in 1899, the South reported 10.6 per cent of the United States. The region, therefore, has not been gaining in manufacturing workers at a noticeably faster rate than the country as a whole, and, so far as total manufacturing is concerned, can scarcely be said to be replacing the non-South, but rather to be sharing in the general

industrialization of the nation. The record for the Southwest so far as change is concerned is slightly more favorable than for the Southeast.

A large increase in employment in retail trade is indicated by the reports of the Census of Business. The data may be summarized in the following manner.

	1929	1935	1939	1948
Number of paid employees (part time included) as of November 15				
Southeast	428,798	416,494	525,092	876,918
Southwest	241,797	208,754	269,829	443,563
South	670,595	625,248	794,921	1,320,481
United States	4,286,516	3,898,258	4,600,217	7,083,315
Per cent of United States				
Southeast	10.0	10.7	11.4	12.4
Southwest	5.6	5.4	5.9	6.3
South	15.6	16.0	17.3	18.6

There seems to be ample evidence that the South increased decidedly in the number of persons employed in retail trade and also that there was a steady increase in its relative position from 15.6 per cent of the national total in 1929 to 18.6 per cent in 1948. The 1948 percentage, however, is still considerably below the South's share of total population, 23.4 per cent.

The following summary indicates that a somewhat similar situation seems to exist with reference to wholesale trade.

	1929	1935	1939	1948
Number of paid employees (part time included)				
Southeast	127,365	118,703	171,846	291,380
Southwest	74,270	56,765	80,038	146,734
South	201,635	175,468	251,884	438,114
United States	1,510,494	1,260,553	1,561,948	2,463,433
Per cent of United States				
Southeast	8.4	9.4	11.0	11.8
Southwest	4.9	4.5	5.1	6.0
South	13.4	13.9	16.1	17.8

These data show that the South's share of wholesale personnel is lower than it is in retail trade and hence suggests a field for expansion.

There were, however, very substantial increases both in total numbers and in relative position.

While information on the number of persons employed in agriculture, manufacturing, retail trade, and wholesale trade leave uncovered large fields of endeavor, the tendencies to decrease in the first and to increase in the three last mentioned classifications are consistent with the population trends toward greater urbanization and suggest that similar increases have taken place in the professions and in the other occupations associated with city dwelling.

Trends Affecting the Ability to Produce

In the preceding paragraphs it has been shown that increasing numbers of the people of the South are working and living under conditions favorable to the use of iron and steel products. The extent to which the market will expand depends largely upon the increase in the purchasing power of the people. A basic factor in such an increase is the ability of a people to produce, because production of goods and services and the purchasing power that a people possess go hand in hand. Brief consideration therefore will be given to two of the factors of production: the supply of capital and conditions affecting the productivity of labor.

Capital, either in the form of capital assets or capital funds, has not been plentiful in the South in the past and this condition, no doubt, has been a barrier to a more rapid development. The seriousness of such a lack is hard to assess. Much of the development has taken the form of large plants and this is likely to continue to be the case. Furthermore, many of these plants are branches or subsidiaries of corporations that operate on a national or even an international scale. For such concerns, access to capital should be no problem. The large independent concerns, likewise, should be able to enter the capital markets outside the South provided they can present convincing evidence of the soundness and probable profitableness of their ventures. The smaller and locally owned enterprises probably must depend on local sources for capital and, for them, the problem may be a serious one. It is well known that there has been a large increase in the resources of the commercial banks of the South and also that quite substantial increases have taken place in the number and the assets of insurance companies in the region. These tendencies indicate that there has been a significant trend toward the accumulation of capital funds in the South, but it seems safe to conclude that the region still must draw most of its capital from outside.

No systematic attempt was made in this study to compile new data on the inherent ability of southern labor to produce, but the literature was examined and, in interviews with industrialists, questions were asked concerning their experience with southern labor. The evidence probably is insufficient to support a definite conclusion, but it seems reasonable to accept the hypothesis that low productivity in the South, where it exists, can be attributed to causes other than lack of innate ability and that these causes are largely associated with lack of general education, insufficient training along mechanical lines, poor health conditions, inadequate industrial equipment, inept managements, and other environmental conditions which are capable of being changed.[3] Such a conclusion points to the question of what has been accomplished in improving the conditions that affect the performance of the people.

To attempt to review the changes in all the environmental factors that influence the productive activities of a people is obviously beyond the scope of this study and so only a general statement will be made. Almost all of the statistical data points to the conclusion that in health measures, educational facilities, and in other similar activities the South is below the average for the nation. On the other hand, there can be no doubt that the past twenty or thirty years have seen very substantial progress.

The story of the efforts to control or eliminate malaria, hookworm, and other infectious diseases in the South should be well known.

[3] For the results of two recent studies see: Richard A. Lester, "Effectiveness of Factory Labor: North-South Comparisons," pp. 74-75 and Glenn E. McLaughlin and Stefan Robock, *Why Industry Moves South.*

Vance suggests that the infant mortality rate is an index of the general cultural level.[4] In twenty years, (as defined by Vance) this rate in the United States fell from 85.8 to 47 and in the Southeast it fell from 87.4 to 57.4. Increases in life expectancy provide another general index of improved health conditions. Life expectancy in the United States rose from 48.2 years at birth in 1900-1902 to 62.9 in 1940 for males and from 51.1 to 67 for females. Vance calculates that there is little difference between life expectancy in the Southeast and that of the nation.[5]

Literacy or illiteracy is often used as an index of educational levels. Actually, a measure of the extent to which the young people of an area are carrying their education beyond the elementary grades is probably a better index of progress toward a desirable condition. The ratio of enrollment in high schools to the number of persons of high school age serves this purpose. In 1900, only two persons in the Southeast of each 100 youths from 14 to 17 years of age were enrolled in high schools. By 1938, the ratio had increased to 46 for each 100. The corresponding figures for the nation were 8.5 and 68.3. During this same period, the average length of school term in the Southeast was increased from 96 to 164 days compared with an increase of 144 to 174 in the United States. The expenditure per pupil increased in the Southeast from four dollars to 40 dollars while the national averages increased from 14 dollars to 86 dollars.[6] The figures representing the Southeast are lower than those of the nation, but the rate of increase is frequently greater for the region. Within the Southeast, a somewhat similar situation exists between the two races. As of any particular date, the ratios representing the negro children are decidedly below the corresponding ratios for the whites, but the percentages of increase are much higher for the negroes.

The few facts cited concerning the changes in health and education can scarcely be considered as conclusive proof of the degree of improvement in conditions affecting the productivity of the people of the South, but they do suggest that fundamental changes are taking place and that sound foundations are being laid for continued improvements in the future.

Trends in Income in the South

The purchasing power of a people is most directly indicated by the amount of income which they receive. This situation makes the trends of income especially significant in any appraisal of the possibilities of the area; therefore the outstanding features of these trends will be reviewed briefly. The estimates of state income payments prepared by the National Income Unit of the United States Department of Commerce were used in preparing Table 136. Since income is usually estimated in terms of the dollars of the year to which the figures apply, comparisons over a period of time are distorted by changes in price levels. Table 137 attempts to correct this trouble by presenting index numbers that have been adjusted for price changes.

The estimates of both total income and per capita income show sharp decreases in 1933, a substantial recovery by 1940, and then very large increases during the war and postwar years. The indexes of the South and the United States react to changing conditions in much the same manner with regard to directions of change, but the South in 1933 was not quite as much below its 1929 income level, percentagewise, as the nation as a whole was and increased much more during the 1940's. This situation resulted quite naturally in a much improved relative position for the South. The principal effects of the deflating process of eliminating price changes were to show the decreases in 1933 as much smaller than the current dollar index and to lower the index in the later years. This of course is entirely logical. Also, the adjusted index shows that the increase in per capita income after 1945 was not enough to offset the increase in prices, with the result that the index tended to decrease. Aside from giving a fairly adequate measure of the changes in

4 Rupert B. Vance, *All These People*, p. 372.

5 Vance, p. 352.

6 Vance, pp. 408-417.

the purchasing power of the income of the nation and the region, the adjusted index shows that there has been a very large increase in the real income in the South, both in terms of total income and per capita income, since the former, in 1948, was 130.3 per cent above 1929 and the latter was 94.2 per cent above 1929.

Such increases in purchasing power have a great market significance, particularly for commodities that are classified as producers goods or luxury or semi-luxury items.

From the point of view of relative position, the South in 1929 had 12.7 per cent of the total income payments of the United States. In 1933,

Table 136

Total Income and Per Capita Income of the South and the United States
(expressed in current dollars)

Year	Total income			Per capita income		
	South	United States	Per cent South of U. S.	South	United States	Per cent South of U. S.
1929	10,478.1	82,617.0	12.7	368	680	54.1
1933	6,050.1	46,273.0	13.1	204	368	55.4
1939	9,928.7	70,601.0	14.1	318	539	59.0
1940	10,517.6	75,852.0	13.9	333	575	57.9
1941	13,277.1	92,268.0	14.4	415	693	59.9
1942	17,984.0	117,196.0	15.3	558	876	63.7
1943	23,331.2	141,831.0	16.5	709	1,059	66.9
1944	25,920.0	153,306.0	16.9	812	1,161	69.9
1945	26,530.2	157,190.0	16.9	844	1,192	70.8
1946	27,911.5	171,548.0	16.3	849	1,215	69.9
1947	31,262.5	189,212.0	16.5	948	1,319	71.9
1948	33,724.2	206,011.0	16.4	999	1,410	70.9

Source: Income Estimates, U. S. Department of Commerce, National Income Unit.

Table 137

Index Numbers of Total Income and Per Capita Income in Terms of Current Dollars and Adjusted to Eliminate the Effects of Price Changes, South and United States

Year	Total income				Per capita income			
	Current dollars		Adjusted		Current dollars		Adjusted	
	South	United States	South	United States	South	United States	South	United States
1929	100.0	100.0	100.0	100.0	100.0	100.0	100.0	100.0
1933	57.7	56.0	76.5	74.3	55.4	54.1	73.5	71.8
1939	94.8	85.5	116.8	105.3	86.4	79.3	106.5	97.7
1940	100.4	91.8	122.9	112.2	90.5	84.6	110.6	103.4
1941	126.7	111.7	147.5	130.0	112.8	101.9	131.3	118.7
1942	171.6	141.9	180.5	149.2	151.6	128.8	159.5	135.5
1943	222.7	171.7	220.9	170.1	192.7	155.7	190.9	154.4
1944	247.4	185.6	241.5	181.1	220.7	170.7	215.4	166.7
1945	253.2	190.3	241.6	181.5	229.3	175.3	218.8	167.2
1946	266.4	207.6	234.3	182.6	230.7	178.7	202.9	157.1
1947	298.4	229.0	229.6	176.2	257.6	194.0	198.2	149.3
1948	321.9	249.4	230.3	178.4	271.5	207.4	194.2	148.4

Source: Income Estimates, see Note B, Table 64.

U. S. Department of Labor, *Handbook of Labor Statistics, 1950.* Consumers' Price Index (used as price adjustment factor), p. 100.

the per cent was 13.1; in 1939, it was 14.0 per cent. With the war, the South's share of the total increased to 16.9 per cent in 1944 and 1945. The postwar years saw slight declines, but the figure of 16.4 per cent for 1948 represents a very substantial gain over the 1929 position. In 1929, the per capita income in the South was only 54.1 per cent of that of the country as a whole. The Southeast was still lower, being 48.7 per cent, and the Southwest was 67.9. During the period covered by the data, the per capita situation improved steadily, although there were some setbacks until, in 1947, the per capita income of the South was 71.9 per cent of the nation's. Throughout the period, the Southwest had a higher per capita income than the Southeast. Both improved very materially, although neither subdivision succeeded in reaching a figure equal to the average for the entire country.

The factors influencing changes in income are very complex—as complex as the economy itself—and consequently cannot be discussed adequately in one section of a chapter.[7] Only a few comments on the income changes will be offered. It must be remembered that the thirties and forties represent wide contrasts in general economic conditions—a severe and prolonged depression and a long period of very intense economic activity. The fact that the South showed a well-sustained tendency to improve its relative position under such varying conditions is evidence of strength. Another important feature is that the changes have tended to bring the income pattern in the South more nearly in line with that of the nation as a whole. A third trend of importance has been the change in the sources of agricultural income in the South. Cotton and cottonseed have decreased in relative importance and tobacco, truck crops, peanuts, pecans, hogs, chickens, cattle and calves, dairy products and eggs have increased in their shares of farm income.[8] Fourth, agricultural income failed to increase as rapidly as other kinds of income in the South or as rapidly as agricultural income in the rest of the country.[9] As a result, agricultural income decreased in relative importance in the South. The fifth, and final, point is that the South sustained its income position in 1946, 1947, and 1948 in a really remarkable fashion. The large gains during the war period can be attributed to a large extent to government payments in the form of salaries to military and civilian personnel, military benefits, and incomes arising from direct war activities. With the decrease in war expenditures, a return of the South to its prewar position might have been expected. The fact that no such drastic decline in total per capita income took place is strong evidence of the strength of the trend toward industrialization and general improvement.

That the improved income position of the South carries through to consumer purchases is indicated by the fact that sales of retail concerns increased faster in the South than in the United States. According to the *Census of Business,* the sales in the South increased from 7,274 million dollars in 1929 to 23,508 million in 1948, or 223 per cent. The corresponding percentage of increase for the United States was 170 per cent. This means that the South gained in relative position from 15.1 per cent of the nation in 1929 to 18.0 per cent in 1948. The data on such trade classifications as furniture and appliances, automotive equipment, and building materials and hardware indicate increases of much the same order as total sales.

Trends in Agriculture in the South

The changes that have been taking place in farming operations in the South have implications of importance. The increased acreages of improved pastures and numbers of livestock imply that more fence, feeding equipment, and shelter houses will be needed. The change to the cultivation of a greater variety of crops can be expected to be accompanied by the purchase of a greater number of specialized farm imple-

[7] For more detailed analyses of income trends in the South see Calvin B. Hoover and B. V. Ratchford, *Economic Resources and Policies of the South,* Chapter III, and John L. Fulmer, *Agricultural Progress in the Cotton Belt Since 1920,* Chapter VIII.

[8] Fulmer, pp. 169-170.

[9] Fulmer, pp. 150-151.

ments. The increase in certain types of facilities should encourage the use of a large number
of auxiliary implements or appliances. A tractor calls for a completely new line of implements specifically designed to be used with that
kind of motive power. Availability of electricity can be expected to be a powerful stimulant to the purchase and use of many types of
equipment and appliances that otherwise would
have no place on a farm. Much the same can
be said of running water. Usually the running
water is provided by mechanical equipment
such as pressure tanks and automatic pumps
operated by electric motors. Such facilities mean
a potential market for washing machines, modern bathroom fixtures, water heaters, fans, and
other household appliances as well as improved
livestock feeders and productive equipment in
barns and feed lots. Such equipment also involves the use of pipe and wire.

A very large increase in the investment in
machinery and implements on farms in the
United States has taken place since 1900. The
Census of Agriculture shows a value of 750 million dollars in 1900 and 5.1 billion dollars in
1945. The Southeast and the Southwest have
shared in this increase: the former by increasing from 98 million to 581 million and the
latter from 40 million to 402 million. The
percentage of increase in the Southeast, however, was not as great as that of the nation;
hence the area did not strengthen its relative
position but dropped from 13.1 per cent of the
national total in 1900 to 11.3 per cent in 1945.

On the other hand, the Southwest increased
faster percentagewise than the nation and increased its share of the national total from 5.4
per cent in 1900 to 7.8 per cent in 1945. However, as seen in Table 138, the Southeast had
a more favorable record for the period from
1930 to 1945.

The items shown in Table 138, for the most
part, indicate that the southern regions are
improving their relative positions or, in other
words, increasing faster than the United States,
but the Southeast still falls short of having as
large a share of the several farm facilities as the
number of farms or the size of its farm population would indicate. Still, the facts indicate an
increasing market for farm implements in the
South.

The Edison Electric Institute reports for the
period from 1941 to 1948 indicate a rapid increase in both the Southeast and the Southwest
in the number of farms with electricity. In
both regions, the increases occurred at a faster
rate than in the nation, with the result that the
two southern regions improved their relative
positions. The per cent changes from 1941 to
1948 were as follows:

	Per cent increase in number of farms with electricity
Southeast	172.2
Southwest	175.2
South	173.0
United States	86.5

Table 138

Relative Position of the Southeast and the Southwest in the United States with Respect to Selected Equipment Items, 1920, 1930, 1940, and 1945

| | Per cent of totals for United States | | | | | | | |
| | Southeast | | | | Southwest | | | |
Kind of item	1920	1930	1940	1945	1920	1930	1940	1945
Value of farm implements and machinery	10.7	8.9	10.4	11.3	6.5	8.3	8.5	7.8
Number of farms with:								
Automobiles	10.4	17.5	15.0	17.0	7.5	10.9	9.9	9.3
Motor trucks	10.5	12.5	15.0	16.4	5.5	8.6	8.3	9.2
Tractors	5.6	5.6	5.2	7.5	6.0	6.5	9.0	9.6
Number of farm dwellings with running water	4.9	5.8	...	13.6	7.0	8.0	...	10.0

Source: Based on *Census of Agriculture, 1945.*

The changes in relative position can be summarized by the figures for 1941, 1945, and 1948.

| | Per cent of United States | | |
	Southeast	Southwest	South
Farms with electricity			
1941	17.6	6.2	23.8
1945	20.3	7.8	28.1
1948	25.7	9.2	34.9
All farms			
1940	30.0	9.8	39.8
1945	30.2	9.4	39.6

These data indicate not only that the two southern regions improved their relative positions in the nation but also that the proportion of farms in the South that had electricity in 1948 was approaching the proportion for the nation as a whole.

KINDS OF IMPLEMENTS ON FARMS IN THE SOUTH

The analysis of kinds of implements on farms in the Southeast and in the Southwest is confined to data for the years 1942, 1945, and 1947. The statistics for 1942 and 1945 on numbers of the various kinds of implements are those prepared by the United States Department of Agriculture. Estimates of the number of tractors on farms by states are available. A survey of Alabama furnished data on numbers, sizes, and kinds of implements in 1947 which were useful in making estimates of implements in the other states. Steel and cast iron requirements per unit of the various kinds of implements were set up and used in connection with the estimates of numbers of implements to compute the estimated quantities of steel and cast iron represented by implements on farms. These latter estimates are presented in Tables 139, 140, and 141. The per unit requirements were based upon Farm Equipment Institute requirements and the Department of Agriculture studies of sizes of implements. While the estimates cannot be considered to have a high degree of precision, they were checked with specialists on farm equipment in agricultural colleges, agricultural extension divisions, and the United States Department of Agriculture in an

effort to get results that give a reasonably accurate representation of the situation.[10]

If the relative position of the Southeast with respect to cultivated acres in farms or the number of workers on farms[11] is taken as a basis for comparison, the region is low in almost all types of tractor-drawn equipment and is relatively high in horse-drawn implements, particularly of the walking varieties—the one-horse and one-row items. The disc plow is the only tractor-drawn item in which the region appears clearly to be strong. In the case of power machines, the Southeast occupies a relatively high position in stationary balers and peanut pickers. The concentration of the crop in the region is the obvious reason for predominance in the peanut pickers.

The Southwest, on the other hand, makes a relatively strong showing in tractors and tractor-drawn equipment. Its per cent of the nation's tractors is practically equal to its share of farm workers. For nine of the fifteen kinds of tractor-drawn equipment in 1945, the region's share of the United States total exceeded its share of farm workers. The showing with respect to horse-drawn equipment is not as strong, but there is little evidence of weakness so far as number and kinds of implements are concerned. The Southwest has a favorable ratio between acres cultivated and the number of workers, and the data indicate that the South-

[10] Sources consulted include the following: U. S. Department of Agriculture, "Age and Size of Principal Farm Machines" and "Number and Duty of Principal Farm Machines"; U. S. Bureau of the Census, "Farm Machinery and Equipment" and "Estimated Material Requirements . . ."

Also used were estimates of machines manufactured in 1940 and requirements per unit in pounds prepared by the Farm Machinery Institute. Useful information and advice was given by the Alabama Extension Service, the Bureau of the Census, U. S. Department of Agriculture, and the Farm and Woodworking Machinery Division, Office of Domestic Commerce, U. S. Department of Commerce.

[11] The Southeast, in 1945, had 13.4 per cent of the total acreage used for crops and 29 per cent of the hired or family workers on farms of the United States. The corresponding percentages for the Southwest were 11.7 for land used for crops and 9.0 for farm workers.

west is quite well equipped with both tractor-drawn and horse-drawn equipment.

A comparison of the percentages of United States totals in 1942 and 1945 indicate a general strengthening of the Southeast's position —a strengthening more pronounced in the tractor-drawn items but applicable also to the horse-drawn. In the Southwest, the increases in relative position of some items are offset to a considerable degree, perhaps more than offset, by decreases in others. It might be said that the statistics suggest that the Southwest tended to maintain its relative position—which was strong—while the Southeast strengthened its position—which was relatively weak, except in the simplest types of implements.

Iron and Steel in Implements on Farms

The accuracy of the estimates of the quantities of steel and cast iron in implements on farms is limited by at least three factors. In the first place, the list of machines or implements is by no means complete although the more important kinds are included. Second, even for the kinds of machines listed, the estimated or reported numbers must be considered as approximations. Third, the various kinds of

equipment are manufactured and sold in a wide variety of models and sizes and the proportions of the various models and sizes in use may vary greatly in different locations. While the effects of these factors are difficult to determine, the resulting estimates should give a usable indication of the quantities of metal involved and, what is probably more important, provide indexes of the changes that have taken place.

The figures on steel and cast iron in implements on farms confirm the conclusions drawn from the analysis of the individual kinds of implements, namely, that power equipment was increasing at a quite rapid rate and horse-drawn equipment was decreasing. In the Southeast, the increase in power equipment was much more rapid percentagewise than in the United States and the decrease in horse-drawn equipment was slower. This situation may be taken as an indication that the trend toward power equipment had not reached the stage where horse-drawn implements were being discarded at a high rate. As a result, the share of the Southeast in the steel in the form of farm power implements increased from 5.6 per cent of the United States total, in 1942, to 7.5 per

Table 139

Steel and Cast Iron in Machines and Equipment on Farms in Southeast, 1942, 1945, and 1947

	January 1, 1942		January 1, 1945		January 1, 1947	
	Tons	Per cent of U. S.	Tons	Per Cent of U. S.	Tons	Per cent of U. S.
Steel						
Farm tractors	84,974	5.5	138,339	6.8	207,650	8.1
Tractor implements	156,398	4.9	232,928	5.9	331,465	6.8
Power machines	53,417	9.1	53,299	9.7	53,234	10.2
Total power equipment	294,789	5.6	424,566	6.5	592,349	7.5
Horse drawn equipment	655,106	13.2	625,045	13.3	599,991	13.4
Total all	949,895	9.3	1,049,611	9.4	1,192,340	9.6
Cast iron						
Farm tractors	105,468	5.8	171,740	7.2	257,735	8.5
Tractor implements	79,885	6.2	115,177	7.5	162,150	8.7
Power machines	41,385	15.0	42,397	15.5	43,224	15.9
Total power equipment	226,738	6.7	329,314	7.8	463,109	9.0
Horse drawn equipment	354,988	12.6	339,507	12.7	326,604	12.9
Total all	581,726	9.4	668,821	9.7	789,713	10.3

Source: Estimates by the Bureau of Business Research, University of Alabama.

cent, in 1947. For the same period, its share in the cast iron so employed increased from 6.7 per cent to 9.0 per cent. These shares for 1947 were still low compared with the general position of the region in agriculture. The relative position of the Southeast in horse-drawn equipment increased slightly, since the decrease in this classification was less in the Southeast than in the nation as a whole.

In the Southwest, the changes were smaller percentagewise than those of the Southeast and were more in line with the United States. The Southwest had little change in its relative position.

Table 140

Steel and Cast Iron in Machines and Equipment on Farms in Southwest, 1942, 1945, and 1947

	January 1, 1942		January 1, 1945		January 1, 1947	
	Tons	Per cent of U. S.	Tons	Per Cent of U. S.	Tons	Per cent of U. S.
Steel						
Farm tractors	148,686	9.6	201,101	9.9	258,682	10.1
Tractor implements	418,663	12.3	481,114	12.3	601,481	12.4
Power machines	34,651	5.9	33,311	6.0	32,234	6.2
Total power equipment	602,000	11.4	715,526	11.0	892,397	11.2
Horse drawn equipment	319,666	6.4	287,584	6.1	265,553	5.9
Total all	921,666	9.0	1,003,110	8.9	1,157,950	9.3
Cast iron						
Farm tractors	187,062	10.3	253,051	10.5	325,448	10.7
Tractor implements	200,349	15.6	225,969	14.8	274,273	14.8
Power machines	21,898	7.9	22,220	8.1	22,471	8.3
Total power equipment	409,309	12.1	501,240	11.9	622,192	12.1
Horse drawn equipment	174,796	6.2	162,565	6.1	152,616	6.0
Total all	584,105	9.4	663,805	9.7	774,808	10.1

Source: Estimates by the Bureau of Business Research, University of Alabama.

Table 141

Percentage Change in Steel and Cast Iron in Implements on Farms in the Southeast, Southwest, and United States, 1942-1945 and 1942-1947

	Steel		Cast iron	
	Per cent change 1942 to 1945	Per cent change 1942 to 1947	Per cent change 1942 to 1945	Per cent change 1942 to 1947
Southeast				
Power equipment	+44.0	+100.9	+45.2	+104.2
Horse drawn equipment	— 4.6	— 8.4	— 4.4	— 8.0
All equipment	+10.5	+ 25.5	+15.0	+ 35.8
Southwest				
Power equipment	+18.9	+ 48.2	+22.5	+ 52.0
Horse drawn equipment	—10.0	— 16.9	— 7.0	— 12.7
All equipment	+ 8.8	+ 25.6	+13.6	+ 32.6
United States				
Power equipment	+22.9	+ 49.9	+24.3	+ 52.4
Horse drawn equipment	— 5.4	— 9.7	— 5.7	— 10.3
All equipment	+ 9.2	+ 21.1	+10.7	+ 23.9

Source: Estimates by the Bureau of Business Research, University of Alabama.

GENERAL CONCLUSIONS CONCERNING AGRICULTURE

In the Southeast power equipment has had large percentages of increase in recent years. These increases have received much attention but certain basic conditions must be kept in mind. The region started with little power equipment and consequently any sizable increases will produce large percentages. The reverse of this is that even very large percentages of increase may leave the general situation much as it was. Still, the increase in power equipment, electrification, and such facilities as running water in farm dwellings indicate that a market is developing on the farms of the Southeast for equipment and appliances which, until very recent years, was largely undeveloped. On the other hand, there are characteristics of the Southeast that cannot be overlooked. Much of the land surface is hilly and rough or swampy and hence not well adopted to mechanization. Also, much of the soil is not well suited to agriculture while the large number of small farms is another limiting factor.

Industrialization and urbanization in the region constitute still another set of factors since farmers in adjacent areas are likely to place more emphasis on dairying, poultry raising, truck crops, and the production of food crops that find markets in nearby urban centers. Such development should create demand for mechanical equipment and for specialized buildings and facilities.

On the whole, the market on the farms of the Southeast for products produced largely from iron and steel seems to present very definite possibilities for future development. The Southwest has been a good market for farm equipment and there seems to be no reason to think that it will not continue to be so.

Trends in Manufacturing

Although allowance must be made for the limitations of the data compiled by the Census of Manufactures, the statistical evidence points to very decided increases in the South. In 1899, the South is shown as having 477,015 production workers. By 1919, the number had reached 973,405 and, by 1929, 1,140,033. The great depression brought decreases, but the number of production workers in 1937 slightly exceeded 1929, being 1,173,823 and, in 1947, stood at 1,721,477. However, similar changes were taking place in the United States as a whole with the result that the South's relative position was not greatly changed. In 1899, the South had 10.6 per cent of the nation's production workers in manufacturing. This share was divided 9.7 for the Southeast and 0.9 for the Southwest. In 1947, the corresponding percentages were 14.4 for the South, divided 12.0 for the Southeast and 2.4 for the Southwest. Thus the South's shares in 1947 were well above those at the beginning of the century although the percentages in 1933 and 1939 had been higher.

The series expressed in values, that is wages and value added by manufactures, show more consistent increases in relative position in the South than do the percentages of the nation's totals based upon the number of production workers. Two explanations may be offered. The first is that the wage differential between the South and the rest of the country has been narrowing and the level of wages paid in the South has been moving closer to that of the remainder of the nation. The second explanation is that there is a tendency for southern industry to produce higher grade products and that this trend has been great enough to bring about an increase in the South's relative position as measured in terms of value added by manufacture.

Comparable statistics for industries or groups of industries are available for the South only for 1939 and 1947 and so the analysis on that basis will be confined to the relatively short period of eight years. Furthermore, the discussion will have to do only with the position in the terminal years, 1939 and 1947, and will not attempt to develop the course taken by manufacturing activities in the intervening years. The number of production workers will be used as the statistical measure of manufacturing development. The data broken down by main industry groups are presented in Table 142.

A comparison of the number of production

workers by main industry groups in the South and the United States brings out an unusual situation. The total number of production workers in the South increased 49.2 per cent from 1939 to 1947. This is a very substantial increase in an eight-year period, but was less than the 52.6 per cent increase of the nation. When the per cent increases of the individual groups in the South are compared with the corresponding percentages of the United States, the South's per cent increases are greater than those of the nation in all cases except chemicals and allied products. In this one group, the South had an increase of 61.5 per cent compared with 69.2 per cent for the United States. In many of the industry groups, the region's per cent of increase was much larger than that of the nation. It seems paradoxical that the

South could increase at a more rapid rate in every main group, but one (and in that one increase only slightly less rapidly) and still, as a whole, have a percentage of growth smaller than that of the nation, thus losing in relative position. Yet this is what happened. The reason for this situation is that the percentage of increase of the total is influenced not only by the percentages of increase of the individual subdivisions or groups but also by the relative importance of the various groups in the total. More specifically, the six fastest growing groups between 1939 and 1947 were electrical machinery, machinery, instruments, fabricated metals, transportation equipment, and rubber products. In the South, the high percentage increases in these groups had comparatively little effect on the region's over-all percentage of

Table 142

Number of Production Workers in Manufacturing; the South and the United States by Main Industry Groups, 1939 and 1947

Main industry groups	South			United States			Per cent South of United States	
	1939	1947	Per cent increase	1939	1947	Per cent increase	1939	1947
Food and kindred products	106,421	166,298	56.3	802,133	1,099,478	37.1	13.3	15.1
Tobacco manufactures	30,923	43,687	41.3	87,525	103,289	18.0	35.3	42.3
Textile mill products	445,377	519,165	16.6	1,081,710	1,147,194	6.1	41.2	45.3
Apparel and related products	68,372	115,856	69.5	752,829	972,897	29.2	9.1	11.9
Lumber and products, except furniture	182,614	265,804	45.6	422,947	596,118	40.9	43.2	44.6
Furniture and fixtures	36,038	55,435	53.8	189,382	282,780	49.3	19.0	19.6
Paper and allied products	30,269	55,676	83.9	270,239	388,901	43.9	11.2	14.3
Printing and publishing industries	25,206	38,336	52.1	324,371	438,135	35.1	7.8	8.8
Chemicals and allied products	54,892	88,664	61.5	275,669	466,458	69.2	19.9	19.0
Petroleum and coal products	29,269	49,654	69.7	107,695	169,610	57.5	27.2	29.3
Rubber products	3,871	13,278	243.0	120,740	214,533	77.7	3.2	6.2
Leather and leather products	9,676	17,064	76.4	327,189	348,529	6.5	3.0	4.9
Stone, clay and glass products	29,004	50,242	73.2	267,094	405,755	51.9	10.9	12.4
Primary metals and machinery*	58,614	118,008	101.3	1,208,520	2,254,190	86.5	4.9	5.2
Fabricated metal products	22,762	44,477	95.4	451,087	822,514	82.3	5.0	5.4
Electrical machinery	1,294	8,611	565.5	247,930	639,147	157.8	0.5	1.3
Transportation equipment	12,193	54,807	349.5	544,553	987,142	81.3	2.2	5.6
Instruments and related products	746	3,756	403.5	84,867	181,939	114.4	0.9	2.1
Miscellaneous manufactures	6,643	12,656	90.6	241,725	397,579	64.5	2.7	3.2
Total all industries	1,154,184**	1,721,477	49.2	7,808,205	11,916,188	52.6	14.8	14.4

*Separate figures are not given for the total of the primary metals industries and the total of the machinery industries in the South in 1939. In 1947 the numbers of production workers in the two industry groups were: primary metals, 70,443 and machinery 47,565; the South's percentages of the national totals were 7.0 per cent and 3.8 per cent respectively.

**This total differs slightly from the total obtained from the individual state reports which is 1,154,162.

Source: *Census of Manufactures, 1947*; figures for the South from a special tabulation made by the Bureau of the Census.

change because of the relatively low development. In the United States, the percentage increases were smaller than in the South but the
much greater weight in the industrial structure
gave these industry groups a powerful influence on the national average. The other side
of the picture is that the South, in 1939, had
over half of its production workers (54.4 per
cent) in two groups, the textile and lumber,
which had relatively low percentages of increase.

The situation discussed in the preceding
paragraph brings out one of the weaknesses of
the industrial structure of the South. The
region failed to improve its relative position
between 1939 and 1947 as an employer of
workers in manufacturing because of the small
share that it had in the industry groups that
showed the greatest strength. Largely these
were the iron and steel processing and fabricating industries.

The fact that the South increased faster percentagewise than the nation in all but one
group[12] means that it strengthened its relative
position in all but the exceptional subgroup.
In 1947, there was no main group in which the
South had less than one per cent of the production workers of the United States, while in
1939 there were two. The tendency of the

Per cent South of the United States number of production workers	Number of industry groups	
	1939	1947
Less than 1 per cent	2	..
1 per cent to 2.49	1	2
2.50 to 4.99	4	2
5.00 to 7.49	1	4
7.50 to 9.99	2	1
10.00 to 12.49	2	2
12.50 to 14.99	1	1
15.00 to 19.99	2	3
20.00 to 24.99	..	..
25.00 to 29.99	1	1
30.00 to 39.99	1	..
40.00 to 49.99	2	3
Total	19	19

[12] Because data were not available for the South in
1939 for the two groups separately, primary metals and
machinery, except electrical, had to be combined and
treated as one group.

South to strengthen its relative position is indicated by the following summary tabulation.

The South, throughout its recent industrial
history, has had its manufacturing activities
concentrated heavily on a very few types of
industries, chiefly textiles and lumber. A comparison of 1947 with 1939 indicates considerable progress in diversification so far as kinds
of industries are concerned. The data in Table
143 shows that the two dominant industry
groups had 54.4 per cent of all production
workers in manufacturing in the South in 1939
and 45.6 per cent in 1947. The only other
group that lowered its per cent of the total of
production workers in the South was tobacco
manufacturing. Thus, the smaller groups generally strengthened their position.

Table 143

Percentage of Total Production Workers in the South in the Several Industry Groups, 1939-1947

Industry group	Per cent of South's total	
	1939	1947
Textile mill products	38.6	30.2
Lumber and products	15.8	15.4
Food and kindred products	9.2	9.7
Apparel and related products	5.9	6.7
Primary metals and machinery,[1] except electrical	5.1	6.9
Chemicals and allied products	4.8	5.2
Furniture and fixtures	3.1	3.2
Tobacco manufactures	2.7	2.5
Paper and allied products	2.6	3.2
Petroleum and coal products	2.5	2.9
Stone, clay and glass products	2.5	2.9
Printing and publishing	2.2	2.2
Fabricated metal products	2.0	2.6
Transportation equipment	1.1	3.2
Leather and leather goods	0.8	1.0
Miscellaneous industries	0.6	0.7
Rubber products	0.3	0.8
Electrical machinery	0.1	0.5
Instruments and related products	0.1	0.2
Total	100.0	100.0

[1] In 1947, primary metals, 4.1 per cent, and machinery, except
electrical, 2.8 per cent.

Source: *Census of Manufactures*, Special tabulation.

To check further into the question of how
general the strengthening of the relative posi-

tion of industries in the South was between 1939 and 1947, a more detailed breakdown was worked out. In some few cases, comparable figures could not be prepared for 1939 and 1947, but direct comparisons could be made in 126 industry classes.[13] A comparison of the percentages of change of the South and the United States is summarized in the following manner.

	Number of industry classes
Total number of classes	126
South had more favorable percentage changes than the United States	
(a) Per cent of increase was greater in South	94
(b) South increased; United States decreased	3
(c) South's per cent of decrease smaller than United States	1
(d) South increased from zero	7
Total	105
South's change less favorable than United States	21

[13] These correspond to the three-digit classification used by the Bureau of the Census except that it was necessary, in a few instances, to add together two or more three-digit classes to get comparable statistics.

The above figures confirm the conclusions indicated by the analysis of the main industry groups. A detailed examination shows that the industry classes that had the more favorable changes are scattered throughout the main industry groups. Of the less favorable changes, four classes occur in chemicals and allied products and three in the fabricated metals group. Generally, the analysis of the more detailed classification shows a growth in manufacturing that is widely distributed throughout the entire industrial structure of the region.

Changes in Geographic Distribution

All of the states included in the South had increases in manufacturing activities during the forty-eight-year period from 1899 to 1947 that are quite significant, but there were differences in the rates of increase of the several states which were large enough to bring about changes in their relative positions in the region. In Table 144, the situation in 1899, 1929, and 1947 is presented to give an indication of the changes that have taken place. Texas has shown the greatest change in relative position. In 1899, it had only 8.09 per cent of the production workers of the South and 12.10 per cent of the value added by manufacture. These

Table 144

Per Cent of Total Number of Production Workers in the South and the Per Cent of Value Added by Manufacture in the South Accounted for by Each of the Several States 1899, 1929, and 1947

State	Per cent of production workers			Per cent of value added		
	1899	1929	1947	1899	1929	1947
North Carolina	15.16	18.40	20.34	12.71	23.72	18.36
South Carolina	9.86	9.54	10.21	7.18	5.45	8.85
Georgia	17.47	13.93	13.12	14.20	10.09	11.33
Florida	7.44	5.69	3.84	6.71	4.64	3.90
Tennessee	9.63	11.26	11.18	12.01	11.05	10.67
Alabama	11.05	10.49	10.78	10.72	8.84	9.78
Mississippi	5.62	4.57	4.04	5.40	3.67	3.35
Arkansas	6.61	3.88	3.38	6.79	3.23	2.96
Louisiana	8.57	7.66	6.48	11.32	8.44	7.74
Oklahoma	0.50	2.78	2.57	0.85	5.11	3.80
Texas	8.09	11.80	14.06	12.11	15.76	19.26
Total South	100.00	100.00	100.00	100.00	100.00	100.00

Source: *Census of Manufactures, 1947.*

proportions increased in 1929 and again in 1947, reaching in the latter year 14.06 per cent for production workers and 19.26 per cent for value added by manufacture. North Carolina seems to have ranked second in strengthening its position as a manufacturing state in the South. This state increased its percentage of the South's production workers from 15.16 in 1899 to 18.40 in 1929 and 20.34 in 1947. Its showing with respect to value added by manufacture is not quite so favorable—its percentage of the South in 1947, 18.36 per cent, was higher than in 1899, 12.71, but was lower than the 1929 percentage.

In 1899, a block of five states consisting of North Carolina, South Carolina, Georgia, Tennessee, and Alabama together accounted for 63.17 per cent of the South's production workers and 56.83 per cent of the value added by manufacture. As a group, these states strengthened their relative position, but not to any great degree, since in 1947 they had 65.63 per cent of the region's production workers and 58.99 per cent of the value added.

On the other hand, Florida, Mississippi, Arkansas, and Louisiana lost in relative position since their share of production workers and value added was lower in 1929 than in 1899 and still lower in 1947. The four states as a whole declined from 28.24 per cent of the South's production workers in 1899 to 17.74 in 1947 and from 30.22 per cent of the value added in 1899 to 17.95 per cent in 1947.

In general, the five states in the North and East of the region maintained their position in the region. Texas greatly strengthened its place and Florida, Mississippi, Arkansas, and Louisiana did not increase fast enough to retain the relative position held at the beginning of the century. Oklahoma greatly increased its relative position from 1899 to 1929, but no more than maintained its position between 1929 and 1947.

To supplement the analysis of changes in geographic location in terms of states, two computations were made to see whether there was evidence of increased concentration in the larger industrial counties. This test was made only for the years 1939 and 1947. Two criteria were set up. The first was the number of production workers in the counties that in 1947 had 2,500 or more production workers. The second was the number of production workers in counties that in 1947 had 10,000 or more production workers. The results are summarized in Table 145.

Neither the wider grouping (counties with 2,500 and more production workers), nor the

Table 145

Concentration of Production Workers in the Larger Industrial Counties of the Southeast, Southwest, and South, 1939 and 1947

	Number of production workers			Per cent of total		
	Southeast	Southwest	South	Southeast	Southwest	South
Total production workers						
1939	1,001,405	152,757	1,154,162	100.0	100.0	100.0
1947	1,435,161	286,316	1,721,477	100.0	100.0	100.0
Per cent increase	43.3	87.4	49.2			
Production workers in counties with 2,500 and more in 1947						
1939	733,796	95,066	828,862	73.3	62.2	71.8
1947	1,028,647	192,638	1,221,285	71.7	67.3	70.9
Per cent increase	40.2	102.6	47.3			
Production workers in counties with 10,000 and more in 1947						
1939	408,765	71,990	480,755	40.8	47.1	41.7
1947	565,061	146,018	711,079	39.4	51.0	41.3
Per cent increase	38.2	101.8	47.9			

Source: *Census of Manufactures, 1947.*

narrower one (counties with 10,000 and more production workers) give evidence of increasing concentration in the Southeast, since the increase in the number of production workers in the selected counties is smaller than in all the counties and the percentage of all the production workers in the Southeast who are employed in the selected counties is smaller in 1947 than in 1939. In the Southwest, the reverse is true, indicating some tendency toward concentration in the more important counties. However, the Southeast so greatly outweighs the Southwest that the statistics for the South as a whole do not show an increased concentration in the larger counties.

The data given in Table 146 show an increase in 1947 (compared with 1939) in the number of counties, with numbers of production workers in excess of 2,500 and 10,000. This simply means that the rapid growth between the two census years has applied to the larger counties as well as to the South as a whole and that more and more counties are getting relatively large numbers of manufacturing employees. This is an evidence of the increasing industrialization of the South.

EXPENDITURES OF MANUFACTURING INDUSTRIES FOR PLANT AND EQUIPMENT

The tendencies in manufacturing in the South have been discussed in the preceding paragraphs. A natural question to raise is, "What do these changes in manufacturing mean to the market for iron and steel products?" The direct consumption of iron and steel as raw materials by manufacturing industries has been discussed in some detail in Chapter XXIII. This consumption covers only a part of the total use of iron and steel by manufacturing plants—the use for one purpose (raw materials) and by a segment of all manufacturing—namely, the iron and steel processing and fabricating industries. The demand of manufacturing concerns for new plant and equipment is also a factor of importance. Factory buildings require structural steel, and machinery and equipment are largely manufactured from iron and steel.

The 1947 Census of Manufactures collected information on expenditures for plant and equipment. The published statistics are for one year only, are in terms of dollars, and do not provide any means of separating iron and steel products from other items. Furthermore, the proportion of iron and steel to the total will vary from industry to industry and perhaps among the establishments of the same industry. Consequently, the market for iron and steel in the form of manufacturing plant and equipment, even for this one year, cannot be determined quantitatively. However, the data provide a basis for some general conclusions concerning the market for industrial plant and equipment in the South.

According to the figures given in Table 147, the reported expenditures in the South for plant and equipment in 1947 was over one billion dollars. This was 16.3 per cent of the total expenditure for the United States—a higher percentage than the South's share in the nation's manufacturing as measured in terms of value added (the South had 11.98 per cent) or number of production workers (the South had 14.45 per cent). The total consisted of the

Table 146

Number of Counties in the South With 2,500 and Over and 10,000 and Over Production Workers in 1939 and 1947

	Counties with 2,500 and more production workers		Counties with 10,000 and more production workers	
	1939	1947	1939	1947
Southeast	90	124	17	29
Southwest	10	16	3	6
South	100	140	20	35

Source: *Census of Manufactures, 1947.*

expenditure for new construction, 367 million dollars; for new machinery and equipment, 604 million; and for used plant, equipment, and land, 111 million. These three categories of expenditures constituted 17.28 per cent, 15.56 per cent, and 17.74 per cent of the total expenditures in the United States in their respective classes. These figures suggest a large total market which is somewhat stronger than the South's relative position in manufacturing would indicate. Such a situation probably arises from the growth of new industries in the region.

On an industry basis, the information available from the published state reports is incomplete, but it is possible to determine that textiles and lumber, the two big industries which together have 45.6 per cent of the production workers of the South, account for only 18 per cent of the South's expenditures for new plant and 24 per cent of the expenditures for new machinery and equipment. On the other hand, several industry groups, including the petroleum and coal products, chemicals, and paper and pulp groups, have new plant and equipment expenditures that are much above their shares of production workers or value added

by manufacture. A probable explanation is that the older, more thoroughly established, and slower growing industries will have less need for new plant and equipment and that those in the process of rapid development will offer the more active markets.

CONCLUSIONS CONCERNING TRENDS IN MANUFACTURING

The analysis of the data on manufacturing in the South may be summarized as supporting the following main conclusions.

1. The South has had a large absolute increase in manufacturing during the period from 1899 to 1947 but has not changed greatly in its relative position in the manufacturing structure of the nation. This large absolute increase is highly significant in providing a larger and better base for the market of iron and steel products.

2. The more detailed comparison of the situation in 1939 and 1947 shows that the increases have been shared by all the main groups and by a large number of the more detailed industry classifications. Also there

Table 147

Expenditures for Plant and Equipment in the Southeast, Southwest, and South, 1947

| | Thousands of dollars | | | | Per cent of United States | | |
	South-east	South-west	South	United States	South-east	South-west	South
Value added by manufacture							
All establishments	6,900,834	2,068,491	8,969,325	74,425,825	9.27	2.78	12.05
Establishments reporting expenditures	6,763,102	2,016,232	8,779,334	73,272,953	9.23	2.75	11.98
Total expenditures on plant and equipment	685,877	395,142	1,081,019	6,627,029	10.35	5.96	16.31
Expenditures on new plant and equipment							
Total	640,037	330,448	970,485	6,003,873	10.66	5.50	16.16
New construction							
Total	205,165	161,478	366,643	2,122,143	9.67	7.61	17.28
Buildings	155,334	55,877	211,211	1,501,430	10.35	3.72	14.07
Other	49,831	105,601	155,432	620,713	8.03	17.01	25.04
New machinery and equipment							
Total	434,872	168,970	603,842	3,881,730	11.20	4.35	15.56
Production machinery and equipment	374,746	132,247	506,993	3,360,408	11.15	3.94	15.09
Other machinery and equipment	60,126	36,723	96,849	521,322	11.53	7.05	18.58
Expenditures for used plant, equipment, and land	45,840	64,694	110,534	623,156	7.36	10.38	17.74

Source: *Census of Manufactures, 1947*, I, Chapter VI.

is evidence of less concentration on a few dominant types of industry and a tendency toward greater diversification. The South, however, remains weak in many of the industries which have been showing the greatest growth in recent years.

3. Geographically, all the states showed important gains from 1899 to 1947, and the distribution among states was not greatly changed. The five states to the north and east of the region—North Carolina, South Carolina, Georgia, Tennessee, and Alabama—retained their position in the industrial structure of the South, approximately 60 per cent of the total. Texas, however, increased decidedly in importance. Florida, Mississippi, Arkansas, and Louisiana, while increasing in absolute terms, lost in relative position.

4. On a more localized area basis the data on the principal industrial counties of the South in 1939 and 1947 indicate that the expansion is not being concentrated disproportionately in a small number of counties.

Taken as a whole, there is much evidence that a large development has taken place and that the growth has been general throughout the area.

From the point of view of an industrial market for plant and equipment, the 1947 data on expenditures for plant and equipment indicate that the general position in manufacturing may be taken as a preliminary index. Industries that are growing rapidly may be assumed to need more in proportion to their size than the older and slower growing industries. The increases in manufacturing in the past suggest that the South has constituted an expanding market for plant and equipment.

General Conclusions

The review of the trends of the South during the past twenty-five or thirty years indicates that the region has moved in much the same direction as the nation. Generally, its rates of increase have been as large or, in a number of cases, larger than those of the nation. However, the South started in low position and the rapid rate of change in the nation as a whole has made it difficult to improve the relative position of the region. The statistics should have a sobering effect upon those who allow their enthusiasm to lead them to the belief that developments in the South will overshadow those in other parts of the country. On the other hand, the study of the trends lends support to the conclusion that real progress has been made in improving conditions in the South and that the markets for iron and steel products, both durable consumers goods and producers goods, should continue to increase. While the South may not be able to reach or exceed the average for the nation for many years, yet in absolute terms the increased quantities of goods required should support a greatly expanded industry.

Some of the factors of importance are enumerated below.

1. The South is an area of increasing population. In the past, the rate of increase has been approximately the same as the nation. The migration from the South provides a source for an increased labor force, if sufficient economic opportunities can be offered to retain in the region the persons born and reared there.

2. The shift toward the cities and into nonagricultural occupations is favorable to increased use of iron and steel.

3. Progress has been made toward creating conditions more favorable to increased production. Banking and insurance statistics indicate a tendency toward capital accumulations. Improvements in health conditions and educational facilities are indicative of general improvements.

4. The incomes of people in the South have increased both absolutely in terms of purchasing power and relatively compared with the nation.

5. The diversification of sources of farm income, improved agricultural methods, and increase in the use of machinery all point toward an increased farm market.

6. Between 1939 and 1947, manufacturing had very substantial increases, but perhaps more important was the tendency toward greater diversity and a more fully rounded industrial structure. Many types of industry remain weak. Among those are many of the metal-working industries, but a continuation of the trends should tend to correct the weaknesses. Also, the new industry stage is one that creates a demand for plant and equip- ment.

The promise of an expanded market seems to exist in the South. Whether that market will be supplied by iron and steel producers and processors and fabricators located in the South or by concerns on the outside is another problem. The answer, to a large extent, is determined by the economic characteristics of the various industries and the framework within which they work.

PART V

POTENTIALS OF IRON AND STEEL INDUSTRIES IN THE SOUTH

INTRODUCTION

The discussions in Parts I through IV have been largely but not wholly factual. The purpose has been to describe the conditions—physical, technical, and economic—that have formed the environment in which the iron and steel industries of the South have developed; to describe the basic and the processing of fabricating industries of the region as accurately and as fully as possible; and to point out the trends that can be discerned. The task has been centered largely on the analysis of geological and technical information and statistical data.

By design, consideration of questions of policy has been postponed until the factual background could be developed and presented. In Part V, the purpose is to examine the potentials of iron and steel in the South. This is a task that is, by its very nature, quite speculative in character. It will be necessary to discuss the influence which various lines of policy may have had on developments of the past or may have in the future.

In general, the data for the past indicate a substantial growth both of the over-all economy of the South and of the iron and steel industries in particular. This situation is an important feature of the background but does not provide a sufficient foundation for arriving at conclusions concerning future possibilities. The existence of a trend may be shown by the statistical information, but this can scarcely be taken as an assurance that the trend will continue in the future. In other words, a trend can scarcely be considered as representing the working of an inevitable line of development that will run its predetermined course uninfluenced by changes in conditions. Furthermore, the fact that a trend has existed in the past cannot be taken as proof that the best possible results were being obtained. There is the possibility that different objectives and different policy decisions might have resulted in a greater growth than that recorded. For reasons such as these, careful consideration should be given

to the economic framework within which the iron and steel industries have been operating and to the possible effects of alternative policies that might be followed by management and government.

In the discussion of the basic industries, particular attention will be given to the implications of the economics of large-scale production, the effects of the ownership organization that characterizes the industry both nationally and in the South, the characteristics of the demand of pig iron and steel, and the effects of pricing policies on developments in the region.

Part IV has centered attention on the development of metal-using industries as constituting one of the important factors in determining the size of the market for iron and steel products. Consequently, much interest attaches to such questions as the following:

What iron and steel processing industries are most likely to develop in the South?
Where are the developments most likely to take place?
What measures can be taken to encourage development?

The problems involved have to do largely with the economics of industrial location.

To give detailed and specific answers to the questions raised in the preceding paragraph would call for a careful analysis of each individual industry. To do this would require the assembling of a vast amount of detailed information, much of which is not readily available. Such a task is beyond the scope of this study. There is, however, the possibility of a more general approach in which the aim is not to pin-point the particular industry or the particular place where development should or is most likely to take place, but rather to point out the characteristics of processing and fabricating industries that are likely to influence their development.

There is a tendency on the part of some of those working in the field of industry location to make decisions on the basis of some relatively simple rule of thumb. One scheme is to classify all industries into what are called market-oriented industries, r a w material-oriented industries, labor-oriented industries and so forth, paralleling a commonly used list of locational factors. Another is to check the representation that a state or region may have in the various industries and to assume that the industries to be encouraged are those in which the area's share is small. Still another is to draw limits around assumed market areas in an effort to determine whether there is a market within the area large enough to support an optimum-sized plant. While the information provided by each of these approaches may be valuable, the view taken in this study is that none is adequate. To arrive at a sound judgment, it

is necessary to have a thorough knowledge of the economic characteristics of the industry under question. This includes not only information on optimum size, capital requirements, and labor and raw material requirements, but also a knowledge of such matters as the ownership organization, price policies, system of distribution outlets, competitive practices, and managerial policies that characterize the industry in question. The chapter on the economic characteristics of the iron and steel processing and fabricating industries will attempt to direct attention to the more important economic factors and to make the discussion as specific as possible by pointing out the effects of these factors on the expansion of the several industries. Still, the discussion must be suggestive rather than final.

CHAPTER XXV

ECONOMIC CHARACTERISTICS AND THEIR REGIONAL IMPLICATIONS: THE BASIC IRON AND STEEL INDUSTRIES

In approaching an appraisal of the prospects of the basic iron and steel industries in the South, a distinction will be made between the characteristics and resulting problems that arise from the economics of production and those that are related to the ownership organization and general management policies of the industries. Under the general heading of the economics of production, attention will be directed to the effects of large-scale production on developments in the industry, the possible effects of changes in sources of raw material on the location of industry, and the effects of technological developments and operating conditions on its future. Consideration of the characteristics of ownership organization raises the question of the consequences to the South of the prominent place held by a relatively small number of large corporations in the industry in the United States and, in particular, the effects of control of iron and steel plants in the South by large corporations that operate on a national, or even international, scale. Under management policies, a very large number of topics could be included. Attention will be given primarily to the characteristics of demand and the market for iron and steel and the policies followed by the operating firms with regard to pricing, competitive practices, and the development of markets.

Economics of Production

THE IMPLICATIONS OF LARGE-SCALE PRODUCTION METHODS

The importance of the place held by large plants in the basic iron and steel industries has been developed in considerable detail in previous chapters. Despite much experimentation with methods of smelting iron that might be adaptable to small plants, the trend to date has been toward larger and larger blast furnaces. The steel-making furnaces are smaller in size than the blast furnaces; however, it seems that steel can be produced economically in relatively small open-hearth furnaces. The capacity of electric furnaces is still smaller. If the problem is limited to producing steel ingots, it would seem that small plants should have a chance to exist. In the production of finished steel products, there are many of the simpler types of shapes that can be rolled by relatively small capacity units. On the other hand, heavy and large shapes, such as rails, heavy structural shapes, large plates, seamless pipe and tubes, and the like, require very large and expensive equipment. Furthermore, the development of the four-high continuous rolling mills has made the rolling of sheets a large-scale operation. The size of the operating plants is also influenced by the savings in heat loss that result from the close integration of blast furnaces, steel-making furnaces, and rolling mills. While there are small plants operating successfully, particularly in the production of the simpler products and low volume specialty items, the great bulk of the nation's iron and steel is produced by large plants. The implications of this situation to possible developments in the South are important.

While it may be possible for an existing plant to expand considerably by the installation of better or more efficient equipment or methods, such as an ore preparation plant, or by the expansion of certain units in order to use the full capacity of other existing units, the large-scale nature of the industry makes a major expansion a matter of an investment of millions of dollars. Such a project involves several factors. Four of these may be mentioned as follows: (1)

an adequate supply of raw materials, (2) a sufficient market for the products, (3) large amounts of capital, and (4) an organization with the technical and managerial know-how needed for successful operation.

If the plant is large, the supply of raw materials must also be large. Furthermore, the nature of the industry is such that the amortization of the investment in plant is relatively slow. This means that operation over a rather long period is needed to make the venture successful. Consequently, there is needed not only a large immediate supply of raw materials but also a source that will maintain a large flow of these materials over a long period of time. The existence of reserves of ore and coal in the South which are sufficient to support the expanded production is not in itself sufficient assurance that this requirement can be met. The important question is the availability of specific deposits to the group that may be contemplating the expansion. Or the problem may be stated in different terms: "Are those who control the resources disposed to make them available?" This impinges on the implications of ownership which will be discussed later.

The large-scale operation has another effect on the raw material problem. It tends to be associated with large-scale operations of mines and the ownership of the transportation facilities needed to get ore and coal from the mines to the iron and steel plants. One effect is to lessen the importance of small mineral deposits.

In its simplest form, the statement that a market large enough to absorb the quantity produced by the new plant must be in prospect is almost axiomatic. If a new mill is to be built in the South to produce an additional one million tons of steel, there must be a prospective market for the one million tons. The problem, however, is more complicated than it seems on the surface. Because of the large-scale nature of the industry, the advantages of the superior equipment and technical methods are attained only when relatively long runs can be made under essentially the same conditions. This tends to favor quantity production of a limited number of products. In other words, the large mill is not likely to be built unless there is a promise of a large market for the products that it can produce in quantity.

The large size of the undertaking means that the capital requirements will be beyond the means of any except organizations that have access to large capital funds, either from their own resources or through investment banking channels. Even admitting the possibility of financing with government support, it is still true that the number of possible organizations qualified to handle the financing of a major plant is not large. Furthermore, financing on such a scale is certain to bring to the front the question of the competence of those who are to operate the new venture. Operators with the required experience and know-how are not numerous. The point is simply that the construction and operation of a major iron or steel plant is a venture that can be undertaken by only a relatively small number of possible groups.

What has been said should not be interpreted as closing the door on small plants. In the Atlantic Steel Company of Atlanta and the Connors Steel Company of Birmingham, the South has examples of relatively small plants that have made a place for themselves. The success of such plants seems to depend on (1) the ability to secure a supply of steel, through either the purchase of ingots or billets for rolling or the purchase of scrap for remelting and rolling, and (2) the successful marketing of products that can be produced in small scale at costs that permit competition with the large mills. With the increasing industrialization of the South, it is entirely possible that there may be opportunities for additional small mills.

POSSIBLE EFFECTS OF SHIFTS IN THE SOURCES OF RAW MATERIALS

Following the close of World War II, a great commotion was caused by statements concerning the approaching exhaustion of the high-grade Lake ores. There was a widespread belief that a drastic relocation of the steel industry was in prospect. In the South, many raised the question as to whether Birmingham might take the place of Pittsburgh or Chicago as the leading steel-producing center. This naturally raised the question as to whether the iron ore and coal reserves of the South were sufficient to provide for such an expansion. With a more careful examination of the situation, the excitement has quieted. New sources of iron ore have been brought to the front, particularly in Labrador, Venzuela, and other foreign countries. Also, the important operating companies have been taking active steps to find ways to meet the situation. Extensive projects have been initiated to discover the best means of fully utilizing the resources at hand. Important work is being done on beneficiating the taconite ores of the northern fields and the Red Mountain ores of Alabama. Furthermore, it seems very possible that the exhaustion of the high grade ores will proceed quite gradually. Ownership of the deposits is likely to result in some steel producers having a supply adequate for a long period in the future, while other companies not so favorably situated may be facing serious problems. Also, it is possible that the actual reserves are considerably larger than the official estimates. Still another factor of very great importance is the fact that location near the deposits is not as essential as might at first appear. Nearness to raw material is an important factor in securing low assembly costs, but previous discussions have shown that bulk movements over long distances have been practical, particularly where water transportation is available. Nearness to consumer markets is also an important factor in the location of iron and steel plants. Considerations such as these cast doubt on the probabilities of any very immediate decline of the present great steel-making centers.

With the development of the Labrador and the Venezuelan deposits, it would seem that a further development of tidewater plants is a decided possibility. The building of the new Fairless plant of the United States Steel Corporation and the Paulsboro, New Jersey, plant of the National Steel Corporation are examples of this movement. However, it is entirely possible that security considerations may limit the number of plants that will be built near the Atlantic Coast. Also, the cost of shipping the finished product may be such that the ability of the tidewater plants to penetrate into the interior markets in competition with such centers

as Pittsburgh and Chicago may be quite limited. Furthermore, it is entirely possible that the St. Lawrence waterway project will be carried to completion and that Labrador and other foreign ores may move readily to the Great Lakes. The Pittsburgh-Ohio River-Great Lakes area may decline gradually in relative importance, but it seems unlikely that a serious absolute decrease will take place.

The building of the Geneva plant to use Utah ores and the development of a western steel industry may tend to reduce the market available to eastern and southern steel makers. However, the long distances are certain to make freight costs high on steel delivered by the western plants to the Pacific Coast. It is possible, therefore, that plants that can ship by water (for example, Sparrows Point and Birmingham) may be able to compete successfully for the market immediately along the coast.

It seems unlikely, therefore, that changes in the locations from which the American steel industry will draw its raw materials will cause a spectacular shift from the North to the South. On the other hand, Birmingham is in position to take advantage of imported ore from Venezuela. Also, it is entirely possible that the availability of foreign ore may make the building of a steel plant at Mobile or some other Gulf port an attractive possibility.

EFFECTS OF TECHNOLOGICAL DEVELOPMENTS AND CHANGES IN OPERATING CONDITIONS

In a field of economic activity which is dynamic, the prospects of any region of the nation depend to a very large extent on whether its enterprisers have the ability to take advantage of technological developments and changes in operating conditions or whether they become the victims of such changes. The discussion of the historical developments of the basic iron and steel industries in the South emphasized the retarding effects of the high phosphorous content of the southern red ores and the lag in perfecting effective means of producing steel. The chapter on technological problems of the iron and steel industries suggested the part that beneficiation of southern ores or the introduction of alternative methods of producing steel might have on the future of the industry. In general, it is probably fair to say that the southern industry in the past has tended to lag in the development of new ideas and new methods and that one of the great needs of the present is a more vigorous attack on the technical problems.

The old problem of the high phosphorus content of southern pig iron still confronts the merchant pig iron sector of the industry. The character of the foundry industry in the South has been strongly influenced by this factor, and the lack of low phosphorus pig iron has much to do with the low position held by the region in malleable iron foundries and in the production of many products needed for a well-balanced line of cast-iron products. The importation of the low phosphorus Venezuelan ores could bring about a decided change in this situation, provided these ores were made available to a company which would make pig iron for the market. The successful beneficiation of the ferruginous sandstones of Red Mountain could have a similar effect.

Recent years have seen the development of several tendencies which can have the effect of changing the relative-cost relationship between Birmingham and the northern steel centers. Although the so-called southern differential did not apply to all occupations, particularly the skilled ones, Birmingham, along with the rest of the South, had relatively low wage rates. In the mining operations, this advantage was offset, at least in part, by the comparatively low production per man-hour due, to a large extent, to difficult underground mining conditions. Still, it seems safe to conclude that Birmingham had relatively low labor costs. More recently the differential has been narrowing, and it is possible that it may disappear entirely. In part, this change has been brought about by the growth of powerful labor unions, but it can also be interpreted as a natural consequence of the industrialization of the South. Whatever their causes and however desirable the higher wage rates may be, there is the possibility that the cost relationships, and hence the competitive position of the South compared with mills in other sections, may be affected unless means

can be found to offset the higher wage rates by improvements in productivity. The expansion and improvement programs and the increased mechanization of many operations indicate that the operating companies are well aware of this problem and are making efforts to cope with it. However, any real appraisal of the effectiveness of these efforts would require information that has not been available in this study.

As pointed out in considerable detail in previous chapters, beneficiation of the southern ores has received the attention of the U. S. Bureau of Mines and operating companies for many years. The development of satisfactory methods could place Birmingham in a more favorable position. The Birmingham iron and steel industry has been built on low-grade iron ore. A beneficiated iron ore would result in important savings in blast furnace costs which would constitute offsets against the cost of beneficiating the ores. On the other hand, the northern furnaces have been accustomed to the use of high-grade ores. The beneficiated taconite ores would probably no more than reach the iron content of the high-grade ores of the present. Thus, the cost of beneficiation would be an added cost with no offsetting gain in quality. However, the successful beneficiation of the southern ores is still an uncertain prospect.

The present discussion of the effect of technological developments and changes in operating conditions will be concluded by suggesting that changes which improve the chances of the relatively small steel mill to operate successfully may have an important place in future prospects. The large scale of the operations of the big mills tends to place the emphasis on quantity production. This probably means that such mills are reluctant to roll products which involve small quantities. In a well-rounded industrial economy, there are many demands that do not fit into the program of the big mills. In an area where metal-working industries are in the early stages of development and the demand for many kinds of products is small, it would be desirable to have mills that could afford to cater to the needs of the new and small concerns.

Effect of the Ownership Situation on the Basic Iron and Steel Industry in the South

That the basic iron and steel industry is one that is largely dominated by a relatively small number of large corporations is a matter of common knowledge. The advantages of large-scale operations in many of the stages of producing iron and steel have encouraged vertical integration—from mines to rolling mills and even to fabricating plants. In addition, in several instances, operating units which are fully integrated vertically have been gathered together as systems under a single ownership, as in the case of the United States Steel Corporation, the Bethlehem Steel Corporation, and the Republic Steel Corporation. It is not the purpose of this study to discuss the problems of national policy that arise from this situation, but rather to consider the possible connections with the development of the industry in a region such as the South.

GENERAL EFFECTS OF CONCENTRATION

The fact that the industry is so largely dominated by a few corporations creates a situation where oligopolistic behavior is highly probable. Under such a condition, decisions on proposed programs or changes in management policies by any member of the small group are likely to be influenced greatly by the reaction that is to be expected from the other iron and steel companies. Furthermore, the company considering the move is in a good position to anticipate with considerable accuracy what the reactions of the others will be. Also, such a company is very conscious that any one of the other companies is a sufficiently strong factor in the market to have a decided influence on competitive conditions. Considerations such as these make concerns operating under oligopolistic conditions very reluctant to take steps that may disturb the status quo. The leader or dominant corporation in the group, particularly, is subject to pressures of this kind. If this line of reasoning is sound, it is reasonable to expect that the policies of the United States Steel Corporation will be influenced not only by what may seem to promise a direct profit to the corporation, but perhaps as much, or more, by the desire to avoid upsetting the general framework within which the whole industry is operating. It follows, then, that developments in a segment of the industry, as for instance the expansion of facilities of the Tennessee Coal, Iron and Railroad Company[1] may be largely determined by general policies that have only remote connections with the production and marketing problems of the subsidiary.

CONCENTRATION AND THE SOUTH

The ownership of the largest units in the South by corporations whose operations are on a national or international scale removes most of the important decisions from the South and tends to place regional interests in a decidedly subordinate position. The control is in the hands of a group to whom the interests of the region and of the plant itself are secondary. Such a group will move only when it is convinced that the interests of the whole corporation are furthered. Even though the members of the controlling group may be sympathetic, they can scarcely be as well informed about the problems, needs, and possible lines of development of a local operation as a group whose major concern is centered on the individual plant and its market. Out of such situations arise many of the criticisms that are made of the basic iron and steel industry in the South. For example, interviews indicated a widespread opinion that fear of endangering investments already made in plants in other areas frequently has blocked developments that seem logical in the region.

If the discussion in the preceding paragraphs seems to imply that concentration of ownership has had an adverse effect on development in the South, it should immediately be pointed out that much can be said on the other side of the question. It may well be that the policies of the large corporations do result in orderly and stabilized operations that are preferable in an industry with high fixed costs to a condition

[1] After January 1, 1952, it became the Tennessee Coal and Iron Division of the United States Steel Corporation.

of unrestrained competition. Furthermore, it may be argued that regional interests, if not restrained, would lead to wasteful duplication of facilities which, from the national point of view, cannot be justified. Arguments such as these are not to be passed by lightly, but the fact remains that concentration of ownership, whether good or bad, is a factor that cannot be ignored in appraising either the past record or the future possibilities of the basic iron and steel industries in the South.

That the United States Steel Corporation has done much for the southern industry can scarcely be questioned. There is no doubt that the securities of the Tennessee Coal, Iron and Railroad Company after 1907 ceased to be a football on the stock market and that the corporation proceeded to put the southern subsidiary on a firm financial and operating basis, a condition that it had never enjoyed previously. Since 1907, the Tennessee Coal, Iron and Railroad Company has had no problem of access to sufficient capital funds, once the corporation has decided on a program. Ownership by the corporation has made available much-needed management and technical resources. The administrative and technical departments have been staffed largely by personnel transferred from other corporation subsidiaries, and, in addition, the research divisions of the parent organization have supplied valuable services on a consulting basis. Under the control of the corporation, the Tennessee Company has been transformed from a weak and unprofitable concern into one that, for the past thirty or forty years, has had a record of strength and very considerable growth.

Still, the question may be raised as to whether much greater growth might not have been possible. George Stocking, in an article in *Law and Contemporary Problems*,[2] expresses the opinion that full advantage was not taken of the low cost of production in Birmingham and that a much greater expansion of the industry was warranted. The staff members working on

[2] George W. Stocking, "The Economics of Basing Point Pricing," *Law and Contemporary Problems* (Spring 1950), pp. 159-180.

this study found many competent persons who expressed the opinion that the United States Steel Corporation generally has been slow in developing and making use of technical improvements and that the Tennessee Coal, Iron and Railroad Company has lagged behind many of the more progressive steel makers in the installation of modern equipment and the adoption of more efficient methods. Another common criticism is that the corporation has been unnecessarily cautious about expanding the line of products made in the South. Lack of markets of sufficient size to justify the step is the reason commonly given for failure to act—a reason which probably is valid in many cases. However, the record with regard to steel pipe is hard to justify on this ground because of the large market in the South. The corporation did nothing in this important field until the Republic Steel Corporation, on the one hand, and Sheffield Steel Corporation and A. O. Smith, on the other, entered the field. Then it proceeded to build the Consolidated Steel Products plant in Orange, Texas. Instances of this kind lend support to the contention that the corporation has been cautious rather than aggressive in its expansion policies.

Statements in the press, including those issued by company officials in defense of their policies, indicate the existence of considerable criticism of the Tennessee Coal, Iron and Railroad Company as lacking in sympathy and helpfulness with regard to regional and local efforts aimed at development. Undoubtedly much of this has not been justified. The company must serve markets that extend over large areas, and it cannot tie its policies to any one city. In its agricultural development work and its programs to buy supplies from local sources, the company has given evidence that disregard of local interests is not characteristic of all its operations. Still, the question remains as to whether the company has been sufficiently aware of the importance of the development of metal-using industries in nearby areas or has taken as vigorous action as it might in encouraging such a development.

The period since the war presents a special situation. The company, in common with all other steel producers, has not been able to supply all the steel that purchasers wish to buy. The policy followed has been one of allocation of available supplies to customers in accordance with the record of past purchases. This policy has generally been accepted by business as fair and just. Still, it has certain implications that should not be overlooked. By its very nature, it tends to freeze the distribution of the product in the old pattern and, consequently, the allocation procedure becomes a factor tending to slow down or to prevent change, even though the change may be in the direction of attaining very desirable objectives. The problem has been intensified by the fact that the postwar years have been marked by many efforts to promote new enterprises. For many of the prospective new plants, a supply of steel is a prime requirement. As a result, conflicts are almost certain to arise between the promoters of new plants and a steel producer operating under an allocation system based on past experience.

Concentration Vs. Absentee Ownership

Involved in the arguments over the effect of ownership are two elements: one has to do with concentration of control in a few hands; the other, with control by groups outside the region—so-called absentee ownership. Both are present in the South. An interesting approach to the regional implications of the situation is to consider two possibilities. The first question is, "What would be the effect of the establishment of new plants owned by companies other than those that now have plants?" The second question is, "What would be the effect if the Tennessee Coal, Iron and Railroad Company were to be separated from the United States Steel Corporation and operated as an independent concern?"

A New Integrated Plant by a New Company

The entry of a new company with a new plant presumably would have the immediate effect of providing more employment for labor, increasing the capital equipment of the region, and creating a larger supply of steel, but the same effect could be obtained by plant expansion of the present companies. The distinctive

purpose to be served by a new company is to provide greater competition for the market and, presumably, a greater stimulus to the aggressive development of markets and to the introduction of more efficient methods and of new products. To accomplish much along this line, a large new plant backed by a strong company would be necessary. This raises the question of the prospects of such a development.

A serious immediate problem is that of obtaining a natural resource base that will place the new plant in position to carry on successful operations. The seriousness of this problem is emphasized by the commonly held opinion that the Republic Steel Corporation is relatively weak in the area and that this condition is largely the result of its unfavorable position with respect to iron ore. The discussions in previous chapters have pointed out that the important ore reserves are closely held by the present companies and that relatively little ore is produced for the market. It would seem that the solution is not an easy one, but several possibilities may be suggested.

One possibility is for an integrated steel plant to be built in connection with one of the existing merchant pig iron concerns. The Woodward Iron Company provides the most inviting possibility because it does have extensive reserves of both coal and iron ore. If such a plan were worked out, the complete withdrawal from the market of all pig iron formerly offered by Woodward would probably react sharply on the gray iron foundry industry of the region. To meet the situation, it would seem that additional capacity of blast furnaces as well as a new steel works would be needed.

Another possibility would be to use imported foreign ores. This is being done to some extent in the Sheffield plant at Houston and by the Tennessee Coal, Iron and Railroad Company in Birmingham. If the plant is to be a large one, the quanitities of raw materials will be large, and the company will wish an assurance of a continued flow. To attain this goal, large capital expenditures would be required to provide the facilities to mine and transport the ore. The coal for coke still must be provided. Coal lands also are closely held, and a considerable problem would probably be met in an attempt to obtain possession of sufficient reserves to insure adequate supplies. On the other hand, there are in operation many mines that produce coal for sale. Decreasing demand for other uses should make the problem of obtaining a suply for metallurgical coke easier.

Still a third possibility is that large new reserves of iron ore may be found in the course of explorations. Mention has been made of the possibility of the extension of the Red Mountain formation below the coal measures to the west of Birmingham. That such beds would be of significance in the near future seems to be only a remote possibility. For one thing, these ore beds, if found to exist, would be deeper underground, and it is doubtful whether present competitive conditions would make their use feasible.

The establishment of a large new integrated plant by a new company is plainly an undertaking that would be attended by many difficulties and would require careful planning and very skillful handling of the arrangements needed to get possession of the necessary natural resources, capital funds, and managerial know-how.

OPERATION OF T. C. I. AS AN INDEPENDENT UNIT

Before attempting any further answer to the first question, attention might be turned to the question of what may be expected if the Tennessee Coal, Iron and Railroad Company were to operate as an independent company. Any attempt at an answer must be based on speculation. Some possible advantages and disadvantages may be listed.

Possible Advantages

1. The company would be more inclined to consider itself a regional concern and to identify its interests more specifically with the region.

2. In its policy decisions, the company would not be restricted to avoiding steps that would endanger the United States Steel Corporation's investments in Pittsburgh and other centers, but would be controlled primarily by what appeared to be good business for the Tennessee Coal, Iron and Railroad Company.

3. The company would have to depend more directly on its own initiative and efforts. It would be more alert to new methods, new products, and new market possibilities. It could be expected to develop a fully-rounded managerial and technical organization.

Possible Disadvantages

1. The Tennessee Coal, Iron and Railroad Company might have difficulty in tapping sources of capital funds for expansion programs. As a subsidiary it has had no occasion to deal with this problem. This raises the question as to whether a company that now appears to be in sound operating condition can get capital through the regular investment banking channels without the sponsorship of one of the super corporations. If it could not, the intervention of the federal government is to be expected.

2. The company would be cut off from the technical services of the United States Steel Corporation and from the possibility of securing experienced personnel by way of transfer. The problem, in this respect, resolves itself into a question of the relative initiative and efficiency of the huge corporation versus the smaller independent concern. A firm as large as the Tennessee Coal, Iron and Railroad Company should be able either to select and train its own staff or to attract to its employment the kind of persons needed. It can also have available on a contract basis the services of the expert staffs of consulting firms.

3. The Tennessee Coal, Iron and Railroad Company would be more subject to dumping in its sales territory than under present arrangements At present, its territory is protected from other United States Steel Corporation subsidiaries which produce competing products and, in many cases, its position is strengthened by being able to offer products that it does not produce itself. The strength of the corporation probably exercises a restraint on unfair competition by other companies.

CONCLUSIONS CONCERNING CONCENTRATION IN THE SOUTH

In both propositions—a new plant by a new company, and the possible divorcement of the

Tennessee Coal, Iron and Railroad Company, or any other subsidiary operation, from the parent corporation—so much depends on the initiative, good judgment, and all-round ability of the group responsible for the venture that there are very real limitations on the validity of conclusions that are based on generalities. Yet it seems reasonable to conclude that the South would benefit from both of the following: (1) an additional large integrated plant not controlled by the concern now dominant in the region, and (2) as high a degree of autonomy as is consistent with good management for the subsidiaries or operating divisions of any of the corporations operating in the region. On the other hand, it would be unwise to expect too much even if both steps were taken. The number of operators still would be small, and the policies of the management might well be controlled by much the same considerations as those which have played such important parts in the past.

Nature of Demand for Steel and Developments in the South

In 1939 the United States Steel Corporation organized a Special Economic Research Section which prepared a series of analyses of the demand and pricing problems of the steel industry for presentation at the hearings on the steel industry that were to be held by the Temporary National Economic Committee. A summary of the conclusions presented in these documents concerning the nature of the demand for steel forms a convenient starting point for the present discussion.

The United States Steel Corporation's Analysis of Demand Factors

With regard to the characteristics of demand for steel, the corporation presents the following three main conclusions:

1. The demand for steel is marked by tremendous cyclical fluctuations;
2. The total demand for steel products is inelastic, i.e., the total quantity of steel bought from the industry would not be greatly different at any particular time if the price were higher or lower;

3. In contrast, the demand for steel from a particular producer usually possesses great potential elasticity. In other words, buyers will readily shift from one producer to another in response to a difference in price.[3]

As factors accounting for these demand characteristics, emphasis is placed on those listed below.

1. The derived nature of the demand
2. The durability of the products manufactured from steel
3. The postponability of purchase of durable goods
4. The low degree of substitution of steel for other materials, or vice versa
5. The relatively low percentage of the total cost of fabricated products accounted for by the cost of steel.

The first three of these factors are presented as being directly related to the variability of demand or the sensitiveness to cyclical changes. The last two factors are given as causes contributing to inelasticity in total demand.

In a study of changes in the demand for steel from 1936 to 1939, the corporation concludes that the changes in the demand for steel during the period under study were largely determined by the following factors:

1. The current and anticipated levels of business activity, income, and profits;
2. The expectations with respect to steel prices in the immediate future compared with current steel prices;
3. The volume of steel inventory accumulated in the immediate past and
4. The length of time required to fill new orders for steel.[4]

It is, of course, quite apparent that the corporation was on the defensive, and it can be assumed that it did not understate its case. With respect to the position that demand for steel is highly inelastic and hence unrelated to the prices of steel, the Federal Trade Commission took direct issue in its rejoinder.[5] It is not the intention of this discussion to attempt

3 United States Steel Corporation, *U. S. Steel Corporation T.N.E.C. Papers*, I, 377.

4 *U. S. Steel Corporation T.N.E.C. Papers*, I, 43.

5 U. S. Temporary Economic Committee, *The Basing Point Problem*, pp. 124-126.

to reach a conclusion as to which of the two may be correct, but rather to explore with respect to developments in a region some of the implications that are inherent in the position taken by the corporation.

REGIONAL IMPLICATIONS OF
CORPORATION'S DEMAND ANALYSIS

It may be conceded, in the restricted sense in which the corporation was discussing demand—the economist's concept of the demand curve at a given point of time—that "the actual level of the buying price of steel" has little "importance in explaining the actual level of steel buying at least in the short run." There are, however, implications of two of the other propositions of the corporation that should be examined. These are: (1) that expectations with respect to levels of business activity and future prices do exercise an important influence, and (2) that the demand for steel from a particular producer possesses great potential elasticity.

The analysts who formulated the first of the two propositions were, of course, thinking particularly of the timing of purchases within a comparatively short period of time in the relatively near future, but it is reasonable to assume that expectancy with reference to levels of business activity and prices constitutes an equally important factor that influences levels of demand over a long period of time. If the policies of the industry are such that they create the impression that plant facilities for producing the kinds of steel needed for particular types of fabricating activities are not likely to be developed in a region, or that steel mills in new and developing regions are being held back to protect investments in mills in older regions, it may be expected that the development of metal fabricating plants in the region affected will be retarded. Similarly, the continuous maintenance of prices in a given region, which place fabricators in that region at a disadvantage compared with those located in other regions, must create an expectancy which will discourage development in the disadvantaged region.

The second proposition—that the demand for the products of a particular producer possesses great potential elasticity—has regional implications that reinforce the reasoning advanced in the preceding paragraph. If the sales of a particular mill can be adversely, or favorably, influenced by relatively small differences in its prices compared with those of other mills, it follows that differences in prices on a regional basis will also exercise a strong influence on the demand for steel produced in the regions affected by such differences. Mills that are in position to offer the better prices have a strong leverage in building up the demand for their products, not only by capturing a larger proportion of the immediate market, but also by inducing long-term developments in their market areas that create larger demands in the future.

Stated more directly, the line of reasoning that has been developed in the last several paragraphs means that characterizing the demand for steel as being inelastic in the short run is not a sufficient approach to an appraisal of the effect of pricing and other management policies on the demand for steel in a region. In some of the discussions, there seems to be a suggestion that there is a sort of "iron law" of demand for steel—just so much in the nation —and that the industry can do nothing about it. It is here suggested that policies followed by the industry can have a powerful influence on the developments within a region. Consequently, policies that retard the utilization of the resources of a region or establish artificially high prices are bound in the long run to depress the volume demanded in that region. Furthermore, policies that result in underdeveloped production facilities and that restrict demand in one part of the nation tend to lower the aggregate for the nation as a whole.

Characteristics of Markets for Iron and Steel

At the risk of undue repetition, it may be well at this point to remind the reader of some of the factual materials which have been developed in previous chapters with regard to the markets for iron and steel. In the chapter on the use pattern of iron and steel, the discussion of the quantities shipped to various classes of users emphasized the importance of the urban and industrial (particularly the metal-working industries) phases of the economy in the demand for steel mill products and assigned a relatively minor place to agriculture. The discussion of the iron and steel processing and fabricating industries brought out in sharp focus the concentration of these industries in the Middle Atlantic and Lake and Ohio River Areas—particularly in the states of Pennsylvania, Ohio, Michigan, Indiana, and Illinois—and the relatively low development in the South. The analysis of the characteristics of the South pointed out the relationship between the market problems of the southern steel mills and the rural and agricultural character of the region. The small number and the wide scatter of large centers of population and the region's vulnerability to invasion by water and rail routes from outside producing centers were also discussed as important market factors. Finally, the chapters on movement and consumption of iron and steel supported the conclusion that the region is a surplus producer of pig iron but a deficit area for steel mill products and iron and steel fabricated products. As a consequence of these conditions, a considerable portion of the region's pig iron found markets outside its boundaries. In contrast, the net movement of steel was to the South. Under these conditions, it may seem paradoxical that a rather large tonnage of steel mill products produced in the South was moved out of the region.

To these pertinent facts concerning the market for iron and steel, certain additional points should be added. The first is that confusion may arise from the manner in which discussions of the market for iron and steel are phrased. For convenience, terms may be used that imply that the demand is for a single commodity, the separate units of which are freely interchangeable as in the case of wheat. While iron and steel has this characteristic at other stages of production, in the sense that a given batch or

heat may be made into any one of a wide variety of products, the market demands are for widely diversified products. Once the iron or steel has been cast or rolled into one of these special shapes or forms, it must find its market in that form. Connected with this market characteristic is the fact that the additional production of many of the most important steel mill products involve large-scale operations. In other words, there is the very real problem of reconciling the demand in a given area for specific products to the ability of the mills in that area to manufacture the products economically.

A second situation that needs a somewhat broader development is the contrast that exists in the degrees of geographic concentration of the markets for iron and steel of mills in the South as compared with the markets of mills in the North. A recent report[6] quotes data from an Interstate Commerce Commission study of territorial movements of carload freight on May 27 and September 23, 1942, indicating that 70.9 per cent of the country's iron and steel railway tonnage originated in the Official Territory and that 78.7 per cent of the traffic so originating remained in the Official Territory. On the other hand, only 53.9 per cent of the iron and steel railway tonnage originating in the Southern Territory remained within that area. This suggests that southern mills go out of their territory to dispose of their product to a much greater extent than do northern mills.

Another view of this situation is presented in Table 148. These data show the very much greater volume of the shipments that originate in the Official Territory compared with those in the Southern Territory, but the contrast of greatest importance is that afforded by the percentage distribution of distances traveled. For the shorter distances, the percentages for the Southern Territory are decidedly smaller than those for the Official Territory, while the reverse is true for the longer distances. One way of summarizing the data is to point out that, in the Official Territory, 52.7 per cent of the ship-

6 Board of Investigation and Research, *The Economics of Iron and Steel Transportation*, pp. 56-57.

ments move less than 300 miles, while, in the Southern Territory, only 34.2 per cent of the total originations were to destinations within this distance limit. On the other hand, only 3.8 per cent of Official Territory originations traveled over 1,000 miles compared with 10.7 per cent for Southern Territory. This difference in the average distance that the mills in the two territories had to ship their products in order to find markets is an important characteristic.

These data emphasize again the need for larger and more concentrated markets in the South and suggest that the development of such markets is one of the most serious problems facing the basic iron and steel industry.

Regional Aspects of Pricing Policies

For almost half a century, steel in the United States was priced under one form or another of a basing-point system. From 1900 to 1924, for the most part, Pittsburgh was the sole basing-point. This was known commonly as Pittsburgh-plus. From 1924 to 1948, a multiple basing-point system was in force. Following the Supreme Court decisions in the cement and corn products cases, the industry abandoned

the basing-point system and adopted pricing on an f.o.b-mill basis. However, efforts to legalize basing-point pricing by federal statute have continued.[7]

BASING-POINT PRICING OF STEEL

Under Pittsburgh-plus, steel was sold at the Pittsburgh base price, plus the cost of transportation from Pittsburgh to the point of delivery, regardless of the location of the steel plant making the sale. As steel manufacture became more decentralized, dissatisfaction with this pricing system accumulated. Finally, as a result of complaints of the Western Association of Rolled Steel Consumers and of the Associated States opposing Pittsburgh-plus, the Federal Trade Commission, in 1924, ordered Pittsburgh-plus to be abandoned, and a multiple basing-point system was substituted.

[7] The National Planning Association through the Committee on the South is sponsoring a study of basing point pricing of steel and the effects on the development of the South. The study is being made by Professor George Stocking of Vanderbilt University. The forthcoming report gives a very thorough discussion of the historical development of the practices and a detailed analysis of the economic consequences.

Table 148

Number of Cars of Iron and Steel Rated Fifth Class in Official Classification (Also Tin and Terneplate) That Originated in Official and Southern Territories by Mileage Blocks
(Board of Investigation and Research Sample, 1939)

Mileage blocks	Number of cars		Percentage distribution			
	Official	Southern	Simple		Cumulated	
	territory	territory	Official	Southern	Official	Southern
0 to 99 miles	6,016	80	26.1	7.6	26.1	7.6
100 to 199 miles	3,085	83	13.4	7.9	39.5	15.5
200 to 299 miles	2,794	197	12.2	18.7	51.7	34.2
300 to 399 miles	3,110	142	13.5	13.5	65.2	47.7
400 to 499 miles	2,600	129	11.3	12.2	76.5	59.9
500 to 599 miles	1,683	108	7.3	10.3	83.8	70.2
600 to 699 miles	1,396	65	6.1	6.2	89.9	76.4
700 to 799 miles	713	70	3.1	6.6	93.0	83.0
800 to 899 miles	408	37	1.8	3.5	94.8	86.5
900 to 999 miles	318	29	1.4	2.8	96.2	89.3
1,000 to 1,999 miles	526	41	2.3	3.9	98.5	93.2
2,000 and over	344	72	1.5	6.8	100.0	100.0
Total	22,993	1,053	100.0	100.0		

Source: 1939 Carload Traffic Survey, Board of Investigation and Research (photostat copies of selected work sheets).

The distinctive feature of a multiple basing-point system is that a number of places are designated as basing-points for pricing the particular products which may be indicated for each. The price at any particular delivery point is the one which makes the lowest combination of mill base price plus freight. This means that a particular basing-point sets the delivered price within the area in which its base price plus freight is lower than the similar figure of any other basing-point. It should further be pointed out that, in practice, the transportation cost used for this purpose is the all-rail freight charge.

At first, the basing-points tended to be places where the United States Steel Corporation had subsidiaries. Also, the practice in the earlier years was to set prices at the basing-points that gave Pittsburgh a substantial favorable differential, generally of $3.00 per ton. On June 24, 1938, the United States Steel Corporation announced price reductions on most products at Pittsburgh, eliminated differentials at many producing centers, and reduced the differentials at other points. Similar action was taken by other companies, many of whom set up additional basing-points for their own mills. Thus, basing-points tended to increase in number and to conform more nearly to natural market areas, but the fact remains that, during the 1940s, prices for a particular steel mill product generally were the same at all basing-points making quotations.

The basing-point pricing system has long been criticized by many economists as a device for monopolistic control of prices and, consequently, as an undesirable and harmful practice. Particularly, the system has been under attack by the Federal Trade Commission. It was this agency that brought the legal action which resulted in the decisions in which the Supreme Court held that the pricing policies followed by the cement companies, Corn Products Refining Company, and the Staley Manufacturing Company were discriminatory and illegal. Influenced by these decisions, the United States Steel Corporation announced in July, 1948, that it was changing to f.o.b.-mill pricing.

The other steel producers concurred in this action almost immediately.

F.O.B.-MILL PRICING OF STEEL

Under f.o.b.-mill pricing, each mill establishes its own price, and the buyer presumably takes possession of the steel at the mill. The cost to the buyer is the price at the mill from which the purchase is made plus the actual transportation charge to the delivery point. Transportation presumably may be by rail, water, or truck, at the buyer's option.

It is not the purpose of this discussion to arrive at conclusions concerning relative merits of basing-point and f.o.b.-mill pricing from the point of view of national policy. The primary interest here is to consider the regional aspects of the problems arising from the pricing policies and practices that have been followed in the past. To accomplish this purpose, however, it is necessary to inquire further into how the various policies operate.

HOW BASING-POINT PRICING AND F.O.B.-MILL PRICING WORK

Perhaps the differences between a basing-point system and f.o.b.-mill pricing can best be brought out by an illustration. For this purpose, the following assumed situation will be used.

There are two steel mills, X and Y, which produce the same kinds of products and are located at two rather widely separated points. Six market points are under consideration, as designated below.

Market points	Freight from plant X	Freight from plant Y
A (location of X)	$ 0.00	$30.00
B	5.00	25.00
C	7.50	22.50
D	10.00	20.00
E	12.50	17.50
F	20.00	10.00

First, the situation under a basing-point system will be developed. X and Y are both basing points, and the price is $50 per ton at each point. Under these conditions, the delivered prices at Markets A, B, C, D, and E will be governed by X as the basing point and will be

$50, $55, $57.50, $60, and $62.50, respectively. The price at market F will be determined by Y and will be $60.

To carry the illustration further, it is assumed that X has been selling entirely in markets A, B, C, D, and E and, on this basis, has a total volume of 800,000 tons at an average cost of $40 per ton, not including transportation. In other words, X has been making a profit of $10 per ton (the difference between the mill net price, $50, and the average cost).

Under the basing-point system, X can sell in market F if the management is willing to meet the delivered price from Y of $60. The freight from X to F is $20 and from Y to F is $10. To sell in F, plant X would have to absorb $10 of the freight or, viewed from a different angle, would have to be satisfied with a mill net price of $40 instead of its base price of $50. On the surface, there would seem to be little incentive for X under the given circumstances to attempt to sell in market F because the average cost is also $40.

Plant X has the ordinary characteristics of an integrated steel mill, namely, the advantage of large-scale production and fixed charges that constitute a large portion of total costs, and has unused capacity. The management is convinced that the plant is operating under decreasing cost conditions. They believe that they can sell 200,000 tons in market F by absorbing freight and that this increased volume will result in a substantial reduction in average cost. On this basis, they embark on the venture.

Let us assume that plant X succeeds in making the additional sales of 200,000 tons and that this results in a reduction of average costs to $38. Now let us calculate the effects on profits. Under the old program, the total profit was $8,000,000 (800,000 tons at a profit of $10 per ton). Under the new program, the plant would retain its profits on its former sales, but these now would be increased by $1,600,000, because of the decrease of $2.00 in average cost, and would be $9,600,000. The profits on the sales to market F would be relatively small but would add $400,000 (200,000 tons at a profit of $2.00, the difference between the mill net price of $40 and the average cost of $38). Thus

a profit of $10,000,000, compared with the former profit of $8,000,000, would result.

For the purpose of contrast, these results may be compared with the situation that would exist with the same set of facts under an f.o.b.-mill pricing arrangement. To get into market F, plant X would have to quote a mill price that would enable a customer in F to get a delivered cost as low as he could get from Y. This would mean a mill price of $40, but if X quotes such a price to a customer from F, presumably the same mill price would have to be offered to all other buyers. According to the conditions of the illustration as formerly set up, X had sales of 800,000 tons at a mill price of $50 and an average cost of $40 per ton or a total profit of $8,000,000. Entering market F on a price basis that would compete with Y was assumed to yield an additional volume of 200,000 tons and a reduction of average cost to $38 per ton. However, the entry into market F under f.o.b.-mill pricing requires a reduction of price on all sales to $40, and this would reduce profits to $2.00 per ton. Under such conditions, profits would fall from $8,000,000 to $2,000,000.

Under the conditions set forth in the preceding paragraph, X would not enter market F under an f.o.b.-mill pricing system. The question might be raised as to how large a reduction in average cost would be needed before X could afford to lower its mill price to get into F. Certainly the anticipated profits from the expanded operations must be as large as from the smaller operation. This sets the condition for the minimum. The former profit on 800,000 tons was $8,000,000. The same over-all profit of 1,000,000 tons would require a profit of $8.00 per ton. Therefore, the average cost achieved by the expanded operation should not be more than $32 ($40, the reduced mill price, less $8.00 profit).

The illustration thus far has presented a quite simplified picture of the workings of basing-point and f.o.b.-mill pricing, but a number of additional possibilities need to be considered. First, some attention will be given to a further examination of problems under a basing-point system, and later, attention will be given to refinements in the application of f.o.b.-mill pricing.

SOME FURTHER CHARACTERISTICS OF BASING-POINT PRICING

One question that may well be raised concerning basing-point pricing might be phrased very directly in this manner, "While X is planning to invade Y's natural market by absorbing freight, what is to prevent Y from taking similar action with regard to X?" The answer is that there is nothing in the system to prevent such retaliatory action, except the calculation of the management of Y as to whether such a move would be profitable or desirable. So long as the basing-point system is working, all plants will respect the prices set by the basing-point plant in its natural market area. Thus, the basing-point system provides a means by which a plant can seek to enter distant markets and still be protected from price competition, although not from the efforts of other plants to sell within its natural market area.

The question may now be asked concerning the conditions that influence a steel mill to seek sales in markets that lie outside its natural market area. In this connection, three typical situations will be mentioned.

The first situation is that in which the natural market area takes practically the full capacity of the plant. Under these circumstances, the mill is under no pressure to absorb freight. In fact, any sales that the producer accepts from outside the natural market area entail a loss of profit, because all the product can be sold without freight absorption.

The second situation is the opposite of the first in that demand in the natural market area is definitely below the capacity of the plant. Under these conditions, the possibility of reducing average costs by increasing the volume of production and sales is a strong incentive to use whatever means may be at hand to obtain the larger volume. Freight absorption under a basing-point system is a relatively safe way to accomplish this result. The disparity between the demand of the market and the capacity of the plant may arise from either of these two situations: the downswing of the business cycle

may bring a severe, though temporary, curtailment of demand; or the plant, at least temporarily, may have overbuilt its market.

The third situation is really a variation of the second. It is the condition in which a plant with heavy fixed charges finds itself when its volume of sales is so low that it fails to yield a profit. Under such circumstances, any additional volume which can be obtained under conditions that will cover variable costs on the new business and provide some contribution to aid in meeting fixed charges is attractive, even though it accomplishes nothing more than a decrease in losses. Such a condition intensifies the drive to expand volume at almost any cost and no doubt is one of the nightmares of industries that have the general economic characteristics of steel. Unrestrained action motivated by this kind of condition might lead to widespread bankruptcy in the industry.

BASING-POINT PRICING AND SMALL NON-BASING-POINT PLANTS

Another feature of the basing-point system is that which concerns its effect on the relationship between the large basing-point plants and small non-basing-point plants. Corwin D. Edwards in an article in the *Georgetown Law Journal* holds that the basing-point system provides a working compromise of the interests of large and small enterprises. "The large enterprise surrenders a part of its ability to attack the small. In effect it guarantees that little business will not be ruthlessly destroyed. In return, the small enterprises surrender most of their initiative in making prices and most of their opportunity to grow in size and power. By this mutual surrender, a situation is created in which the small concerns live impotently but not unsuccessfully under the large concern's umbrella."[8] He further expresses the opinion that "a second broad characteristic of an industry-wide basing-point system is that it tends to facilitate the growth of large enterprises and to limit the growth of small enterprices, so that discrepancies in size within the

---

[8] Corwin D. Edwards, "Geographic Price Formulas," *Georgetown Law Journal* (January 1949), p. 136.

industry are maintained and may even be enhanced."[9] Much the same theme is further developed and is illustrated with a series of models in an accompanying article by William Summers Johnson in the same journal.[10] The topic is one of importance in an examination of the regional implications of basing-point pricing and so need further elaboration. One approach is to return to the illustration already used and add a third plant, designated as Z, which is small in size, has an average cost of $45 per ton, and is located at D, a non-basing point. The situation in which such a plant would find itself can be inferred from the data.

Though somewhat repetitious, the following tabulation is given to get the facts in mind:

| Market points | Freight from | | Delivered Price | Plant Z | |
	Plant X	Plant Y		Freight	Cost plus freight
A (location of X)	$ 0.00	$30.00	$50.00	$10.00	$55.00
B	5.00	25.00	55.00	5.00	50.00
C	7.50	22.50	57.50	2.50	47.50
D (location of Z)	10.00	20.00	60.00	0.00	45.00
E	12.50	17.50	62.50	2.50	47.50
F	20.00	10.00	60.00	10.00	55.00

Operating under a basing-point pricing system, Z would sell at the delivered prices set by X or Y, the two basing-point plants involved. Presumably, Z could enter any of the markets where the sum of its average cost and freight is lower than the delivered price. This would mean that, under the conditions as presented, it would sell at a profit in all of the market points except A. It will be observed that selling becomes less attractive for Z the nearer the market point is to the basing-point from which the delivered price is determined. The most attractive markets pricewise are at D (the point where Z is located) and the points lying between D and the limit of the territory for which plant X is the basing-point mill.

While the illustration does not present the

complete picture, because it assumes that the market points lie in a straight line, enough is brought out to show the situation in which Z must operate as a non-basing-point mill. The following important characteristics can be seen.

1. While X and Y have a fixed mill net price, $50, and profit per ton, $10 (under the previously assumed average cost of $40 per ton), Z will have a variable net price and profit. The net prices will be $50 at B, $55 at C, $60 at D and E, and $50 at F. The profit will be $5.00 at B, $10 at C, $15 at D and E, and $5.00 at F.

2. Z can sell in a part of the markets of X and Y, but the action of decreasing delivered prices and increasing freight imposes a limit on the extent to which it is profitable for Z to expand its market. At the same time, X and Y have access to all markets within their respective territories without sacrifice of profit per ton.

3. While Z is guaranteed high prices and hence high profit margins per ton in nearby markets, these high prices probably place customers at disadvantage in competing with firms located near X and Y. Hence it is logical to conclude that Z will have access to small volume markets and will be excluded from the large markets. These limitations on the non-basing-point mill would seem to place handicaps that would be hard to overcome and would discourage the establishment of new plants.

The question might be raised as to why a plant, located as Z is, cannot declare itself a basing-point and set its own base price. Under the assumptions previously set up, the answer is easily seen. Situated between two basing-

9 Corwin D. Edwards, p. 139.

10 William Summers Johnson, "The Restrictive Incidence of Basing Point Pricing on Regional Developments," *Georgetown Law Journal* (January 1949), pp. 149-165.

points, Z would have only a limited area within which it could set prices. This area would probably be one with quite limited demand because of the high prices which have previously existed. X, therefore, would have only a limited market in which it would recover the full freight charges. To sell beyond these limits, it would have to absorb freight. On the other hand, the big mills could sell in the home market of Z by absorbing freight and would have large home markets to act as a base from which to operate. The immediate result is that Z would be worse off as a basing-point mill than it formerly was. In a long-term attempt to profit by building up a home market, Z would be in an unequal contest with more powerful concerns which are in position to share in whatever increase may take place. The ultimate result might well be the complete failure and elimination of Z.

UNIFORM SPECIFICATIONS AND PRICING POLICIES

A factor of importance in this situation is that steel mill products are made to meet specifications that are uniform for the entire industry.[11] As a result of little or no differentiation between products of different mills and of identical prices, the choice of a supplier from two or more mills becomes either a matter of indifference to the purchaser or a question as to which producer can give the best assurance for the future. Under these conditions, the smaller and apparently weaker firm is at a disadvatnage. As Johnson points out, "It is not necessary for distant producers to undersell the local producer in order to take away a large share of his customers; it is only necessary that they offer identical products and services at identical prices."[12] If pricing is on an f.o.b.-mill basis, the small mill has a degree of protection within its home market in that outside mills must reduce their prices to all customers in order to match prices in the home market of the small mill.

[11] U. S. Steel Corporation T.N.E.C. Papers, I, 377.
[12] William Summers Johnson, p. 154.

ATTITUDE OF IRON AND STEEL COMPANIES TOWARD BASING-POINT PRICING

No doubt the steel industry has been convinced that the basing-point system serves a useful purpose. It provides plants whose natural markets are too small to absorb their total product with a means of seeking additional markets. At the same time, it avoids the undesirable results that could come from the kind of cutthroat competition which almost ruined the railroads in the closing decades of the last century. It should also be pointed out that basing-point pricing does not entirely eliminate price competition because, in a portion of the shipments of steel products, specifications must be met that differ from those on which the quoted prices are based. On such shipments, the steel mill has considerable latitude in charging "extras" and consequently of varying its effective delivered price. Still, the extent to which price competition can enter is quite limited and it is very unlikely that any serious disturbance of the general price and competitive situation in the industry will take place so long as the basing-point system works. From the large companies' point of view, the system can be accepted as a stabilizing device.

REGIONAL IMPLICATIONS OF BASING-POINT PRICING

Since the operation of a basing price system has been discussed in some detail, the regional aspects may now be considered. One factor of importance is the relationship between the general conditions of demand for steel mill products and the market area in which a plant seeks to sell its products. A significant feature of this relationship is that it is not stable. In fact, it might almost be thought that instability is inherent. When conditions are poor, steel mills make strenuous efforts to secure customers in distant markets. When conditions are good and demand in the natural market area is strong, steel mills lose their incentive to accept orders from the customers that their previous efforts may have obtained. These customers may suddenly find themselves without suppliers. The geographic distribution of steel shortages and the consequent appearance of gray markets in the postwar years can be traced, at least to some extent, to this feature of the operation of basing-point pricing. In former years, steel mills in the North and East, operating under basing-point pricing, built up sales in many parts of the South and in the St. Louis area which they could reach only by absorbing freight. With the strong demand of the postwar years, these mills no longer needed to absorb freight to sell all they could produce and, consequently, cut off their former customers. These, thus, were left without suppliers and without much prospect of being able to form a connection with a steel mill located within their marketing area. Such a condition creates uncertainties that are scarcely conducive to the industrial development of the areas affected.

Another question may be raised concerning the effect of basing-point pricing on the geographic development of the basic iron and steel industries. It is one that directs attention to the possible connection of such pricing with the policy of large corporations in developing specialized large-scale plants to serve territories that are much larger than the factors determining natural market areas would seem to justify. The advantages of integration and large-scale production certainly are such as to make large plants in the iron and steel industry a normal expectancy. The technical methods of producing certain products such as steel rails, seamless tubes and pipe, continuous rolled sheets, and tin plate are particularly applicable to large plants, and this is a factor which might well point to the need for a relatively small number of plants producing such items. Still, the question may be raised as to whether the concentration on a few highly specialized plants (that sell at great distances) represents as healthy a situation as one where there is greater geographic distribution of productive facilities and greater diversification and balance in the industrial structure of the component regions of the country. A further question may be raised as to the extent to which the basing-point system of pricing has acted as a device that has permitted the steel producers to carry this proc-

ess of concentration on large and specialized plants to an extent greater than technical and other economic considerations warrant. The argument is advanced by the industry that the abandonment of basing-point pricing would have disastrous results on certain highly developed steel-producing centers, particularly those in western Pennsylvania and eastern Ohio, because the capacity in those centers greatly exceeds the demand in their natural market areas. Such a line of argument tends to confirm the idea that basing-point pricing has had a part in bringing about this high degree of concentration. It would seem, therefore, that its continuance would be a factor in perpetuating the concentration in the present areas and, hence, an influence in retarding the development of plants in the areas that are less developed at present.

Another connection with regional development is the influence that prices, as set under the basing-point system, have had on regional development. Two aspects of this problem may be mentioned. The first is that prices have been held in line with the price in the older and larger centers, more specifically Pittsburgh. Under Pittsburgh-plus, fabricators or other consumers in the South had to pay higher prices for steel (even though they may have been located next door to a steel mill) than their opposite numbers who happened to be located near Pittsburgh, and the differential had no direct connection with costs of production. During the first years of the multiple-basing-point system, the Birmingham price was higher than the Pittsburgh price by what appears to have been an arbitrary differential of $3.00 per ton. Since 1938, the base prices at Birmingham have never been lower than the Pittsburgh prices. Viewed historically, it would seem that steel prices have tended to protect Pittsburgh in its position rather than to encourage the development of regional plants. The second aspect is that basing-point pricing diverts the efforts of a plant desiring to expand volume toward securing the increased volume by absorbing freight to distant markets and away from building up demand in its natural market area by offering lower prices. By making it possible for a mill to obtain a higher mill net price on sales within its market area than on sales outside the area, basing-point pricing makes it possible for the plant to retain all the advantage of savings in average cost and pass none on to consumers in the natural market area. These aspects of basing-point pricing seem to work in the direction of retarding development in line with natural advantages. In other words, if a region has an advantage in production costs, the working of the basing-point system seems to prevent fabricators or consumers in the region from benefiting from that situation by getting lower prices.

A final point with respect to the regional impact of basing-point pricing on a regional economy has to do with the effects on the development of small plants. In a well-developed industrial economy, there should be a place for a number of small steel plants, operating on scrap or purchased ingots, and there should be an opportunity for such plants to develop into larger operations if the growth of market permits. The South has had relatively few such mills, and even such a plant as the Gadsden plant, formerly operated by the Gulf States Steel Company and now by Republic Steel Corporation, has had a difficult time in maintaining profitable operations. The analysis of the problems that face the small non-basing-point mill suggests that, at least in part, the development of new steel mills in the South has been restricted by the operation of basing-point pricing.

REGIONAL IMPLICATIONS OF F.O.B.-MILL PRICING

The discussion of the assumed situation faced by plant X and plant Y indicated that f. o. b.-mill pricing has an entirely different result on prices in the natural market area than does basing-point pricing. Under f. o. b.-mill pricing, the mill price is the same to everyone. This means that advantages, obtained by expanding the volume of sales through making concessions in prices to anyone, are shared by all. The illustration as set up had the defect that there was a big jump in the freight costs from X to market E and from X to market F.

The former was $12.50 and the latter $20 per ton. Very probably markets will be located quite close to each other, and the increments of increase in freight costs between market points as they become more distant from a mill will be quite small. If this is the case, the pressure to reduce prices to enlarge the sales territory will be stronger because it is possible to accomplish results of consequence by much smaller reductions than would have been necessary under the illustration given above. This would be particularly true if there happened to be important market points that were located just beyond X's market territory as determined by current prices. If X had the opportunity of capturing 200,000 additional tons by reducing prices $1.00 per ton, the result would work out quite differently from the calculations under the assumptions previously used. The profit on the 800,000 ton volume as previously shown was $8,000,000. The reduction of price by $1.00 and the resulting expansion of market territory would yield a volume of 1,000,000 tons. The price would be $49 instead of $50, but the average cost of 1,000,000 tons (by previous assumption) would be $38 instead of $40. The profit then is $11 per ton, or $11,000,000 on the total volume. Thus, the cut in price under these conditions would be very profitable.

The situation described in the preceding paragraph perhaps assumes a greater increase in the volume to be obtained by a relatively small decrease in price than is likely to occur, but the important point is that the attempt to expand the market by decrease in price need not involve large decreases in order to move the boundary of the market back by great distances, but may be made in small increments and may involve relatively small shifts so far as miles are concerned. It should be pointed out also that the volume increases that may be expected should include not only the sales obtained from the new area, but also increases in the former market area that are stimulated by the lower prices. If the steel industry is correct in its contention that the demand for steel is inelastic, this latter type of increase may be small so far as the immediate future is concerned, but the long-run effect should be of considerable importance, particularly in those regions in which the basic industry is operating at relatively low costs.

LIMITATIONS OF F. O. B.-MILL PRICING

F. o. b.-mill pricing should not be described as a cure for all the troubles that have been attributed to the policies followed in pricing steel. One opinion that is often expressed is that the effect of f. o. b.-mill pricing will be to place each mill in a monopoly position in its natural market area. This may be true in the sense that the mill may become the only seller in much of the area. However, it would seem that steel mills generally are operating under decreasing cost conditions or have such heavy fixed charges that they are under pressure at most times to use their production facilities more fully. The means that most mills are continually seeking to expand their volume. If the expansion is to be obtained by reducing the prices charged to all, the buyers in the marketing area are receiving considerable protection from being overcharged. A more serious problem arises from the danger that f. o. b.-mill pricing may precipitate a price war that would be ruinous to all. As previously pointed out, a firm which has heavy fixed charges may feel under such pressure to compete for a larger market that it will sell for prices that little more than cover variable costs. Thus, it is entirely possible that f. o. b.-mill pricing might release competitive forces which, if not restrained, would be disasterous. However, it is doubtful that this would occur under the oligopolistic conditions that characterize the industry.

CONCLUSIONS CONCERNING PRICING POLICIES

The discussion of the characteristics of basing-point and f. o. b.-mill pricing suggests the following conclusions.

1. A shift from basing-point to f. o. b.-mill pricing should lessen the incentive to secure volume by efforts to get into distant markets. Under the basing-point system, absorption of freight did not involve price reduction in the natural markets. The situation under f. o. b.-

mill pricing is quite different. A cut in prices in a new market means reducing prices to all customers. The price decreases required to enter distant markets probably will be too large to be profitable.

2. F. o. b.-mill pricing should put more pressure on producers to make relatively small price reductions in order to meet competition around the periphery of the market area, particularly if a large market point lies just outside the area.

3. Presumably, f. o. b.-mill pricing may be expected to make adherence to an agreed price structure more difficult to maintain. It should tend to bring prices more in line with costs of production, but, on the other hand, it might encourage cutthroat competition.

4. Presumably, a system of basing-point pricing that uses all-rail freight rates in calculating delivered prices makes the manner of shipment a matter of indifference to the buyer. F. o. b.-mill pricing would make the choice of the cheapest manner of shipping a matter of concern to the buyer since he would receive any savings in freight.

5. F. o. b.-mill pricing may be expected to cause mills to direct more attention to the needs of their natural market areas and to adjust their production facilities more directly to those needs. Probably such a pricing program would discourage concentration on huge special product plants and encourage the building of plants designed for more numerous and diversified products. Another aspect of this phase of the subject is that f. o. b.-mill pricing may exert considerable influence in encouraging location of processing and fabricating plants in areas where they can obtain supplies of steel at low transportation costs.

6. Once an adjustment has been made to an f. o. b.-mill price basis, the relation between buyer and seller should no longer be dependent on the question of whether or not it is profitable for the seller to absorb freight. A more stable situation insofar as the buyer is concerned should result.

7. Basing-point pricing, as it has been practiced in the past, appears to have provided protection to the older steel centers and the larger

mills and to have restrained the new centers and smaller mills from deriving the full benefits from any advantages they may have had in the way of lower costs of production or nearness to markets.

The examination of the workings of basing-point pricing in the past points toward the conclusion that the system is not designed to stimulate growth in metal-using industries in regions that have the characteristics of the South. F. o. b.-mill pricing has many features that indicate that such a system of pricing would encourage development in conformity with the natural advantages of a region and would seem in the long run to be advantageous to the South. There are, however, serious problems that need to be faced. It is entirely possible that an abrupt change from basing-point to f. o. b.-pricing could result in serious dislocations of industries and markets. In other words, steel mills located in areas where capacity is larger than the demand in their natural markets might be suffering from lack of markets for their products at the same time that consumers, who previously had been buying steel on a freight absorption basis, were finding that they could buy steel only by paying a much higher freight and hence a much higher total price than their competitors. In part, this situation has characterized the last few years, when the extremely active demand has caused steel companies to discontinue absorbing freight. Presumably, such dislocations would disappear as producers and consumers adjusted themselves to the change. Another difficulty connected with the adoption of f. o. b.-pricing is the possibility of ruinous competition in the steel industry.

So far as the immediate consequences to the South are concerned, it is entirely possible that too much emphasis is given to the debate over basing-point versus f. o. b.-mill pricing because the decision with regard to prices in the region will remain largely in the hands of the United States Steel Corporation. The management of the corporation will have the problem of deciding what prices will be quoted on steel produced by its Birmingham plants and what relationship those prices will have to costs of production and to prices at its other plants. The Republic Steel Corporation is in a similar position, and the two constitute practically the whole of the steel industry in the Birmingham area. In many respects, the most important problem with respect to price is how the price at Birmingham compares with prices in Pittsburgh, Chicago, and other steel centers with which Birmingham has to compete. Under present ownership, it is questionable if changes in these relationships will depend to any great extent on whether prices are determined by a basing-point or f. o. b.-mill system.

Most economists probably would agree that the most desirable prices would be those that result when price-making forces, including the self-interest of producers, are free to operate. Such a statement carries the implication of what the economist refers to as pure, or perfect, competition. Under conditions as they exist in an industrialized economy, consideration must be given to the peculiar conditions under which a particular class of producers and consumers must operate. In large scale industries, the number of producers must, of necessity, be small and, with heavy investment, entry into or withdrawal from the industry is not easy. On the other hand, consumers are likely to be numerous, scattered, and varied in size. These conditions make it unreasonable to assume perfect competition. It might be pertinent, however, to ask what considerations would influence a producer in setting prices in a place like Birmingham on the assumption that he was the sole producer, that his production costs were relatively low, and that he was free to work out his own quotations. In attempting an answer, two alternative assumptions concerning the situations with regard to the market in which the producer has a freight advantage will be made. These are as follows: (1) the territory has a demand much greater than the capacity of the producer, and (2) the territory has a demand much smaller than the capacity.

It would seem that, under the first condition, the immediate policy of the producer probably would be to set prices that would maximize his gross take from sales. This would be a price that would meet the delivered price of competitors at the points bounding the area with a demand sufficiently large to take his total product. Under the conditions assumed, this might mean giving up part of the freight advantage in order to secure the higher price per unit. In the longer view, however, the fact that he is a low cost producer and that he has a freight advantage should be an incentive to increase capacity and absorb a larger portion of the total market. The extent to which the process of expanding capacity and reducing prices to get a larger market will be carried presumably would be a matter of securing the largest net return. The degree to which the producer operates with decreasing costs is a factor of importance.

In the second situation a quite different approach to the problem can be expected. The producer, instead of having relatively little immediate concern about the size of his market, will be strongly moved to build up his volume of sales. Presumably this might be done by (1) increasing the demand within his territory or (2) expanding the limits of his territory. If he were operating on an f. o. b.-mill basis and charging the same mill net price to all customers, it would seem that the producer would take advantage of his low costs and of any opportunity for decreasing his average cost in order to quote lower prices than his competitors. Such an action should have the effect of encouraging the development of steel-consuming industries in his territory and also of extending the limits. The final results would, of course, be dependent on the action taken by competitors. The anticipation of those reactions may well influence the extent to which the producer in question may push his policy of low prices.

The record of prices of steel in Birmingham and of price differentials, when compared with other steel centers, is scarcely one that corresponds with what would be expected if pricing had been done with the interests of steel production in Birmingham as a central consideration. The evidence that could be assembled in this study indicates that Birmingham has been a relatively low-cost producer. The reason for

being slow in expanding facilities that has most commonly been advanced is the lack of markets in the South. Yet prices of steel until 1938 were held above Pittsburgh and have never been permitted to fall below the base prices of other competing markets. This situation stands in sharp contrast with that of pig iron. As is shown by Table 149, Birmingham

Table 149

Annual Average Prices of Foundry Pig Iron No. 2, Mahoning, Shenango Valley, and Birmingham, 1920-1950

	Average price per ton	
Year	Mahoning, Shenango Valley	Birmingham
1920	$43.21	$40.60
1921	23.22	22.19
1922	25.23	19.63
1923	26.37	23.86
1924	20.73	19.86
1925	19.90	19.71
1926	18.87	21.16
1927	18.00	17.47
1928	17.12	16.01
1929	18.23	15.13
1930	18.00	14.14
1931	16.72	12.27
1932	14.73	11.04
1933	15.91	12.32
1934	18.19	14.15
1935	18.67	14.60
1936	19.60	15.76
1937	23.49	19.87
1938	22.20	18.58
1939	21.59	17.96
1940	23.03	19.38
1941	24.00	20.17
1942	24.00	20.38
1943	24.00	20.38
1944	24.00	20.38
1945	25.02	21.40
1946	27.64	24.06
1947	34.36	31.43
1948	42.12	40.43
1949	46.50	40.74
1950	47.58	43.53

Source: *Iron Age,* Annual numbers, 1920-1950.

foundry iron usually has sold at a lower price than comparable grades of Mahoning and Shenango Valley foundry iron. The differential in favor of Birmingham was at least $1.00

per gross ton in all except four of the years of the period between 1920 and 1950. The average differential was around $3.50. It seems reasonable to conclude that this situation has been a very important factor in the development of the cast-iron pipe and gray iron foundry industries in the South and in the extension of the market for southern pig iron much farther to the north than the market for steel.

General Conclusions

Although much that has been said in the preceding discussions may seem critical, it should be pointed out in conclusion that the slow development of metal-using industries and the markets for steel in the South cannot be charged too heavily to the policies of the big iron and steel companies. The South is a large area. Its characteristics have their roots in a wide variety of conditions, most of which have been brought about by factors which have, at most, only indirect connections with steel. Consequently, such general conditions

as the predominance of agriculture, the low degree of urbanization, and the late response to industrialization, all of which have a great influence on demand for steel, can scarcely be considered as resulting from the policies of the steel companies to any great degree. Furthermore, it must be emphasized that substantial progress has been made in the southern industry, and that the United States Steel Corporation and the other steel makers have had an important place in that record of progress.

Still, the opinion can be advanced that policies have not always been those that would stimulate the greatest development. The corporations do have the power to initiate and to put in practice policies that will have much to do with future developments, and it is hoped that those making decisions will give regional interests an important place in their deliberations. A good case can be made for the argument that a well-rounded development that makes full use of the natural resources and people of a region will in the long run prove profitable for the entire country.

CHAPTER XXVI

ECONOMIC CHARACTERISTICS AND THEIR REGIONAL IMPLICATIONS: THE IRON AND STEEL PROCESSING AND FABRICATING INDUSTRIES

While the same general topics as were used in the preceding chapter can be used to describe the iron and steel processing and fabricating industries, there are differences in the data and the characteristics of the industries that prevent paralleling the discussion of the basic industries with any great degree of exactness. The basic industries consist of only three important separate industries; some 144 industries are included as constituting the processing and fabricating industries. The basic industries employ techniques and processes that are closely related and the products are quite similar in their nature—pig iron and steel are closely associated with each other in common usage and thought. The processing and fabricating industries are varied in their operations and their products are diverse. Because of these factors, an analysis of their economic characteristics can scarcely be as specific in dealing with particular industries as it was possible to be with the basic industries. Consequently, extensive use will be made of groupings of industries, classified according to selected criteria. This kind of treatment has definite limitations, particularly to those whose interest is in a specific industry or who desire to choose the best industry to promote. However, limits of time and space make it necessary to confine the analysis to the general features of important characteristics.

The general outline that will be followed is quite similar to that used for the discussion of the basic industries except that more attention will be given to the problems of promoting expansion. This latter feature arises from the conviction that a well-rounded and vigorous development of the metal-using industries is one of the most important needs both for the development of the basic iron and steel industries and for the strengthening of the industrial structure of the South. The topics which will be discussed are as follows: the economics of production, present locational pattern, ownership characteristics, nature of demand and markets, market organization and methods, pricing policies, and problems of expansion.

Economics of Production

In previous chapters, the typical operations used by the processing and fabricating industries in shaping the metal parts, giving them the proper physical characteristics such as hardness or toughness, and assembling or erecting the final finished products have been described in some detail[1] and these descriptions scarcely need to be repeated. The reader is reminded, however, that individual plants vary greatly in the kinds of equipment used and the operations performed and that a similar diversity exists with regard to the product both with respect to form and to end use. These differences present many opportunities for the exploration of a wide variety of particular problems of individual industries, but the analysis will be confined to certain general characteristics such as the size of establishments, average wages paid, importance of administrative, office, and sales personnel, and the use of power.

SIZE OF ESTABLISHMENTS

To represent the size of the establishments of the 144 processing and fabricating industries, two measures were used. Both were cal-

[1] See Chapter XIX.

culated from the data published in the reports of the *Census of Manufactures*, 1947. The first is the median size of the establishments of an industry in terms of the number of production workers. The second is the percentage of the total number of production workers of an industry who are employed in plants of 249 or fewer employees. The first measure is an average which does not give heavy weight to the extremely large plants and indicates the frequency with which small plants occur—fifty per cent are as small or smaller than the median. The second indicates the weight that small plants as a whole have in the entire in-

dustry. Table 150 presents a summary of the results of this analysis in which the interrelations of the two measures are shown.

In general, the median establishments of the processing and fabricating industries are small compared with those of the basic iron and steel industries. The medians of the latter group are as follows: blast furnace industry, 324; steel works and rolling mills, 1591; and electrometallurgical plants, 231 production workers. The processing and fabricating industries with the largest medians together with the corresponding percentages of total employees in plants with 249 employees or less are listed below.

Title of industry	Production workers in median establishments	Percentage of production workers employed in plants of 249 or fewer employees
Aircraft	625	1.0
Malleable iron foundries	260	18.4
Steam engines and turbines	218	5.8
Railroad and street cars	207	3.8
Wire drawing	197	10.3
Steel foundries	191	18.9
Domestic laundry equipment	163	6.0
Welded and heavy riveted pipe	142	16.8
Vitreous enameled products	140	19.9
Typewriters	130	6.5*
Aircraft engines	108	4.3

*500 or less employees.

Table 150

Size of Establishments of Iron and Steel Processing and Fabricating Industries, Median Size of Establishment as Related to Percentage of Employees in Plants of 249 Employees or Less, 1947

Median establishment (in terms of production workers)	Total number of industries	Number of industries with indicated percentage in plants with 249 or less employees				
		50% or more	30% to 49.9%	15% to 29.9%	0 to 14.9%	not available
Under 25	93	34	31	9	5	14*
25 to 74	33	2	12	10	6	3**
75 to 149	11	0	1	4	5	1***
150 and over	7	0	0	2	5	0
Total	144	36	44	25	21	18

Source: Calculated from *Census of Manufacturers*, 1947.
*Of these 14 industries, 7 had 50 per cent or more of their employees in plants with 500 or less employees; 3 had from 30 per cent to 49.9 per cent of their employees in plants with 500 or less employees; and one had 16.4 per cent of its employees in plants with 500 or less employees.
**One of these industries had 7.8 per cent of its employees in plants with 500 or less employees.
***This industry had 6.5 per cent of its employees in plants with 500 or less employees.

All of these have a small proportion of their total employees in plants employing 249 or less, indicating that small plants play a relatively small part in these eleven industries.

In industries that have one-half of their plants with less than 100 production workers, it would seem that small plants should be considered as having a good chance for existence. This condition is met by 133 of the 144 processing and fabricating industries. An examination of the distribution of employees by size of plant suggests, however, that a number of the industries with low medians are dominated by the large plants. Examples of such industries are given in the following list.

of the industries consist of relatively small units, and efficient working combinations of these units are possible in small plants.

The 1947 Census of Manufactures published information on the metal-working operations performed which throws more light on size of operations. The data do not cover all the industries included in this study and are for twelve selected operations only, but the more important industries and operations are included. These data are summarized in Table 151. A further qualification that must be kept in mind is that the industries specializing in a particular line are not included in the figures for the similarly named operation. Thus,

Title of industry	Production workers in median establishments	Percentage of production workers employed in plants of 249 or fewer employees
Files	7	12.0
Small arms ammunition	9	0.2
Tractors	18	2.8
Watches, clocks, and parts	17	12.3
Refrigerators	19	14.2
Measuring and dispensing pumps	30	11.9
Power and distribution transformers	32	12.4
Vacuum cleaners	38	7.8*
Small arms	40	8.4
Computing machines	45	**
Motor vehicles and parts	46	4.3
Telephone and telegraph equipment	46	**
Aircraft propellers	63	7.3
Motors and generators	70	14.6
Shipbuilding and repairing	90	12.2
Locomotives and parts	93	5.3
Internal combustion engines	99	6.1
Ball and roller bearings	99	9.5

*Plants with 500 or less employees.   ** Not available, but low.

Table 150 shows that there are 36 industries in which 50 per cent, or more, of the employees are in plants employing 249 or fewer. Furthermore, there are 44 additional industries in which from 30 to 49.9 per cent of the employees are in plants employing 249 or fewer employees. Only one of these has a median of over 75. In general, the processing and fabricating industries seem to have considerable room for small plants. This conclusion seems reasonable. Compared with the blast furnace and steel works industries, the machinery and other production equipment required by many

the foundry and die-casting operations do not include commercial foundries; forging does not include commercial forge shops; nor does galvanizing include the galvanizing industry, or machine shops, the machine shop industry. In other words, the table reflects the use of the designated operation by industries other than those specializing in the performance of the operation. The industries are largely those that are engaged in making a finished product.

The table serves to give some indication of the frequency with which the twelve operations constitute a part of the manufacturing process of the metal-working industries. By far the most common are the machine shops; with stamping, blanking, forming, or drawing as second; and tool and die rooms, third. Perhaps more important is the evidence that most of these operations tend to be relatively small-scale. Of the twelve operations, five have more than half of their occurrences in establishments that employ four or fewer production workers on the operation. These are die casting, electroplating, galvanizing, heat treating, and pattern shops. A sixth, automatic screw machine department, has almost one-half of its establishments in this class. Furthermore, all operations except foundries have at least half of their occurrences in establishments that employed 19, or fewer, production workers on the operation and six (die casting, electroplating, galvanizing, heat treating, automatic screw machine department, and pattern shops) have 80 per cent, or more, of their occurrences so classified. In so far as these data can be considered as representative, they give further evidence

that the fundamental operations of the iron and steel processing and fabricating industries are being successfully performed on a small-scale basis.

OTHER OPERATING CHARACTERISTICS

Data from the *Census of Manufactures* can also be used to indicate other characteristics that are significant in the economics of production of the processing and fabricating industries. A series of tables (Tables 152, 153, 154, 155 and 156) present such information. These deal with the level of wages paid, the importance of administrative, technical, and office personnel, value added by manufacture as related to the number of man hours of labor, the relative importance of wages and salaries in costs, and the use of electric power in manufacturing operations. The more outstanding conclusions that can be drawn from these data will be pointed out.

The most conspicuous characteristics that are indicated by these tables are: (1) wages as

Table 151

Number of Establishments Performing Selected Metal Working Operations in
Iron and Steel Processing and Fabricating Industries, 1947

Metal working operation	Number of establishments distributed by number of production workers on operation					
	Total	1-4	5-19	20-49	50-99	100 and over
Foundry, except die casting*.....................	1,477	284	337	341	239	276
Die casting, nonferrous metals only*..............	420	262	103	27	17	11
Forging-presses, hammers on upsetters**..........	1,518	722	476	185	68	67
Electroplating***................................	1,865	955	575	218	64	53
Galvanizing and other hot-dip coating†..........	691	357	202	100	25	7
Heat treating or annealing metal.................	3,911	2,637	861	273	84	56
Automatic screw machine department...........	3,441	1,701	1,084	415	132	109
Machine shop††..............................	15,157	4,755	5,211	2,592	1,235	1,364
Tool and die room............................	5,694	2,295	2,059	808	307	225
Pattern shop	3,377	2,131	956	205	56	29
Plate or structural fabrication....................	4,995	1,560	1,613	893	473	456
Stamping, blanking, forming or drawing..........	9,423	3,839	2,812	1,426	638	708

*Data shown do not include commercial foundries. (Number of establishments, 1947: malleable-iron, 78; gray-iron 1654; steel, 204; nonferrous, 1724.)

**Data shown do not include commercial forge shops. (Number of establishments, 1947: 250.)

***Data shown do not include figures for the plating and polishing industry. (Number of establishments, 1947: 1802.)

†Data shown do not include establishments in the galvanizing industry. (Number of establishments, 1947: 125.)

††Data shown do not include establishments classified in the machine shops industry. (Number of establishments, 1947: 3112.)

Source: *Census of Manufacturers, 1947,* I, 252-258, after eliminating industries not considered as iron and steel processing and fabricating industries, namely, steel works and rolling mills, copper rolling and drawing, aluminum rolling and drawing, nonferrous metal rolling n.e.c. and electric lamps.

measured by the wage per man-hour are relatively high; (2) wages and salaries as measured in terms of percentages of value added by manufacture are much more important elements of cost than in manufacturing as a whole; and (3) the use of power as measured in kilowatt hours per production worker is low. When compared with all-industry figures, wages per man-hour are higher in 100 of the 144 iron and steel processing and fabricating industries and wages and salaries account for higher percentages of value added by manufacture in 121 industries. On the other hand, only four processing and fabricating industries have figures for consumption of electricity per production worker that are higher than the all-manufacturing average. To some, these results may not seem consistent with the idea that most of the iron and steel processing and fabricating industries are highly mechanized. Nearly all the processing is mechanical in nature and the machines and equipment that have been developed to aid in performing the operations are highly specialized and are power operated, but intelligence and skill is an even more important requirement and the rates of pay are relatively high.

With regard to the other two measures that are used in the series of tables, the processing and fabricating industries on the whole do not seem to differ markedly from the all-manufacturing averages. For value added by manufacture per man-hour, the processing and fabricating industries seem to be somewhat on the low side, since only 59 of the 144 industries are higher than the all-manufacturing average.

Table 152

Average Wage Per Man-Hour in the Iron and Steel Processing and Fabricating Industries, United States, 1947

Wage per man-hour (in cents)	Number of industries
80 to 89	1
90 to 99	2
100 to 109	9
110 to 119	19
120 to 129	30
130 to 139	50
140 to 149	22
150 to 159	10
160 to 169	0
170 to 179	1
Total	144

Note: All-industry average wage per man-hour—$1.24.
Source: *Census of Manufactures, 1947.*

Table 153

Per Cent of All Employees Classified as Administration, Sales, and Office in the Iron and Steel Processing and Fabricating Industries, United States, 1947

Per cent administration, sales, and office employees of total	Number of industries
8 to 9.9	8
10 to 11.9	8
12 to 13.9	20
14 to 15.9	19
16 to 17.9	23
18 to 19.9	19
20 to 21.9	10
22 to 23.9	12
24 to 25.9	5
26 to 27.9	13
28 to 29.9	4
30 and over*	3
Total	144

*One industry each, 30.0, 33.6, and 36.1 per cent.
Note: All-industry average per cent of administration employees —16.5 per cent.
Source: *Census of Manufactures, 1947.*

Table 154

Value Added by Manufacture Per Man-Hour, in the Iron and Steel Processing and Fabricating Industries, United States, 1947

Value added per man-hour	Number of industries
$1.75 to $1.99	1
2.00 to 2.24	8
2.25 to 2.49	18
2.50 to 2.74	27
2.75 to 2.99	28
3.00 to 3.24	20
3.25 to 3.49	21
3.50 to 3.74	12
3.75 to 3.99	5
4.00 and over*	4
Total	144

*One industry each, $4.45, $4.48, $4.63, and $5.63.
Note: All-industry average—$3.06.
Source: *Census of Manufactures, 1947.*

Table 155

Per Cent of Value Added by Manufacture Accounted for by Wages and Salaries in the Iron and Steel Processing and Fabricating Industries, United States, 1947

Wages and salaries as per cent of value added	Number of industries
40.0 to 44.9	2
45.0 to 49.9	7
50.0 to 54.9	28
55.0 to 59.9	38
60.0 to 64.9	36
65.0 to 69.9	21
70.0 to 74.9	8
75.0 per cent and over*	4
Total	144

*One industry each—76.4, 80.4, 88.9, 96.2 per cent.
Note: All-industry average—53.3 per cent.
Source: Census of Manufactures, 1947.

Table 156

Kilowatt Hours of Electric Energy Consumed Per Production Worker in the Iron and Steel Processing and Fabricating Industries, United States, 1947

Kilowatt hours (1000) per production worker (per year)	Number of industries
0 to 999	2
1,000 to 1,999	16
2,000 to 2,999	20
3,000 to 3,999	37
4,000 to 4,999	26
5,000 to 5,999	18
6,000 to 6,999	8
7,000 to 7,999	5
8,000 to 8,999	4
9,000 to 9,999	2
10,000 and over*	4
Total	142**

*One industry each—11,941; 15,643; 17,867, and 19,221.
**Total is shown as 142 because of two combinations of two industries each.
Note: All-industry average—11,828 kilowatt hours (1000) per production worker.
Source: Census of Manufactures, 1947.

For the per cent of all employees classified as administrative, technical, office, and sales, the processing and fabricating industries have 78, or slightly more than one-half the industries with higher percentages than the all-manufacturing percentage. However, a more detailed examination of the figures shows an important situation. The manufacturers of machinery, appliances, instruments, and specialized apparatus tend to be high in both respects. This undoubtedly is a reflection of the relatively high prices commanded by the products of these industries, on the one hand, and the need for more than the average amount of attention to problems involving design, technology, and selling, on the other.

CONCLUSIONS CONCERNING ECONOMICS OF PRODUCTION

The data presented suggest a wide range in the characteristics of the industries being studied and this should serve as a caution against categorical conclusions. The industries vary widely in size and in kinds of products. Some products, such as automobiles, are highly standardized and are mass produced. Others, such as turbines for a hydroelectric power plant and many items of industrial equipment are custom-made for a particular use. Some products, such as needles, hand tools, and surgical instruments are small, while others—diesel locomotives and ships — are extremely large. Typewriters, washing machines, refrigerators, and many other products leave the factory finished and ready for use, while structural steel products for buildings, water tanks, and bridges have to be assembled and erected at the place where they are to stand. These differences call for many variations in the operations and operational procedures best suited to the particular industry. For these reasons, the present general analysis cannot substitute for complete information about the particular industry which may be under consideration. The present analysis does serve to suggest that design and technical competence on the part of management and skilled labor are important to successful operation in this group of industries. Also, while there are exceptions, as for example in manufacturing automobiles, the data suggest that the processing and fabricating industries stand in contrast to the basic industries in that small scale operations have an important place.

Present Locational Pattern

In discussing industrial location, it has become customary to list the common location factors such as raw materials, labor, markets, taxes, transportation facilities and so forth, appraise the situation with regard to each of these factors, and attempt to come to a conclusion by weighing the good and bad features. This approach may be appropriate for a particular industry or a single plant, but is extremely difficult to apply to a group of industries as numerous or diverse as that under study. Consequently, a detailed consideration of the factors of locations as they may influence the future of the metal products industries of the South will not be attempted. All that will be done now is to review the outstanding features of the present location pattern.

From the geographical point of view, the concentration in the Middle Atlantic and Lake and Ohio River states and the relatively low development in the South were discussed in considerable detail in previous chapters. Another aspect of the locational pattern had to do with the degree of geographic concentration or dispersion that characterizes an industry. The approach was to determine for each industry the number of states that had at least one establishment. On the basis of these counts, the 144 processing and fabricating industries were classified according to the degree of concentration with the following results.

Number of industries with establishments in 38 or more states (widely dispersed) 25

Number of industries with establishments in 25 to 37 states (moderately dispersed) 44

Number of industries with establishments in 13 to 24 states (moderately concentrated) 62

Number of industries with establishments in fewer than 13 states (highly concentrated) 13

Total 144

It also appeared that the concentrated industries tended to be those which had relatively few establishments and that manufactured highly specialized products. In contrast, wide dispersion tended to be associated with large numbers of establishments in the industry and with the production of the simpler and more generally used products. In the analysis of the processing and fabricating industries in the South, it was found that the region had only a weak representation in many of the widely dispersed industries, or those that seemed to have a general tendency to localize, and almost no representation in the concentrated industries.

Ownership Characteristics

The problem of studying the ownership organization of the processing and fabricating industries is much more complicated than was the case with the basic industries. In the latter, general similarity of products and vertical and horizontal integration made the situation easy to describe. In the processing and fabricating industries, the number of industries and the great diversity of products make a simple and direct approach impossible. Certainly there is no combination of two or three corporations which holds the dominant position in the entire classification that the United States Steel Corporation, the Bethlehem Steel Corporation, and the Republic Steel Corporation occupy in the basic industry. The great variety of products has the effect of breaking up the entire classification into a large number of parts, and concentration of ownership becomes largely a matter of dominence in particular individual industries or in the manufacture of particular products or groups of products. Because of this division of the field into a large number of segments, control of the production of a particular product through ownership of plants or patents or possession of the necessary know-how may be largely in the hands of two or three relatively small corporations.

There are, of course, a number of giant corporations operating in the field. The situation in several industries is well known. Outstanding examples are General Motors, Ford, and Chrysler, in motor vehicles; General Electric, Westinghouse, and Western Electric, in electrical machinery; American Can and Continental Can, in the production of tin cans; Singer Sewing Machine Company and White Sewing Machine Company, in sewing machines; International Harvester Company, Deere and Company, and Allis-Chalmers Manufacturing Company, in farm machinery; International Business Machines Company, in mechanical tabulating equipment; and Monroe, Marchant, Friden, and Burroughs, in adding and calculating machines. Also, there is a tendency for a single large company to enter and secure an important position in several industries. Numerous examples could be cited, but the following will suffice. General Motors is much more than a manufacturer of motor vehicles; it is also an important factor in refrigerators and electric ranges. Chrysler Motor Company produces air conditioning equipment and gas and oil furnaces. General Electric not only produces generating equipment

for public utilities and electric lamps, but radio and television receiving sets as well. It is easy to point out these comparatively familiar examples of concentration of ownership in large corporations. An over-all analysis of the total situation is more difficult.

There are two fairly comprehensive types of information on ownership that are available in *Structure of Industry,* a T.N.E.C. Monograph.[2] One is based upon data on control of production operations through central offices and is expressed in terms of the percentage of the total operations in an industry that is accounted for by establishments of companies with central offices—in other words, multiplant concerns. The report gives figures based on the number of establishments, number of wage earners, wages, value of product, and the cost of raw materials. For the present pur-

[2] Temporary National Economic Committee, *The Structure of Industry,* Monograph No. 27.

Table 157

The Importance of Central Office Control in the Iron and Steel Processing and Fabricating Industries, 1937

Industry classification* and measure	Number of industries	Number of industries controlled by central offices in:			
		75% and over of total	50% to 74.9% of total	25% to 49.9% of total	less than 25% of total
Iron and steel and their products**					
Wage earners	25	3	7	14	1
Value of product	25	2	7	14	2
Selected nonferrous industries					
Wage earners	4	0	1	2	1
Value of product	4	0	1	3	0
Machinery					
Wage earners	17	1	8	6	2
Value of product	17	1	8	6	2
Transportation equipment					
Wage earners	6	3	2	1	0
Value of product	6	3	3	0	0
Miscellaneous industries selected					
Wage earners	4	0	1	1	2
Value of product	4	0	1	1	2
Total of above industries					
Wage earners	56	7	19	24	6
Value of product	56	6	20	24	6

*The old census classification.
**Excluding blast furnaces and steel works.
Source: Compiled from U.S.T.N.E.C., *Structure of Industry,* Monograph No. 27, pp. 211-225.

poses, the data on number of wage earners and value of product were chosen. The other measure is based on information on some 1807 products selected to represent the entire range of manufacturing. The figures g i v e n are termed concentration ratios and represent the percentages of the total value of each of the several products that was produced by the four largest concerns. Both kinds of data are for the year 1937[3] and use the old census classification of industries. Neither completely covers

[3] The general concensus seems to be that concentration of ownership in American industry increased during World War II and is probably greater at present than it was in 1937. This view is expressed by the authors of *Economic Concentration and World War II,* Senate Document No. 206, 1946.

all the industries under study and it is possible that the industries or products selected are not completely representative, but the situations that are indicated seem reasonable and significant.

The industries and the products belonging in the iron and steel processing and fabricating industries were selected and the data presented in Tables 157 and 158 were compiled.

The data on central office control indicate that the multiplant companies hold a strong position in many of the iron and steel processing and fabricating industries. In 26, or almost half, of the 56 industries for which data are available, central offices control 50 per cent or more of the number of wage earners and value of product and in only six indus-

Table 158

Distribution of Concentration Ratios (Percentage of Total Value of Product Produced by the Four Largest Concerns) for All Selected Products, Iron and Steel Products, and Machinery, 1937

Concentration ratios (percentage of total value by four largest concerns)	Number of products		Cumulated percentage of totals	
	All products	Products of iron and steel processing and fabricating	All products	Products of iron and steel processing and fabricating
0.1 to 5.0	1	0	0.1	0.0
5.1 to 10.0	7	0	0.5	0.0
10.1 to 15.0	10	2	1.1	0.4
15.1 to 20.0	28	5	2.6	1.3
20.1 to 25.0	44	6	5.0	2.4
25.1 to 30.0	46	7	7.6	3.8
30.1 to 35.0	54	11	10.6	5.8
35.1 to 40.0	69	13	14.4	8.3
40.1 to 45.0	91	17	19.4	11.5
45.1 to 50.0	75	10	23.5	13.3
50.1 to 55.0	85	30	28.2	19.0
55.1 to 60.0	98	24	33.6	23.5
60.1 to 65.0	100	26	39.1	28.4
65.1 to 70.0	130	39	46.3	35.7
70.1 to 75.0	124	32	53.2	41.7
75.1 to 80.0	135	44	60.7	50.0
80.1 to 85.0	117	36	67.2	56.8
85.1 to 90.0	101	48	72.8	65.8
90.1 to 95.0	75	32	76.9	71.8
95.1 to 100.0	89	36	81.8	78.6
Withheld to avoid disclosure				
(1) of individual companies	153	49	90.3	87.8
(2) of remaining companies	175	65	100.0	100.0
Total	1,807	532		

Source: U.S.T.N.E.C., *The Structure of Industry,* Monograph 27. All products p. 275, products iron and steel processing and fabricating compiled from pp. 420-480.

tries are the proportions less than 25 per cent. Among the industries with the highest percentages for central office control are files; tin cans and other tinware; wire drawn from purchased rods; steel barrels, kegs and drums; agricultural implements; electrical machinery and apparatus; refrigerators and refrigerating apparatus; cars, electric and steam railway; and motor vehicles. Those with the smallest percentages include screw machine products; cutlery and edge tools; sheet metal works; lighting equipment; toys; and signs and advertising displays.

The data on the concentration ratios of the selected products indicate a quite high degree of concentration of ownership both for all the commodities included in the T.N.E.C. study and for those that can be classed as belonging in the iron and steel processing and fabricating group. In the former, Table 158 shows that 1,382 of the 1,807 products, or 77.5 per cent, either had 50 per cent or more of their value produced by the four largest firms or had a concentration of ownership so great that the figures could not be disclosed. For the processing and fabricating products, the corresponding figures were 461 of the total of 532 products, or 86.7 per cent. The cumulated percentages indicate that the degree of concentration is considerably higher for the processing and fabricating items than for all products taken as a whole. An examination of the detailed figures indicates that the degree of concentration tends to be camparatively low for the simpler and more common products and high for the highly complicated and specialized products such as machinery, appliances, and transportation equipment.

A further point of importance is brought out by a comparison of the concentration ratios of products with the percentage of central office control in the industry in which the product belongs. In a number of cases, the two sets of figures do not seem to agree. For example, the central office percentages are low for the cash register, adding and calculating machine, and other business machine industry, being 32.8 per cent as based on wage earners and 23.9 per cent, on value, while the concen-

tration ratios on the individual products are high. A similar situation exists in the machine tools industry. The point is that the industry classifications and the organization of corporations for production and marketing purposes do not necessarily follow the same pattern. Generally, it seems that concentration of ownership is greater when viewed from the standpoint of a product than an industry. It is concentration of control of products that has the greatest significance to the present or prospective manufacturer.

While ownership of production facilities for processing and fabricating iron and steel products is not concentrated in the hands of a few giant corporations as it is in the basic iron and steel industry, still it can be concluded that the manufacture of a large proportion of the individual products of the processing and fabricating industries is in the hands of a few corporations. In such products, a new entrant has the problem of meeting the competition of large and powerful concerns. On the other hand, there are quite a number of products where concentration of ownership is not great.

Nature of Demand and Markets

CHARACTERISTICS OF IRON AND STEEL PRODUCTS

A discussion of the nature of the demand and markets for products of the iron and steel processing and fabricating industries may well be initiated by considering such characteristics of these products as type of purchaser, type of ultimate user, degree of durability, degree of fabrication, and whether the market is regional or national. Such a classification of products was used in *Structure of Industry*.

The pertinent data for the 532 processing and fabricating products may be summarized in the following manner:

Characteristics	*Number of products*
Type of purchaser	
Consumer	93
Producer	439
Type of ultimate user	
Consumer	121
Producer	289
Degree of durability	
Nondurable	0

Semidurable	25
Durable	385
Degree of fabrication	
Semimanufactured	51
Finished	474
Type of market	
Regional	54
National	478
Construction materials	115
Producers' supplies	7

The characteristics set forth in this summary and their influence on the market will be used as the basis for the discussion that follows.[4]

The durable nature of the products is a factor of great importance since it introduces the element of postponability of purchases. Replacement sales play an important place in the market of most established products and ultimately in almost all. With durable products, the user has considerable latitude in the timing of replacements and this tends toward greater variability in demand.

The importance of other producers as purchasers of products is the second factor to be considered. A producer becomes a purchaser for at least two purposes. One is to secure raw or partly finished materials or supplies for use in his production operations. The other is to provide his company with machines, equipment, and tools — the instruments of production. Many foundries, forge shops, machine shops, galvanizing plants, and similar establishments receive major portions of their revenues from parts produced for, or services rendered to, other producers. In addition, the manufacturers of engines, motors, condensers, pumps, compressors, and similar products sell a large part of their total production to the manufacturers of finished units.[5] In the case of industrial machinery and equipment, the purchasers are largely other manufacturers. This situation has a number of market impli-

cations that will be developed later. For the present, discussion will be restricted to the effect on the variability of demand. Immediately, the manufacturer of the partly finished products is separated from direct contact with the ultimate consumer. If the purchasing manufacturer is disposed to stabilize his purchases by accumulating inventories in slack times, the situation could operate to assure the parts producer a steady market, but the chances are strong that the actual results will be in the opposite direction. In the case of industrial machinery and equipment, the demand is dependent on the sales of the commodities produced by the equipment. Derived demands of this kind are highly variable.

The T.N.E.C. data assign a place to the consumer as purchaser and ultimate user which is considerably smaller than that of the producer, but it is still very important. For many products, of course, the consumer constitutes the main or the sole market. The products vary from relatively cheap and commonly used commodities such as needles and pins, cast iron heating stoves, metal beds, garden and other hand tools, metal chairs, kitchenware, and steel and plated cutlery to large and expensive products such as refrigerators, central heating units, washing machines, air-conditioning units, radio and television receiving sets, and automobiles. In this wide range of products, some may be classed as necessities and others as luxuries. Characteristics such as these are certain to influence the variability of demand and the marketing methods used in their distribution.

Another factor of importance is the place that construction materials have in the list of products. A large segment of the entire group of industries finds its primary outlet in supplying the construction industry with materials. This is particularly true of structural steel works and manufacturers of plumbers' supplies, building hardware, and metal doors and window sash and frames. To a considerable extent, building construction is an important source of sales to such concerns as the producers of heating and cooking equipment, sheet metal work, lighting fixtures, ventilating

---

[4] *The Structure of Industry*, Monograph No. 27, pp. 506-553.

[5] It should be pointed out that the data presented above tends to underemphasize the purchase of raw or partly finished products because the production of parts is not adequately represented and custom processing for another manufacturer is not included as a product.

fans, and air-conditioning units. Building activity, then, is an important factor in determining the size and the location of markets for many iron and steel products. Along with durability, the derived nature of demand of producers' purchases and the importance of luxury items in consumers' products, construction is an element making for a high degree of variability in demand in the several phases of the business cycle.

Of the characteristics presented by the T.N.E.C. data, the type of market remains to be discussed. The presentation probably does not do full justice to regional markets. For example, all the agricultural implement items were assigned to the national market because none of those selected were directly associated with crops that are primarily regional in nature. Omitted also were machinery and equipment for industries that tend to be localized, such as the textile industry, petroleum production, and coal and other mineral mining. Still, the data give approximately the correct presentation in indicating that the large proportion of the products will find use and sales in all parts of the nation and, for that reason, their market should be termed national. This characteristic is also one that must be taken into account in any consideration of marketing problems of the processing and fabricating industries.

DIFFERENTIATION OF IRON AND STEEL PRODUCTS

An important additional characteristic which should be kept in mind is the degree to which products can be differentiated. With such items as needles and pins, sash weights, cabinet hinges, kitchen knives, and other similar objects, the opportunity for product differentiation is very small and the products of different manufacturers can be considered as practically identical. Price competition is likely to be extremely keen in such lines. In the case of parts manufacture and customs processing, the producer in general must meet the specifications of the purchaser and consequently has little control over the design or properties of the product. However, in the machinery, apparatus and appliance field, prod-

ucts can be, and are, differentiated to a very great degree. Designs that are easily recognized and can be identified with the maker are much in evidence, and brands, trademarks, and trade names are in extensive use. If a manufacturer can use product differentiation to establish a preference for his product among buyers, he can attain a considerable freedom from price competition. This, in the minds of most producers, is highly desirable. The form, functions, and technical and specialized nature of many finished metal products, together with their national market, make product differentiation an important factor in a large segment of the field under study. Consequently, much effort and money is expended in efforts to establish preference for the manufacturer's particular make or brand of product through advertising, demonstration, and other extensive and expensive sales methods.

SERVICE AS A MARKET FACTOR

The durability of the products and product differentiation combine to produce another important factor that influences the demand and marketing problems of the machinery, apparatus, and appliance items, namely, the problem of repair parts and maintenance service. In many lines, the experienced and intelligent buyer is much concerned about being able to keep the purchased item in continuous operation. This involves the ability to buy repair parts promptly when needed and to have ready access to maintenance mechanics who know the product and can correct difficulties with the minimum expense and loss of time. As a result, the ability to assure the buying public that such service will be available is an important factor in attaining and holding a position in the market.

MARKET DEMANDS AND THE LOCAL ECONOMY

The final topic that will be discussed under the general heading of nature of demand and markets is the influence that association of use with other general conditions has on the location and size of markets. An elaborate development of this subject is not needed because many particular examples have already been given and need now only to be mentioned. Reference has frequently been made to the relationship of urbanization to the market for such products as cast-iron pipe, plumbers' supplies, structural steel, and many kinds of appliances. The size and distribution of personal income is an important factor in determining the market for almost all consumer products but particularly those that are in the expensive and luxury class. The market for particular kinds of agricultural implements depends directly on the type of agriculture and the agricultural methods in use. Finally, the localization of industry has much to do with where special industry machinery can be sold.

Market Organization and Methods

In Chapter XIX, the data on the distribution outlets used by the iron and steel processing and fabricating industries were presented and discussed. In general, these data emphasized the important place held by sales to other producers and to wholesalers. At the same time, it was pointed out that many of the constituent industries made extensive use of direct sales to retailers or to consumers and that a very large percentage of the industries found an outlet for a portion of their products in export trade.[6] It is the purpose of this section to point out some of the additional characteristics of m a r k e t organization and methods. Four topics will be considered. These are sales of parts and customs processing to manufacturers of finished products, sales of undifferentiated consumer products, sales of industrial machinery and equipment, and sales of differentiated consumer products.

SALE OF PARTS AND CUSTOMS PROCESSING

A large establishment for the production of a fabricated product often has associated with it a number of auxiliary plants that produce and sell parts or perform some of the processes on a customs basis. Many of the plants and the owning organizations in this latter classification are small but there are concerns which

[6] For greater detail, see Table 81 and Chart 22 and the discussion in Chapter XIX.

are large and that sell to many fabricators. Examples are the manufacturers of automobile engines and compressors. It is probably safe, however, to say that typical concerns are those that seek contracts to manufacture according to the fabricator's specifications such items as brake shoes, axles, axle housings, bushings, valves and fittings, and other relatively simple parts. Where the fabricating concern is large and in a position to make contracts for sizable quantities and where suppliers are small, the bargaining position of the latter is weak. Interviewers for this study found that many concerns were very hesitant to tie up any considerable portion of their facilities in contracts to produce parts for large companies. On the other hand, there are companies which occupy, because of patents or highly specialized know-how, such an important place in the production of an essential unit of a fabricated product that they are in as strong, or even stronger, a bargaining position as the fabricator. In any case, the relationship between buyer and seller tends to be on a direct firm-to-firm basis and is often handled through contracts.

SALE OF UNDIFFERENTIATED CONSUMER PRODUCTS

The producer of undifferentiated consumer products usually finds his outlets through jobbers or wholesalers. Many such items are handled on narrow profit margins and price competition tends to be severe. The nature of the operations tends to make entry into the industries easy. Capital requirements are relatively small and, for the common products, production techniques are easily acquired. On the other hand, many wholesalers consider that dealing with small producers of single and small products is too troublesome and costly to be profitable. The critical problem is to find an outlet at prices that permit a profit.

SALE OF DIFFERENTIATED CONSUMER PRODUCTS

The differentiated products, to a very large extent, are produced and sold by large firms. In consumer products, the leading firms have gone to great expense to make the buying public conscious of the distinctive appearance and the brand names of their products through advertising in periodicals of national circulation and over radio networks. Many of them distribute their products through dealers on the basis of exclusive contracts or through factory-owned sales branches or retail outlets. Dealer helps of many kinds, such as advertising displays, visits by factory representatives to advise on sales methods, and special demonstrations of new models, are in common use. Elaborate tests and contests to prove the excellence of the product and to furnish sales promotion material constitute additional devices for impressing the prospective buyer. In the case of many products, accessibility to repair parts and specialized repair service is an important factor. As a result, the new firm is faced either with being satisfied with a small local market or with expending large sums on a sales promotion program which carries no assurance of success in breaking into the market.

In case the outlet is sought through wholesalers, the small producer is likely to find that the wholesaler has a preference for the firm that can furnish a full line covering a general type of product. The new firm will be confronted with a similar preference for products with established brands or trade names. Staff members on this study were told of the experience of a prospective producer of a piece of equipment for use in raising poultry. In attempting to develop contacts with wholesalers, he found none who was willing to handle the single item because the wholesaler, by buying from producers of full lines of poultry raising equipment, could make up carload lots of assorted items, get the benefit of lower freight rates, and, in addition have a well-known product to sell.

SALES OF INDUSTRIAL MACHINERY

In the case of industrial machinery and equipment, established reputation and the familiar characteristics of specialized machines produced by manufacturers favorably known to the purchaser are elements of importance. Reputation for prompt and efficient service is another factor, as is also the ability of the engineering, technical, and sales staff of the manufacturer to see the customer's problems and suggest the equipment best suited to meet his needs, or, if necessary, to design and build special units. New concerns, however, often are able to find a place for themselves by detecting needs not seen by the older producers. A number of instances of this kind were brought to the attention of those working on this study. In some cases, a former factory representative who was well and favorably known in the industry which he served was able to produce and market successfully a device that was superior to the older products. In others, a small foundry and machine shop, whose business formerly consisted largely of welding broken pieces of casting and machining replacement parts of a group of plants, was able to devise improvements or substitute units and gradually changed from being essentially a service establishment to a manufacturer. In any case, skill, ability to meet specific needs, and direct contacts are essential elements in the marketing of industrial equipment.

PRICE POLICIES IN METAL PRODUCTS

Basing-point and f.o.b.-mill pricing were discussed in the preceding chapter and do not need to be described again. Both have been used by metal-working industries in pricing their products. A number of types of delivered pricing methods other than the basing-point system are also in common use, and two of the more important of these will be discussed. They are freight equalization and zone pricing.

FREIGHT EQUALIZATION PRICING

Under a freight equalization system, a producer establishes a price at his mill and quotes delivered prices which are the sum of his mill price plus freight to the point of delivery, but if he makes sales in a territory where another mill has a lower delivered price, he absorbs or equalizes freight sufficiently to meet the lower price. In many respects, the freight equalization scheme is similar to multiple basing-point except that every mill is a basing-point. When systematically practiced in an industry, it does give to each mill a territory in which it has a freight advantage over competitors located at other points, but it also gives the dominant firms much the same power that exists under a basing-point system to punish smaller mills which resort to price cutting. Freight equalization is practiced by many producers of industrial machinery.[7]

UNIFORM ZONE PRICING

In zone pricing, a uniform delivered price is quoted to all points in a designated area. There may be a single zone covering the entire country or there may be several zones. The producer, in setting such a price, includes in his calculation an allowance for freight costs, but it is an estimate of average freight on sales to all points in a zone rather than the freight to specific points. As a result, the nearby customers pay a price which includes an allowance for freight which is greater than that actually paid on the products they buy, while the distant customers pay less. In other words, the manufacturer, in effect, receives phantom freight on customers in neighboring territories and absorbs freight on sales in distant markets.

In an article in *Law and Contemporary Problems,* Vernon A. Mund[8] gives a list of commodities priced under one form or another of zone price system which includes many products of the iron and steel processing and fabricating industries. Among these the following are listed:

Uniform prices for the entire country— arc welding machines; tire chains; multiblade fans, blowers, and air washers; household electrical appliances; machine knives; flexible steel and aluminum conduit; steam condensers; sheet metal fittings; water meters; Stillson pipe wrenches; industrial motors; dictating machines a n d accessories; typewriters; and cash registers, accounting machines, adding machines, and check writing machines.

Uniform prices, but in several zones— water works valves; scales, meat choppers, slicers, and coffee mills; street lighting equipment; distribution transformers; portable elevators; electric grinders; gasoline service pumps; hydraulic lifts (gasoline station); folding chairs and school chairs; hand lift trucks; portable electric tools; electric fans; plumbing fixtures; firearms; pliers, wrenches and small tools; and road machinery.

Zone pricing evidently applies quite extensively in the field under study.

REGIONAL IMPLICATIONS OF ZONE PRICING

The implication of uniform zone prices, particularly on a national basis to fabricators in a region such as the South, perhaps can best be brought out by an illustration. For the purpose of this illustration, it is assumed that A is a leading producer of product X and is located at Point P and that A follows the policy of selling his product at a uniform price in the entire country. A has set the price in the following manner: factory cost per unit is $100, estimated average freight, $15 and selling price, $138 or 20 per cent over factory cost plus freight. It is further assumed that B is a new producer of X product and is located in Q, a point at a sufficient distance from P for freight on product X from P to Q to be $25 per unit. Factory costs for producing product X tend to vary in the following manner:

For a plant producing 1,000 units—$125 per unit

For a plant producing 2,000 units—$115 per unit

For a plant producing 5,000 units—$100 per unit

Over 5,000 units—no appreciable decrease in average cost but rather a tendency for costs per unit to increase.

The problem is to discover the implications of this situation to A and to B.

If B can produce as cheaply as A and keep the average freight on his deliveries at $15 or lower, it would seem that he should make as high a per unit profit as A. There are, however, two serious questions. One is whether

[7] Charles E. Landon, "Geographic Price Structure," *Law and Contemporary Problems* (Spring 1950), p. 135.
[8] Vernon A. Mund, "The Development and Incidents of Delivering Prices in American Industry," *Law and Contemporary Problems* (Spring 1950), pp. 141-158.

there is a potential market near enough to Q to give B an opportunity to produce and sell enough units to attain costs comparable to those of A and also keep his average freight costs within the prescribed limits. The other question has to do with B's ability to break into the market in his own area. It is entirely possible that A is so well provided with dealer outlets and has been so successful in establishing preference for his product by advertising and by other means that B can capture a sufficiently large portion of the market only by incurring promotion and selling costs that he cannot afford.

The effect of the uniform pricing policy of A can be seen by contrasting the situation with what it would be if A's prices were determined on an f.o.b.-mill basis. Under such a plan, the price of A's product X at point Q would be determined somewhat as follows: factory cost per unit $100 plus $20 (20 per cent to cover other costs and profits) plus freight $25 or a total of $145 as compared with the uniform price of $138. This would mean that B would have an additional advantage of $7.00 per unit to allow either for higher production costs per unit or for quoting somewhat lower prices than his competitor. As a newcomer in the field, a lower price is likely to be one of B's most effective means of breaking into the market. The uniform price established by a leading concern located at a distant point lessens the opportunity for the new and smaller local plant to use this weapon.

For A, the situation has implications that may be important from the point of view of regional industrialization. To bring this out, it is assumed that there is a potential market for 5,000 units of product X in an area centering on Q within the limits of freight charges of $15 and $30, based on A's present plant site at P as the originating point, and that the average freight costs to sell in this market from Q is $5.00 per unit. Under such circumstances, a strong argument can be made that A should establish a branch plant at Q. Such a plant would have as low a factory cost as the plant at P. There should be a substantial saving in freight costs since the average costs of products

distributed from Q would be $10 under the estimated freight on which the uniform price is based. In addition, A would not be absorbing freight on shipments made from P into a territory all of which lies beyond the $15 freight limit. The result would be a decrease in average freight costs to A, but, under a uniform pricing system, it is doubtful that any reduction in price would result. It would seem, therefore, that a branch plant would become feasible when the market accessible from the proposed site is large enough to support an optimum sized plant and the average freight from that site is equal to, or less than, the average freight cost from the nearest existing plant of the firm, providing that the new plant does not cut the market of any of the existing plants below optimum size.

The illustration which has been developed in the preceding paragraphs is intended only to highlight the workings of a uniform delivered price system. It is not entirely realistic because it has not attempted to bring in any factor affecting costs except the question of size of plant. In an actual case, there might well be a problem of balancing the cost of raw materials delivered to prospective sites against the cost of delivering the finished products from these sites to their markets. Also, the illustration did not attempt to estimate the advantage that B migh have as a local producer who knows his market area and its needs and is in a position to appeal to buyers on a buy-at-home basis. These limitations must be acknowledged, but still, the difficulty that a new firm faces in breaking into a market, compared with the relative ease with which an established firm can move into an area under a delivered price system, is quite apparent.

Delivered pricing has the general effect of eliminating, or at least limiting, price competition. Under such plans, prices tend to be set at relatively high levels, and this tends to provide an umbrella for the new and, presumably, high cost producer. The concern that attempts to break into a market by lowering prices, however, is likely to invite punitive measures from large and powerful firms if their position in the market is endangered by the price cutter.

Stabilized prices are attained, but the result is failure to pass on savings in costs and thus to obtain the advantage of the increased volume that would be obtained from lower prices.

This section will be ended by quoting a conclusion that Vernon Mund reached in the article to which reference has previously been made, "Basing point and zone delivered pricing systems operate not only to eliminate price competition, but also to prevent a decentralization of industry."[9]

Problems of Expansion

The preceding sections of this chapter have been devoted to an examination of the outstanding economic characteristics of the iron and steel processing and fabricating industries. Attention can now be directed to the application of conclusions to the problems that confront the South. The relatively low degree of development in the region places primary emphasis on the task of securing new plants and encouraging expansion generally. Consequently, the remainder of the chapter will be concerned with the problems of securing a sound development.

At the beginning of the chapter, it was pointed out that the processing and fabricating classification includes a wide variety of industries and products and that each industry has its own distinctive characteristics and problems. As a result, a well-planned program of expansion must necessarily give consideration to two aspects of the total task. On the one hand, there are the problems that have to do with the technical, economic, and business characteristics which apply generally to the processing and fabricating industries and with the conditions conducive to a well-balanced and healthy development. On the other hand, effective promotion efforts must be directed toward specific industries and, consequently, must be based on an understanding of the specific problems of the industry under consideration and of the conditions that must be met if that particular industry is to prosper. This

9 Vernon A. Mund, p. 155.

requires the detailed study of specific industries. Such studies will naturally give consideration to the common location factors—accessibility and cost of raw materials, labor supply, markets, industrial power, transportation facilities—and will attempt to come to conclusions as to feasibility of establishing new enterprises in the particular industry under study. The scope and objectives of the present study require that the discussions be restricted to the problems of most general concern, but this must not be interpreted as in any way depreciating the importance of specific industry studies.

The analysis of the economic characteristics brought out a number of conditions which form important features of the situation in which expansion must take place. While large plants occur in many of the industries and are predominant in some, iron and steel processing and fabricating as a whole can scarcely be said to be characterized by large-scale operations. This means that, in most industries, small plants may be operated successfully. In general, the operations are highly mechanized, but the consumption of power in terms of man-hours is not high. The several industries tend to pay relatively high wages and to require more than the average proportion of skilled labor. In many, there is a special need for competence in design of product and control of operations. Selling is an important function in almost all. These operating characteristics are important and, in many of the industries, are exacting, but they do not impose conditions that persistence and intelligent effort cannot meet.

On the ownership and marketing side, there are characteristics which have regional implications of very great importance. Despite the relatively small size of plants, ownership of the plants producing a particular product, or group of products, tends to be concentrated. To a considerable extent, this is related to the specialized nature of many of the products and to the fact that product differentiation is highly developed in a large proportion of the industries. Highly developed methods of sales promotion and closely knit systems of distribution outlets are widely used in marketing the products of many industries. Furthermore, the uniform pricing policies that are followed by many of the established producers tend to discourage the establishment of new concerns, especially in under-developed areas.

In the further development of the subject, the following three groups of problems will be considered: (1) problems of providing necessary operating facilities; (2) problems arising from the kind of products to be produced; and (3) problems arising from the m a n n e r in which expansion is to be accomplished.

PROBLEMS OF PROVIDING OPERATING FACILITIES

Under the general heading of problems of providing necessary operating facilities comes the whole group of questions concerning the optimum size of plant, raw materials, labor, industrial power and water, transportation and freight rates, and the like. These questions cannot be discussed in detail, and only a few comments will be offered concerning the problems related to raw materials, labor, and the general institutional factors needed for satisfactory operations.

With reference to raw materials, the ability to buy the appropriate iron and steel mill products at prices comparable to those paid by competitors is the important consideration. In the past, fabricators in the South have been at a disadvantage in that many products needed were not produced by southern mills and had to be obtained from a distance at a price disadvantage. Also, as pointed out in the previous chapter, the price policies of the steel industry have not been those that lent active encouragement to processing and fabricating in regions such as the South. The variety of steel mill products has gradually been increased, but there are still important items that are not produced in the region. Under f.o.b.-mill pricing, there should be increased emphasis on the regional market for steel mill products with the result that more aggressive measures will be taken to meet regional needs. It will also be helpful if a means, by use of imported ore or otherwise, can be found to produce at least limited quantities of low phosphorous pig iron at reasonable cost because such a development would have a healthy effect on foundry products.

Many discussions of labor in the South center around two questions. One is the so-called southern differential and the other is the productivity of southern labor. As stated in other places in this report, it is scarcely reasonable to predicate expansion of industry in the South on the perpetuation of low wage rates. The process of industrialization in and of itself tends to eliminate such differences while recent history indicates a tendency toward lessening differentials. Such tendencies, of course, put more emphasis on productivity. While the subject has been much discussed and a number of studies have been made, the problem of comparative productivity has not been solved in any convincing manner. The reported experience of concerns that operate plants both in the North and the South can be cited on both sides of the controversy. Therefore, the m o s t reasonable conclusion seems to be that, when properly trained and supervised, southern labor is capable of very satisfactory performance. The one important point that can be made with certainty is that the South lacks persons experienced and skilled in the production and marketing of metal products. This shortage ranges all the way from skilled mechanics to engineers and management personnel. This puts the emphasis on programs of education and training.

With increasing industrialization and the accompanying increases in density of population and concentration of industry in industrial areas, institutional factors are taking on increasing importance. Housing, educational and recreation facilities, sewage and sewage disposal, industrial water supply, access roads, health and welfare services are all matters of importance in creating the conditions needed for successful operations. These are not distinctive to metal products plants, but they do apply, and they are factors for which the communities and states, through their public and private agencies, are responsible.

PROMOTION AND THE KIND OF PRODUCT

It has already been pointed out that the kind of product that is to be produced has a great influence on the marketing problems of the producer. Likewise, the problems of promotion are very greatly affected by this factor. All the questions concerning production facilities are directly dependent on the product desired. Consequently, sound decisions as to what is needed and how well the region or a particular location can provide the necessary conditions can scarcely be formed except when related to specific products. However, the major emphasis here will be placed on the connection with markets. A division of the subject similar to that already set up will be used: manufactured parts and customs processing, undifferentiated consumer products, industrial machinery and equipment, and differentiated consumer products.

The presence of a large plant fabricating a product that consists of many component parts suggests the possibility of establishments that manufacture at least some of the parts. For instance, the establishment of large assembling plants in the South by several of the major automobile manufacturing companies, no doubt, has caused many to think that this situation presents an opportunity to manufacture automobile parts in the region. This idea occurred also to the staff working on this study and inquiries were made. A number of manufacturing plants were found that had contracts with automobile companies. Among these was a southern company that was producing, on contract, parts for brake shoes and housings. However, these parts were not shipped to Atlanta, or other southern assembly plants, but to the factory in Detroit. The reason given was that the automobile manufacturer found it more economical to make a complete subassembly of the axle, and ship these subassemblies to the assembly plants. This might mean cross hauling, but even so, the total costs were said to be less. Furthermore there are parts of automobiles in the manufacture of which the advantages of large scale production are so great that it seems

better to have the entire supply produced at one plant. A case of this kind is the shaping of steel bodies. The point is that the presence of a fabricating plant cannot be taken as final evidence that a market for parts exists. A knowledge of the economics of the industry and the policies of management is needed to decide whether a possibility exists and, if so, what parts may be demanded. Further study will be needed to arrive at a conclusion as to whether a local producer can meet the requirements.

It is reasonable to expect that any sizable concentration of fabricating plants will present opportunities which, if seen and developed, can bring into being additional establishments. Such plants may be small, but can constitute very significant parts of the industrial structure. For example, several plants may require a certain process, such as galvanizing or enameling, but the volume of each may make it questionable that any one of these plants can afford to set up such a department. A separate enterprise may be able to make a place for itself by handling the needs of the other establishments on a contract basis. Also, a small die-making shop may provide a vital service for a number of metal-working plants. Filling in gaps and rounding out production facilities requires an intimate knowledge of needs and, often, considerable imagination. It is very probable that many opportunities of this kind are overlooked in programs of industrial promotion.

The problems of marketing undifferentiated consumer products have already been discussed and perhaps little more needs to be added. The production of such items ordinarily requires a relatively small amount of specialized knowledge and skill and seems to offer a good chance for the small shop to get started. This very fact probably means that there will be many competitors and much difficulty in securing sufficient outlets to make the venture profitable. Many such ventures originate with a man who has acquired the required skills as an employee in a larger concern and has accumulated savings of a modest sum, but has little or no experience in selling. In other words, such enterprisers lack the very thing that they most need in the highly competitive field they seek to enter. Occasionally, someone hits on some relatively simple idea that succeeds without great difficulty because the commodity or service offered is unique in some respect. The manager of the sales promotion department of a large concern gave an example of this kind. A man got the idea of making and selling a single strand wire clothes line because his wife had injured her hand on a broken strand of a twisted wire line. After some experimentation, he found a wire of the required gauge, strength, toughness, and flexibility. His manufacturing process consisted only of cutting the wire in lengths of 50 or 100 feet and tying the lengths in coils with an appropriate label. Little difficulty was met in marketing because the wholesalers who were approached did not have such an item and thought that it would sell. Difference or novelty may help, but the opportunities are limited. If the object is to encourage the establishment of manufacturers of this type, the critical problem seems to be selling rather than the problems ordinarily included under industrial engineering.

The market for industrial machinery and equipment quite naturally is with the plants that use the particular kind of item that is being offered. Some kinds of machinery, such as lathes and drill presses, are used by many different kinds of industries and others, such as looms, printing presses, shoe repairing machinery, and deep-well drilling outfits, are used only by specific industries. Some of these industries are widely scattered over the entire country and some are concentrated in relatively small areas. The machinery manufacturer has to find his market and he has to demonstrate his ability to produce equipment that will do a job.

The opportunities in a new industrial area such as the South are likely to seem limited during the early stages of industrialization but should grow as industrialization progresses. Naturally, the best opportunities will be associated with the activities that are distinctive to the region. In agricultural implements,

special equipment needed by such distinctive crops as cotton, peanuts, tobacco, and citrus fruits seem to be logical products for plants located in the South. As pointed out previously, the oil field machinery and equipment industry is one in which the South holds a prominent place. Also, considerable progress has been made in the manufacture of textile machinery. This industry in the South seems to have grown from small machine shops that did repair work for textile mills. As time went on, some of the shops devised improvements and gradually build up a clientele for their products. The important lumber and furniture industries have been accompanied by the presence of concerns manufacturing saw mills and other wood working equipment. The important developments in the papermaking and chemical industries should present opportunities for equipment manufacturers. Generally, a high degree of engineering competence and imagination is required to produce machines that will meet the needs, and marketing methods must be those designed to deal with experienced and highly critical buyers.

The marketing problems that arise from differentiation of consumer products have also been discussed in some detail. Also, it has been pointed out that delivered pricing policies are in common use in this group of products. A new entrant into the field should be fully acquainted with these conditions if he is to be prepared to handle the problems that are almost certain to face him in attempting to compete with established concerns. If the product is a new one, the new concern may be in a good position to establish itself before the older companies can get into the field, but even so, the capture of a large market under present day marketing methods calls for the expenditure of large sums of money. To attain such an objective, it is usually necessary, through advertising or by other means, to establish brands or trade names in the minds of consumers and to create a preference for the product of a particular manufacturer. If the product is an old one, the choice seems to be either to manufacture on a small scale, if that is feasible from a cost standpoint, and gradually build up sales or to be prepared to expend large sums to establish a place in the market.

Any agency or group of individuals attempting to promote the establishment of new plants in any of the iron and steel processing and fabricating industries should certainly seek to know the problems presented by the kind of product they will make if they are to make plans that have a reasonable chance of success.

METHODS OF ACCOMPLISHING EXPANSION

In this final topic of the chapter, little more will be attempted than to point out the general methods of accomplishing an expansion that are available. These are: (1) a new independent plant, (2) a relocated plant, (3) a branch plant of a multi-plant company, and (4) the expansion of an existing plant. The general problems involved in each will be pointed out briefly.

The establishment of a new independent plant has all the problems of creating an operating organization, securing adequate financing, and creating a market. Generally, the creation of such an enterprise is considered highly desirable, but it is faced with difficulties that make most promotional organizations seek other means. New enterprises of this kind have a way of appearing as the result of the efforts of an exceptionally capable and persistent person who succeeds in creating a place more or less unaided. Perhaps the encouragement of this kind of enterprise is the most neglected phase of organized industrial promotion. A relocated plant presumably has a working organization and an established market. If it is to be a real addition to the region, there must be sound reasons for relocation. Branch plants of existing firms have operating organizations, established reputations, and established markets. If the parent organization can be convinced that the establishment of such a branch will increase its profits, this seems to be the easiest way of getting a new plant. Expansion obtained by the increase in capacity of an established plant ordinarily is looked upon as a development that will occur automatically if conditions warrant. It is, however, a mode of industrial growth of great importance, not only because of the increases directly created, but also because of the indirect effects arising from the easily seen evidence of successful operation in a region or a community. To the extent that successful operation can be influenced by general conditions, expansion of existing plants is a matter of concern to promotion agencies.

No doubt active efforts will continue to be made which have as their purpose the attraction of new industries and aid in the desired developments. City chambers of commerce or other promotional groups, state planning and development departments, state chambers of commerce, and electric power companies are among those actively engaged in work of this kind, and it is important that the methods employed be those best adapted to securing sound and lasting results. A well-rounded development of the iron and steel industries is badly needed in the South. The record of past trends provides a basis for hope, but the study of the economic characteristics of the industries suggests that the way is not without obstacles. Effective programs of promotion need to be based on adequate knowledge of these characteristics and on careful analysis of facts.

CHAPTER XXVII

POTENTIALS OF THE IRON AND STEEL INDUSTRIES IN THE SOUTH

The task of this, the last chapter of the report, is to attempt to arrive at conclusions concerning the developments that can reasonably be expected in the iron and steel industries of the South. A logical first step in the direction of formulating such conclusions is to summarize in some detail the findings of the preceding chapters.

Situation with Regard to Raw Materials

The conclusion presented at the end of Part II was that availability of suitable raw materials was not likely to be a limiting factor to future development of the basic industry. Like other iron and steel producing areas, the South, principally the Birmingham District, has both favorable and unfavorable features. The advantages most widely publicized are the large deposits of iron ore in Red Mountain, coal in the Warrior Basin, and limestone in the valley in which Birmingham is located. This constitutes a favorable situation of very great importance, but is offset at least to some extent by the low grade of the ore and its high phosphorus content, the need for washing the coal, and the difficult underground mining conditions for both ore and coal. The reserves seem adequate for many years. Furthermore, the South has numerous red and brown ore deposits which have considerable significance as supplementary sources. Improved mining methods and beneficiation of ore may play a large part in making it possible to use the region's ore and coal resources to a much better advantage. Two other conditions are of importance. The South is a surplus iron and steel scrap area, and the industrialization of the region should increase the opportunity for accumulating large quantities of the desired kinds of scrap. The other factor of importance is the accessibility to foreign ores, particularly those of Venezuela. The raw material situation is such as to support a large future development.

Trends in the Basic Industries

The study of the history of the blast furnace and steel works industries in the South showed a long struggle against adverse conditions. On the technical side, the southern ores had characteristics that produced poor results when the methods developed in the older iron and steel centers were applied. The development of appropriate techniques for producing steel was slow, and this slowness held back the use of the region's resources. From the market point of view, the impoverished and rural South did not provide quantity markets for pig iron and steel. Consequently there was a continual battle to find markets, and the efforts largely took the form of trying to find products such as cast-iron pipe, steel rails, and tin plate that could be sold in distant markets.

Despite the difficulties of the earlier period, the trends in the basic industries during the last twenty-five or thirty years have shown growth. Long-term statistics on the South's production of pig iron, steel ingots, and hot rolled iron and steel products have indicated tendencies of growth at least as strong as those for the United States as a whole. In general, the increases have been greater percentagewise for steel ingots than for pig iron and for hot rolled products than for steel ingots. In years of decline, the South has tended to have milder downward movements and, in recovery and prosperity periods, the reaction of the region to increasing demands has been stronger than for the nation as a whole. Capacity for production has been increasing in a manner that parallels national trends. Particularly in steel mill products, the past has seen the expansion and diversification of the South's capacity. Such information as could be assembled indicates that costs of production at Birmingham have been low and, despite recent increases, still compare favorably with other centers.

While the long-term trends have not been sufficient to enable the South to overcome its slow start or to change, in any spectacular manner, its relative position in the nation, there is no evidence of the industry's languishing. The increases in the South have been taking place while the nation as a whole has been going through one of the greatest industrial developments ever known.

The Situation with Regard to Metal-Using Industries

The South has a relatively low development of the metal-using industries. It is particularly deficient in such high-ranking steel users as motor vehicles, industrial and electrical machinery, and domestic and commercial apparatus and appliances. It has a highly developed oil field equipment manufacturing industry and cast-iron pipe and fittings industry and has made substantial progress in textile machinery, agricultural implements, woodworking machinery, and a number of lines where local markets have developed. In shipbuilding and construction fabrication, its development is approximately proportionate to its general stage of industrialization.

The comparison of the situation in 1947 with that of 1939 shows a more rapid expansion percentagewise in the South than in the nation in most of the individual industries and also a decided tendency to diversify and strengthen the metal-using industries of the region. The South is overshadowed by the great developments in the area north of the Ohio and east of the Mississippi. This area has a head start and has the advantage of short distances to the largest concentrated markets of the nation. The rates of increase for the

South are encouraging, but it must be remembered that the small 1939 figures tend to make percentage increases less significant.

The Situation with Regard to Steel Consumption in the South

Estimates for 1947 indicate consumption of approximately seven million tons of steel mill products in the South. This seems to be almost double the consumption in 1939. Also, it is approximately twice the quantity produced in the South. Large quantities, therefore, come into the South from the northern steel centers. Furthermore, large quantities of finished products such as automobiles, machinery, and commercial and domestic appliances are shipped into the region from the outside. There is a large over-all market for steel mill products and for products which are made largely from steel. However, the region is large in area, easily accessible to the older and more firmly established producing areas, and the demands are varied and widely scattered geographically.

Conditions in the South Affecting the Market for Iron and Steel

The South has lacked many of the conditions that create quantity markets for iron and steel. It has been predominately rural and agricultural, and its agriculture has made relatively little use of machinery and other types of equipment that use sizable quantities of steel. This is particularly true of the Southeast. Cattle raising and tractor farming in the Southwest, particularly Texas, have created a much more favorable situation there. The South's cities have been widely scattered and, compared with the North and East, the number of large cities or of large concentrations of population has been small. The degree of industrialization is relatively low, and the industries of the South on the whole have not been those that have used large quantities of iron and steel as raw materials or as necessary supplies. The big exception has been the petroleum industry of Texas, Oklahoma, Arkansas, Louisiana, and Mississippi which has used millions of tons of pipe, tubing and plate, and oil field supplies, although this did not result in the manufacture of pipe in the South until very recently. Finally, the low income of people of the South has been a limiting factor in the market for consumers' durable goods.

Again, if the situation is examined from the dynamic, rather than the static, point of view, conditions are more favorable. The number of persons living on farms and deriving a living from agriculture has been decreasing, and population changes are definitely toward a higher degree of urbanization.

Southern agriculture has made decided strides toward extension and greater mechanization. Livestock and livestock products have been increasing in importance. Methods of agriculture have improved and rural electrification has made it possible for the farming population to use many of the modern home and farm appliances.

While per capita income in the South is still below the average for the nation, there has been a decided improvement, both in absolute terms and relatively, when compared with the national per capitas. Educational and health facilities and other conditions conducive to increasing the productive capacity of a people have been steadily improving. These changes have been reflected in greatly increased volume of wholesale and retail trade and improvement in general living conditions.

While manufacturing does not occupy as high a position in the economic structure of the South as in the nation as a whole, the industrialization of the region has been progressing steadily. Part of this increase has been obscured by a rather peculiar situation. Between 1939 and 1947, the South lost in relative position in the total number of production workers. At the same time, its percentages of increase were greater than the nation's in all but one of the main industry groups. The difficulty was that the South has a large proportion of its workers in two slow-growing industry groups—textiles and lumber—and has relatively small numbers in the fast-growing industries. For this reason, an apparently contradictory condition exists: the region im-

proved its relative position in almost all of the individual industries or industry groups and yet lost in relative position in the total of all manufacturing. The data for the last forty or fifty years show decided increases in manufacturing, and the detailed comparisons that can be made between 1939 and 1947 show strong tendencies to diversify the industrial structure of the region both by the establishment of new industries and by reducing the dependence on textiles and lumber. Furthermore, established manufacturing centers have grown and many new ones have come into existence.

The examination of data provides convincing evidence of trends that indicate larger markets for iron and steel and their products. These improved conditions are not entirely the result of changes during the last few years; they are not entirely war induced, but have their beginnings in the developments that were taking place before the discovery in the early thirties that the South was the nation's Number One problem. On the other hand, the increases have not been sufficient to greatly change the South's relative position in the nation. While the large increases in the region were taking place, the rest of the nation was moving ahead at almost as rapid a pace.

Implications of Economic Characteristics

THE BASIC INDUSTRIES

The economic characteristics of the basic industries affect regional development in many ways. On the one hand, they explain, in part, past developments or lack of development and, on the other, they lay down conditions that are certain to influence the future.

Large-scale production is a very prominent feature of the economics of production of the basic iron and steel industries. An important result of this feature is that any program for the future that will change the situation materially must deal with large units which necessitate large capital investment, big sources of raw materials, and large operating organizations. Changes in sources of raw materials are not likely to cause a major shift from North to South but may have the effect of cutting off a part of Birmingham's market in the Far West. Another change that may be encouraged by the Venezuelan ore discoveries is the development of a tidewater industry at one or more points along the Gulf Coast.

The ownership of most of the plants in the nation and in the region by a relatively small number of large corporations is an additional factor of importance. Generally, under conditions of this kind, the companies tend to behave as oligopolies and are interested primarily in maintaining their own positions and the status quo generally. From the point of view of the South, the control of the steel plants of the region by corporations whose major interests are in the more highly developed areas is a condition that has influenced developments. Under such circumstances, the interest of those in final control is likely to be centered on the well-being of their major investments and largest operations. There is not likely to be much disposition to push the interests of outlying regions, especially if such a move threatens to affect the profits of the major plants in any way.

While the steel industry maintains that demand for steel is inelastic and defends its price policies on that ground, there is good reason to conclude that the comparative prices of steel in different geographic areas over a long term do exercise a considerable influence on the location and development of metal-using industries. The predominant pricing policy during most of the last half century—the basing-point system—has not tended to encourage fabrication in the South. Under Pittsburgh-plus and the first years of multiple basing-point pricing, southern fabricators had to pay higher prices than their northern competitors, even though they may have been located close to a steel mill with low production costs. Even with the equalization of base prices in Birmingham and Pittsburgh, fabricators did not receive the benefit of the low production costs that seem to have existed in the South. Also, they have been handicapped by not being able to buy many of the needed kinds of steel mill products from a near-by steel mill but had

to pay higher delivered prices from distant basing-points. Furthermore, the basing-point system tends to discourage the establishment of small mills at non-basing-point locations. While f.o.b.-mill pricing has its disadvantages and dangers, it should have the general effect of placing more emphasis on the demand in the natural market area of a mill.

There is no doubt that the large corporation lends strength and stability to a local operation. The acquisition and subsequent control of the Tennessee Coal, Iron and Railroad Company by the United States Steel Corporation unquestionably resulted in adequate financial backing, the management of the operations by experienced and competent men, and important expansions of plant and facilities. On the other hand, the dominance of the large corporations and at least some of their characteristic policies have not tended to promote the maximum degree of regional development.

THE PROCESSING AND FABRICATING INDUSTRIES

With several notable exceptions, such as the manufacture of motor vehicles, railroad and street cars, and electric generating equipment, the data on size of establishments and important operating departments indicate that small establishments account for a significant segment of production in the iron and steel processing and fabricating industries. This suggests that from the production point of view, the advantages of large-scale operations are not so great as to exclude the small plant. On the other hand, the information on the importance of central office control and the concentration ratios of individual products of the processing and fabricating industries give evidence that large firms hold very important places in the production and marketing of a large proportion of the products of the industries under study. The complete explanation of this situation would lead to a study of the entire subject of concentration in industry and was not attempted in this report. Two factors are important in the present connection. The first is that the character of many of the products, particularly machinery, appliances, and apparatus, is such as to encourage elaborate methods of establishing preference for the products of a particular manufacturer by the use of brands, trade names, and highly organized sales promotion techniques. These are very costly and can best be used by larger concerns that are distributing their products over wide geographic areas. The second is that the use of delivered prices, particularly uniform national or zone prices based on average freight calculations, tends to strengthen the position of the large firm.

The varied characteristics of the products of the processing and fabricating industries suggest that wide differences exist in the operating and marketing problems of the several industries and, consequently, in the measures that should be taken to best promote development. This emphasizes the importance of accurate information and a thorough understanding of the characteristics and requirements of each particular industry that may be under consideration. A classification of products that helps to bring out many of the distinctive problems is the one with these subclasses: (1) parts and customs processing, (2) undifferentiated consumer products, (3) differentiated consumer products, and (4) industrial machinery and equipment. The products in each subclass have distinctive problems, especially with reference to markets. Products in the last two subclasses lend themselves readily to easy identification of the maker and, consequently, the producers of such products typically make use of the highly developed sales methods mentioned in the preceding paragraph. The ability of the maker to back his product with repair parts and service is another important factor in marketing products of these kinds. For all the processing and fabricating industries, securing appropriate sales outlets is a problem of critical importance.

The relatively high average wage and the large percentages of value added that is accounted for by wages and salaries suggest that competent labor is especially important in the processing and fabricating industries. Also, the high percentage of the total employees of the industries producing the more complicated products that are classed as administrative,

technical, office, and sales employees is a reflection of the important place held by design, technical excellence, and selling in such industries.

With reference to geographic scatter, a large proportion of the processing and fabricating industries are widely dispersed throughout the nation, while a limited number of the industries, usually those with the more complicated and specialized products, are quite definitely concentrated. A point of interest to the South is the fact that the region has relatively weak representation in many of the widely dispersed industries. Southern plants in the highly concentrated industries, geographically, are few in number.

Finally, four methods of accomplishing an expansion were mentioned. These are (1) a new independent plant, (2) relocation of an existing plant, (3) a branch plant of a multiplant concern, and (4) expansion of an existing plant. In general, the second and the third seem easier and more likely to produce quick results and are perhaps the methods most commonly used by promotional agencies. While the problems may be more difficult, the first and the fourth types of expansion are highly important and should not be overlooked.

General Significance of Developments

The iron and steel industries of the South have been passing through several stages in their development. First were the rather fumbling and uneven beginnings that lasted until the early 1900's. During this period, the economy of the South was largely built around producing and shipping raw materials or semifinished products to fabricators located outside the region and buying back finished products. Pig iron, cast-iron pipe, and, later, steel were relatively minor items in this flow of commodities. Quite naturally, arrangements to facilitate this kind of trade tended to develop. For example, low commodity freight rates on the materials shipped out of the South were mutually advantageous to buyer and seller and to the railroad as well.

The acquisition of the Tennessee Coal, Iron and Railroad Company in 1907 by the United

States Steel Corporation put the steel industry in the South definitely on sound financial footing and initiated a period of relatively steady and continuous growth. The older ideas of finding a market for large quantities at distant points continued not only in iron and steel, but in other important southern products as well. The adoption of basing-point pricing by the steel industry provided an additional device that facilitated selling in distant markets and, to this extent, fitted into the general scheme of marketing southern products. The first half of the twentieth century also saw the development in the nation of the manufacture of fabricated metal products on a large scale, and here again the problem of finding markets over wide areas was encountered. The systems of delivered prices that came into being served the purpose of making it easy to sell at a distance although it is highly improbable that this particular feature constituted the sole, or even the main, reason for their adoption.

The other side of the story is that basing-point pricing of steel mill products, slowness in installing facilities that might compete with other plants owned by the same company, and the delivered price policies of manufacturers of fabricated products (while they may be justified from the point of view of corporation policy, at least in times past) are not conducive to developing fabricating industries in an under-developed region or to building up the local markets of such an area.

Still, the metal products industries of the South have grown, the consumption of steel mill products has increased decidedly, and the general economic and industrial development of the region has been moving at a pace that many observers have termed phenomenal. These changes at least make it reasonable to raise the question as to whether a new stage has been reached in the South. It is possible that it may be to the interest not only of the region, but also of the corporations in the basic and fabricating industries, that production and marketing activities should be decentralized and that policies be adopted which allow the maximum autonomy to the plants in each area and which give positive encouragement to

the maximum industrialization within the natural market of each plant. In other words, it may be time to abandon ideas of protecting the interests of plants at distant points and to permit each plant or each branch to act as nearly like a free enterprise as possible.

The Future

The analysis of past trends and present conditions certainly lends support to the conclusion that continued growth of the iron and steel industries and the market for iron and steel products in the South can be expected. However, the growth can scarcely be looked upon as inevitable or as a condition that will be attained without facing difficulties. Certainly, a southern plant can establish itself in many of the processing and fabricating industries only by meeting the keenest kind of competition of established concerns. Hence, it is reasonable to think that the future is conditioned to a very considerable extent by the attitudes and actions of several interested groups, of which four will be mentioned.

The first group consists of the nation's big corporations in the basic and processing and fabricating industries. Because of the nature of the operations, and the problems involved in marketing many of the products, a very large part of the future development is almost certain to be in the hands of the leading corporations in the several fields. Consequently, their policies are certain to have a strong influence on what takes place and it is in their power to hasten or to retard developments in the region.

The second group consists of the public officials, particularly those who have legislative powers. Without question, arbitrary and discriminatory laws, ordinances, or regulations can have an adverse effect on development. On the other hand, it is questionable if preferential treatment is wise. Special privilege for one interest too often means a handicap for another. The really important function of state and local government are to develop a legal framework that protects the rights of all parties, to provide the services required by a modern industrialized and urbanized civilization, and to finance its operations by a revenue system that has equity as its guiding principle rather than protection of some or the punishment of others.

The third group includes the promotional agencies. Many such agencies expend the major portion of their funds and effort in advertising the assumed advantages of their particular state or city. Some seem to make a fetish of action. Some practically refuse to face the unfavorable factors present in the localities that they represent. While optimism and drive no doubt are essential characteristics of a promoter, still there is another side to sound development. There are difficult problems that should be faced. A town with a poor sewage system, a water supply inadequate for domestic and industrial use, or poor school facilities may be an unattractive site for the industry that it seeks to attract, but these are conditions that concerted action by the citizens can change. There should be a place, also, for long term programs of research and careful planning. Certain particular problems might be selected for investigation. For example, the possibility of manufacturing automobile parts for southern assembly plants might be an approriate project. To achieve significant results, it would be necessary to make a careful study of the economics of automobile production to determine what locally manufactured parts, if any, could be used by an assembly plant. The specifications of the parts would have to be obtained. The interest and co-operation of the automobile manufacturer would need to be solicited and possibly a program of acquainting foundries or other manufacturers with the opportunities and needs might be required. Such programs would, of course, be expensive and probably would be within the reach only of large organizations. However, a large steel-producing center has so much at stake in the development of metal-using industries within its immediate market area that it might well undertake a thorough study of selected industries.

The fourth group comprises the enterprisers engaged in the iron and steel industries in the South. The important question has to do with how effectively those actually engaged in production and selling will attack their problems. Will they show resourcefulness in devising new methods or overcoming technical difficulties? Will they see opportunities to develop and market new products? Will they show a disposition to co-operate in legitimate ways to solve problems that trouble all of them? There are many examples that might be cited to show that such a spirit of co-operation is present among southern enterprisers. The establishment of the Southern Research Institute is one such example. The co-operative action of the southern foundry men to provide facilities for research and training in foundry practice at the University of Alabama is another. There are many examples with respect to particular products. A good one is the story of the manufacturers of the autosoler and the autonailer machines of Atlanta, who developed the designs for their machines and now market them in all parts of the United States and many foreign countries. It is this sort of spirit that has much, many would say most, to do with the industrial potentials of a region or group of industries.

BIBLIOGRAPHY

A. Books, Pamphlets, and Documents

Adamson, W. M., *Industrial Activity in Alabama, 1913-1932*, Mimeo. Ser. 1 (University, Alabama: Bureau of Business Research, University of Alabama, 1933)

Alabama Department of Industrial Relations, *Annual Statistical Report, 1948-49* (Montgomery: 1949)

Alabama Geological Survey.
Iron Ore Outcrops of the Red Mountain Formation in Northeast Alabama by E. F. Burchard and Thomas G. Andrews, Special Report 19 (University, Alabama: 1937)
Iron Making in Alabama, Chapter XI, "Steel Making in Alabama," by Frank H. Crockard (University, Alabama: 1912)
Report on the Geology of Northeastern Alabama by C. W. Hayes (Montgomery: 1892)
Brown Ore of the Chulafinnee District by J. W. Huddle, Circular 17, (University, Alabama: 1941)
Report on the Coal Measures of the Plateau Region of Alabama by Henry McCalley, Special Report 3, (University, Alabama: 1891)
Report on the Valley Regions of Alabama by Henry McCalley, Special Reports 8 and 9 (Montgomery: J. P. Armstrong, 1896-97)
Reports on the Warrior Coal Basin by Henry McCalley, Special Report 10 (University, Alabama: 1900)
Report on the Cahaba Coal Field by Joseph Squire, Special Report 2 (University, Alabama: 1890)

Alabama, University of, State Mine Experiment Station.
Coal Losses in Alabama by J. J. Forbes, Bulletin I (University, Alabama: 1925)

American Iron and Steel Institute.
Annual Statistical Report, 1920-1949 (New York: 1920-1949)
Directory of Iron and Steel Works of the United States and Canada, 1890, 1900, 1910, 1920, 1925, 1930, 1935, 1938, 1940, 1945, 1948 (New York: dates as above)
Yearbook, 1951 (New York: 1951); *Yearbook, 1950*, "Present and Prospective Sources of Supply of Steel Making Raw Materials" by C. C. Henning and R. W. Braund (New York: 1951)
Address by E. H. Rose, Preprint Regional Technical Meeting (New York: October 1949)

American Institute of Mining and Metallurgical Engineers.
Coal Preparation, "Use Specifications for Coal" by J. H. Kerrick, J. E. Tobey, and D. R. Mitchell (New York: 1943)
The Manufacture and Properties of Killed Bessemer Steel by E. C. Wright (New York: 1944)

American Steel Warehouse Association, *Roster* (Cleveland, Ohio: August 1947)

Armes, Ethel, *The Story of Coal and Iron in Alabama* (Birmingham: Birmingham Chamber of Commerce, 1910)

Barger, Harold and S. H. Schurr, *The Mining Industries, 1899-1939* (New York: National Bureau of Research, 1943)

Bayley, W. S., *Magnetic Iron Ores*. See Tennessee Geological Survey.

Bethlehem Steel Corporation, *Annual Report*, 1947, 1949, 1950 (Pittsburgh: dates same as above)

Bishop, J. L., *A History of American Manufacture*, I (Philadelphia: Edward Young and Company, 1868)

Board of Investigation and Research, *The Economics of Iron and Steel Transportation*, 79th Congress, Senate Document No. 80 (Washington: 1945)

Brodell, A. P., and James W. Birkhead, *Age and Size of Principal Farm Machines*. See U. S. Department of Agriculture.

Brodell, A. P., and M. R. Cooper, *Number and Duty of Principal Farm Machines*. See U. S. Department of Agriculture.

Bryson, H. J., *The Mining Industry in North Carolina from 1929 to 1936* (Raleigh, N. C.: North Carolina Department of Conservation and Development, 1937)

Burchard, E. F.
——, "The Birmingham District, Alabama." See International Geological Survey.
——, "Brown Ores, Russellville District." See U. S. Geological Survey.
——, *Brown Ores, Western Highland Rim*. See Tennessee Geological Survey.
——, *The Red Iron Ores of East Tennessee*. See Tennessee Geological Survey.
——, "Preliminary Report on the Red Iron Ores." See U. S. Geological Survey.
——, and Thomas G. Andrews, *Iron Ore Outcrops of the Red Mountain Formation*. See Alabama Geological Survey.
——, and Charles Butts, *Iron Ores, Fuels and Fluxes*. See U. S. Geological Survey.

Butts, Charles, *Alabama Coals*. See U. S. Bureau of Mines.
——, *Montevallo-Columbiana*. See U. S. Geological Survey.
——, *Northern Part, Cahaba Coal Field*. See U. S. Geological Survey.
——, *Southern Part, Cahaba Coal Field*. See U. S. Geological Survey.
——, "Warrior Coal Basin . . . Brookwood Quadrangle." See U. S. Geological Survey.
——, and W. A. Nelson, *The Crossville Quadrangle*. See Tennessee Geological Survey.

Camp, J. M., and C. B. Francis, *The Making, Shaping, and Treating of Steel* (Pittsburgh: Carnegie-Illinois Steel Corporation, 1940)

Census of Agriculture, Business, Construction, Manufactures, Minerals Industry, Population. See U. S. Bureau of the Census.

Clark, Victor S., *History of Manufactures in the United States,* II (New York: McGraw-Hill, 1929)

"Consumption of Metal Mill Shapes . . ." See U. S. Bureau of the Census.

"Consumption of Steel Mill Shapes and Forms . . ." See U. S. Bureau of the Census.

Crane, M. R., *Development, Mining and Handling of Ore, Birmingham District.* See U. S. Bureau of Mines.

——, *Iron Ore (Hematite) Mining in the Birmingham District, Alabama.* See U. S. Bureau of Mines.

——, *Red Iron Ores and Ferruginous Sandstones.* See U. S. Bureau of Mines.

Crockard, Frank H., "Steel Making in Alabama." See Alabama Geological Survey.

Deming, Frederick L. and Weldon A. Stein, *Disposal of Southern War Plants,* Mimeo. Report No. 2 (Washington: N. P. A. Committee of the South, 1949)

DeVaney, F. D., B. W. Gandrud, and W. H. Coghill, *Gravity Concentration of Alabama Oolitic Iron Ores.* See U. S. Bureau of Mines.

Directory of Iron and Steel Works. See American Iron and Steel Institute.

Distribution of Oven and Beehive Coke in 1946. See U.S. Bureau of Mines.

Echel, E. C., *Iron Ores and Iron Industries.* See Tennessee Geological Survey.

Economics of Iron and Steel Transportation, The. See Bureau of Investigation and Research.

Edison Electrical Institute, *Statistical Bulletin, 1948; 1931.* (New York: June 1949, July 1932)

Fabricant, Solomon, *The Output of Manufacturing Industries, 1899-1937* (New York: National Bureau of Economic Research, 1940)

Facts for Industry. See U. S. Bureau of the Census.

Forbes, J. J., *Coal Losses in Alabama.* See Alabama Geological Survey.

Foreign Commerce and Navigation of the United States. See U. S. Bureau of Census.

Fulmer, John Leonard, *Agricultural Progress in the Cotton Belt Since 1920* (Chapel Hill: University of North Carolina Press, 1950)

Gandrud, B. W. [and others], *Alabama Red Iron Ores.* See U. S. Bureau of Mines.

Georgia Department of Natural Resources. *The Geology of the Sand-Lookout Mountain Area, Northwest Georgia* by J. Wentwood Sullivan, Information Circular 15 (Atlanta: July 1942)

Georgia Geological Survey. *Iron Ore Deposits of Georgia* by R. H. Haseltine, Bulletin 41 (Atlanta: 1924)

Glenn, L. C., *The Northern Tennessee Coal Field.* See Tennessee Geological Survey.

Harder, E. C., "Iron Ores, Pig Iron and Steel." See U. S. Bureau of Mines.

Haseltine, R. H., *Iron Ore Deposits of Georgia.* See Georgia Geological Survey.

Hayes, C. W., *Geology of Northeastern Alabama.* See Alabama Geological Survey.

Henning, C. C. and R. W. Braund, "Present and Prospective Sources of Supply of Steel Making Raw Materials." See American Iron and Steel Institute.

Hotchkiss, W. E., F. G. Tryon [and others], *Mechanization, Employment, and Output per Man in Bituminous Coal Mining* (Philadelphia: National Research Project, WPA, 1939)

Hoover, Calvin B. and B. U. Ratchford, *Economic Resources and Policies of the South* (New York: Macmillan, 1951)

Huddle, J. W., *Brown Iron Ores of the Chulafinnee District.* See Alabama Geological Survey.

International Geological Congress, *Mining Districts of the Eastern States,* "The Birmingham District, Alabama" by E. F. Burchard, Guidebook 2: Excursion A-2 (Washington: 1933)

Iron Age, *Basic Marketing Data,* II (New York: 1948)

Kerrick, J. H., J. E. Tobey, and D. R. Mitchell, "Use Specifications for Coal." See American Institute of Mining and Metallurgical Engineers.

McCalley, Henry, *Coal Measures of the Plateau Region of Alabama.* See Alabama Geological Survey.

——, *Valley Regions of Alabama.* See Alabama Geological Survey.

——, *Warrior Coal Basin.* See Alabama Geological Survey.

McLaughlin, Glenn E. and Stefan Robock, *Why Industry Moves South,* Report No. 3 (Washington: N.P.A. Committee of the South, 1949c.)

Mills, Mable D., *Coke Industry in Alabama,* Mimeo. Ser. 11 (University, Alabama: Bureau of Business Research, University of Alabama, September 1947)

Mineral Resources of the United States. See U. S. Bureau of Mines.

Minerals Yearbook. See U. S. Bureau of Mines.

Morgan, Charles, *Prospecting, Mining and Washing the Brown Ores of Alabama,* Tech. Pub. 860 (New York: American Institute of Mining and Metallurgical Engineers, 1937)

National Resources Planning Board, *Industrial Location and National Resources* (Washington: 1943)

Nelson, James C. and Robert C. Smith, *Transportation Factors in the Location of the Cast Iron Pipe Industry.* See U. S. Department of Commerce.

Nelson, Wilbur A., *The Herbert Domain.* See Tennessee Geological Survey.

——, *The Southern Tennessee Coal Field.* See Tennessee Geological Survey.

Noble, Henry Jeffers, *History of the Cast Iron Pressure Pipe Industry in the United States of America* (Birmingham: Newcomen Society, 1940)

Parker, Charles M., *Steel in Action* (Lancaster, Pennsylvania: Jaques Catell Press, 1943)

Payne, H. M., *The Undeveloped Mineral Resources of*

the South (Washington: American Mining Congress 1928)

Rose, E. H., *Address*. See American Iron and Steel Institute.

Smaller War Plants Corporation, *Economic Concentration and World War II*, 79th Congress, 2nd Session, Senate Document No. 206 (Washington: 1946)

Squire, Joseph, *Cahaba Coal Field*. See Alabama Geological Survey.

Statistical Abstract of the United States. See U. S. Bureau of the Census.

Steel Making at Birmingham. See T. C. I.

"Steel Warehouses, General Steel Products, Shipments, Receipts, and Inventories, . . ." See U. S. Bureau of the Census.

"Steel Warehouses, Merchant Trade Products, . . ." See U. S. Bureau of the Census.

Steven, W. H. S. [and others], *Distribution of Natural Resources*. See U. S. Interstate Commerce Commission.

Sullivan, J. Wentwood, *Sand-Lookout Mountain Area*. See Georgia Department of Natural Resources.

T. C. I., *Steel Making at Birmingham* (Birmingham, Alabama: Tennessee Coal, Iron and Railroad Company, 1940)

Tennessee Geological Survey.

The Magnetic Iron Ores of East Tennessee and Western North Carolina by W. S. Bayley, Bulletin 29 (Nashville: 1923)

The Brown Ores of the Western Highland Rim, Tennessee by E. F. Burchard (Nashville: 1934)

Red Iron Ores of East Tennessee by E. F. Burchard, Bulletin 16 (Nashville: Brandon Printing Company, 1913)

Geology and Mineral Resources of the Crossville Quadrangle by Charles Butts and Wilbur A. Nelson, Bulletin 33d (Nashville: 1925)

Iron Ores and Iron Industries of the Tennessee Valley Region by E. C. Echel, Bulletin 10 (Nashville: 1938)

The Northern Tennessee Coal Field by L. C. Glenn, Bulletin 33b (Nashville: Williams Printing Company, 1925)

The Coals and Geology of the Herbert Domain by Wilbur A. Nelson, Bulletin 33c (Nashville: 1925)

The Southern Tennessee Coal Field by Wilbur A. Nelson, Bulletin 33b (Nashville: 1925)

Tennessee. State Planning Commission. *Industrial Resources of Tennessee* by George I. Whitlatch (Nashville: 1945)

United Nations, *World Iron Ore Resources and Their Utilization, With Special Reference to the Use of Iron Ore in Underdeveloped Areas* (Lake Success, New York: 1950)

U. S. Bureau of the Census.

Census of Agriculture, 1945, II, (Washington, 1947)

Census of Business, 1939, "Construction," IV (Washington: 1943); "Wholesale Trade," II (Washington, 1942); "Distribution of Manufacturers' Sales," V (Washington: 1942)

Census of Business, 1948, "Wholesale Trade," V (Washington: 1951)

Census of Manufactures, 1860; 1939;1947 (Washington: 1860, 1941, 1949)

Census of Manufactures, 1947, "Consumption of Steel Mill Shapes and Forms by Metal Fabricating Establishments by State, Standard Metropolitan Area, and Selected Counties: 1947," Series MC100-13 (Washington: April 9, 1951)

Census of Manufactures, 1947, "Consumption of Metal Mill Shapes and Forms and Castings by Individual Manufacturing Industries: 1947," Series MC100-12 (Washington: March 23, 1950)

Census of Manufactures, 1947, "Geographic Distribution of Consumption of Metal Mill Shapes and Forms and Castings: 1947," Series MC100-10 (Washington: December 30, 1949)

Census of Manufactures, 1947, II, "Statistics by Industry" (Washington: 1949). Also for years 1860, 1900, X, 1910, 1920, 1921, 1923, 1925, 1927, 1930, 1931, 1933, 1935, 1937, 1940.

Census of Minerals Industry, 1939, I (Washington: 1944)

Census of Population, 1860 (Washington, 1864); *1940*, III, "Labor Force," (Washington: 1943)

Facts for Industry,

"Fabricated Metal Products," Series 50-3; "Facilities Expansion," Series 50-4; "Quarterly Summary of Materials Consumption for New Construction in the United States," (Washington: 1944-1946)

"Farm Machinery: Estimated Carbon Steel Requirements," Series 52-3-1 (Washington: 1944)

"Farm Machines and Equipment," Series M35A-05, M35A-06, M35A-07 (Washington: 1946, 1947, 1948)

"Steel Warehouses, General Steel Products, Shipments, Receipts, and Inventories, 1942, 1943, and 1944," Series 30-8-1 (Washington: 1945)

"Steel Warehouses, Merchant Trade Products, October 1942-June 1945 and Prewar Periods," Series 30-8-2 (Washington: 1946)

"U. S. Consumption of Carbon Steel," Series 52-8-1 (Washington: 1942)

Foreign Commerce and Navigation of the United States (Washington: 1920-44)

Statistical Abstract of the United States, 1947; 1948 (Washington: 1947, 1948)

U. S. Bureau of Mines.

Analyses of Alabama Coals by Charles Butts, Tech. Paper 347 (Washington: 1925)

Development, Mining, and Handling of Ore in Folded and Faulted Areas, Red Ore Mines, Birmingham District, Alabama by W. R. Crane, Tech. Paper 407 (Washington: 1927)

Iron Ore (Hematite) Mining Practice in the Birmingham District, Alabama by W. R. Crane, Bulletin 239 (Washington: 1926)

Red Iron Ores and Ferruginous Sandstones of the Clinton Formation in the Birmingham District, Alabama by W. R. Crane, Tech. Paper 377 (Washington: 1926)

Gravity Concentration of Alabama Oolitic Iron Ores by F. D. DeVaney, B. W. Gandrud, and W. H. Coghill, RI 2937, Mimeo. (Washington: May 1929)

Distribution of Oven and Beehive Coke in 1946, MMS 1541 (Washington: 1947)

Classifications and Tabling of Alabama Red Iron Ores by B. W. Gandrud, A. C. Richardson, and B. S. Followill, RI 3224, Mimeo. (Washington: 1934)

Mineral Resources of the United States, 1913-1929 (Washington: 1914-1932); *1886* (Washington: 1887); *1908,* Part I, "Iron Ores, Pig Iron and Steel" by E. C. Harder (Washington: 1909)

Minerals Yearbook, 1900-1949 (Washington: 1901-1951) "U. S. Consumption of Carbon Steel." See U. S. Bureau of the Census.

U. S. Department of Agriculture.

Age and Size of Principal Farm Machines by A. P. Brodell and James W. Birkhead, Series FM41 (Washington: November 1943)

Number and Duty of Principal Farm Machines by A. P. Brodell and M. R. Cooper, Series FM46 (Washington: November 1944)

U. S. Department of Commerce.

Construction and Construction Materials, "State Distribution of Construction Activity, 1939-1947" (Washington: June 1948)

Transportation Factors in the Location of the Cast Iron Pipe Industry by James C. Nelson and Robert C. Smith, ES 63 (Washington: 1947)

U. S. Department of Labor.

Estimates of Employment in Manufacturing Industries, by State, 1943-1946, Mimeo. (Washington: 1948)

Handbook of Labor Statistics, 1950, Bulletin No. 1016 (Washington: 1951)

U. S. Engineer Department, *Annual Report,* Part 2, 1939, 1947, 1948 (Washington: 1940, 1948, 1949)

U. S. Federal Communications Commission, *Statistics of the Communications Industry in the United States, 1939; 1945* (Washington: 1941, 1947)

Distribution of the Natural Resources of the United States by Freight Rate Territories by W. H. S. Stevens, G. M. Saharov, and E. C. Bryant, Mimeo. (Washington: 1941)

U. S. Geological Survey.

Contributions to Economic Geology,
"The Brown Iron Ores of the Russellville District, Alabama" by E. F. Burchard, Bulletin 315-D (Washington: 1907)

"Preliminary Report on the Red Iron Ores of East Tennessee, Northeast Alabama, and Northwest Georgia" by E. F. Burchard, Bulletin 540-G (Washington: 1914)

"The Northern Part of the Cahaba Coal Field, Alabama" by Charles Butts, Bulletin 316a (Washington: 1907)

"The Southern Part of the Cahaba Coal Field, Alabama" by Charles Butts, Bulletin 431b (Washington: 1911)

"Warrior Coal Basin in the Brookwood Quadrangle, Alabama" by Charles Butts, Bulletin 260 (Washington: 1905)

"Iron Ores, Fuels and Fluxes of the Birmingham District" by E. F. Burchard and Charles Butts, Bulletin 400 (Washington: 1910)

Montevallo-Columbiana, Alabama by Charles Butts, Folio 226 (Washington: 1941)

U. S. Interstate Commerce Commission.

Statistics of Oil Pipe Line Companies Reporting to the ICC for the Year Ended December 31, 1941; 1945 (Washington: 1943, 1947)

Statistics of Railways in the United States for the Year Ended December 31, 1946 (Washington: 1948)

Tons of Revenue Freight Originated and Tons Terminated in Carloads by Groups of Commodities and by Geographic Areas, 1940; 1946-1948 (Washington: 1941, 1947-1949)

U. S. Office of Price Administration, *Survey of Commercial Bituminous Coal Mines,* Econ. Data Series 15 (Washington: 1947)

U. S. Senate, *Economic Concentration in World War II,* Doc. 206 (Washington: 1946)

U. S. Steel Corporation, *U. S. Steel Corporation T.N.E.C. Papers,* "An Analysis of Changes in the Demand for Steel and in Steel Prices, 1936-1939," TNEC Exhibit No. 1412; "Some Factors in the Pricing of Steel," TNEC Exhibit No. 1410, I (New York: 1940)

U. S. Temporary National Economic Committee, *The Basing Point Problem,* "An Analysis of the Basing-Point System or System of Delivered Prices as Presented by United States Steel Corporation in 'Exhibits Number 1410 and 1418'" by Walter B. Wooden and Huge E. White, Mono. 42 (Washington: 1941)

The Structure of Industry, "Investigation of Concentration of Economic Power," Mono. 27 (Washington: 1941)

U. S. War Production Board, *Directory of Warehouse Distributors of General Steel Products,* Multi. (Washington: April 1944)

Vance, Rupert B., *All These People* (Chapel Hill: University of North Carolina Press, 1945)

White, C. M., *"Iron Ore and the Steel Industry,"* pamphlet (n.p.: Republic Steel Corp., 1947)

White, J. G., Engineering Corporation, *Economic Analysis of the State of Minnesota,* II (New York: 1945)

Wooden, Walter B. and Hugh E. White, "An Analysis of the Basing-Point System." See U. S. Temporary National Economic Committee.

Woodward Iron Company, *Alabama Blast Furnaces* (Woodward, Alabama: 1940)

Wright, E. C., *The Manufacture and Properties of Killed Bessemer Steel.* See American Institute of Mining and Metallurgical Engineers.

Yaworksi, O. E. [and others], *Technology, Employment, and Output per Man in Iron Mining,* Report E-13 (Philadelphia: National Research Project, 1940)

B. Newspapers and Periodicals

Alabama Today and Tomorrow, X (October 1947); XI (February 1948); XII (December 1949); XIII (May, June, October, November 1950)

Barloon, Marvin, "Steel: the Great Retreat," *Harper's,* CXCV (August 1947)

Benitez, Alberto Terrone, "Cerro de Mercado, Mexico's Iron Mountain," *Engineering and Mining Journal,* CXLV, 9 (September 1944)

"Bethlehem Ship Comes in at Sparrow's Point," *Iron Age,* CLXVII, 13 (March 29, 1951)

Birmingham *Post-Herald.*
  (April 17, 1951) p. 14, col. 4.
  (November 23, 1951) p. 6, col. 1.

Bulletin, American Iron and Steel Association, VIII, 173 (June 4, 1874); VIII, 337 (November 12, 1874); XI, 205 (August 1, 1877); XI, 257 (October 3, 1877); XIII, 331 (December 24 and 31, 1879)

"Cerro Bolivar—Saga of an Iron Ore Crisis Averted," *Mining Engineering,* CLXXXVII, 2 (February 1950)

Conference Board Business Record, VII, 8 (August 1950)

Davis, E. W., "Iron Ore Reserves of the Lake Superior District," *Mining and Metallurgy,* XXVIII, 481 (January 1947)

DeSollar, T. C., "The Red Iron Mines of the Woodward Iron Company at Bessemer, Alabama," *Transactions,* American Institute of Mining and Metallurgical Engineers, CIX (1934)

Dorr, John N., "How Much Iron Ore in Brazil," *Iron Age,* CLXVI (August 17 and 24, 1950)

Edwards, Corwin D., "Geographic Price Formulas and the Concentration of Economic Power," *Georgetown Law Journal,* XXXVII (January 1949)

The Farm Income Situation, U. S. Department of Agriculture (May 1947)

"First Pipe Leaves New Twin Mills," *Iron Age,* CLXV, 15 (April 13, 1950)

"Foreign Sources of Iron Ore," *Mining World,* XIII, 11 (October 1951)

Hall, E. M. and A. W. Beck, "Iron Mining in Muscoda Number 6," *Engineering and Mining Journal,* CXXXVIII (September and October, 1937)

Hubbell, A. H., "The Problem of Iron Ore and How It Will Be Solved," *Engineering and Mining Journal,* CL, 7 (July 1949)

Iron Age, CLXII (November 4, 1948); CLXIV (December 1, 1949); CLXVI (August 31, September 21, October 19, 1950); CLXVII (February 8, September 27, November 9, December 7, 1951). Also "Annual" numbers, 1920-1950; First monthly issue, 1930-1939.

Johnson, William Summers, "The Restrictive Incidence of Basing Point Pricing on Regional Development," *Georgetown Law Journal,* XXXVII (January 1949)

Journal of Metals, III (November 1951). 969

"Laborador Ore Sooner Than You Think," *Iron Age,* CLXVI (August 31, 1950)

Lake, M. C., "Cerro Bolivar, U. S. Steel's New Iron Ore Bonanza," *Engineering and Mining Journal,* CLXI, 8 (August 1950)

Landon, Charles E., "Geographic Price Structures," *Law and Contemporary Problems,* XV, 2 (Spring 1950)

Lee, Oscar, "Birmingham's Future Depends on Concentration," *Engineering and Mining Journal,* CXLV (October 1944)

Lester, Richard A., "Effectiveness of Factory Labor: North-South Comparisons," *Journal of Political Economy,* LIV (February 1946)

Lippert, W. W., "Cerro Bolivar," *Journal of Metals,* CLXXXVIII, 2 (February 1950)

"Local Market Mill to be Built in Tennessee," *Iron Age,* CLXVII, 2 (January 11, 1951)

Manufacturer's Record, VII (July 11, 1885)

Martin, John Bartlow, "North to Find Iron," *Harper's,* CCIII (December 1951); CCIV (January 1952)

Malozemoff, A., "The United Nations' Newest Source of Iron," *Engineering and Mining Journal,* CXLIII, 12 (December 1942); CXLIV (January 1943)

Metaxes, Ted, "Renaissance of Steel in South America," *Iron Age,* CLXVI (September 28, 1950)

Mobile Register, "2,400,000 Order for Freight Cars Placed by GM&O," (August 4, 1951) p. 1, col. 7.

Mund, Vernon A., "The Development and Incidents of Delivered Pricing in American Industry," *Law and Contemporary Problems,* XV, 2 (Spring 1950)

Nelson, A. A., and Roy Yingling, "Remote Control, a Feature of Ore-Conditioning Plant," *Engineering and Mining Journal,* CXLVIII, 4 (April 1947)

"New Company Records Set by Atlantic Steel," *Alabama Purchaser,* VII, 3 (April 1951)

"New Lone Star Mill Rated at 500,000 Tons," *Manufacturer's Record,* CXX, 4 (April 1951)

"New Ore for Republic," *Engineering and Mining Journal,* CL, 7 (July 1949)

Place, P. B., "Tennessee Coals, Their Classification and Analyses," *Combustion,* VIII, 3 (September 1936)

"Pipe Production in Houston Plant Slated to Open August 1," *Iron Age,* CLXV, 12 (March 23, 1950)

Randall, Clarence B., "The Iron We Need," *Atlantic Monthly,* CLXXI (June 1948)

"Republic, Hanna Seek Venezuelan Ore," *Iron Age,* CLXVII (January 11, 1951)

"Republic Gets First Liberian Ore," *Iron Age,* CLXVII (June 28, 1951)

Retty, J. A., "Laborador, North America's Newest Iron Ore Field," *Mining and Metallurgy,* XXIX (September 1948)

Sims, E. C. and F. Toy, "The Turbo-Hearth," *Transactions,* American Institute of Mining and Metallurgical Engineers, CLXXXVIII (1950)

Steel, CXXX (February 25, 1942)

Stocking, George W., "The Economics of Basing Point Pricing," *Law and Contemporary Problems,* XV, 2 (Spring 1950)

"T. C. I's. Concord Mine is World's Most Modern," *Alabama Today and Tomorrow,* XIII, 12 (November 1950)

Thompson, N. E., "Red Ore from Raimund," *Engineering and Mining Journal,* XXXIX (March 1938)

"Venezuelan Iron Ore," *Mining Congress Journal,* XXXVII, 4 (April 1951)

INDEX